Phytotechnology

Urbanization, Industrialization, and the Environment

Series Editor
Dr. Viduranga Waisundara

Crisis Management of Chronic Pollution: Contaminated Soil and Human Health
Edited by Magalie Lesueur Jannoyer, Philippe Cattan, Thierry Woignier, and Florence Clostre

Biochar: Production, Characterization, and Applications
Edited by Yong Sik Ok, Sophie M. Uchimiya, Scott X. Chang, Nanthi Bolan

Phytotechnology: A Sustainable Platform for the Development of Herbal Products
Edited by Wanderley Pereira Oliveira

For more information on this series, please visit: https://www.routledge.com/Urbanization-Industrialization-and-the-Environment/book-series/CRCURBINDENV

Phytotechnology

A Sustainable Platform for the Development of Herbal Products

Edited by

Wanderley Pereira Oliveira

CRC Press
Taylor & Francis Group
Boca Raton London New York

CRC Press is an imprint of the
Taylor & Francis Group, an **informa** business

First edition published 2022
by CRC Press
6000 Broken Sound Parkway NW, Suite 300, Boca Raton, FL 33487-2742

and by CRC Press
2 Park Square, Milton Park, Abingdon, Oxon, OX14 4RN

CRC Press is an imprint of Taylor & Francis Group, LLC

Library of Congress Cataloging-in-Publication Data

Names: Oliveira, Wanderley Pereira, editor.
Title: Phytotechnology : a sustainable platform for the development of herbal products / edited by Wanderley Pereira Oliveira.
Description: First edition. | Boca Raton : Taylor and Francis, 2022. | Series: Urbanization, industrialization, and the environment, 2572-4150 | Includes bibliographical references and index.
Identifiers: LCCN 2021038013 (print) | LCCN 2021038014 (ebook) | ISBN 9781032126111 (hardback) | ISBN 9781032126166 (paperback) | ISBN 9781003225416 (ebook)
Subjects: LCSH: Herbs--Therapeutic use. | Natural products. | Drug development.
Classification: LCC RM301.25 .P49 2022 (print) | LCC RM301.25 (ebook) | DDC 615.3/21--dc23/eng/20211001
LC record available at https://lccn.loc.gov/2021038013
LC ebook record available at https://lccn.loc.gov/2021038014

ISBN: 9781032126111 (hbk)
ISBN: 9781032126166 (pbk)
ISBN: 9781003225416 (ebk)

DOI: 10.1201/9781003225416

Typeset in Times
by KnowledgeWorks Global Ltd.

Dedication

To my mom and dad (in memoriam), who spent their lives taking care of their children and supporting my career and intellectual growth. Thank you for all!

To Professor José Teixeira Freire, master and advisor, who introduced me to the fascinating world of science and technology.

Contents

Foreword ix
Series Preface xi
Preface xiii
Editor xv
Contributors xvii

PART I General Aspects

Chapter 1 Research and Development of Herbal Medicines: Perspectives and Challenges 3

Luis Carlos Marques, Lucio Ferreira Alves, and Cléverson Luiz dos Santos Vigo

Chapter 2 Importance of Historical Records for the Development of Herbal Medicines: The Example of COVID-19 21

Fernanda Lins Brandão Mügge, Leopoldo Clemente Baratto, and Maria Graças Lins Brandão

PART II Processing Technologies

Chapter 3 Drying of Medicinal and Aromatic Plants 53

Maria do Carmo Ferreira, Fábio Bentes Freire, and José Teixeira Freire

Chapter 4 Extraction, Isolation, and Identification of Phytopharmaceuticals 85

João Carlos Palazzo de Mello and Larissa Valone

Chapter 5 Standardisation of Herbal Extracts by Drying Technologies 105

Wanderley Pereira Oliveira

Chapter 6 Drying of Phytochemical Compositions by Spouted Bed: An Update 141

Cláudia Regina Fernandes Souza and Wanderley Pereira Oliveira

Chapter 7 Drying of Lipid Systems Loaded with Phytochemicals 173

Elizabeth Céspedes-Gutiérrez and Diego Francisco Cortés-Rojas

Chapter 8 Encapsulation of Essential Oils in Lipid-Based Nanosystems 197

Iara Baldim, Cláudia Regina Fernandes Souza, and Wanderley Pereira Oliveira

PART III Technological Applications

Chapter 9 Plant-Based Cosmetic Products 233

Patrícia Maria Berardo Gonçalves Maia Campos, Gabriela Maria D'Angelo Costa, and Cláudia Regina Fernandes de Souza

Chapter 10 Uses of Herbal-Derived Products in the Food Sector 255

Karen Elbert Leal Mazza, Tamires Sousa de Oliveira, André Mesquita Magalhães Costa, Humberto Ribeiro Bizzo, and Renata Valeriano Tonon

Chapter 11 Essential Oil and Herbal Compounds in the Agroindustry 285

Thaís Aparecida Santos Oliveira, Livia Stenico Tanajura, and Antônio Eduardo Miller Crotti

PART IV Regulation Aspects

Chapter 12 Registration of Phytomedicines: Technical Requirements and Highlights on Regulation Instruments 309

Wagner Luiz Ramos Barbosa, Wanderley Pereira Oliveira, Andressa Santa Brígida da Silva, and Ailton Castro Pinheiro

Chapter 13 Phytopharmacovigilance 327

Ricardo Tabach

Index 347

Foreword

Human beings from ancient times have been reliant on nature for managing their basic needs such as foods, spices, clothing, and shelters. Medicinal plants have been a rich source of numerous therapeutic agents used in various traditional medicinal systems from prehistoric time to the cure of different kinds of ailments and diseases (D.J. Newman and G.M. Cragg 2020, Natural Products as Sources of New Drugs over the Nearly Four Decades from 01/1981 to 09/2019, *Journal of Natural Products*, 83(3): 770–803). Furthermore, the World Health Organization revealed that most of the world's occupants (>80%) essentially utilise folk medicines for their basic medical needs. Those residing in rural areas across the globe have been using phytomedicines for their basic health problems (Yuan, H., Ma, Q., Ye, L., Piao, G. 2016, The Traditional Medicine and Modern Medicine from Natural Products, *Molecules*. 21: 559–576).

As more data are coming forward, the desire for specific information on local medicines, including taxonomic names connecting to local names, sources, preparations, etc., is critical, as these plants are valued by indigenous populations. Herbal preparations require good sourcing and should be prepared based on safety considerations and chemically standardised, leading to evidence-based testing in a clinical setting.

The pharmaceutical industry has always maintained a high-level quality process for the development of its products, but this industry is not involved to any significant extent in the commercialisation of plant products. However, it is fair to say that quality processes have been lacking uniformly, in many of the other industries, which use plants or plant extracts.

Phytotechnology: A Sustainable Platform for the Development of Herbal Products covers a large area in scientific technology, and processes related to herbal products, which require a multidisciplinary approach. This book addresses fundamental and technological concepts directed to the manufacture of high-quality herbal products, thereby recognising there is a need to address weaknesses of processes in the preparation of phyto-products and the lack of consistency.

There is a need to integrate new scientific platforms, to enhance the understanding of botanicals and natural products. A road map forward is needed to

a. better understand and gain acceptance of these preparations and formulae and
b. to integrate the challenges of government, regulation, safety, and culture

and help industry find the path to successful commercialisation.

For example, there are opportunities for harmonising standards, adapting the latest research methodologies including a *Total Quality System* beginning at the "farm" to the final product. The systematic studies of the health effects of botanicals and natural products require the collaboration of experts from many different disciplines including the proper collection or cultivation of source materials, botanical identification and authentication, chemical analysis, evaluation of the biological response, and clinical studies leading to a total quality system. There are other important techniques to authenticate the herbal samples that are covered in the book, which are crucial for all scientific investigation of botanicals. As more scientific processes develop, we shall witness the incorporation of DNA fingerprinting, "omics" and spectroscopic tools to evaluate the actions of botanicals and natural products for development leading to better remedies and health claims to support a wider acceptance of botanicals and herbs in the world. Despite the worldwide efforts in the last century, scientific inquiry of botanicals remains a particularly challenging task. Botanicals usually contain complex chemical mixtures and their interaction in the human body may be much more complicated.

Professor Oliveira is to be congratulated for producing this scientific text in collaboration with his contributing authors, to address some of the key issues of phytotechnology strategies, provide scientific processes and strategies that could substantiate the health claims, and contribute to a wider acceptance of botanicals and herbs in the world.

Raymond Cooper, PhD
The Hong Kong Polytechnic University
Hong Kong

Series Preface

URBANIZATION, INDUSTRIALIZATION, AND THE ENVIRONMENT

This book series addresses current critical environmental issues resulting from rapid urbanization and industrialization, particularly in the developing world. Modern technologies and industrial chemicals have given rise to unique problems of ecosystem degradation, pollution, deprivation, and disease. The books in this series will present case studies from different parts of the world, with the aim to stimulate discussion and make policy makers aware of the current state of play.

Major themes include *Waste and Technology, Climate Change, Food and Land, Biodiversity, Energy, Food Safety and Security*, but interdisciplinary areas including *Environmental Governance, Human Behavioral Change,* and *Bridging Science and Policy* will also be explored, from both natural and social science perspectives. It is hoped that the series will serve as a discussion forum for major environmental issues of modern demographic transition, allowing authors and editors to present strategies for mitigation and remediation.

Dr. Viduranga Waisundara
Series Editor

Series Preface

URBANIZATION, INDUSTRIALIZATION, AND THE ENVIRONMENT

Preface

Herbal products have traditionally been used in several industrial sectors, like pharmaceutical, food, cosmetic, chemical, veterinary, and agroindustry. Noteworthy examples of applications include the production of fine chemicals, herbal remedies, natural dyes, natural food preservatives, and natural pesticides. The natural origin of these products is a positive marketing differential, considering the current trend of society and industry, which seeks natural and healthier products obtained by eco-friendly and sustainable protocols. Since herbal materials have a complex and variable chemical composition, processing is a key factor to producing a high-quality standardised product. This task involves numerous sequential steps, namely obtaining the vegetable raw material (cultivation, harvesting, or wildcrafting), pre-processing (stabilisation, cleaning), technological processing (e.g., drying, grinding, extraction of active constituents), the guarantee of quality and stability throughout the production and storage processes, and the final product development. The number of sequential unit operations is driven by the degree of technological transformation required. In this book, the production chain of herbal products was named *Phytotechnology*—the science and engineering involved to obtain high-quality and high-value plant-based products by eco-friendly and sustainable processing. Phytotechnology integrates knowledge from several areas, namely biology, ethnobotany, ethnopharmacology, pharmacology and toxicology, agronomy, chemistry and pharmacognosy, engineering, pharmaceutical technology, among others. To be marketed, the final product must be manufactured in compliance with the requirements specified in resolutions and regulations, according to the desired application.

This book intends to provide clearly and objectively the main fundamental and technological concepts involved in the manufacture of high-quality and high-value herbal products. The book is divided into four sections, comprising 13 chapters, written by experts in the field from academia and industry. The first section contains two chapters. The first is a general chapter that presents issues in the research and development of herbal medicines, examining the challenges and prospects. Chapter 2 focuses on the importance of historical records for the development of herbal medicines, presenting as a case study the search for plants with potential for the treatment of COVID-19. The second section contains six chapters related to processing technologies—drying of medicinal plants; methods of extraction, isolation, and identification of phytopharmaceuticals; standardisation of herbal extracts by drying; the use of spouted beds for drying of phytochemical compositions; and two chapters focused on encapsulating and drying of phytochemicals and essential oils in lipid-based systems. The third section has three chapters focusing on applications of herbal products in cosmetics, food, and agroindustry. The final section contains two chapters with a focus on regulatory aspects and phytopharmacovigilance of herbal medicinal products. Although the information presented here is focused on herbal medicines, the processing steps are general and can be applied to prepare innovative products in various industrial sectors. The information can be easily used to implement a sustainable production chain of high-value herbal products, contribute to the sustainable use of biodiversity, and improve the population's quality of life in underdeveloped regions.

The information presented provides good reference material for professionals of different specialities who wish to enter this fascinating and innovative field. It may contribute to the academia and industry with valuable information for the manufacture of high-quality herbal products. Finally, I would like to thank the chapter authors who spent time in their busy schedules to contribute to this project and the publisher's team for supporting the editorial issues.

Wanderley Pereira Oliveira
Editor

Editor

Prof. Dr W. P. Oliveira is a Senior Associate Professor at the University of São Paulo/USP. Dr. Oliveira received his PhD from the Federal University of São Carlos/UFSCar, working with Spouted Bed Drying of Pastelike Materials (1996), and held a post-doctorate in the Department of Chemical and Biological Engineering at the University of British Columbia/UBC (2006–2007), working with Monitoring of Fluid-Particle Systems by Acoustic and Pressure Fluctuation Signals. He is the founder and coordinator of LAPROFAR's group (https://sites.usp.br/laprofar), dedicated to developing basic and applied research in pharmaceutical and phytopharmaceutical processes. Recent projects include drying, coating, agglomeration, and microencapsulation of pharmaceuticals, volatile oils, and plant extracts; drying and immobilisation of enzymes/proteins. Currently, his research projects have been directed to the study of micro- and nanoencapsulation of active phytopharmaceutical ingredients in lipid-based nanosystems, aiming to improve their physicochemical properties, bioavailability, and biological activity. His research has been continuously supported by grants from the São Paulo State Research Foundation (FAPESP), the National Council for Scientific and Technological Development (CNPq), and the Coordination for the Improvement of Higher Education Personnel (CAPES), in the form of research funds, infrastructure provision, multiuser equipment grants, and student and research fellowships. He has extensive experience as an advisor of undergraduate, master's, and PhD students, post-doctoral scholars, and industry personnel. He has published more than 200 full papers (various in collaboration with groups from Canada, the United States, Chile, and Portugal), 103 in refereed journals and proceedings, 10 book chapters (5 international), 2 Brazilian patents granted, and 4 pending. Moreover, he has worked as a scientific advisor of national and international funding agencies and journals, organises workshops and conferences, and is a member of the Bioencapsulation Research Group (http://bioencapsulation.net).

Editor

Contributors

Lúcio Ferreira Alves, Senior PhD Researcher, Oswaldo Cruz Foundation/FIOCRUZ, Institute of Pharmaceutical Technology—Biodiversity and Health Management Center, Rio de Janeiro, Brazil. Email: lucioferreiraalvesfarma75@gmail.com

Iara Baldim, DSc Student, Faculty of Pharmaceutical Sciences of Ribeirão Preto, University of São Paulo, Ribeirão Preto, SP, Brazil. Email: ib.iara.baldim@gmail.com

Leopoldo Clemente Baratto, Associate Professor, Faculty of Pharmacy, Laboratory of Applied Pharmacognosy, Federal University of Rio de Janeiro, Cidade Universitária-Ilha do Fundão, Rio de Janeiro, Brazil. Email: leopoldo@pharma.ufrj.br

Wagner Luiz Ramos Barbosa, Professor, Department of Pharmacy, Federal University of Pará, R. Belém, PA, Brazil. Email: barbosa@ufpa.br

Humberto Ribeiro Bizzo, Senior PhD Researcher, Embrapa Agroindústria de Alimentos, Laboratory of Essential Oils, Rio de Janeiro, Brazil. Email: humberto.bizzo@embrapa.br

Maria Graças Lins Brandão, Professor, Founder, and Coordinator of Specialized Center on Aromatic, Medicinal and Toxic Plants, Museum of Natural History, Federal University of Minas Gerais, Belo Horizonte, MG, Brazil. Email: mglinsbrandao@gmail.com

Patrícia Maria Berardo Gonçalves Maia Campos, Professor, Faculty of Pharmaceutical Sciences of Ribeirão Preto, University of São Paulo, Ribeirão Preto, SP, Brazil. Email: pmcampos@usp.br

André Mesquita Magalhães Costa, Postdoctoral Researcher, Institute of Chemistry, Federal University of Rio de Janeiro, Rio de Janeiro, Brazil. Email: andreme_1@hotmail.com

Gabriela Maria D'Angelo Costa, DSc Student, Faculty of Pharmaceutical Sciences of Ribeirão Preto, University of São Paulo, Ribeirão Preto, SP, Brazil. Email: costagmdc@gmail.com

Antônio Eduardo Miller Crotti, Associate Professor, Department of Chemistry, Faculty of Philosophy, Sciences, and Letters of Ribeirão Preto, University of São Paulo, Ribeirão Preto, SP, Brazil. Email: millercrotti@ffclrp.usp.br

Maria do Carmo Ferreira, Professor, Department of Chemical Engineering, Federal University of São Carlos, São Carlos, SP, Brazil. Email: mariaf@ufscar.br

Fábio Bentes Freire, Associate Professor, Department of Chemical Engineering, Federal University of São Carlos, São Carlos, SP, Brazil. Email: fabiobefreire@gmail.com

José Teixeira Freire, Emeritus Professor, Department of Chemical Engineering, Federal University of São Carlos, São Carlos, SP, Brazil. Email: jotefreire@gmail.com

Elizabeth Céspedes Gutierrez, Researcher, Bioproducts Department, Colombian Corporation for Agricultural Research—AGROSAVIA, Bogotá, Mosquera, Colombia. Email: ecespedes@agrosavia.co

Luís Carlos Marques, PhD, Independent Consultant, Fitoscience Consulting Ltd., São Paulo, SP, Brazil. Email: luis.marques08@hotmail.com

Karen Elbert Leal Mazza, DSc Student, Institute of Chemistry, Federal University of Rio de Janeiro, Cidade Universitária, Rio de Janeiro, RJ, Brazil. Email: karenelbert@gmail.com

João Carlos Palazzo de Mello, Professor, Laboratory of Pharmaceutical Biology/PALAFITO, Pharmaceutical Sciences Graduate Program, State University of Maringá, Maringá, Brazil. Email: mello@uem.br

Fernanda Lins Brandão Mügge, PhD, Postdoctoral Fellow, IFZ—Research Centre for Biosystems, Land Use and Nutrition; Universität Gießen, Gießen, Germany. Email: fernandalbm@gmail.com

Tamires Sousa de Oliveira, DSc Student, Institute of Chemistry, Federal University of Rio de Janeiro, Rio de Janeiro, RJ, Brazil. Email: tamiresoliveira1412@gmail.com

Thaís Aparecida Santos Oliveira, DSc Student, Department of Chemistry, Faculty of Philosophy, Sciences, and Letters of Ribeirão Preto, University of São Paulo, Ribeirão Preto, SP, Brazil. Email: thaisoliveira@usp.br

Wanderley Pereira Oliveira, Associate Professor, Faculty of Pharmaceutical Sciences of Ribeirão Preto, Laboratory of R&D on Pharmaceutical Processes—LAPROFAR, University of São Paulo, Ribeirão Preto, SP, Brazil. Email: wpoliv@fcfrp.usp.br

Ailton Castro Pinheiro, DSc Student, Federal Institute of Education, Science and Technology of Pará, Av. João Paulo II, 514, Postcode: 66645-240 Belém, PA, Brazil. Email: ailton.ufpa@hotmail.com

Diego Francisco Cortés Rojas, PhD Researcher, Bioproducts Department, Colombian Corporation for Agricultural Research—AGROSAVIA, Bogotá, Mosquera, Colombia. Email: dfcortes@agrosavia.co

Andressa Santa Brígida da Silva, Associate Professor, University of Amazonia, Ananindeua, PA, Brazil. Email: andressabriggida@gmail.com

Claudia Regina Fernandes Souza, PhD Researcher, Faculty of Pharmaceutical Sciences of Ribeirão Preto, University of São Paulo, Ribeirão Preto, SP, Brazil. Email: souzacrf@gmail.com

Ricardo Tabach, Senior PhD Researcher, Brazilian Center for Information on Psychotropic Drugs (CEBRID), Federal University of São Paulo, and Professor of Biological Sciences, Universidade Santo Amaro/UNISA, São Paulo, SP, Brazil. Email: rtabach@gmail.com

Livia Stenico Tanajura, Undergraduate Student, Department of Chemistry, Faculty of Philosophy, Sciences and Letters of Ribeirão Preto, University of São Paulo, Ribeirão Preto, SP, Brazil. Email: liviastenico@gmail.com

Renata Valeriano Tonon, PhD Researcher, Embrapa Agroindústria de Alimentos, Pilot Plant of Food Processing, Rio de Janeiro, RJ, Brazil. Email: renata.tonon@embrapa.br

Larissa Valone, Pharmacist, Laboratory of Pharmaceutical Biology/PALAFITO, Pharmaceutical Sciences Graduate Program, State University of Maringá, Maringá, PR, Brazil. Email: larissavalone@hotmail.com

Cleverson Luiz dos Santos Vigo, PhD, Head of Open Innovation, Herbarium Botany Laboratory, Colombo, PR, Brazil.

Part I

General Aspects

1 Research and Development of Herbal Medicines

Perspectives and Challenges

Luis Carlos Marques, Lucio Ferreira Alves, and Cléverson Luiz dos Santos Vigo

CONTENTS

1.1 Introduction 3
1.2 History of R&D on Medicinal Plants: The Brazilian Know-How 4
1.3 The Market of Medicines and Herbal Products 5
1.4 Effective Herbal Product Development 10
1.5 Current Challenges in R&D of Herbal Products 14
 1.5.1 Complexity of Biological Materials 14
 1.5.2 Economic Costs of the Innovation Process 14
 1.5.3 Integration between Industry and University 15
 1.5.4 Unreasonable Legal Requirements 15
 1.5.5 Other Related Difficulties 16
1.6 Final Remarks 17
References 17

1.1 INTRODUCTION

The research and development (R&D) of medicines is a strategic activity for all countries. Pharmaceutical products are important not only to treat people's diseases but also for preventive health care. The economic expenditures in the R&D of medicines are very high and have grown consistently over the years, being a complex mix of public and private funding [1]. On average, the Organisation for Economic Co-operation and Development (OECD) pharmaceutical companies spent about 14% of their gross value added in R&D. The pharmaceutical industry applies the knowledge gained from basic research to develop the medicines, and perform the clinical assays on a large scale, to get approval from regulating agencies. Although most R&D works are carried out in developed countries, the participation of developing nations is increasing [1]. Therefore, it is important to attempt to build adequate legal, technical, and scientific bases—among others—so that the R&D of suitable medicines may be possible, especially in developing countries.

DOI: 10.1201/9781003225416-2

Brazil, in this scenario, unfortunately, does not have good performance, being a country almost totally dependent on imports in the medicine area, with few examples of local products. According to estimates, around 95% of pharmaceutical raw materials, pharmaceutical active ingredients, adjuvants, and even finished medicines consumed in our country are imported [2]. Currently, well marked by the COVID-19 pandemic, the lack of autonomy for the independent manufacture of local pharmaceutical products is much more striking. It places the Brazilian population at the mercy of commercial negotiations with international vaccine producers and evident competition for their purchase. The same occurs with other categories of drugs and pharmaceutical inputs used in the treatment of COVID-19.

Among the various possible sources of drug manufacturing, plant species stand out, accounting for about 20% of the most widely used medicines in the world. Herbs also mainly provide model molecules for the synthesis of new drugs, raw material for semi-synthesis, and even in the form of standardised plant extracts that make up herbal products [3].

This book is contextualised with the following objective: to reinforce and improve drug research and, in particular, to contribute to the development of phytomedicines (herbal medicines), presenting concepts and technologies suitable for this class of products. Brazil has an impressive biodiversity, expressed in about 46,000 species of plants and more than 116,000 species of animals recognised today [4]. Theoretically, this contingent of species should translate into an equally significant number of pharmaceutical products based on vegetal species, but it has not been happening.

Theoretically, this number of species should reflect an equally significant number of herbal medicines on the market, which unfortunately did not happen. In this chapter, we seek to explore the historical and current relationships between research usually carried out in public universities and the phytopharmaceutical industry. Thus, it is expected to contribute to understanding problems and weaknesses and point out present and future challenges and opportunities of the herbal medicine sector, which we hope will be more productive.

1.2 HISTORY OF R&D ON MEDICINAL PLANTS: THE BRAZILIAN KNOW-HOW

Medicinal plants have been used in all cultures since antiquity. Archaeological and historical evidence, such as that found on an Egyptian papyrus from Ebers (c. 1600 BC) and on cuneiform clay tablets from the Ashurbanipal Library (c. 650 BC), indicate the use of herbal remedies. Physicians such as Hippocrates (406–377 BC), Galen (129–199 DC), Avicenna (980–1037 DC), and Paracelsus (1493–1541 DC), to name a few, have also described the therapeutic properties of medicinal herbs [5–7]. However, the use of natural products as therapeutic agents seems to be much older. According to Hardy and colleagues, Neanderthals (30,000–24,000 years ago) already possessed a sophisticated knowledge of the selection and use of herbs for health purposes [8].

Brazil has a long tradition in the herbal medicine area since Colonial and Imperial times [9, 10], mostly linked to its huge biodiversity [11], a potential source of dyes, fragrance, aroma, flavours, cosmetics, perfumes, insecticides, and medicines.

Brazilian biodiversity is distributed in six biomes: the Amazon Forest, the Atlantic Forest, Caatinga, Cerrado, Pampas, and the Pantanal.

The first description of Brazilian natural wealth is in the letter that Pero Vaz de Caminha, scribe of the fleet, sent to D. Manoel—King of Portugal—shortly after the arrival of the Portuguese fleet in 1500. The letter is considered the birth certificate of Brazil [12]. Aware of the wealth of the new colony and the impossibility of defending it, Portugal adopted a restrictive policy, prohibiting the entry of any foreigner into the territory. Due to this policy, the first scientific description of Brazilian flora and fauna was made by William Piso, the personal physician of Count Maurício de Nassau, who came to Brazil in 1637 to colonise the northeast of the country. In 1648, Piso published the *História Natural do Brasil* with the German naturalist George Marc Grave. They described hundreds of plants with their vernacular names and their use to treat some common diseases in the northeast Brazil. The book is considered the most complete treatise on Brazilian flora and fauna created in the 17th century [13, 14]. According to Alcantara-Rodriguez et al. [15, 16], from 378 species found in the *Natural History of Brazil*, 256 (68%) were useful, mainly used for healing and feeding in a similar way (80%) both in the 17th century and in modern times.

The weak knowledge of Brazilian biodiversity began to change when the Portuguese royal family arrived in Brazil in 1808, fleeing French troops. The Colony then became the centre of the empire, and a new era in the study of Brazilian biodiversity began. Many naturalists such as Carl Friedrich Philipp von Martius, Johann von Spix, Johann Natterer, Johann Christian Mikan, Johann Emanuel Pohl, and Giuseppe Raddi were invited to participate in an expedition to study the Brazilian tropical flora and fauna. Carl Friedrich von Martius's reports are most relevant for the purpose of this chapter. He is the author of the books *Systema de materia medica vegetal brasileira* and *Natureza, doenças, medicina e remédios dos índios brasileiros.* According to Martius, the first one contains the catalogue and classification of all Brazilian plants known for their taxonomy, habitat, and medicinal uses. In the second, he mentions the medicinal properties not only of some plants but also of other products, such as deer antlers (against snake bites), roasted frog meat (to relieve the pain of childbirth), and dog skin against sciatica [10].

In *Travels in Brazil* [17], Martius, with Spix's collaboration, described in detail the climate, people, commerce, Indian music, and flora and fauna, among other information obtained during the 3 years he spent in Brazil. They also collected hundreds of plant species and sometimes described their medicinal use, such as in the treatment of ulcers, wounds, intestinal constipation, as laxatives, purgatives, among others. However, many of the medicinal plants described by Spix and Martius have not yet been scientifically studied [18]. Researchers such as August Sant-Hilaire, among others, also contributed to the knowledge of the Brazilian flora.

1.3 THE MARKET OF MEDICINES AND HERBAL PRODUCTS

The global drug market includes products from all sources, whether synthetic or natural (plants, animals, and biotechnology). According to a survey by STATISTA, the global pharmaceutical market reached a figure of **US$1.27 trillion** in sales in 2020 [19], having a heterogeneous distribution among various parts of the world [20]. The

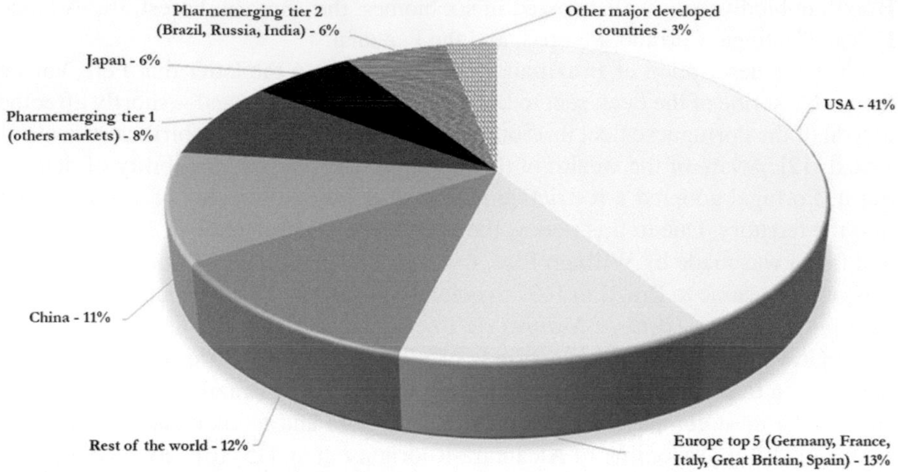

FIGURE 1.1 Forecast for the worldwide distribution of medicine spending in 2020. (Adapted from Ref. [20].)

drugs sales in the United States represent 41% of the total, the main European countries (Germany, France, Italy, United Kingdom, and Spain) representing 13%, and China 11% (Figure 1.1). The Brazilian market for medicines in general (synthetic and natural) had a dimension for 2020 estimated at about **US$24.6 billion** [21], representing just under 2% of the world market, but placing the country between the sixth and seventh position in global terms [22].

Regarding the registration of patents, a parameter indicative of advances in R&D that can lead to new launches and discoveries, of the approximately 3,300,000 applications placed in 2018, China stands out with 1.5 million applications (45%), the United States has 597,000 (18%), Japan has 314,000 (9.5%), and the rest of world has 889,000 (26.9%) applications. Brazil has placed less than 25,000 requests—about 0.8% of the total, below the 10th country with the highest number in this area [22].

However, scaling is more difficult in the global herbal medicine market due to the lack of harmonisation of technical parameters and regulatory requirements in different nations. Depending on the region, the criteria of efficacy, safety, and quality required for herbal medicines (phytopharmaceuticals) are similar to those for conventional medicinal products. However, herbal products can also be classified as foods (nutraceuticals, dietary, or nutritional supplements), like vitamins, minerals, fatty acids, and other ingredients. They can also be registered in specific formats based on the tradition of use (traditional medicines), with proof of their efficacy and safety based on popular knowledge and information available in the literature [23].

A proposal considered adequate to assess the global size of the herbal medicine sector was made by Jaenicke in 2010 at the VIII International Forum of Herbal Medicines in São Paulo, Brazil [24], calling them 'botanical products'. Then, global

TABLE 1.1
The Worldwide Market for Botanical Products According to the Industry of Origin (2010)

Food industry (US$228 billion)	Botanical supplements	US$12 billion	14%
	Botanical functional foods	US$15 billion	17%
Pharmaceutical industry (US$850 billion)	Drugs from botanical precursors	US$31 billion	36%
	Registered botanical medication (phytopharmaceuticals)	US$14 billion	16.5%
Cosmetic industry (US$270 billion)	Botanical beauty and skin-care products	US$14 billion	16.5%
Total		US$86 billion	

Source: Adapted from Ref. [24].

estimates were established for these various categories, which at the time represented $86 billion in sales (Table 1.1).

From this set of possibilities for classifying plant-derived products and their performance of turnover, in the context of this book, the categories and items of botanical supplements and also the most typical registered botanical medications, then named phytopharmaceuticals, are considered related. Adding to the turnovers of these two subclasses, we obtain a total value of US$26.3 billion—30.5% of the set. Searching the growth estimates for these segments over the years in different sources, it is predicted for 2020 that the world market for phytopharmaceuticals will represent around *US$30 billion* [25].

This estimated global value shows the regional distribution comparatively expressed in Table 1.2 with the previous two estimates [24, 26]. In percentage terms, these data are similar. European Community countries stand out with 45% of the total (estimating half of this percentage to Germany), Asia including China with 30%, Latin America with a stabilised consumption in the range of 5%, and other countries comprising the remaining 20%. It is also possible to verify in Table 1.2 a resumption of growth in the European Community in 2020 compared to 2010, a minimum growth for the Asian market, maintaining the same level in Latin American

TABLE 1.2
Distribution of Worldwide Consumption of Phytopharmaceuticals

	Gruenwald 1998 [26]	Jaenicke 2010 [24]	Reis 2019 [25]
European Community	48%	30%	45%
Asia	19%	29%	30%
Latin America	4%	5%	5%
Rest of the world	29%	36%	20%
Total market	US$12.4 billion	US$26.3 billion	US$30 billion

markets, and an undeclared fluctuation in other countries of the world, including the United States.

The relevance of the German market as the most outstanding in this scenario can be explained by the professional work done with Commission E, with its approximately 300 positive monographs, officially published over a decade, to which were added the R&D efforts carried out by German private companies, which manufactured herbal medicines of great importance and performance around the world. This is the case of extracts of *Ginkgo biloba*, *Hypericum perforatum*, *Hedera helix*, and *Pelargonium sidoides*, among many others.

This development in the American market was leveraged in 1994 with the *Dietary Supplement Health and Education Act of 1994 (DSHEA)* edition. It facilitated the commercial release of plant-derived products without therapeutic claims and provided substantial growth in these products from that period onwards. The DSHEA rules were complemented in 2006 by the *Dietary Supplement and Non-prescription Drug Consumer Protection Act (DSNDCPA)*, which required communication and reporting of adverse events associated with herbal products without negatively impacting the performance of the class as a whole [27].

However, over the decades, this model has already shown clear signs of weakness, as the products are established as commodities, with lots of practically identical offers and fierce competition for prices, leading to a gradual decrease in consumption. Alongside, there has been an appreciation of differentiated products, especially those that carry out clinical studies that seek registration in the US Food and Drug Administration (FDA), and may present themselves with well-founded therapeutic indications [24, 28].

The Brazilian phytopharmaceuticals market represents about half of the 5% of consumption attributed to Latin America, a value of approximately US$1.5 billion in 2020 [25]. Thus, it can be inferred that we have a consumption of phytopharmaceuticals in the range of US$750 million, representing 2.5% of the world's herbal medicine market. Therefore, it is a still small market that reflects specific issues in the herbal medicines area and general economic problems, since the low-income population does not consume the products expressed in these statistics, probably using homemade herbal remedies for their treatment. Table 1.3 highlights the evolution of the top 12 most commercialised phytopharmaceuticals in Brazil from October 2018 to October 2020 [29].

By using the data presented in Table 1.1 as a representative sample of the Brazilian plant market, it can be verified that of the estimated value of US$750 million in sales, when evaluated in terms of the origin of the species that make up the products, about 95% of the products are composed of exotic species, imported or acclimated in the country (e.g., *Passiflora incarnata, P. sidoides, Rhamnus purshiana, Peumus boldus, Aesculus hippocastanum, H. helix, G. biloba, Bacopa monnieri*, and others), with an estimated meagre 5% produced with native species from Brazil or Latin America (*Cordia verbenacea, Mikania glomerata*; Figure 1.2). Again, it is clear that significant efforts are needed for the R&D of phytopharmaceuticals and other herbal products to increase the use of the wealth of local biodiversity of the country.

TABLE 1.3
Turnover Evolution of Top 12 Phytopharmaceuticals in the Brazilian Market (2018–2020)

Phytopharmaceutical (Company)	Species in the Composition	Annual Revenues (US$ million)		
		2018	2019	2020
Seakalm® (Natulab)	*Passiflora incarnata*	9.440	11.514	11.200
Kaloba® (Herbarium)	*Pelargonium sidoides*	10.208	12.970	8.910
Eparema® (Takeda)	*Peumus boldus, Rhamnus purshiana, Rheum palmatum*	13.660	12.870	8.455
Sintocalmy® (Aché)	*P. incarnata*	6.937	7.282	7.751
Acheflan® (Aché)	*Cordia verbenacea*	8.166	7.472	5.455
Varicell Phytos® (Farmacoquímica)	*Aesculus hippocastanum*	9.363	7.266	4.863
Abrilar® (Farmoquímica)	*Hedera helix*	13.823	12.390	4.825
Ritmoneuran® (Kley Hertz)	*P. incarnata*	5.545	5.389	4.640
Varicell Pele Norm® (Farmoquímica)	*A. hippocastanum*	3.604	3.175	2.324
Tebonin® (Herbarium)	*Ginkgo biloba*	4.000	3.170	2.074
Cognitus® (Herbarium)	*Bacopa monnieri*	2.861	2.756	2.062
Xarope de Guaco® (Natulab)	*Mikania glomerata*	5.090	2.993	1.141

Source: Adapted from Ref. [29].

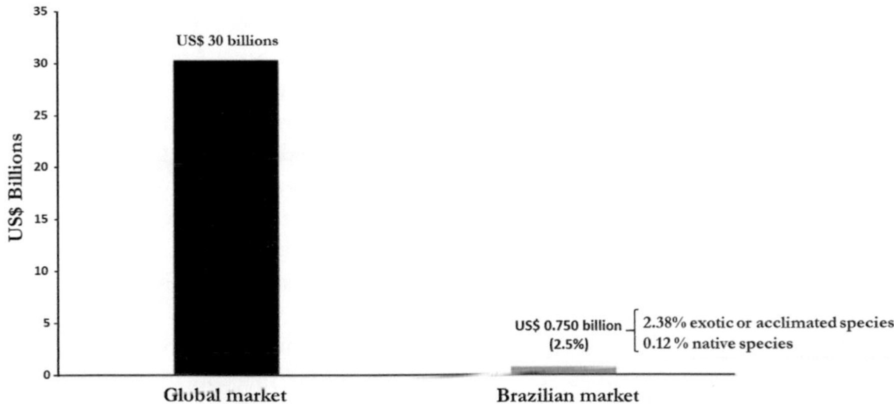

FIGURE 1.2 World and Brazilian phytopharmaceutical markets and participation of exotic and native species.

1.4 EFFECTIVE HERBAL PRODUCT DEVELOPMENT

The development of the international pharmaceutical industry took place markedly after World War I, which showed the economic and strategic importance of medicines. Thus emerged the multinational conglomerates, mainly in the United States, which began to use the resources of chemical synthesis and have remarkably integrated with universities and research institutes. This relationship led to the discovery of new molecules and medicines [30].

In the context of the first decades of the 20th century, Brazil had a little impact from the World Wars that did not influence its characteristics, maintaining a profile of generally family-owned pharmaceutical companies, originating from the master, low-tech pharmacies, and employing workshop formulations (constants of pharmacopoeias); many of them based on plant extracts of exotic and native species. Simultaneously, the legal norms in force conceived the concept of 'officinal medical preparation' in 1931. In 1945, the 'equivalent to officinal' was added, exempting them from technical requirements and evidence of safety and efficacy, a typical normative profile of a relationship of self-protection and government paternalism. These rules kept the national companies and their products in the market, although without any relevant technological evolution or innovation [31].

The establishment of strong and technologically advanced multinational conglomerates with chemical synthesis and new drugs that generated progressive and expressive revenues led them to search new markets. They found, in Brazil and also in other developing countries, a favourable scenario for what was called the national pharmaceutical industry's denationalisation process, from 1930. From this period until the 1970s, dozens of national laboratories were associated or integrated with large multinational companies, leading to eliminating their own products and consolidating innovative drugs developed by the pharmaceutical conglomerates [32]. In this context, many companies producing numerous herbal medicines were extinguished. This happened with the Silva Araújo Laboratory, founded in 1891, which focused on vaccines and biological products and had a significant production of herbal medicines, including its own proprietary documentation. It was incorporated in 1936 to the Roussel Laboratory, with the French capital, becoming Silva Araújo Roussel S/A (SARSA) and losing all documentation and herbal products in its portfolio [33, 34].

The lack of official policies to reverse this process consolidated the multinational domain. On the other hand, the discontinuity of the industrial sector of chemical synthesis and the lack of patent law in the country favoured the development of national companies, based on the importance of pharmaceutical ingredients and production similar to the innovative pharmaceuticals of multinationals. This condition led the Brazilian pharmaceutical field to a vegetative situation, totally dependent on pharmaceutical raw materials and records by similarity [30].

The enactment of the patent law [35] created obvious restrictions for national companies to copy new drugs. The dependence on pharmaceutical raw materials remained due to the absolute lack of measures to stimulate local chemical synthesis. Thus, the options for future developments were evaluated, placing as one of the potential and interesting possibilities to search for drugs and medicines from plant species, bearing in mind the great Brazilian biodiversity.

The government efforts made in the Medicinal Plants Research Program (PPPM), a program of the former Medicine Center of the Brazilian Ministry of Health (CEME), contributed to the consolidation of this path. This program selected 74 plant species as a priority for investigation and, from 1983 to 1997, invested around US$8 million in research incentives for 55 species from the initial list, generally in the preclinical phases, with 15 reaching the clinical stage, and 9 had confirmed the traditionally reported effects. The investments allowed laboratory structuring and training of human resources in this area. Thus, various research with positive results in terms of safety and efficacy were developed, and groups of researchers and industrial partnership laboratories were created, mostly in public universities [36, 37].

In line with these scientific studies and with the attention that herbal medicines have received, mainly in Germany, and with the personal and visionary effort of a Brazilian entrepreneur, the first genuinely national herbal medicine was developed and launched in 1993, the Giamebil®, obtained from the *Mentha crispa* species and recommended for the treatment of giardiasis, developed by the Hebron Laboratory in partnership with the Federal University of Pernambuco, Brazil [38, 39].

In 1995, the process of renewing the sanitary regulations for herbal medicines began in Brazil with the publication of Ordinance No. 06 of the Health Surveillance Department, which defined the requirements for the adequate development of phytopharmaceuticals in modern terms of safety, efficacy, and quality, the process that has evolved over the years [40]. Based on this regulatory impulse and taking advantage of the infrastructure of laboratories and permanent employees made available by the PPPM, some companies that produce herbal medicines have entered into partnerships with universities to improve existing products and possibly also to search for innovations.

Although auspicious, this form of development of Brazilian herbal medicines was also impacted by other factors, such as the approval of the sale of generic drugs in 1999 by Federal Law No. 9,787. This opening also promoted a great stimulus to national companies, which directed their R&D efforts in the area of bioequivalence, with federal government support [30]. If on the one hand there was a change in the focus of research on herbal medicines, on the other it provided an increase in the market share of Brazilian pharmaceutical companies such as EMS, Aché, Eurofarma, and others, which started to obtain expressive revenues, which in theory would allow the sponsorship of innovative research, whether in synthetic drugs or herbal derivatives.

Thus, this period was marked by some R&D initiatives with phytopharmaceuticals and other classes of herbal products, with research being carried out at the initiative and sponsorship of national pharmaceutical companies. In addition to the pioneering herbal product Giamebil, previously reported, the same company—Hebron Laboratory—continues to sponsor research alongside the Federal University of Pernambuco, developing and launching the Kronel® vaginal gel product (phytopharmaceutical) and liquid soap (phytocosmetic) for bacterial vaginosis treatment and intimate hygiene in 1999 [41]. Other phytopharmaceutical products were also launched on the market, for example: (i) Acheflan®—from the Aché laboratory, in 2005 as a topical anti-inflammatory phytopharmaceutical, developed in partnership with the Federal University of Santa Catarina and other institutions [30]; (ii) the product Imunomax®—from the Herbarium Laboratory in 2010, recommended for topical treatment of cold sores, developed in partnership with the Federal University of Santa Catarina and the Federal Fluminense University [42]; and (iii) the product Fitoscar®—from the Apsen Farmacêutica laboratory, also in 2010, and recommended as a healing agent for levels I and II bedsores, developed in partnership with the University of Ribeirão Preto [43], among others.

In parallel to the products promoted by the pharmaceutical companies themselves, based on the results of the PPPM and their open disclosure, without patent applications, Brazilian researchers started to investigate many of the species on the CEME list, generating a progressive accumulation of scientific evidence about them. Thus, it has been possible to register several phytopharmaceuticals at the Brazilian Health Surveillance Agency (ANVISA), allowing the release of dozens of national herbal products developed in the open format, that is, without exclusive financing from one or another company and without patents.

Results of this process of collective development includes, among others, 28 phytopharmaceuticals based on leaves of espinheira santa (*Maytenus ilicifolia* and *Maytenus aquifolium*) intended for cases of gastritis and gastric ulcers, 8 of them are still in use (Ulcerazine®, Gastrosil®, Gastroplantas®, Gastrinon®, Espinheira Santa Herbarium®, Espinheira Santa Natulab®, Espinheira Santa Vidora®, and Tintura de Espinheira Divina Composta®), and 41 products made from guaco leaves (*M. glomerata* and *Mikania laevigata*), of which 19 are currently marketed (Apiguaco®, Biotos edulite®, Biotoss Xarope®, Expectrat®, G500 Balsâmico®, Guaco EdulitoHerbarium®, Guacoflus®, Guacolin®, Guaconat®, Guacotoss®, Guacovita®, Livtós®, Melagrião®, Peitoral Martel®, Xarope de Guaco Belfar®, Xarope de Guaco Cimed®, Xarope de Guaco Herbarium®, Xarope de Guaco Natulab®, and Xarope de Guaco Melpoejo®) [44].

Unfortunately, the vast majority have a simple extracts profile, not purified or differentiated, without therapeutic or commercial distinctions regarding the degree of technological innovation of Brazilian phytopharmaceuticals. A single highlight can be made to the product Sintocalmy® from the Aché laboratory. It is produced from the leaves of *P. incarnata*, indicated as a central nervous system depressant, promoting a sedative effect and prolonging sleeping time. The company sought to develop an extract different from the other numerous products offered in the Brazilian market. Thus, it produced a standardised extract with a high concentration of flavonoids (7% compared to 2–4% of its competitors) and undetectable amounts of the indole alkaloids (harmane, harmine, and harmol) [45], being reported as bradycardia and ventricular arrhythmias inducers [46]. Table 1.4 presents the turnover of main phytopharmaceuticals developed by Brazilian companies and some of those generated by the open collective development process.

Unfortunately, this important R&D process with acclimated native and exotic species, which was at an incipient, albeit progressive stage, was negatively impacted by issues of legal norms of access to biodiversity and associated traditional knowledge, in particular, Provisional Measure 2.186-16 of 2001 and the resulting administrative measures, related to the country's compliance with the Convention on Biodiversity, signed in Rio de Janeiro in 1992. These norms created many bureaucratic obstacles

TABLE 1.4
Turnover of Genuine Brazilian R&D of Phytopharmaceuticals with Native and Exotic Acclimated Species—PMB 2015

Phyto-Pharmaceutical	Species in the Composition	Pharmaceutical Form	Units	Turnover (US$ million)
Melagrião®	*Mikania glomerata* e associações	Syrup, spray	1,726,000	13,500
Kronel®	*Schinus terebinthifolius*	Liquid soap, vaginal gel	326,000	7,840
Giamebil®	*Mentha crispa*	Drops, syrup	441,000	6,310
Acheflan®	*Cordia verbenacea*	Cream, aerosol	674,000	5,200
Peitoral Martel®	*M. glomerata*	Syrup	242,000	1,950
Fitoscar®	*Stryphnodendron adstringens*	Ointment	130,000	1,540
Xarope de guaco G500 balsâmico®	*M. glomerata*	Xarope	71,000	670
Espinheira-santa Herbarium®	*Maytenus ilicifolia*	Capsules	37,400	337
Imunomax®	*Uncaria tomentosa*	Lip gel	18,600	182
Ginseng brasileiro®	*Pfaffia glomerata*	Capsules	12,300	110
Ulcerazine®	*M. ilicifolia*	Capsules	2,100	28

Source: Adapted from Ref. [47].

to research with native species. It was allowed excessive inspections and punishments to researchers, university institutions, and sponsoring companies. It established a regulatory framework with substantial legal uncertainties, particularly concerning the future possibility of traditional communities' questioning concerning traditional use and sharing benefits. These uncertainties discouraged pharmaceutical companies that had already made or were preparing to start financing the development of phytopharmaceuticals and other products from native biodiversity [48].

Thereby, in recent years, from the entire Brazilian industrial field in the pharmaceutical area, it is only possible to highlight the launch in 2017 of a single innovative product from an exotic species acclimated in Brazil, which is prepared with essential oil fraction from *Alpinia zerumbet* leaves, called Ziclague®—from Hebron Laboratory, intended to adjunctive treatment in muscular spasticity states [49].

The legal rules to access biodiversity and traditional knowledge have been adjusted in recent years with the publication of Federal Law no. 13,123 [50]. However, it is still a risk factor for companies, which have been trying to adapt to their requirements, considering that it is a global issue and that it will end up involving all countries, and it will impact the economy and international trade relations. The implementation of the Nagoya Protocol, an international agreement, which regulates the fair and equitable sharing of benefits arising from the use of genetic resources and associated traditional knowledge between user and supplier countries (parties), will add new concerns in the field of herbal medicine research since many questions remain unresolved [51]. Even though it is expected that new R&D initiatives for products derived from biodiversity will be completed and launched soon.

1.5 CURRENT CHALLENGES IN R&D OF HERBAL PRODUCTS

The R&D in the area of bioproducts is very important for several sectors of the health and economy. However, some challenges that need to be overcome to improve productivity in these areas are presented as follow.

1.5.1 Complexity of Biological Materials

This aspect is inherent to the R&D of herbal products, whether due to the large number of species existing in biodiversity, or its remarkable biological variability, influenced by environmental factors that generate chemical and functional changes, or even by the particular chemical complexity of plants and other biological organisms [52]. Taking control of the main factors interfering in the chemical complexity can become a source of innovation, compared to different competitors or even a differential, making it difficult to copy and obtain similar products.

In any case, it is an area that requires a wide range of professionals from different specialities, such as botany, agronomy, phytochemistry, quality control, and pharmaceutical technology, but also involved in proving the aspects of safety and therapeutic efficacy. This group of professionals requires the involvement of different institutions. Obviously, there is also the risk of difficulties inherent to the specificity of each sub-area.

1.5.2 Economic Costs of the Innovation Process

The complexity mentioned in the previous topic gives an idea of the costs to be covered by the R&D of herbal products, as each step requires the search for multiple materials, equipment, suitable professionals, etc., their respective certifications and documentation, in addition to the high costs of proof needed in the phytochemical aspects, safety, and therapeutic efficacy.

Studies show that, for the complete development of a new drug, the cost is usually in the order of US$1 billion [53], an amount that is certainly only available in large multinational companies and which can also represent a significant obstacle for developing nations.

In this sense, the R&D of phytopharmaceuticals has advantages over synthetic drugs, with much lower cost estimates, 2–3% of the value for synthetic medicine. The lower costs are due to the traditional aspects, that is, the effectiveness of herbal drugs can be based on the popular and documented use by diverse traditional populations [54]. This also provides safety indicators that make toxicity studies more flexible, as these species have been used for decades or even longer without significant detrimental effects. The efficacy studies towards therapeutic targets can be also well characterised from traditional documentation, reducing the probability of negative results. These and other recommendations were issued by the World Health Organization to guide the proper establishment of regulations on herbal medicines in member states [55].

In another aspect, the sustainability of the chains related to the supply of phytoproducts is another problem that can represent risks and perhaps increase the costs. Thus, at the stage of selecting the species to be investigated, the possibilities of agronomic domestication of the plant material that makes cultivation viable must be evaluated. If this activity negatively impacts the content of the phytoactives, the possibility of carrying out forest management must be considered. By following these recommendations, it is possible to have the material in volume and quality suitable for future scale production if the stages of development are positive.

In Brazil, despite the lack of official diagnoses, wildcrafting is one of the main procedures for obtaining the vast majority of species used in popular and industrialised herbal medicine. Unfortunately, these activities can negatively affect sustainability at an unpredictable level in the future [56].

1.5.3 Integration between Industry and University

This approach is necessary for synergy between academic research competence and companies' market vision and investment potential. However, for different reasons, this approach is not always easy or productive. In Brazil, for example, there is a lack of official instruments such as fairs and exhibitions. At these fairs, the companies can present their opportunities or needs and interests, while researchers can evaluate if the company's needs fit into their competence and propose forms of collaboration.

In addition, university researchers are under academic pressure to produce and publish research results, a condition used to measure and evaluate postgraduate courses and their professional growth. On the other hand, for companies, publications make it impossible the privacy and confidentiality they need so that competitors don't know about their future releases. In Brazil, this is one of the main problems which evidence the different concepts and needs between universities and pharmaceutical companies.

In another aspect, although the open and collective development model has generated the greatest number of opportunities, registration, and commercialisation for Brazilian companies, its consolidation lacks alignment with a list of priorities, whether potential plant species or diseases selected and considered preferential targets. Furthermore, research tends to be dispersed by individual researcher initiatives and the search for knowledge frontiers, often with little concern for market priorities.

The PPPM carefully prepared a list with 74 species [36, 37] which could be a way to generate validated phytoproducts in a short time. Another list of 71 species issued by the Ministry of Health in 2007, initially called RENISUS [57], aimed to meet this concentration of attention and research efforts. However, after more than a decade, the goals were not reached, which still needs to be defined and implemented.

1.5.4 Unreasonable Legal Requirements

The health regulatory framework for herbal products in Brazil has been implemented and adjusted over the last 3 decades, both in the area of phytopharmaceuticals and in related areas, such as functional foods, nutritional and dietary supplements, phytocosmetics, and more recently, also in products derived from Traditional Chinese Medicine. If, on the one hand, we currently have a well-structured scenario in regulatory terms; on the other hand, it is admitted that some regulatory excesses have been developed, mainly in the requirements related to quality control tests of industrialised phytopharmaceuticals, which have progressively increased over the years [40].

This rigour has not been observed in other areas that use plant-derived products or in the compounding pharmacies segment. This disparity has led to the obvious shift of the R&D efforts of phytopharmaceuticals to different categories, in which the requirements for proof of efficacy and quality are lower and equally more superficial. Marketing actions are carried out either on social networks or directly to prescribers and in the compounding segment to counteract the lack or need of therapeutic indications, thus circumventing the lack of robust documentation and registration as medicine [58]. It is therefore a serious deviation that must be corrected at some point.

1.5.5 Other Related Difficulties

In Brazil and several other countries, there is still some resistance from medical categories in accepting phytomedicines. This is mainly because these products are not fully aligned with the modern concepts of scientific evidence, which guide decisions and therapeutic selection in the medical field in general. Therefore, there is a need for further studies with plants, especially with clinical trials. The difficulty of patenting herbal products due to their traditional use also alienates most sponsors and can reduce researcher interest in this segment [59].

Another complicating factor is the absence of a harmonised global regulation for these products, a factor that causes serious problems. Thus, products with different qualities and compositions of actives can be produced depending on the country, which can cause issues with quality and efficacy, low bioavailability, and adverse effects. These differences in active compositions are also responsible for contradictory results obtained in different clinical trials reported for products from the same botanical species.

All of this drives away orthodox prescribers and therefore reduces the interest of pharmaceutical companies, who see difficulties in future medical promotions that can be carried out with such products [60] and hinder their commercialisation between different countries. However, the German experience in which more than 50% of prescriptions contain one or more herbal medicines shows that the incorporation of phytomedicines in modern medical practice is feasible, as long as the peculiar characteristics of these products are understood in terms of scientific evidence, increasing their acceptance [61].

Other difficulties in the production of herbal medicines are related to issues of biodiversity and sustainability. They involve developing ecologically correct and sustainable production processes, compliance with local and universal laws for the preservation of biodiversity, international property rights, and benefit-sharing among nations and traditional communities as established by the Nagoya Protocol, among others.

1.6 FINAL REMARKS

Herbal medicines represent a significant portion of primary health care, particularly in developing countries. However, R&D in herbal medicine is quite complex and presents several challenges to be overcome to meet the modern requirements of safety, efficacy, quality, reproducibility, and sustainability, essential factors for this class of products and any other category of medicines. The main difficulties lie in the variability of raw materials produced in different regions, the absence of harmonised global regulations, poor quality raw materials, distinct processing conditions, patenting technologies issues, genetic resources, environment protection laws, etc. These bottlenecks hinder the growth of the phytopharmaceutical industry, as the production control parameters usually differ from country to country.

Although there is a plethora of research groups in the academia and industry carrying out studies on various aspects of herbal medicines, efforts are not organised and integrated. In many cases, there is a repetition of studies or production of results aimed only at producing scientific papers without focusing on the real sector's needs. The integration between research groups from academia and industry can lead to the more productive and practical use of the considerable resources invested in the area. Otherwise, wastage of time and money will continue, and the evolution will happen at a snail's pace.

REFERENCES

1. OECD Indicators. Research and development in the pharmaceutical sector. Health at a Glance. Paris: OECD Publishing, 2017, pp. 194–195.
2. Silveira, E. Entendendo a dependência nacional de medicamentos importados. 2021. Available at: https://www.revistaquestaodeciencia.com.br/questao-de-fato/2021/02/24/entendendo-dependencia-nacional-de-medicamentos-importados. Accessed in 22/06/2021.
3. Atasanov, A.G.; Zotchev, S.B.; Verena, M.; Dirsch, V.M.; The International Natural Product Sciences Taskforce; Supuran, C.T. Natural products in drug discovery: Advances and opportunities. Nature Reviews Drug Discovery 2021, 20, 200–216.
4. Brasil. Ministério do Meio ambiente. Biodiversidade. Available at: https://www.gov.br/mma/pt-br/assuntos/biodiversidade. Accessed in 21/06/2021.
5. Zarshenas, M.M.; Zagaran, A. A review on the Avicena's contribution to the field of cardiology. International Journal of Cardiology 2015, 182, 237–241.
6. Alves, L.F.; Santos, P.F.P. Brazilian biodiversity as a source of new medicines. Revista Brasileira de Farmácia 2013, 94 (3), 307–320.
7. Péres-Arantegui, J.; Ribechin, E.; Colombini, M.P.; Escudero, F. Characterization of an ancient 'chemical' preparation: pigments and drugs in medieval Islamic Spain. Journal of Archaeological Sciences 2011, 38 (12), 3350–3357.
8. Hardy, K.; Buckley, S.; Collins, M.J.; Estalrrich, A.; Brothwell, D.; Coperland, L. … ; Rosas, A. Neanderthal medics? Evidence for food, cooking, and medicinal plants entrapped in dental calculus. Naturwissenschaften 2012, 99 (8), 617–626.
9. Alves, L.F.; Ming, L.C. Chemistry and pharmacology of some plants mentioned in the letter of Pero Vaz de Caminha. Ethnobiology and Conservation 2015, 4 (3), 1–5.
10. Alves, L.F. Produção de fitoterápicos no Brasil: História, problemas e perspectivas. Revista Virtual de Química 2013, 5 (3), 450–513.
11. Wilson, E.O. A situação atual da diversidade biológica (Cap. 1, p. 3–24). In: Wilson, E.O. (Org). Biodiversidade. Rio de Janeiro: Nova Fronteira, 1997, p. 675.

12. Caminha, P.V. Letter from Pero Vaz de Caminha. Available at: http://objdigital.bn.br/Acervo_Digital/livros_eletronicos/carta.pdf. Accessed in 10/10/2013.
13. Andrade-Lima, D. A botânica na carta de Pero Vaz de Caminha. Rodriguesia 1984, 36 (58), 5–8.
14. Filgueiras, T.S.; Peixoto, A.L. Flora e vegetação do Brasil na carta de Pero Vaz de Caminha. Acta Botanica Brasilica 2002, 16 (3), 263–272.
15. Alcantara-Rodriguez, M.; Françozo, M.; van Andel, T. Plant knowledge in the Historia Naturalis Brasiliae (1648): Retentions of seventeenth-century plant use in Brazil. Economic Botany 2019, 73 (3), 390–404.
16. Alcantara-Rodriguez, M.; Geertsma, I.P.; Franço, M.; van Andel, T. Marcgrave and Piso's plants for sale: The presence of plant species and names form the Historia Naturalis Brasiliae (1648) in contemporary markets. Journal of Ethnopharmacology 2020, 259, 112911.
17. von Spix, J.B.; von Martius, C.F.P. Viagem ao Brasil. Companhia Editora Nacional. National Publishing Company, Rio de Janeiro, 1981, 3 volumes.
18. Breitbach, U.B.; Niehues, M.; Lopes, N.P.; Faria, J.E.Q.; Brandão, M.G.L. Amazonian Brazilian medicinal plants described by CFP von Martius in the 19th century. Journal of Ethnopharmacology 2013, 147 (1), 180–189.
19. Mikulic, M. Global pharmaceutical industry – statistics & facts. 2020. Available at: https://www.statista.com/topics/1764/global-pharmaceutical-industry/. Accessed in 08/6/2021.
20. Krugmann R. Pharma market 2020: Upswing turn for global production. 2018. Available at: https://www.manufacturingchemist.com/news/article_page/Pharma_market2020_Upswing_turn_for_global_production/139701. Accessed in 08/6/2021.
21. Sindusfarma. Mercado farmacêutico Brasil, canal farmácia, vendas do mercado total em dólares 2003-2021. Available at: https://sindusfarma.org.br/mercado/indicadores-economicos. Accessed in 10/06/2021.
22. Interfarma. Guia 2020. Available at: https://www.interfarma.org.br/app/uploads/2021/04/guia-2020.pdf. Accessed in 10/06/2021.
23. David, B.; Wolfender, J-L.; Dias, D.A. The pharmaceutical industry and natural products: historical status and new trends. Phytochemistry Reviews 2015, 14, 299–315.
24. Jaenicke, C. International herbal medicines market: trends and opportunities. In: VIII International Forum of Herbal Medicines. Anais: São Paulo, Sindusfarma, 2010.
25. Reis, R.D. Cenário do mercado brasileiro de fitoterápicos (palestra). In: XX Congresso do Conselho Regional de Farmácia de São Paulo, 2019.
26. Gruenwald, J. The emerging role of herbal medicine in health care in Europe. Drug Information Journal 1998, 32, 151–153.
27. Zayets, V. Comparing dietary supplement regulations in the US and abroad. Food and Drug Law Institute, 2020. Available at: https://www.fdli.org/wp-content/uploads/2020/06/ZAYETS-Final.pdf. Accessed in 12/06/2021.
28. EPA—United States Environmental Protection Agency. Commonly consumed food commodities, 2021. Available at: https://www.epa.gov/minimum-risk-pesticides/commonly-consumed-food-commodities. Accessed in 12/06/2021.
29. IQVIA Brazil. Dataset PMB—Pharmaceutical market Brazil, MAT—moving annual total. October 2020.
30. Calixto, J.B.; Siqueira Jr, J.M. The drug development in Brazil: challenges. Gazeta Médica da Bahia 2008, 1 (142), 98–106.
31. Marques, L.C.; Petrovick, P.R. Normatização da produção e comercialização de fitoterápicos. In: Farmacognosia: da planta ao medicamento, 5th ed. UFRGS/UFSC: Porto Alegre/Florianópolis, 2003, pp. 327–369.
32. Rodrigues, G.K. Ciência a preço de garrafada: a transnacionalização de fármacos no pós-segunda guerra (1945-1961). Khronos 2019, 8, 1–28. Available at: http://revistas.usp.br/khronos. Accessed in 18/06/2021.

33. Viriato, E.P. Discurso de posse como Membro Titular na Academia Nacional de Farmácia. Available at: http://www.academiafarmacia.org.br/ezequielviriato.php. Accessed in 20/06/2021.
34. Coimbra, R. Notas de fitoterapia: catálogo dos dados principais sobre plantas utilizadas em medicina e farmácia. Silva Araújo: Rio de Janeiro, 1942.
35. Brasil. Lei no 9279 de 14 de maio de 1996. Regula direitos e obrigações relativos à propriedade industrial. Diário Oficial da União, 15 de maio de 1996. Available at: http://www.planalto.gov.br/ccivil_03/leis/l9279.htm. Accessed in 20/06/2021.
36. Sant'Ana, P.J.P.; Assad, A.L.D. Programa de pesquisa em produtos naturais: a experiência da CEME. Química Nova 2004, 27(3), 508–512.
37. Luz Netto Junior, N. O Programa de Pesquisas com Plantas Medicinais da Central de Medicamentos: contribuição ao estudo da flora medicinal brasileira. Dissertação de Mestrado, Universidade de Brasília, Brasília, DF, 2005, p.178.
38. Henrique J. Empreender na prática são outros 500 ... milhões. Ed Agathos: São Paulo, 2013, pp. 253–254.
39. Santana, C.F.; Almeida, E.R.; Santos, E.R.; Souza, I.A. Action of *Mentha crispa* hidroethanolic extract in patients bearing intestinal protozoan. Fitoterapia 1992, 63, 409–410.
40. Oliveira, D.R.; Oliveira, A.C.D.; Marques, L.C. O estado regulatório dos fitoterápicos no Brasil: um paralelo entre a legislação e o mercado farmacêutico (1995–2015). Visa Em Debate 2016, 4 (4), 139–148.
41. Santos, L.C.; Amorim, M.M.R. Uso da aroeira (Schinus terebinthifolius Raddi) para tratamento de infecções vaginais. Femina 2002, 30 (6), 339–342.
42. Viana, M.N. Estudo de caso de desenvolvimento de medicamento fitoterápico inovador e dos instrumentos adotados para sua proteção intelectual. Dissertação de Mestrado. Instituto Nacional da Propriedade Industrial, Rio de Janeiro, 2014.
43. Marques, L.C.; Souza, C.M. Research and development of phytomedicines: report of experience on a Brazilian pharmaceutical company. Revista Fitos 2012, 7 (1), 50–66.
44. Anvisa—Agência Nacional de Vigilância Sanitária. Banco de dados de medicamentos: registros à base de Maytenus e Mikania. Available at: https://consultas.anvisa.gov.br/#/medicamentos/. Accessed in 20/06/2021.
45. Pianowski, L.F. Processo para preparação de um produto à base de *Passiflora incarnata* L., produto farmacêutico, composição farmacêutica, usos e método de tratamento de ansiedade e insônia. Patente de Invenção PI 0602106-9 A, 25 de Maio de 2006.
46. Fisher, A.A.; Purcell, P.; Le Couteur, D.G. Toxicity of *Passiflora incarnata* L. Journal of Toxicology: Clinical Toxicology 2000, 38 (1), 63–66.
47. IMS Health Brazil. Dataset PMB—Pharmaceutical Market Brazil, MAT—moving annual total. September 2015.
48. Gilbert, B.; Marques, L.C. Avaliação da legislação de acesso à biodiversidade e seus impactos na fitoterapia brasileira. In Ferreira, S.N.; Sampaio, M.J.A.M. (Org). Biodiversidade e conhecimentos tradicionais associados: implementação da legislação de acesso e repartição de benefícios no Brasil, 1st ed., vol. 1. Sociedade Brasileira Para o Progresso da Ciência: Brasília, 2013, pp. 127–132.
49. Hebron. Comunicado de progresso Junho 2018–Junho 2019. Available at: https://s3-us-west-2.amazonaws.com/ungc production/attachments/cop_2019/478139/original/COP_2019.pdf. Accessed in 21/06/2021.
50. Brasil. Lei Federal no 13.123 de 20 de maio de 2015. Regulamenta o inciso II do § 1º e o § 4° do art. 225 da Constituição Federal, o Artigo 1, a alínea j do Artigo 8, a alínea c do Artigo 10, o Artigo 15 e os §§ 3° e 4° do Artigo 16 da Convenção sobre Diversidade Biológica, promulgada pelo Decreto No. 2.519, de 16 de março de 1998; e dá outras providências. Diário Oficial da União, 21/05/2015. Available at: http://www.planalto.gov.br/ccivil_03/_ato2015-2018/2015/lei/l13123.htm. Accessed in 21/06/2021.

51. Heinrich, M.; Scotti, F.; Andrade-Cetto, A.; Berger-Gonzalez, M.; Echeverría, J.; Friso, F. … ; Spadafora, R. Access and benefit sharing under the Nagoya Protocol—Quo Vadis? Six Latin American case studies assessing opportunities and risk. Frontiers in Pharmacology 2020, 11, 765.
52. Hesse, H.; Hoefgen, R. On the way to understand biological complexity in plants: S-nutrition as a case study for systems biology. Cellular & Molecular Biology Letters 2006, 11 (1), 37–56.
53. Mestre-Ferrandiz J, Sussex J, Towse A. The R&D Cost of a New Medicine. Office of Health Economics: London, 2012. Available at: https://www.researchgate.net/publication/290441583 _The_RD_cost_of_a_new_medicine/link/5698e65808aec79ee32cacb9/download. Accessed in 21/06/2021.
54. Calixto, J.B. Biodiversidade como fonte de medicamentos. Ciência e Cultura 2003, 55 (3), 37–39.
55. Organización Mundial de la Salud. Pautas para la evaluación de medicamentos herbarios. Ginebra: 1991. WHO/TRM/91.4. Available at: http://apps.who.int/iris/bitstream/handle/10665/61330/WHO _TRM_91.4_spa.pdf. Accessed in 22/06/2021.
56. Sene, R.F.S. Valorização e proteção de nossa flora medicinal diante do extrativismo predatório e da pirataria de nossos recursos naturais. 2018. Available at: https://www.eadplus.com.br/blog/valorizacao-e-protecao-de-nossa-flora-medicinal-diante-do-extrativismo-predatorio-e-da-pirataria-de-nossos-recursos-naturais/. Accessed in 22/06/2021.
57. Cesarno, L. Plantas medicinais e fitoterapia. Available at: https://www.xn–farmacutico-sbb.com/plantas-medicinais-renisus. Accessed in 22/06/2021.
58. Marques, L.C. Comparação entre fitoterápicos industrializados e manipulados. Revista A Flora 2021, 1 (2), 21. Available at: https://revista-aflora.com.br/atual. Accessed in 23/06/2021.
59. Seixlack, A.C. Os médicos prescrevem fitoterápicos? Influência da formação do médico na sua prescrição. Revista Medicina Integrativa, 2018. Available at: https://revistamedicinaintegrativa.com/author/revis971_wp/page/15/. Accessed in 23/06/2021.
60. Pelkonen, O.; Xu. Q.; Fan, T-P. Why is research on herbal medicinal products important and how can we improve its quality? Journal of Traditional and Complementary Medicine 2014, 4, 1–7.
61. Joos, S.; Glassen, K.; Musselmann, B. Herbal medicine in primary healthcare in Germany: the patient's perspective. Evidence-Based Complementary and Alternative Medicine 2012, Article ID 294638, 10 pages.

2 Importance of Historical Records for the Development of Herbal Medicines

The Example of COVID-19

Fernanda Lins Brandão Mügge, Leopoldo Clemente Baratto, and Maria Graças Lins Brandão

CONTENTS

2.1 Introduction 21
2.2 Records on Plants from Brazilian Traditional Medicine: A Brief History 23
2.3 The Dataplamt 26
2.4 Searching Data on the Traditional Use of Brazilian Plants with Potential Benefits to Treat COVID-19 27
2.4.1 Results and Discussion 27
2.5 Concluding Remarks 37
References 38

2.1 INTRODUCTION

In the 1970s, the World Health Organization (WHO) recognised medicinal plants as an important therapeutic resource. It instituted a program to encourage the use of validated species in public health [1]. Validating a medicinal plant means evaluating its pharmacological potential and confirming the absence of toxicity. After the validation, medicinal plants can be transformed into medicines, with the same requirements for efficacy, safety, and quality required for synthetic products. The validated plant remedies are called herbal medicines or phytomedicines, which have been developed worldwide. Since 2002, the WHO has also encouraged herbal medicinal products based on traditionality [2, 3]. In these cases, it is considered that the secular use of a plant for a specific purpose can attest to its effectiveness. In Europe, for example, herbal medicines have been used and studied for many decades, and most of them are standardised and prescribed by medical doctors.

Brazil has one of the most diverse floras of the world, with 49,987 species, including 4,993 algae; 35,547 angiosperms; 1,610 bryophytes; 114 gymnosperms; and

DOI: 10.1201/9781003225416-3

1,403 ferns and lycophyte [4], which corresponds to 26.5% of the total of known species [5]. In addition to its vast biodiversity, the country also has a rich socio-diversity, constructed along the centuries of miscegenation of Amerindian, African, and European cultures. However, despite its recognised potential, Brazil's native vegetation has undergone an intense destruction process, caused by a sequence of highly impacting economic cycles that started with the exploration of Brazilwood [*Paubrasilia echinata* (Lam.) Gagnon, H.C. Lima & G.P. Lewis] in the 16th century. Currently, only 12% of the Atlantic Forest is preserved. Other ecosystems such as the Amazon, the Cerrado, and the Caatinga are being rapidly replaced by monocultures of eucalyptus, sugar cane, and soybeans, or livestock [6, 7]. The harmful consequences of these processes on the useful and medicinal plant availability are dramatic. A study carried out by our research group among the population of the mining areas of the State of Minas Gerais showed that even for the older inhabitants of rural areas, the knowledge about the medicinal applications of native plants was forgotten. Due to this intense cultural erosion, most plants species used today as medicines are exotic mostly observed throughout Brazil's south-central part [8, 9]. However, the huge biodiversity still found in Brazilian territory shows great potential for developing herbal medicines, cosmetics, nutraceuticals, and other innovative products with high commercial value. Coupled with the sustainable use of natural resources, this could be an important tool to reduce genetic and cultural erosion, especially in the more remote regions.

The Resolution of the Collegiate Board Nr. 26/2014 of the Brazilian National Health Surveillance Agency (RDC no. 26/2014—ANVISA) strictly regulates the herbal medicines and traditional herbal products available in the country, with the same efficacy/effectiveness, safety, and quality exigencies as required for synthetic drugs. Although the increase of sanitary surveillance in the last decades, the number of licensed herbal medicines decreases by 30% in the last 8 years, evidencing the low interest from the pharmaceutical industry to invest in these products. Despite Brazil's huge biodiversity, only a few native plants are active ingredients in herbal medicines, approximately 27% of all licensed phytomedicines. Some examples of important native species used as active raw materials for herbal drug manufacture are guaraná (*Paullinia cupana* Kunth), espinheira-santa (*Monteverdia ilicifolia* [Mart. ex Reissek] Biral), guaco (*Mikania glomerata* Spreng.), erva-baleeira (*Varronia curassavica* Jacq.), barbatimão (*Stryphnodendron adstringens* [Mart.] Coville), and unha-de-gato (*Uncaria tomentosa* [Willd. ex Roem. & Schult.] DC) [10]. Specifically, *V. curassavica* is the plant ingredient of the first Brazilian licensed herbal medicine used as a topical anti-inflammatory agent launched in 2005, which was considered a best seller in the drug market in Brazil for many years and is considered more effective than diclofenac diethylammonium [11]. Many reasons may justify the nonsignificant number of herbal products based on native flora: (a) absence of clinical data of Brazilian plant extracts; (b) reduced data regarding plants with traditionality of continuous use for more than 30 years with effectiveness and safety, as preconised by WHO; (c) low public and private investment in research on local flora; and (d) no interaction between Universities or Research Institutes and Pharmaceutical Companies. Conversely, non-native plants, especially from Europe, are used by national industries to produce some medications, usually sold as over-the-counter [10].

2.2 RECORDS ON PLANTS FROM BRAZILIAN TRADITIONAL MEDICINE: A BRIEF HISTORY

Even with the current loss of traditional knowledge on the use of native plant species by the local populations, several strategic information about traditional uses of Brazilian plants is recorded in bibliography and other documents from the past centuries. These data are important because they are primary; that is, they were collected when native vegetation was conserved, and the population used, almost exclusively, medicinal plants from Brazilian biodiversity. The first registers on the use of Brazilian plants were recorded, for example, by Jesuit priests, who had direct contact with the Amerindians. The Jesuits repeatedly attracted the attention of the Portuguese to the potential of Brazilian plants. However, in the Portuguese colonial project, there was no interest in evaluating native products. On the contrary, already in the 16th century, the colonisers celebrated the successful cultivation in Brazil of Asian species such as Ceylon cinnamon (*Cinnamomum verum* J. Presl), ginger (*Zingiber officinale* Roscoe), mango (*Mangifera indica* L.), and jackfruit (*Artocarpus heterophyllus* Lam.).

Table 2.1 presents European naturalists that travelled through Brazil at the beginning of colonisation and described the use of plants by the Amerindians. Among them is the Portuguese Gabriel Soares de Souza, who described the uses of several plants from the Atlantic Forest in his book *Tratado descritivo do Brasil em 1587.* In the 17th century, the northeast of Brazil was invaded by the Dutch, which allowed the doctor Wilhelm Piso to live for 8 years in that region. In his work *Historiae Naturalis Brasiliae*, published in 1648 in the Netherlands, Piso described the use of several indigenous medicinal plants. It can be found in these works, the description of the primary uses of important Brazilian plant, such as copaiba balsam (*Copaifera* spp.) and ipecac (*Carapichea ipecacuanha* [Brot.] L. Andersson).

By the end of the 18th century, the Brazilian naturalist Frei Mariano da Conceição Velloso (Frei Vellozo) organised the *Flora Fluminensis*, with more than 200 useful species of the Atlantic Forest and Cerrado. In Rio de Janeiro, the Portuguese doctor Bernardino A. Gomes also published some works about medicinal plants such as caroba (*Jacaranda caroba* [Vell.] A. DC.) and barbatimão (*Stryphnodendron* spp.).

In 1808, the Portuguese royal family moved to Rio de Janeiro, fleeing Napoleon Bonaparte's invasion. They lived in Brazil for 13 years, a period characterised by remarkable progress in the economy, culture, and local sciences. Foreigners were finally allowed to enter Brazil. Several European naturalists travelled extensive areas of the vast Brazilian territory to study the biodiversity and search for native plant species of commercial value. The naturalists recorded observations about natural resources, the customs of the inhabitants, economic and ecological aspects, among other important activities developed at that time. Among these scientists who described the uses of medicinal plants by the Brazilians are the Englishman George Gardner (1836–1841), the Germans Karl F.P. von Martius (1817–1820) and Grigory I. Langsdorff (1821–1836), and the French Auguste de Saint-Hilaire (1779–1853) (Table 2.1).

Subsequent works from the 19th century also reported the use of many native plants, some of them published by doctors, who prescribed Brazilian plants to treat

TABLE 2.1
Authors' Nationalities, Phytogeographical Domains, and Period of Studies in Brazil

Author/Nationality	Area of Study	Period in Brazil
Gabriel Soares Sousa/Portuguese	Atlantic Forest (Bahia)	1575–1592
Guilherme Piso/Dutch	Atlantic Forest, Caatinga (Pernambuco)	1637–1644
Mariano C. Vellozo/Brazilian	Atlantic Forest, Cerrado (MG/RJ)	Natural
Bernardino A. Gomes/Portuguese	Atlantic Forest (RJ)	1798–1802
Grigory I. Langsdorff/German	Atlantic Forest, Cerrado, Pantanal, Amazonia	1803–1830
Auguste de Saint-Hilaire/French	Atlantic Forest, Cerrado, Pampa	1816–1822
Karl F.P. von Martius/German	Atlantic Forest, Caatinga, Cerrado, Amazonia	1817–1820
José F.X. Sigaud/French	Atlantic Forest	1825–1856
George Gardner/English	Caatinga, Cerrado (PI, BA, TO, GO, MG)	1836–1841
Pedro Napoleão Chernoviz/Polish	All regions of Brazil	1840–1855
Theodor Peckolt/German	All regions of Brazil	1847–1912
Manuel Pio Corrêa/Portuguese	All regions of Brazil	1926–1934

Publications containing the original works:

Chernoviz PLN. A Grande Farmacopeia Brasileira. Formulário e Guia médico. Vols. 1–2. 19a Edição. Belo Horizonte: Ed. Itatiaia; 1996. 1475p.

Correa MP. Dicionário das plantas úteis do Brasil e das exóticas cultivadas. Vols. 1–6. Rio de Janeiro: Ministério da Agricultura, IBDF; 1984.

Gardner G. Viagem ao Interior do Brasil. Belo Horizonte: Itatiaia; São Paulo: Editora da Universidade de São Paulo; 1975. 260p.

Gomes BA. Observações botanico-medicas sobre algumas plantas do Brasil, Memorias da Real Academia das Sciencias de Lisboa, t. III, 1812, 1812, pp. 1–104. Em B. A. Gomes, Plantas medicinais do Brasil, São Paulo, Editora da Universidade de São Paulo; 1972. 226p.

Piso G. História Natural do Brasil Ilustrada. Tradução Prof. Alexandre Correia. Rio de Janeiro: Companhia Editora Nacional; 1948. 434p.

Saint-Hilaire A. Plantas Usuais dos Brasileiros. Belo Horizonte: Fino Traço; 2014. 342p.

Sigaud JFX. Do Clima e das Doenças do Brasil ou estatística médica deste império. Rio de Janeiro: Editora Fiocruz; 2009. 422p.

Silva DB. Diários de Langsdorff. Vols. 1–3. Rio de Janeiro: Editora da FIOCRUZ; 1997.

Sousa GS. Tratado Descritivo do Brasil em 1587. São Paulo: Companhia Editora Nacional; 1987. 389p.

Peckolt T, Peckolt G. História das Plantas Medicinais e Úteis do Brasil. 1. ed. Belo Horizonte: Fino Traço; 2016. 900p.

Spix JB, Martius CFP. Viagem pelo Brasil (1817–1820). Vols. 1–3. Belo Horizonte: Itatiaia; São Paulo: Editora da Universidade de São Paulo; 1981.

Vellozo JMC. Florae Fluminensis, seu Descriptionum Plantarum Praefectura. Flumine Januario, Apud Machado & C.: Rio de Janeiro; 1881. 461p.

various ailments. Examples of these works are those produced by doctors Xavier Sigaud and Pedro Chernoviz, the pharmacist Theodor Peckolt, and the botanist Manuel Pio Corrêa (Table 2.1). Sigaud (1796–1856) was a French doctor who arrived in Brazil shortly after independence and developed his medical career in Rio de Janeiro. He has recorded the history of Pharmacy in Brazil, which he considered the most important profession, given the available vegetable wealth. The therapeutic indication for several native plants was described in detail in his book, thus representing an important source of medical information. Chernoviz (1812–1881) was Polish, studied medicine in Montpellier, and came to Rio de Janeiro in early 1840, where he lived for 15 years. Chernoviz wrote, a year after his arrival, the "Medical Dictionary and Guide" (*Dicionário e Guia Médico*), followed by the "Dictionary of Popular Medicine" (*Dicionário de Medicina Popular*). His interest in the properties of native plants was great, and he started to incorporate several of them in subsequent editions of his books. The first edition of the Medical Dictionary and Guide, published in 1841, includes the description and use of 37 species. The latest edition, published by one of his sons in Paris in 1920, provides information on 224 Brazilian plants. Theodor Peckolt (1822–1912) was a German pharmacist who came to Brazil in 1847 under the influence of Von Martius. He spent his entire life in Rio de Janeiro, where he built a chemistry laboratory. In that he was a pioneer in identifying active substances from Atlantic Forest plants. In his work History of Medicinal and Useful Plants of Brazil (1888–1902), divided into eight issues, he left important references on the best use of Brazilian plants and some exotic cultures. The Portuguese Manuel Pio Corrêa (1874–1934) lived in Rio de Janeiro and was linked to the Botanical Garden. He was also a member of the Société Botanique de France. The works developed by this author gave rise to important publications, the six volumes of the *Dictionary of Useful Plants of Brazil and Exotic Cultivated*, which preparation began in 1926. His work contains botanical information of traditional use and places where almost 5000 species occur, 2000 natives to Brazil.

Some native species, registered by the authors cited in Table 2.1, were included in the first edition of the Brazilian Pharmacopoeia, attesting to their importance in both traditional and conventional medicine practised at the time. The Portuguese Pharmacopoeia was used in Brazil until the beginning of the 20th century. However, a group of Brazilian pharmacists then started a movement to elaborate an official Brazilian Pharmacopoeia completed in 1926. The pharmacist Rodolpho Albino Dias da Silva (known as Rodolpho Albino) was responsible for this important work. Rodolpho Albino was born in 1889 and graduated in Pharmacy in Rio de Janeiro in 1909.

Many species described by Saint-Hilaire, for example, were also included in the Brazilian Pharmacopoeia, such as mate (*Ilex paraguariensis* A. St.-Hil.), quina-do-campo (*Strychnos pseudoquina* A. St.-Hil.), butua (*Chondrodendron platyphyllum* [A. St.-Hil.] Miers), and quina-mineira (*Remijia ferruginea* [A. St.-Hil.] DC). However, despite the importance of these and other native medicinal species as remedies, the number of monographs was drastically reduced in the following editions. Among the species described by Saint-Hilaire, for example, only the monograph for butua (*C. platyphyllum* [A. St. Hil.] Miers) was maintained in the second edition, published in 1959. In its third edition, published in 1977, there are monographs for only four native species: guaraná (*P. cupana*), passion fruit (*Passiflora alata* Curtis), ipecac (*C. ipecacuanha*), and jaborandi (*Pilocarpus jaborandi* Holmes). The reduction of the number of monographs for native herbs in the Brazilian Pharmacopoeia resulted from the intense transformations occurring in Brazilian society in the 20th century, especially from the 1950s. There was a diversification of the country's economy, with the implantation of a Brazilian industrial park and a major cultural reorganisation. The arrival of international pharmaceutical companies and the massive introduction of synthetic medicines also contributed to replacing herbal-based medicines with synthetic ones. The decade of the 1970s is also characterised by intense repression against mysticism, including the traditional use of plants. These processes contributed to a lack of interest from the industry and the population in medicinal plants and products native to Brazil.

Recently, however, two new editions of the Brazilian Pharmacopoeia (fifth and sixth) have presented an increase in the number of monographs for Brazilian plants, showing an increasing awareness of the importance of native plant species to produce phytomedicines. The latest editions were organised by the Brazilian government agency responsible for the regulation of medicines, pharmaceuticals, among others (ANVISA), and incorporates the needs for the development of herbal products with the highest standards of quality, efficiency, and safety similar to those required for synthetic products in Brazil.

2.3 THE DATAPLAMT

As described in the previous sections, traditional knowledge associated with plant species is very valuable, and historical records are a rich source of this information. To contribute to the valorisation of useful native plant species and subsequent development of an economy based on the sustainable use of biodiversity, during the last decade, our research group has focused on retrieving traditional information about useful Brazilian plants from manuscripts and bibliographies published until the 1950s. Each work is carefully revised, searching for data regarding the use of plants, and some of the updated information is then publicised [9, 12–14]. Furthermore, the recorded information is organised into an online database named Dataplamt (www.dataplamt.org.br), built to organise and make it readily available.

In Dataplamt, the search for information can be done through links referring to popular and scientific names, traditional uses, places where the plant occurs, and in addition to the text about the plant extracted entirely from the original books or documents. To date, Dataplamt contains information on 3,400 different species of useful Brazilian plants, recovered from 75 documents. The most representative botanical family is Fabaceae, with 468 species, followed by Poaceae with 164, Arecaceae 137, Asteraceae 108, Malvaceae 101, Myrtaceae and Rubiaceae 95, Bromeliaceae 94, and Euphorbiaceae 87. Other 138 botanical families also have species described in the database. It is important to note that Dataplamt is still not completed—only 40% of the information about the plant is included to date, and including new data is a continuous work.

Considering the WHO recommendations on the traditionality and validation of useful plant species, it is shown here specifically how to find in the Dataplamt database plant species with registered uses to treat respiratory diseases (RD). The reason for that choice is the current global health emergency imposed by COVID-19, the disease caused by the SARS-CoV-2 virus. COVID-19 is a disease that begins as a respiratory infection. However, it can quickly evolve into a systemic inflammatory syndrome, which has caused more than five million deaths, having infected more than 250 million people worldwide (November, 2021, official data from WHO).

2.4 SEARCHING DATA ON THE TRADITIONAL USE OF BRAZILIAN PLANTS WITH POTENTIAL BENEFITS TO TREAT COVID-19

Our search in Dataplamt for traditional uses of medicinal plants to treat RDs was divided into three keywords: "respiratory disease" (RD), "pulmonary disease" (PD), and "chest *affection*" (CA). The last term lacks anatomic precision in the current days but was frequently used in older scientific texts. It was included to increase the chances of finding useful information because the texts added to Dataplamt are direct transcripts of the original materials published in previous centuries.

A list of species found for each category was formulated and presented in Table 2.2. The website Flora do Brasil was used to confirm the current botanical names and whether the species was native of Brazil. It is necessary to point out the difficulties in identifying the species from books published between the 16th and 18th centuries because Taxonomy as a field of knowledge as it is known today was only established in the late 18th century, and the rules of botanical nomenclature did not exist until the beginning of the 20th century.

Data on recent laboratory studies on the bioactivity of the plant species found in the first search were obtained from PubMed and included in Table 2.2. The search was conducted using the plant species name followed by the keywords: pulmonary; respiratory; cough; pneumonia; anticoagulant; coagulation; asthma; lung; trachea; relaxant; antibacterial; and antiviral. Concerning antibacterial activity, studies with the following respiratory pathogens were selected: *Klebsiella pneumoniae*; *Streptococcus pneumoniae; Pseudomonas aeruginosa; Staphylococcus aureus;* Methicillin-resistant *Staphylococcus aureus; Mycobacterium tuberculosis; Mycobacterium abscessus; and Streptococcus pyogenes.* Works citing the Influenza virus, Rhinovirus, Adenovirus, and Human coronavirus were also selected for being respiratory pathogens. We also decided to include studies with rotavirus and HIV-1 because their replication mechanisms and some molecular targets might be similar to coronavirus. When found on PubMed, studies about taxonomic correlated plant species (for example, same genus but not necessarily a native species from Brazil) were also included in Table 2.2, considering the possibility of similar chemical compositions of the native Brazilian ones.

2.4.1 Results and Discussion

The current global health emergency imposed by COVID-19 has brought several challenges to pharmaceutical development, which are currently being addressed by different strategies, such as *in silico* analysis and *in vitro* screenings aimed at drug repurposing. Ten months after WHO officially declared it a pandemic, supportive care and nonspecific treatments for a wide variety of symptoms are still the main options found to improve the disease outcomes. In China, where the SARS-CoV-2 virus emerged, many patients have been treated with formulations from the traditional Chinese medicine system (TCM), in a similar approach to the SARS-CoV outbreak from 2002 to 2003. Traditional medicine systems from India, Iran, and South Africa, for example, are also being investigated for useful plant species and formulations to treat COVID-19 [127, 215].

TABLE 2.2
Species Studied from the Dataplamt with Their Proven Biological or Pharmacological Activities

Family/Species in Dataplamt/ Traditional Uses/Studies	Other Related Species with Studies, Activities, and Chemical Substances	Ref.
ADOXACEAE *Sambucus australis* Cham & Schlecht./CA Antibacterial (*K. pneumoniae*); antiviral (Influenza A H1N1, FluA H1N1); Influenza virus type A and B (clinical study); Rhinovirus B subtype 14 (HRV14), (RSV); Adenovirus C subtype 5 (Adeno 5); Human coronavirus NL63 (*HCoV-NL63*)	*S. formosana; S. nigra* respiratory Phenolic compounds: caffeic acid, chlorogenic acid, rutin, quercetin, anthocyanins (cyanidin-3-glucoside and cyanidin 3-sambubioside), triterpene acids (ursolic acid)	[15–21]
ARECACEAE *Syagrus macrocarpa* Barb. Rodr./CA	*S. coronata* antibacterial (*S. aureus*)	[22]
ARISTOLOCHIACEAE *Aristolochia arcuata* Mast./PD	*A. brevipes* and *A. taliscana* antituberculosis (in vitro/ mice) (*M. tuberculosis*); *Aristolochia* sp. acute lung injury; *A. papillaris* tracheal muscle relaxant (guinea pig isolated tracheal chain) Neolignans: licarin A, licarin B, and eupomatenoid-7; aristolactam I—antituberculosis Alkaloids: magnoflorine—reduce acute lung injury (inflammation) induced by LPS; coclaurine, moupinamide, and isoboldine—tracheal muscle relaxant	[23–25]
ASTERACEAE *Acanthospermum hispidum* DC./CA Antibacterial (*S. aureus, S. pyogenes*)	Sesquiterpene lactone: acanthospermal B—antibacterial (MRSA)	[26–29]
Elephantopus mollis Kunth./CA Anti-asthmatic (preclinical, rats, and Guinea pigs), anti-RSV	—	[30, 31]
Pluchea sagittalis (Lam.) Cabrera/CA	*P. indica* antibacterial (*M. tuberculosis*), antiviral (HIV-1), *P. ovalis* tracheal muscle relaxant	[32–34]

(Continued)

TABLE 2.2 ***(Continued)***
Species Studied from the Dataplamt with Their Proven Biological or Pharmacological Activities

Family/Species in Dataplamt/ Traditional Uses/Studies	Other Related Species with Studies, Activities, and Chemical Substances	Ref.
Mikania guaco Kunth./RD	*M. glomerata* antibacterial (*S. aureus*), lung injury (preclinical), chronic obstructive pulmonary disease (preclinical), tracheal muscle relaxant (preclinical), anticoagulant *M. laevigata* anti-asthmatic (anti-inflammatory activity in the allergic inflammation) (preclinical), anticoagulant (preclinical), lung injury (preclinical), tracheal muscle relaxant (preclinical), anticoagulant, *M. micrantha* antiviral (RSV, parainfluenza type 3), and antibacterial (*S. aureus*) *M. cordata* antibacterial (*S. aureus*) Germacrene type-sesquiterpene, sesquiterpene dilactones (*M. micrantha*) Coumarin and o-coumaric acid	[35–47]
Stomatanthes oblongifolius (Spreng.) H. Rob./PD	*S. africanus* antibacterial (*S. aureus*)	[48]
BIXACEAE *Bixa orellana* L./CA Antibacterial (*S. aureus* [*in vitro*/ mice], *S. pyogenes, P. aeruginosa, M. abscessus*); anti-histaminic (preclinical)		[49–54]
BORAGINACEAE *Heliotropium elongatum* (Lehm.) I.M. Johnst/RD	*H. strigosum* bronchodilator; *H. subulatum* antibacterial (*S. aureus*) Flavonoids: pinocembrin	[55, 56]
BROMELIACEAE *Bromelia antiacantha* Bertol./CA	*B. balansae* antibacterial (*M. tuberculosis*) (moderate), anticoagulant; *B. hieronymi*—pro and anticoagulant (dose dependent) Flavonol glycosides: kaempferol-3-O-α-L-rhamnopyranoside, kaempferol-3-O-α-L-rhamnopyranosyl-(1-->6)-ß-D-glucopyranoside, quercetin-3-O-α-L-rhamnopyranosyl-(1-->6)-ß-d-glucopyranoside, kaempferol 3,7-di-O-α-L-rhamnopyranoside	[57, 58]
Ananas comosus (L.) Merrill./PD Allergic asthma (preclinical); no benefit on cough (clinic-controlled placebo trial); antibacterial (*M. tuberculosis*)	Bromelain	[59–63]

(Continued)

TABLE 2.2 ***(Continued)***
Species Studied from the Dataplamt with Their Proven Biological or Pharmacological Activities

Family/Species in Dataplamt/ Traditional Uses/Studies	Other Related Species with Studies, Activities, and Chemical Substances	Ref.
BURSERACEAE *Protium heptaphyllum* March/RD Antibacterial (*S. aureus*)	*P. confusum* antibacterial (*S. aureus*) Oleoresin: essential oil/monoterpenes	[64–68]
CAPPARACEAE *Crataeva tapia L./CA* Anticoagulant (preclinical/mice)	*C. nurvala* antibacterial (*P. aeruginosa*) Lectin, lupeol	[69–71]
CARYOCARACEAE *Caryocar coriaceum* Wittm./PD Antibacterial (*S. aureus*, MRSA); prevent lung injury	Fixed oil	[72–75]
CECROPIACEAE *Cecropia hololeuca* Miq./RD	*C. glaziovii:* bronchodilator (preclinical—guinea pigs), tracheal muscle relaxant	[76–80]
CONVOLVULACEAE *Cuscuta racemosa* Mart./CA	*C. reflexa* thrombolytic, antifungal (*A. niger*); *C. kotchiana* antiviral (HIV-1); *C. pedicellata* antibacterial (*Acinetobacter baumannii, S. aureus, K. pneumoniae, P. aeruginosa*) Pratensein, pratensein glucoside	[81–86]
CYATHEACEAE *Cyathea microdonta* (Desv.) Domin./RD	*C. gigantea* antibacterial (*S. aureus, P. aeruginosa*)	[87]
EUPHORBIACEAE *Euphorbia hirta* L./RD Anti-asthma (preclinical/mice and rats); bronchodilator (preclinical/guinea pigs); antiviral (HIV-1 and 2, Dengue); fribrinolytic/ anticoagulant; antibacterial (*P. aeruginosa, S. aureus, K. pneumoniae*)	*E. thymifolia* (anti-asthma), *E. prostrata* anti-asthma (preclinical/guinea pigs); *E. maculata* anticoagulant (preclinical); *E. nivulia* procoagulant *E. humifusa* antiviral (Influenza type A and B) *E. jolkinii* antiviral (RSV); *E. lathyris* reduces acute lung injury (preclinical/mice); *Euphorbia* cf. *lactea* anticoagulant *Euphorbia granulata, Euphorbia helioscobia* (*K. pneumoniae, S. aureus*) and antifungal (*Aspergillus fumigatus*) Tannins: 1,3,4,6-tetra-O-galloyl-b-D-glucopyranoside (TGBG); diterpenes, caffeic acid, epicatechin-3-gallate; flavonoids: quercetin, kaempferol, latex	[88–107]
FABACEAE *Amburana cearensis* (Allemao) A.C.Sm./CA Trachea muscle relaxant; antibacterial (*S. aureus; K. pneumoniae*)	Flavonoids: isokaempferide; coumarin; Methoxy-methylphenol compounds	[108–112]

(Continued)

TABLE 2.2 *(Continued)*
Species Studied from the Dataplamt with Their Proven Biological or Pharmacological Activities

Family/Species in Dataplamt/ Traditional Uses/Studies	Other Related Species with Studies, Activities, and Chemical Substances	Ref.
Anadenanthera colubrina (Vell.) Brenan/CA/RD Antibacterial (*S. aureus; P. aeruginosa*) Condensed tannins	—	[108, 113–115]
Enterolobium gummiferum (Mart.) J.F. Macbr./PD	*E. contortisiliquum* anti-asthma, attenuates bronchial hyperresponsiveness, chronic obstructive pulmonary disease, haemolytic, anticoagulant; antibacterial (*S. aureus, K. pneumoniae*)	[116–118]
Dipteryx odorata (Aubl.) Willd./ RD Anticoagulant	*D. micrantha* antibacterial (*S. aureus*—low activity) coumarin	[119–121]
Geoffroea spinosa Jacq./CA Anticoagulant; antibacterial (*S. aureus, P. aeruginosa, K. pneumoniae*)	*G. decorticans* antibacterial (*S. aureus, P. aeruginosa, K. pneumoniae*), anticoagulant Polysaccharides	[122–124]
Hymenaea courbaril L./ CA Antiviral (rotavirus); antibacterial (*S. aureus, P. aeruginosa*) tracheal muscle relaxant; asthma	*H. verrucosa* preventive measure/sanitising for COVID-19; *H. rubriflora* antibacterial (*S. aureus, P. aeruginosa, K. pneumoniae*), *H. eriogyne* antibacterial (*P. aeruginosa*), *H. cangaceira* antibacterial (*S. aureus, P. aeruginosa, K. pneumoniae*); *H. martiana* antibacterial (*S. aureus*); *H. parvifolia* anti-asthma Flavonoids: astilbin; coumarins; volatile oil	[125–130]
Hymenaea stigonocarpa Mart. ex Hayne/CA Antibacterial (*S. aureus*)	Flavonoids: astilbin Coumarins, condensed tannins	[131]
Libidibia ferrea (Mart. Ex Tul.) L.P. Queiroz/PD/CA Antibacterial (*S. aureus*)	Tannins	[132, 133]
Mimosa caesalpiniifolia Benth./ CA Antibacterial (*S. aureus*)	*M. pigra* attenuates hypoxic pulmonary hypertension (preclinical/rats), *M. pudica* anti-asthma (preclinical/ mice); *M. himalayana* antibacterial (*P. aeruginosa*) Tryptophane, quercetin glycosides	[108, 134–137]
Myroxylon peruiferum L./CA Antibacterial (*S. aureus*)	Many studies with the genus as a cause of allergies Isoflavones; volatile oil	[138]
Piptadenia polyptera Benth./CA	*P. stipulacea* trachea muscle relaxant (preclinical/ guinea pig) Flavonoids: galetin 3,6-dimethyl ether	[139–141]

(Continued)

TABLE 2.2 *(Continued)*
Species Studied from the Dataplamt with Their Proven Biological or Pharmacological Activities

Family/Species in Dataplamt/ Traditional Uses/Studies	Other Related Species with Studies, Activities, and Chemical Substances	Ref.
LAMIACEAE *Cunila spicata* Benth./CA Antiviral (Adenovirus type 2); antibacterial (*S. pneumoniae, S. pyogenes, S. salivarius*)		[142, 143]
Hyptis radicans (Pohl. Harley & J.F.B. Pastore)/CA	*H. lantanifolia* antiviral (HIV-reverse transcriptase); *H. capitata* antiviral (HIV-1), procoagulant; *H. verticillata* antibacterial (*S. aureus*); *Hyptis fasciculata* antibacterial (*S. pneumoniae, S. pyogenes, S. salivarius*); *H. crenata* antibacterial (*S. aureus*) Lignans; alkaloids; mono and diterpenes; pomolic acid; oleanolic acid	[65, 143–147]
Vitex megapotamica (Spreng.) Moldenke/CA	*V. negundo*—antitussive (preclinical), bronchodilator (preclinical) *V. rotundifolia*—anti-asthma (preclinical) *Vitex agnus-castus*—prevent acute lung injury (preclinical) 1H,8H-pyrano[3,4-c]pyran-1,8-dione; casticin; vitexin	[148–156]
LORANTHACEAE *Struthanthus marginatus* (Desr.) Blume/CA	*S. concinnus* antibacterial (*M. tuberculosis*) *S. orbicularis* procoagulant	[51, 157]
Tripodanthus acutifolius (Ruiz & Pav.) Tiegh./CA Antibacterial (*S. aureus, P. aeruginosa*)	Flavonoids: rutin, nicotiflorin, isoquercitrin, hyperoside and rutin, isoquercitrin, hyperoside, quercetin, kaempferol; tripodantoside	[158, 159]
MALPIGHIACEAE *Byrsonima crassifolia* (L.) Kunth./RD Antibacterial (*S. aureus, K. pneumoniae, S. pneumoniae, P. aeruginosa*)	*Byrsonima intermedia* antibacterial (*S. aureus*) *Byrsonima verbaascifolia* antiviral (rotavirus)	[126, 160, 161]
MALVACEAE *Guazuma ulmifolia* Lam./CA Antibacterial (*S. aureus, P. aeruginosa*)	— Proanthocyanidins; flavon coumarins: epiphyllocoumarin-[4β→8]-epicatechin, epiphyllocoumarin-[4β→8]-epicatechin-[4β→8]-epicatechin	[65, 162–166]
Helicteres pentandra L./CA	*H. angustifolia* anti-complement activity (excess of complement activity can lead to acute respiratory distress syndrome) Phenalenon derivatives, lignans, flavonoid glycosides	[167–169]

(Continued)

TABLE 2.2 *(Continued)*
Species Studied from the Dataplamt with Their Proven Biological or Pharmacological Activities

Family/Species in Dataplamt/ Traditional Uses/Studies	Other Related Species with Studies, Activities, and Chemical Substances	Ref.
Urena lobata L./CA Antibacterial (*S. aureus*)	*U. sinuata* thrombolytic	[170, 171]
Waltheria communis A. St.-Hil./ PD/CA	*W. indica* tracheal muscle relaxant, anti asthma (–)–epicatechin	[172]
MYRTACEAE *Eugenia uniflora* L./CA Antibacterial (*S. aureus*)	*E. brasiliensis* treatment of chronic obstructive pulmonary disease (COPD) Anthocyanins	[126, 173–176]
PASSIFLORACEAE *Passiflora edulis* Sims./RD Reduction of pulmonar fibrosis (preclinical); anticough and anti-asthma (clinical); anticoagulant	*P. incarnata* antitussive (preclinical) *P. quadrangularis* procoagulant (pre-clinical) Vitexin-rich extracts of *Passiflora* spp. anti-asthma	[155, 177–180]
POLYGALACEAE *Caamembeca spectabilis* (DC.) J.F.B.Pastore/CA	*P. caudata* influenza H1N1 Polygalasaponin F	[181, 182]
PTERIDACEAE *Adiantum subcordatum* Sw./CA	*A. capillus-veneris* antibacterial (*K. pneumoniae, S. aureus*), anti-asthma (preclinical), prevent hypoxia-related lung injury (preclinical); *A. philippense* thrombolytic Triterpenoids	[183–185]
Pityrogramma calomelanos (L.) Link./PD/CA Antibacterial (*S. aureus*)	—	[186]
SAPOTACEAE *Manilkara excelsa* (Ducke) Standl./CA	*M. zapota* antiviral (anti-HIV-1 reverse transcriptase); antibacterial (*S. aureus, K. pneumoniae, P. aeruginosa*); *M. subsericea* (*S. aureus*) Amyrin esters; prenylated coumarins	[187–190]
Pouteria caimito (Ruiz & Pav.) Radlk./PD	*P. viridis* antiviral (HIV)	[191]
SIPARUNACEAE *Siparuna guianensis* Aubl./CA Antibacterial (*S. aureus*)	Volatile oil	[192]
VERBENACEAE *Lantana fucata* Lindl./CA Antibacterial (*M. tuberculosis*)	*L. camara, L. trifolia, L. hispida* antibacterial (*M. tuberculosis*) Flavonoids: linaroside, lantanoside, acetyl linaroside; oleanane- and ursane-type triterpenes; volatile oil (sesquiterpenes)	[193–198]

(Continued)

TABLE 2.2 ***(Continued)***
Species Studied from the Dataplamt with Their Proven Biological or Pharmacological Activities

Family/Species in Dataplamt/ Traditional Uses/Studies	Other Related Species with Studies, Activities, and Chemical Substances	Ref.
Lippia brasiliensis (Link.) T.R.S. Silva/CA	*L. alba* antibacterial (*S. aureus*), antiviral (influenza virus type A); *L. sidoides* reduces lung emphysema; *L. origanoides* tracheal muscle relaxant, *L. alnifolia* tracheal muscle relaxant; *L. graveolens* antiviral (RSV); *L. dulcis* bronchospasms; *L. microphylla* antibacterial (*S. aureus, S. pyogenes*)	[199–211]
	Volatile oil (monoterpenes): *p*-cymene, carvacrol, thymol, carvone	
Verbena bonariensis L./CA	*V. carolina* antibacterial (*S. aureus*—slightly active)	[212, 213]
VOCHYSIACEAE	—	[214]
Vochysia thyrsoidea Pohl./ RD/CA Anticoagulant	Gum exudate (glycoglucuronomannan)	

Abbreviations: CA = chest affections; RD = respiratory diseases; PD = pulmonary disease.

In Brazil, the records on the traditional use of plants are scarcer and more scattered. However, Dataplamt, created by our group, is a vast source of primary information on useful native Brazilian plant species. Using the keywords RD, PD, and CA, we found a total of 96 Brazilian plant species, 29 of them already submitted to bioactivity studies (usually *in vitro* or preclinical) that have confirmed activities correlated to various RDs and infections. Table 2.2 shows these studied species, their demonstrated bioactivity, and when described, chemical composition. Data from studies done with other species taxonomically correlated were also included, showing the potential of the genus and botanical families in substances to treat respiratory affections. Another 36 plants present in Dataplamt have not yet been be studied to verify bioactivity and were included in Table 2.3.

The 29 studied species from Dataplamt belong to 18 botanical families. The family with higher number of species is Fabaceae (9), followed by Asteraceae and Malvaceae (2 species each). The other 15 families have one studied species each. These results suggest a wide variety of structurally different chemical substances but useful to treat problems in respiratory system. Table 2.3 shows that among the nine Fabaceae species, three are traditionally used to treat chest affection (CA) (*Amburana cearensis* [Allemão] A.C.Sm; *Dipteryx odorata* [Aubl.] Willd, and *Geoffroea spinosa* Jacq.) and have coumarins, showing anticoagulant and/or trachea muscle relaxant effects. It is currently very well established that blood coagulation disorders are the basis of the most serious symptoms of COVID-19, among them respiratory failure and pulmonary fibrosis. It occurs due to clogging of small vessels in the lung and causing microinfarctions. Heparin-treated patients are usually better

TABLE 2.3
Species from Dataplamt Not Yet Studied

Family/Species from Dataplamt	Traditional Uses
Amaryllidaceae	PD
Hippeastrum vittatum (L'Her) Herb.	
Apocynaceae	PD/CA
Parahancornia fasciculata (Poir.) Benoist	
Arecaceae	CA
Syagrus romanzoffiana (Cham.) Glassman	
Araucariaceae	PD
Araucaria angustifolia (Bertol.) Kuntze	
Asteraceae	CA
Moquiniastrum polymorphum (Less.) G. Sancho	
Bignoniaceae	CA
Anemopaegma arvense (Vell.) Stellfeld ex de Souza	
Cactaceae	PD/CA
Cereus jamacaru D.C.	
Fabaceae	PD
Anadenanthera peregrina L.	
Cenostigma bracteosum (Tul.) E. Gagnon & G.P. Lewis	CA
Periandra mediterranea (Vell.) Taub.	PD
Cunila microcephala Benth.	PD
Lauraceae	CA
Aniba canelilla (Kunth.) Mez	
Malvaceae	CA
Helicteres ovata Lam.	
Sidastrum micranthum (A. St.-Hil.) Fryxell	CA
Sphaeralcea cisplatin A. St.-Hil	CA
Sphaeralcea bonariensis (Cav.) Griseb.	
Sterculia apetala (Jacq.) H. Karst.	CA
Ochnaceae	PD/CA
Sauvagesia erecta L.	
Orchidaceae	CA
Cyrtopodium glutiniferum Raddi.	
Passifloraceae	PD
Passiflora quadrangularis L.	
Polygalaceae	CA
Acanthocladus brasiliensis (A.St.-Hil. & Moq.) Klotzsch ex Hassk.	
Pteridaceae	PD
Adiantopsis chlorophylla (Sw.) Fée.	
Adiantopsis radiata (L.) Fée.	CA
Adiantum trapeziforme L.	CA
Rubiaceae	PD
Carapichea ipecacuanha (Brot.) L. Andersson	

(Continued)

TABLE 2.3 *(Continued)*
Species from Dataplamt Not Yet Studied

Family/Species from Dataplamt	Traditional Uses
Rutaceae	CA
Ertela trifolia (L.) Kuntze	
Sapotaceae	CA
Pouteria procera (Mart.) K. Hammer	
Pradosia lactescens (Vell.) Radlk.	CA
Siparunaceae	CA
Siparuna brasiliensis (Spreng.) A SDc	
Thelypteridaceae	CA
Thelypteris patens (Sw.) Small.	
Urticaceae	CA
Urera aurantiaca Wedd.	
Urera caracasana (Jacq.) Griseb.	PD/CA
Verbenaceae	CA
Lippia geminata H.B.K.	
Lippia macrophylla Cham.	CA
Lippia pseudothea Schauer	CA
Violaceae	CA
Anchietea pyrifolia (Mart.) G.Don	

Abbreviations: CA = chest affections; RD = respiratory diseases; PD = pulmonary disease.

between the 10th and 14th days of intensive treatment. This occurs by two mechanisms: the drug breaks up the microthrombi that prevent oxygen from passing the alveolus into small pulmonary arteries and, in addition, helps in the recovery of the vascular endothelium [216, 217]. Considering that coumarins have the same effects as heparin, it can be speculated that some plants used in Brazilian traditional medicine could be useful in preventing the worst outcomes of COVID-19 in a hospital environment, possibly with fewer side effects than heparin.

Although *M. guaco* was not studied yet, the species is registered in Dataplamt as useful to treat RD. It was included in Table 2.2 because three other species of *Mikania* (*M. glomerata*, *M. laevigata,* and *M. cordata*) have shown antibacterial, anti-asthma, and anticoagulant effects, which are also correlated with the presence of coumarins. In a recent review in 2020, Silveira et al. showed data on 39 plant species used to treat RDs worldwide and discussed their potential for use as adjuvants in the treatment of COVID-19 [218]. Only three species are native to Brazil, which produce coumarins: *Justicia pectoralis* Jacq. (Acanthaceae) and *M. glomerata*/*Mikania laevigata* Sch.Bip. ex Baker (Asteraceae). *M. glomerata* and *M. laevigata* are very well-known medicinal plants, and their efficacy to treat respiratory troubles is recognised by the Brazilian Health Surveillance Agency (ANVISA).

Patients with SARS-CoV-2 develop a strong inflammatory reaction in the lung, leading to the development of a condition known as acute respiratory distress syndrome. The pulmonary alveoli are filled with dead cells, pus, and other inflammatory molecules. The lungs become hard and prevent proper oxygenation of the body [219, 220]. Anti-inflammatory drugs, such as dexamethasone, are currently used to treat these affections and have drastically reduced mortality of hospitalised COVID-19 patients [221, 222]. Table 2.2 shows that magnoflorin, an alkaloid from *Aristolochia* species, reduced acute lung injury (related to inflammation) in preclinical studies. A recent double-blinded placebo-controlled clinical trial, available as a preprint, has shown promising results on the efficacy of alkaloid colchicine to treat systemic inflammation in patients with severe acute respiratory syndrome [223]. *Mikania* spp. also show anti-inflammatory activity. Another study has shown the potential of flavonoids, like rutin and quercetin, in reducing the level of interleukin 6, a pro-inflammatory cytokine involved in the "cytokine storm", responsible for some severe infection-related complications [219, 220]. Flavonoids are widely distributed in plants and emerge as potential candidates for the development of drugs against SARS-Cov-2. Since 1951, the antiviral potential of flavonoids is known. Computational screenings show that these phenolic compounds present interesting results against key proteins involved in the infective virus cycle. The phenolic structure containing many hydroxyl moieties and glucosyl units is linked to glucosyl flavonoid's high ability to bind proteins by hydrogen bonds [224–226].

Many studies have been done with plants searching specific antiviral substances to treat COVID-19 [227–229]. Among species recorded in Dataplamt, only four were evaluated to date as antiviral. Some of them showed specific activity against types of coronavirus, as *Sambucus australis* Cham & Schlecht (Adoxaceae). In this case, a study of bioguided fractionation could be very useful in discovering molecules with anti-coronavirus activity and allowing the description of specific mechanisms of action.

Several species of the Dataplamt also exhibit broad-spectrum antibacterial activity against respiratory pathogens (including gram-positive and gram-negative bacteria). Although not directly related to the symptoms of COVID-19 and the disease progression, it is relevant to emphasise that hospitalised patients with COVID-19, especially those on mechanical ventilation, are highly prone to acquire secondary respiratory infections, which can aggravate the primary disease. It is possible that adjuvant antibacterial therapies can be useful in preventing secondary infections and improving patient outcomes. Therefore, it can be highlighted that some species found in our research have multiple biological activities that can be useful in the treatment of COVID-19. In addition to *Mikania*, another example is *Euphorbia hirta* L. (Euphorbiaceae), which has activities such as anti-asthma, anticoagulant, antibacterial, and antiviral that are also observed for other species of the genus *Euphorbia*.

2.5 CONCLUDING REMARKS

Traditional uses of plants are a valuable source of information for the discovery of new drugs and development of herbal medicines. Biodiversity loss and cultural erosion make urgent the necessity to register the traditional knowledge associated to the native flora. On the other hand, the study of data already documented by naturalists and scientists who came to Brazil or lived in the country between the

16th to the first half of the 20th centuries is extremely prominent and can be used for selection of plant species with potential to develop herbal medicines for new diseases. In this chapter, we showed a smart procedure to select relevant Brazilian plants that have the potential to be successfully used in the treatment of COVID-19. Relevant information on the traditional use and bioactive properties were acquired from the historical records of Dataplamt database, accomplished with the websites *Flora do Brasil* and PubMed. Finally, it is important to emphasise that incentives for the development of products based on Brazilian biodiversity used in traditional medicine should be strongly encouraged, especially in times of health emergencies such as the current global pandemic.

REFERENCES

1. WHO, *The World Medicines Situation 2011. Traditional Medicines: Global Situation, Issues and Challenges.* 2011, World Health Organization, Geneva.
2. WHO, *WHO Traditional Medicine Strategy: 2014–2023.* 2013, World Health Organization, Geneva.
3. Ricardo, L.M., et al., *Evidence of traditionality of Brazilian medicinal plants: The case studies of* Stryphnodendron adstringens *(Mart.) Coville (*barbatimão*) barks and* Copaifera *spp. (copaíba) oleoresin in wound healing.* J Ethnopharmacol, 2018. **219**: pp. 319–336.
4. Flora do Brasil, e.c. *Flora do Brasil.* 2020 11th September 2021; Available from: http://floradobrasil.jbrj.gov.br/.
5. Ulloa Ulloa, C., et al., *An integrated assessment of the vascular plant species of the Americas.* Science, 2017. **358**(6370): pp. 1614–1617.
6. Bockmann, F.A., et al., *Brazil's government attacks biodiversity.* Science, 2018. **360**(6391): pp. 865–865.
7. Mügge, F.L.B., et al., *Native plant species with economic value from Minas Gerais and Goiás: A discussion on the currentness of the data recovered by the French naturalist Auguste de Saint-Hilaire.* Horticultura Brasileira, 2016. **34**(4): pp. 455–462.
8. Palhares, R.M., et al., *The use of an integrated molecular-, chemical- and biological-based approach for promoting the better use and conservation of medicinal species: A case study of Brazilian quinas.* J Ethnopharmacol, 2014. **155**(1): pp. 815–822.
9. Teixeira, N., et al., *Edible fruits from Brazilian biodiversity: A review on their sensorial characteristics versus bioactivity as tool to select research.* Food Res Int, 2019. **119**: pp. 325–348.
10. Carvalho, A.C.B., et al., *The Brazilian market of herbal medicinal products and the impacts of the new legislation on traditional medicines.* J Ethnopharmacol, 2018. **212**: pp. 29–35.
11. Dutra, R.C., et al., *Medicinal plants in Brazil: Pharmacological studies, drug discovery, challenges and perspectives.* Pharmacol Res, 2016. **112**: pp. 4–29.
12. Brandão, M.G.L., et al., *Useful Brazilian plants listed in the field books of the French naturalist Auguste de Saint-Hilaire (1779–1853).* J Ethnopharmacol, 2012. **143**(2): pp. 488–500.
13. Fagg, C.W., et al., *Useful Brazilian plants listed in the manuscripts and publications of the Scottish medic and naturalist George Gardner (1812–1849).* J Ethnopharmacol, 2015. **161**: pp. 18–29.
14. Breitbach, U.B., et al., *Amazonian Brazilian medicinal plants described by C.F.P. von Martius in the 19th century.* J Ethnopharmacol, 2013. **147**(1): pp. 180–189.

15. Benevides Bahiense, J., et al., *Potential anti-inflammatory, antioxidant and antimicrobial activities of* Sambucus australis. Pharm Biol, 2017. **55**(1): pp. 991–997.
16. Fal, A.M., et al., *Antiviral activity of the "Virus Blocking Factor" (VBF) derived i.a. from* Pelargonium *extract and* Sambucus *juice against different human-pathogenic cold viruses in vitro.* Wiad Lek, 2016. **69**(3 pt 2): pp. 499–511.
17. Glatthaar-Saalmüller, B., et al., *Antiviral activity in vitro of two preparations of the herbal medicinal product Sinupret® against viruses causing respiratory infections.* Phytomedicine, 2011. **19**(1): pp. 1–7.
18. Hawkins, J., et al., *Black elderberry (*Sambucus nigra*) supplementation effectively treats upper respiratory symptoms: A meta-analysis of randomized, controlled clinical trials.* Complement Ther Med, 2019. **42**: pp. 361–365.
19. Weng, J.R., et al., *Antiviral activity of* Sambucus formosana *Nakai ethanol extract and related phenolic acid constituents against human coronavirus* NL63. Virus Res, 2019. **273**: pp. 197767.
20. Zakay-Rones, Z., et al., *Inhibition of several strains of influenza virus in vitro and reduction of symptoms by an elderberry extract (*Sambucus nigra *L.) during an outbreak of influenza B Panama.* J Altern Complement Med, 1995. **1**(4): pp. 361–369.
21. Zakay-Rones, Z., et al., *Randomized study of the efficacy and safety of oral elderberry extract in the treatment of influenza A and B virus infections.* J Int Med Res, 2004. **32**(2): pp. 132–140.
22. Souza Dos Santos, B., et al., *Anti-staphylococcal activity of* Syagrus coronata *essential oil: Biofilm eradication and in vivo action on* Galleria mellonela *infection model.* Microb Pathog, 2019. **131**: pp. 150–157.
23. Gómez-Cansino, R., et al., *Natural compounds from Mexican medicinal plants as potential drug leads for anti-tuberculosis drugs.* An Acad Bras Cienc, 2017. **89**(1): pp. 31–43.
24. Guo, S., et al., *Magnoflorine ameliorates lipopolysaccharide-induced acute lung injury via suppressing NF-κB and MAPK activation.* Front Pharmacol, 2018. **9**: pp. 982.
25. León-Díaz, R., et al., *Antitubercular activity and the subacute toxicity of (-)-Licarin A in BALB/c mice: A neolignan isolated from* Aristolochia taliscana. Arch Med Res, 2013. **44**(2): pp. 99–104.
26. Arena, M.E., et al., *In vivo and in vitro antibacterial activity of acanthospermal B, a sesquiterpene lactone isolated from* Acanthospermum hispidum. Phytother Res, 2011. **25**(4): pp. 597–602.
27. Rocha Martins, L.R., et al., *In vitro antiviral activity from* Acanthospermum australe *on herpesvirus and poliovirus.* Pharm Biol, 2011. **49**(1): pp. 26–31.
28. Summerfield, A., et al., *Antiviral activity of an extract from leaves of the tropical plant* Acanthospermum hispidum. Antiviral Res, 1997. **36**(1): pp. 55–62.
29. Cartagena, E., et al., *Natural sesquiterpene lactones enhance oxacillin and gentamicin effectiveness against pathogenic bacteria without antibacterial effects on beneficial lactobacilli.* Phytother Res, 2015. **29**(5): pp. 695–700.
30. Li, Y., et al., *Antiviral activities of medicinal herbs traditionally used in southern mainland China.* Phytother Res, 2004. **18**(9): pp. 718–722.
31. Sagar, R. and Sahoo, H.B., *Evaluation of antiasthmatic activity of ethanolic extract of* Elephantopus scaber *L. leaves.* Indian J Pharmacol, 2012. **44**(3): pp. 398–401.
32. Agbonon, A., et al., *The effect of* Mangifera indica *stem bark and* Pluchea ovalis *roots on tracheal smooth muscle in vitro.* Fitoterapia, 2002. **73**(7–8): pp. 619–22.
33. Locher, C.P., et al., *Antiviral activity of Hawaiian medicinal plants against human immunodeficiency Virus Type-1 (HIV-1).* Phytomedicine, 1996. **2**(3): pp. 259–264.
34. Mohamad, S., et al., *Antituberculosis potential of some ethnobotanically selected Malaysian plants.* J Ethnopharmacol, 2011. **133**(3): pp. 1021–1026.

35. But, P.P., et al., *Antiviral constituents against respiratory viruses from* Mikania micrantha. J Nat Prod, 2009. **72**(5): pp. 925–928.
36. Collaço, R.e.C., et al., *Protection by* Mikania laevigata *(guaco) extract against the toxicity of Philodryas olfersii snake venom.* Toxicon, 2012. **60**(4): pp. 614–622.
37. dos Santos, S.C., et al., *LC characterisation of guaco medicinal extracts,* Mikania laevigata *and M. glomerata, and their effects on allergic pneumonitis.* Planta Med, 2006. **72**(8): pp. 679–684.
38. Fierro, I.M., et al., *Studies on the anti-allergic activity of* Mikania glomerata. J Ethnopharmacol, 1999. **66**(1): pp. 19–24.
39. Freitas, T.P., et al., *Effects of* Mikania glomerata *Spreng. and* Mikania laevigata *Schultz Bip. ex Baker (Asteraceae) extracts on pulmonary inflammation and oxidative stress caused by acute coal dust exposure.* J Med Food, 2008. **11**(4): pp. 761–766.
40. Graça, C., et al., *In vivo assessment of safety and mechanisms underlying in vitro relaxation induced by* Mikania laevigata *Schultz Bip. ex Baker in the rat trachea.* J Ethnopharmacol, 2007. **112**(3): pp. 430–439.
41. Justino de Araújo, A.C., et al., *GC-MS-FID characterization and antibacterial activity of the* Mikania cordifolia *essential oil and limonene against MDR strains.* Food Chem Toxicol, 2020. **136**: pp. 111023.
42. Leite, P.M., et al., *In Vitro Anticoagulant activity of* Mikania laevigata*: Deepening the study of the possible interaction between guaco and anticoagulants.* J Cardiovasc Pharmacol, 2019. **74**(6): pp. 574–583.
43. Li, Y., et al., *Antimicrobial constituents of the leaves of* Mikania micrantha *H. B. K.* PLoS One, 2013. **8**(10): pp. e76725.
44. Maiorano, V.A., et al., *Antiophidian properties of the aqueous extract of* Mikania glomerata. J Ethnopharmacol, 2005. **102**(3): pp. 364–370.
45. Possebon, L., et al., *Anti-inflammatory actions of herbal medicines in a model of chronic obstructive pulmonary disease induced by cigarette smoke.* Biomed Pharmacother, 2018. **99**: pp. 591–597.
46. Soares de Moura, R., et al., *Bronchodilator activity of* Mikania glomerata *Sprengel on human bronchi and guinea-pig trachea.* J Pharm Pharmacol, 2002. **54**(2): pp. 249–256.
47. Yatsuda, R., et al., *Effects of* Mikania *genus plants on growth and cell adherence of mutans streptococci.* J Ethnopharmacol, 2005. **97**(2): pp. 183–189.
48. Ngezahayo, J., et al., *In vitro study of five herbs used against microbial infections in Burundi.* Phytother Res, 2017. **31**(10): pp. 1571–1578.
49. Castello, M.C., et al., *Antimicrobial activity of crude extracts from plant parts and corresponding calli of* Bixa orellana *L.* Indian J Exp Biol, 2002. **40**(12): pp. 1378–1381.
50. Pierpaoli, E., et al., *Supplementation with tocotrienols from* Bixa orellana *improves the in vivo efficacy of daptomycin against methicillin-resistant Staphylococcus aureus in a mouse model of infected wound.* Phytomedicine, 2017. **36**: pp. 50–53.
51. Núñez, V., et al., *Neutralization of the edema-forming, defibrinating and coagulant effects of* Bothrops asper *venom by extracts of plants used by healers in Colombia.* Braz J Med Biol Res, 2004. **37**(7): pp. 969–977.
52. Rojas, J.J., et al., *Screening for antimicrobial activity of ten medicinal plants used in Colombian folkloric medicine: A possible alternative in the treatment of non-nosocomial infections.* BMC Complement Altern Med, 2006. **6**: p. 2.
53. Yong, Y.K., et al., *Chemical constituents and antihistamine activity of* Bixa orellana *leaf extract.* BMC Complement Altern Med, 2013. **13**: p. 32.
54. Yong, Y.K., et al., Bixa orellana *leaf extract suppresses histamine-induced endothelial hyperpermeability via the PLC-NO-cGMP signaling cascade.* BMC Complement Altern Med, 2015. **15**: p. 356.

55. Janbaz, K.H., et al., *Validation of ethnopharmacological uses of* Heliotropium strigosum *Willd. as spasmolytic, bronchodilator and vasorelaxant remedy.* BMC Complement Altern Med, 2015. **15**: p. 169.
56. Singh, B. and Sharma, R.A., *Anti-inflammatory and antimicrobial properties of flavonoids from* Heliotropium subulatum *exudate.* Inflamm Allergy Drug Targets, 2015. **14**(2): pp. 125–132.
57. Errasti, M.E., et al., *Effects on fibrinogen, fibrin, and blood coagulation of proteolytic extracts from fruits of* Pseudananas macrodontes, Bromelia balansae, *and* B. hieronymi *(Bromeliaceae) in comparison with bromelain.* Blood Coagul Fibrinolysis, 2016. **27**(4): pp. 441–449.
58. Coelho, R.G., et al., *Chemical composition and antioxidant and antimycobacterial activities of* Bromelia balansae *(Bromeliaceae).* J Med Food, 2010. **13**(5): pp. 1277–1280.
59. Secor, E.R., et al., *Bromelain limits airway inflammation in an ovalbumin-induced murine model of established asthma.* Altern Ther Health Med, 2012. **18**(5): pp. 9–17.
60. Secor, E.R., et al., *Bromelain inhibits allergic sensitization and murine asthma via modulation of dendritic cells.* Evid Based Complement Alternat Med, 2013. **2013**: p. 702196.
61. Dutta, S. and Bhattacharyya, D., *Enzymatic, antimicrobial and toxicity studies of the aqueous extract of* Ananas comosus *(pineapple) crown leaf.* J Ethnopharmacol, 2013. **150**(2): pp. 451–457.
62. Mahajan, S., et al., *Stem bromelain-induced macrophage apoptosis and activation curtail* Mycobacterium tuberculosis *persistence.* J Infect Dis, 2012. **206**(3): pp. 366–376.
63. Peixoto, D.M., et al., *Use of honey associated with* Ananas comosus *(Bromelin) in the treatment of acute irritative cough.* Rev Paul Pediatr, 2016. **34**(4): pp. 412–417.
64. de Lima, E.M., et al., *Essential oil from the resin of* Protium heptaphyllum*: Chemical composition, cytotoxicity, antimicrobial activity, and antimutagenicity.* Pharmacogn Mag, 2016. **12**(Suppl 1): pp. S42–S46.
65. Violante, I.M., et al., *Antimicrobial activity of some medicinal plants from the Cerrado of the central-western region of Brazil.* Braz J Microbiol, 2012. **43**(4): pp. 1302–1308.
66. Cabral, R.S.C., et al., *Chemical composition of essential oils from different parts of* Protium heptaphyllum *(Aubl.) Marchand and their in vitro antibacterial activity.* Nat Prod Res, 2018: pp. 1–6.
67. Mobin, M., et al., *Gas Chromatography-Triple Quadrupole Mass Spectrometry Analysis and Vasorelaxant Effect of Essential Oil from* Protium heptaphyllum *(Aubl.) March.* Biomed Res Int, 2017. **2017**: p. 1928171.
68. Santana, A.I., et al., *Composition and biological activity of essential oils from* Protium confusum. Nat Prod Commun, 2009. **4**(10): pp. 1401–1406.
69. Batista, F.P., et al., Crataeva tapia *bark lectin (CrataBL) is a chemoattractant for endothelial cells that targets heparan sulfate and promotes in vitro angiogenesis.* Biochimie, 2019. **166**: pp. 173–183.
70. Salu, B.R., et al., *CrataBL, a lectin and Factor Xa inhibitor, plays a role in blood coagulation and impairs thrombus formation.* Biol Chem, 2014. **395**(9): pp. 1027–1035.
71. Zhang, F., et al., *Structural studies of the interaction of* Crataeva tapia *bark protein with heparin and other glycosaminoglycans.* Biochemistry, 2013. **52**(12): pp. 2148–2156.
72. de Lacerda Neto, L.J., et al., *Modulation of antibiotic activity by the hydroalcoholic extract from leaves of* Caryocar coriaceum *WITTM.* Nat Prod Res, 2018. **32**(4): pp. 477–480.
73. de Oliveira, L.M., et al., *Endothelium-dependent vasorelaxant effect of butanolic fraction from* Caryocar brasiliense *Camb. Leaves in rat thoracic aorta.* Evid Based Complement Alternat Med, 2012. **2012**: p. 934142.

74. Pereira, F.F.G., et al., *Characterization, antibacterial activity and antibiotic modifying action of the* Caryocar coriaceum *Wittm. pulp and almond fixed oil.* Nat Prod Res, 2020. **34**(22): pp. 1–5.
75. Silveira Serra, D., et al., *Effects of fixed oil of* Caryocar coriaceum *Wittm. Seeds on the respiratory system of rats in a short-term secondhand-smoke exposure model.* J Ethnopharmacol, 2020. **252**: p. 112633.
76. Delarcina, S., et al., *Inhibition of histamine-induced bronchospasm in guinea pigs treated with* Cecropia glaziovi *Sneth and correlation with the in vitro activity in tracheal muscles.* Phytomedicine, 2007. **14**(5): pp. 328–332.
77. Petronilho, F., et al., *Hepatoprotective effects and HSV-1 activity of the hydroethanolic extract of* Cecropia glaziovii *(embaúba-vermelha) against acyclovir-resistant strain.* Pharm Biol, 2012. **50**(7): pp. 911–918.
78. Tanae, M.M., et al., *Chemical standardization of the aqueous extract of* Cecropia glaziovii *Sneth endowed with antihypertensive, bronchodilator, antiacid secretion and antidepressant-like activities.* Phytomedicine, 2007. **14**(5): pp. 309–313.
79. Caldas Dos Santos, T., et al., *In vitro antiherpes effect of C-glycosyl flavonoid enriched fraction of* Cecropia glaziovii *encapsulated in PLGA nanoparticles.* Mater Sci Eng C Mater Biol Appl, 2017. **75**: pp. 1214–1220.
80. Guerrero, E.I., et al., *Vasoactive effects of different fractions from two Panamanians plants used in Amerindian traditional medicine.* J Ethnopharmacol, 2010. **131**(2): pp. 497–501.
81. Awasthi, L.P., *The purification and nature of an antiviral protein from* Cuscuta reflexa *plants.* Arch Virol, 1981. **70**(3): pp. 215–223.
82. Azad, A.K., et al., *In vitro evaluation of* Cuscuta reflexa *Roxb. for thrombolytic, antioxidant, membrane stabilizing and antimicrobial activities.* Nat Prod Res, 2018: pp. 1–4.
83. Behbahani, M., *Anti-human immunodeficiency virus-1 activities of pratensein and pratensein glycoside from* Alhaji maurorum *and its parasite* Cuscuta kotchiana. Chin J Integr Med, 2017. pp. 1–6. DOI: 10.1007/s11655-017-2820-2
84. Kim, H.J., et al., *Ameliorating effects of* Cuscuta chinensis *Lamak extract on hind-limb ischemia, and angiogenic- or inflammatory associated factors in ovariectomized mice.* Mol Med Rep, 2019. **19**(4): pp. 3321–3329.
85. Paudel, P., et al., *Volatile analysis and antimicrobial screening of the parasitic plant* Cuscuta reflexa *Roxb. from Nepal.* Nat Prod Res, 2014. **28**(2): pp. 106–110.
86. Naz, R., et al., *Antimicrobial activity, toxicity and anti-inflammatory potential of methanolic extracts of four ethnomedicinal plant species from Punjab, Pakistan.* BMC Complement Altern Med, 2017. **17**(1): p. 302.
87. Nath, K., et al., Cyathea gigantea *(Cyatheaceae) as an antimicrobial agent against multidrug resistant organisms.* BMC Complement Altern Med, 2019. **19**(1): p. 279.
88. Amos Samkumar, R., D. Premnath, and R.S. David Paul Raj, *Strategy for early callus induction and identification of anti-snake venom triterpenoids from plant extracts and suspension culture of.* 3 Biotech, 2019. **9**(7): p. 266.
89. Chang, S.Y., et al., *A natural component from* Euphorbia humifusa *Willd displays novel, broad-spectrum anti-influenza activity by blocking nuclear export of viral ribonucleoprotein.* Biochem Biophys Res Commun, 2016. **471**(2): pp. 282–289.
90. Gopi, K., et al., *Quercetin-3-O-rhamnoside from* Euphorbia hirta *protects against snake Venom induced toxicity.* Biochim Biophys Acta, 2016. **1860**(7): pp. 1528–1540.
91. Gyuris, A., et al., *Antiviral activities of extracts of* Euphorbia hirta *L. against HIV-1, HIV-2 and SIVmac251.* In Vivo, 2009. **23**(3): pp. 429–432.
92. Huang, C.S., et al., *Antifeedant and antiviral diterpenoids from the fresh roots of* Euphorbia jolkinii. Nat Prod Bioprospect, 2014. **4**(2): pp. 91–100.

93. Mir, M., R. Khurshid, and R. Aftab, *Management of thrombocytopenia and flu-like symptoms in dengue patients with herbal water of* Euphorbia hirta. J Ayub Med Coll Abbottabad, 2012. **24**(3–4): pp. 6–9.
94. Patel, G.K., A.A. Kawale, and A.K. Sharma, *Purification and physicochemical characterization of a serine protease with fibrinolytic activity from latex of a medicinal herb* Euphorbia hirta. Plant Physiol Biochem, 2012. **52**: pp. 104–111.
95. Perumal, S., R. Mahmud, and S. Ramanathan, *Anti-infective potential of caffeic acid and epicatechin 3-gallate isolated from methanol extract of* Euphorbia hirta *(L.) against* Pseudomonas aeruginosa. Nat Prod Res, 2015. **29**(18): pp. 1766–1769.
96. Siritapetawee, J., et al., *Characterization of the binding of a glycosylated serine protease from* Euphorbia cf. lactea *latex to human fibrinogen*. Biotechnol Appl Biochem, 2017. **64**(6): pp. 862–870.
97. Sundari, S.K., et al., *Bronchodilator effect of alcoholic extract of* Euphorbia hirta *linn.* Anc Sci Life, 2004. **23**(3): pp. 1–5.
98. Xia, M., et al., *Anti-inflammatory and anxiolytic activities of* Euphorbia hirta *extract in neonatal asthmatic rats*. AMB Express, 2018. **8**(1): p. 179.
99. Youssouf, M.S., et al., *Anti-anaphylactic effect of* Euphorbia hirta. Fitoterapia, 2007. **78**(7–8): pp. 535–539.
100. Zhang, Q., et al., Euphorbia *factor L2 alleviates lipopolysaccharide-induced acute lung injury and inflammation in mice through the suppression of NF-κB activation*. Biochem Pharmacol, 2018. **155**: pp. 444–454.
101. Parmar, G., K. Pundarikakshudu, and R. Balaraman, *Anti-anaphylactic and antiasthmatic activity of*. J Tradit Complement Med, 2019. **9**(1): pp. 60–65.
102. Siritapetawee, J., P. Sojikul, and S. Klaynongsruang, *Biochemical characterization of a new glycosylated protease from* Euphorbia cf. lactea *latex*. Plant Physiol Biochem, 2015. **92**: pp. 30–38.
103. Badgujar, S.B., *Evaluation of hemostatic activity of latex from three* Euphorbiaceae *species*. J Ethnopharmacol, 2014. **151**(1): pp. 733–739.
104. Wang, T.T., et al., *Mechanisms of vasorelaxation induced by total flavonoids of* Euphorbia humifusa *in rat aorta*. J Physiol Pharmacol, 2017. **68**(4): pp. 619–628.
105. Kwon, S.U., et al., *Chloroform fraction of* Euphorbia maculata *has antiplatelet activity via suppressing thromboxane B2 formation*. Mol Med Rep, 2015. **11**(6): pp. 4255–4261.
106. Sharma, G.D. and S.N. Tripathi, *Experimental evaluation of dugdhika (*euphorbia prostrata *w. Ait) for the treatment of 'tamaka svasa' (bronchial asthma)*. Anc Sci Life, 1984. **3**(3): pp. 143–145.
107. Awaad, A.S., et al., *Comparative nutritional value and antimicrobial activities between three*. Saudi Pharm J, 2017. **25**(8): pp. 1226–1230.
108. Figueredo, F.G., et al., *Modulation of the antibiotic activity by extracts from* Amburana cearensis *A. C. Smith and* Anadenanthera macrocarpa *(Benth.) Brenan*. Biomed Res Int, 2013. **2013**: p. 640682.
109. Leal, L.K., et al., *Anti-inflammatory and smooth muscle relaxant activities of the hydroalcoholic extract and chemical constituents from* Amburana cearensis *A C Smith*. Phytother Res, 2003. **17**(4): pp. 335–340.
110. Leal, L.K., et al., *Mechanisms underlying the relaxation induced by isokaempferide from* Amburana cearensis *in the guinea-pig isolated trachea*. Life Sci, 2006. **79**(1): pp. 98–104.
111. Sá, M.B., et al., *Phytochemistry and preliminary assessment of the antibacterial activity of chloroform extract of* Amburana cearensis *(Allemão) A.C. Sm. against* Klebsiella pneumoniae *carbapenemase-producing strains*. Evid Based Complement Alternat Med, 2014. **2014**: p. 786586.

112. Oliveira, M.T.A., et al., *Serine protease inhibition and modulatory-antibiotic activity of the proteic extract and fractions from* Amburana cearensis. Food Chem Toxicol, 2020. **135**: p. 110946.
113. Barreto, H.M., et al., *Enhancement of the antibiotic activity of aminoglycosides by extracts from* Anadenanthera colubrine *(Vell.) Brenan var. cebil against multi-drug resistant bacteria*. Nat Prod Res, 2016. **30**(11): pp. 1289–1292.
114. Trentin, D.S., et al., *Tannins possessing bacteriostatic effect impair* Pseudomonas aeruginosa *adhesion and biofilm formation*. PLoS One, 2013. **8**(6): p. e66257.
115. Rodrigo Cavalcante de Araújo, D., et al., *Bioguided purification of active compounds from leaves of* Anadenanthera colubrina *var. cebil (Griseb.) Altschul*. Biomolecules, 2019. **9**(10): p. 590.
116. de Sousa, M.V. and L. Morhy, *Enterolobin, a hemolytic protein from* Enterolobium contortisiliquum *seeds (Leguminosae–Mimosoideae). Purification and characterization*. An Acad Bras Cienc, 1989. **61**(4): pp. 405–412.
117. Rodrigues, A.P.D., et al., *A plant proteinase inhibitor from* Enterolobium contortisiliquum *attenuates airway hyperresponsiveness, inflammation and remodeling in a mouse model of asthma*. Histol Histopathol, 2019. **34**(5): pp. 537–552.
118. Sampaio, C.A., et al., *Proteinase inhibitors in Brazilian leguminosae*. Mem Inst Oswaldo Cruz, 1991. **86**(Suppl 2): pp. 207–209.
119. López-Briz, E. and A. Vázquez-Polo, *[Coumarins: Interaction with vitamin K antagonists and safety of tonka bean]*. Gac Sanit, 2012. **26**(2): p. 193; author reply 194.
120. Sarker, S.D. and L. Nahar, *Progress in the chemistry of naturally occurring coumarins*. Prog Chem Org Nat Prod, 2017. **106**: pp. 241–304.
121. Kloucek, P., et al., *Antimicrobial activity of some medicinal barks used in Peruvian Amazon*. J Ethnopharmacol, 2007. **111**(2): pp. 427–429.
122. Cotabarren, J., et al., *GdTI, the first thermostable trypsin inhibitor from* Geoffroea decorticans *seeds. A novel natural drug with potential application in biomedicine*. Int J Biol Macromol, 2020. **148**: pp. 869–879.
123. Souza, R.O., et al., *Purified polysaccharides of* Geoffroea spinosa *barks have anticoagulant and antithrombotic activities devoid of hemorrhagic risks*. Carbohydr Polym, 2015. **124**: pp. 208–215.
124. Salvat, A., et al., *Antimicrobial activity in methanolic extracts of several plant species from northern Argentina*. Phytomedicine, 2004. **11**(2–3): pp. 230–234.
125. Bezerra, G.P., et al., *Phytochemical study guided by the myorelaxant activity of the crude extract, fractions and constituent from stem bark of* Hymenaea courbaril *L*. J Ethnopharmacol, 2013. **149**(1): pp. 62–69.
126. Cecílio, A.B., et al., *Screening of Brazilian medicinal plants for antiviral activity against rotavirus*. J Ethnopharmacol, 2012. **141**(3): pp. 975–981.
127. Nikhat, S. and M. Fazil, *Overview of Covid-19; its prevention and management in the light of Unani medicine*. Sci Total Environ, 2020. **728**: p. 138859.
128. Oliveira de Veras, B., et al., *Chemical composition and evaluation of the antinociceptive, antioxidant and antimicrobial effects of essential oil from* Hymenaea cangaceira *(Pinto, Mansano & Azevedo) native to Brazil: A natural medicine*. J Ethnopharmacol, 2020. **247**: p. 112265.
129. da Silva, G.C., et al., *Chemical composition, antimicrobial activity and synergistic effects with conventional antibiotics under clinical isolates by essential oil of* Hymenaea rubriflora *Ducke (Fabaceae)*. Nat Prod Res, 2020: pp. 1–5. DOI: 10.1080/14786419.2020.1729150
130. Silva, S.L., et al., *Phytochemical analysis and evaluation of the antimicrobial and antioxidant activities of extracts and fractions of* Hymenaea eriogyne *Benth*. Nat Prod Res, 2021. **35**(17): pp. 2937–2941.

131. Dimech, G.S., et al., *Phytochemical and antibacterial investigations of the extracts and fractions from the stem bark of* Hymenaea stigonocarpa *Mart. ex Hayne and effect on ultrastructure of* Staphylococcus aureus *induced by hydroalcoholic extract.* ScientificWorldJournal, 2013. **2013**: p. 862763.
132. de Oliveira Marreiro, R., et al., *Evaluation of the stability and antimicrobial activity of an ethanolic extract of* Libidibia ferrea. Clin Cosmet Investig Dent, 2014. **6**: pp. 9–13.
133. da Silva, L.C., et al., *Anti-*Staphylococcus aureus *action of three Caatinga fruits evaluated by electron microscopy.* Nat Prod Res, 2013. **27**(16): pp. 1492–1496.
134. Rakotomalala, G., et al., *Extract from* Mimosa pigra *attenuates chronic experimental pulmonary hypertension.* J Ethnopharmacol, 2013. **148**(1): pp. 106–116.
135. Santos, M.E., et al., *Hypotensive and vasorelaxant effects induced by the ethanolic extract of the* Mimosa caesalpiniifolia *Benth. (Mimosaceae) inflorescences in normotensive rats.* J Ethnopharmacol, 2015. **164**: pp. 120–128.
136. Yang, E.J., et al., *Suppression of ovalbumin-induced airway inflammatory responses in a mouse model of asthma by* Mimosa pudica *extract.* Phytother Res, 2011. **25**(1): pp. 59–66.
137. Silva, S.W.C., et al., *Antimicrobial activity of* Mimosa caesalpiniifolia *Benth and its interaction with antibiotics against* Staphylococcus aureus *strains overexpressing efflux pump genes.* Lett Appl Microbiol, 2019. **69**(1): pp. 57–63.
138. Pereira, R., et al., *Evaluation of the antimicrobial and antioxidant activity of 7-hydroxy-4', 6-dimethoxy-isoflavone and essential oil from* Myroxylon peruiferum *L.f.* An Acad Bras Cienc, 2019. **91**(2): p. e20180204.
139. Macêdo, C.L., et al., *Spasmolytic effect of galetin 3,6-dimethyl ether, a flavonoid obtained from* Piptadenia stipulacea *(Benth) Ducke.* J Smooth Muscle Res, 2011. **47**(5): pp. 123–134.
140. Macêdo, C.L., et al., *Mechanisms underlying the relaxant effect of Galetin 3,6-dimethyl ether, from* Piptadenia stipulacea *(Benth.) Ducke, on guinea-pig trachea.* Z Naturforsch C J Biosci, 2014. **69**(11–12): pp. 434–442.
141. Macêdo, C.L., et al., *Mechanisms underlying vasorelaxation induced in rat aorta by galetin 3,6-dimethyl ether, a flavonoid from* Piptadenia stipulacea *(Benth.) Ducke.* Molecules, 2014. **19**(12): pp. 19678–19695.
142. Simões, C.M., et al., *Antiviral activity of south Brazilian medicinal plant extracts.* Phytomedicine, 1999. **6**(3): pp. 205–214.
143. Isobe, T., et al., *[Biological activity tests of chemical constituents from two Brazilian Labiatae plants].* Yakugaku Zasshi, 2007. **127**(2): pp. 389–395.
144. Picking, D., et al., Hyptis verticillata *Jacq: A review of its traditional uses, phytochemistry, pharmacology and toxicology.* J Ethnopharmacol, 2013. **147**(1): pp. 16–41.
145. Kashiwada, Y., et al., *Anti-AIDS agents. 30. Anti-HIV activity of oleanolic acid, pomolic acid, and structurally related triterpenoids.* J Nat Prod, 1998. **61**(9): pp. 1090–1095.
146. Matsuse, I.T., et al., *A search for anti-viral properties in Panamanian medicinal plants. The effects on HIV and its essential enzymes.* J Ethnopharmacol, 1999. **64**(1): pp. 15–22.
147. Nascimento, P.F., et al., Hyptis pectinata *essential oil: Chemical composition and anti-*Streptococcus *mutans activity.* Oral Dis, 2008. **14**(6): pp. 485–489.
148. Bae, H., et al., Vitex rotundifolia *L. prevented airway eosinophilic inflammation and airway remodeling in an ovalbumin-induced asthma mouse model.* Int Immunol, 2013. **25**(3): pp. 197–205.
149. Haq, R.U., et al., *Antitussive and toxicological evaluation of* Vitex negundo. Nat Prod Res, 2012. **26**(5): pp. 484–488.
150. Ibrahim, S.R.M., et al., Vitex agnus-castus *safeguards the lung against lipopolysaccharide-induced toxicity in mice.* J Food Biochem, 2019. **43**(3): p. e12750.

151. Khan, M., A.J. Shah, and A.H. Gilani, *Insight into the bronchodilator activity of Vitex negundo*. Pharm Biol, 2015. **53**(3): pp. 340–344.
152. Lee, H., et al., *A new compound, 1H,8H-pyrano[3,4-c]pyran-1,8-dione, suppresses airway epithelial cell inflammatory responses in a murine model of asthma*. Int J Immunopathol Pharmacol, 2009. **22**(3): pp. 591–603.
153. Lee, H., et al., *Casticin, an active compound isolated from* Vitex Fructus*, ameliorates the cigarette smoke-induced acute lung inflammatory response in a murine model*. Int Immunopharmacol, 2015. **28**(2): pp. 1097–1101.
154. Lee, G., et al., *Pyranopyran-1,8-dione, an active compound from* Vitices Fructus*, attenuates cigarette-smoke induced lung inflammation in mice*. Int J Mol Sci, 2017. **18**(7): p. 1602.
155. Venturini, C.L., et al., *Vitexin inhibits inflammation in murine ovalbumin-induced allergic asthma*. Biomed Pharmacother, 2018. **97**: pp. 143–151.
156. Wang, C., et al., *Casticin inhibits lipopolysaccharide-induced acute lung injury in mice*. Eur J Pharmacol, 2016. **789**: pp. 172–178.
157. Leitão, F., et al., *Medicinal plants from open-air markets in the State of Rio de Janeiro, Brazil as a potential source of new antimycobacterial agents*. J Ethnopharmacol, 2013. **149**(2): pp. 513–521.
158. Soberón, J.R., et al., *Antibacterial activity of plant extracts from northwestern Argentina*. J Appl Microbiol, 2007. **102**(6): pp. 1450–1461.
159. Soberón, J.R., et al., *Purification and identification of antibacterial phenolics from* Tripodanthus acutifolius *leaves*. J Appl Microbiol, 2010. **108**(5): pp. 1757–1768.
160. Martínez-Vázquez, M., et al., *Antimicrobial activity of* Byrsonima crassifolia *(L.) H.B.K.* J Ethnopharmacol, 1999. **66**(1): pp. 79–82.
161. Yaseen, R., et al., *In Vitro testing of crude natural plant extracts from Costa Rica for their ability to boost innate immune cells against* Staphylococcus aureus. Biomedicines, 2017. **5**(3): p. 40.
162. Magos, G.A., et al., *Hypotensive and vasorelaxant effects of the procyanidin fraction from* Guazuma ulmifolia *bark in normotensive and hypertensive rats*. J Ethnopharmacol, 2008. **117**(1): pp. 58–68.
163. Maldini, M., et al., *Flavanocoumarins from* Guazuma ulmifolia *bark and evaluation of their affinity for STAT1*. Phytochemistry, 2013. **86**: pp. 64–71.
164. Pereira, G.A., et al., *Phytochemicals and biological activities of mutamba (*Guazuma ulmifolia *Lam.): A review*. Food Res Int, 2019. **126**: pp. 108713.
165. Felipe, A.M., et al., *Antiviral effect of* Guazuma ulmifolia *and* Stryphnodendron adstringens *on poliovirus and bovine herpesvirus*. Biol Pharm Bull, 2006. **29**(6): pp. 1092–1095.
166. Jacobo-Salcedo, M.e.R., et al., *Antimicrobial and cytotoxic effects of Mexican medicinal plants*. Nat Prod Commun, 2011. **6**(12): pp. 1925–1928.
167. Huang, Q., et al., *Antiviral activity of methyl helicterate isolated from* Helicteres angustifolia *(Sterculiaceae) against hepatitis B virus*. Antiviral Res, 2013. **100**(2): pp. 373–381.
168. Pohocha, N. and N.D. Grampurohit, *Antispasmodic activity of the fruits of* Helicteres isora *Linn*. Phytother Res, 2001. **15**(1): pp. 49–52.
169. Yin, X., et al., *Anti-complementary components of* Helicteres angustifolia. Molecules, 2016. **21**(11): p. 1506.
170. Emran, T.B., et al., *Effects of organic extracts and their different fractions of five Bangladeshi plants on in vitro thrombolysis*. BMC Complement Altern Med, 2015. **15**: p. 128.
171. Yang, Y., et al., *The antibacterial effect of* Urena lobata *L. fromv guangxi on mice with Staphylococcus aureus pneumonia*. Afr J Tradit Complement Altern Med, 2017. **14**(1): pp. 73–88.

172. Zongo, F., et al., *Bioguidage search of active compounds from* Waltheria indica *L. (Malvaceae) used for asthma and inflammation treatment in Burkina Faso.* Fundam Clin Pharmacol, 2014. **28**(3): pp. 323–330.
173. Flores, G., et al., *Anthocyanins from* Eugenia brasiliensis *edible fruits as potential therapeutics for COPD treatment.* Food Chem, 2012. **134**(3): pp. 1256–1262.
174. John, K.M., et al., *Metabolic variations, antioxidant potential, and antiviral activity of different extracts of* Eugenia singampattiana *(an endangered medicinal plant used by Kani tribals, Tamil Nadu, India) leaf.* Biomed Res Int, 2014. **2014**: p. 726145.
175. Lee, M.H., et al., *EBV DNA polymerase inhibition of tannins from* Eugenia uniflora. Cancer Lett, 2000. **154**(2): pp. 131–136.
176. Wazlawik, E., et al., *Analysis of the role of nitric oxide in the relaxant effect of the crude extract and fractions from* Eugenia uniflora *in the rat thoracic aorta.* J Pharm Pharmacol, 1997. **49**(4): pp. 433–437.
177. Chilakapati, S.R., et al., *Passion fruit peel extract attenuates bleomycin-induced pulmonary fibrosis in mice.* Can J Physiol Pharmacol, 2014. **92**(8): pp. 631–639.
178. Dhawan, K. and A. Sharma, *Antitussive activity of the methanol extract of* Passiflora incarnata *leaves.* Fitoterapia, 2002. **73**(5): pp. 397–399.
179. Sato, A.C., et al., *Effects of compounds from* Passiflora edulis *Sims f. flavicarpa juice on blood coagulation and on proteolytic enzymes.* Protein Pept Lett, 2012. **19**(5): pp. 501–508.
180. Watson, R.R., et al., *Oral administration of the purple passion fruit peel extract reduces wheeze and cough and improves shortness of breath in adults with asthma.* Nutr Res, 2008. **28**(3): pp. 166–171.
181. Lin, L.L., et al., *Xanthones from the roots of* Polygala caudata *and their antioxidation and vasodilatation activities in vitro.* Planta Med, 2005. **71**(4): pp. 372–375.
182. Ye, Y., et al., Polygalasaponin *F treats mice with pneumonia induced by influenza virus.* Inflammopharmacology, 2020. **28**(1): pp. 299–310.
183. Kashkooe, A., et al., A review on pharmacological properties and toxicological effects of Adiantum capillus-veneris L. Curr Drug Discov Technol, 2021. **18**(2): pp. 186–193.
184. Rastogi, S., M.M. Pandey, and A.K.S. Rawat, *Ethnopharmacological uses, phytochemistry and pharmacology of genus* Adiantum*: A comprehensive review.* J Ethnopharmacol, 2018. **215**: pp. 101–119.
185. Yadegari, M., et al., *The TNF-α, P53 protein response and lung respiratory changes to exercise, chronic hypoxia and* Adiantum capillus-veneris *supplementation.* Adv Respir Med, 2019. **87**(4): pp. 226–234.
186. Souza, T.M., et al., *Herbs in association with drugs: Enhancement of the aminoglycoside-antibiotic activity by* Pityrogramma calomelanos *(L.) Link.* J Young Pharm, 2013. **5**(4): pp. 188–190.
187. Fernandes, C.P., et al., *Triterpene esters and biological activities from edible fruits of* Manilkara subsericea *(Mart.) Dubard, Sapotaceae.* Biomed Res Int, 2013. **2013**: p. 280810.
188. Liu, Y.P., et al., *Prenylated coumarins from the fruits of* Manilkara zapota *with potential anti-inflammatory effects and anti-HIV activities.* J Agric Food Chem, 2019. **67**(43): pp. 11942–11947.
189. Rodríguez-García, C.M., et al., *Antioxidant, antihypertensive, anti-hyperglycemic, and antimicrobial activity of aqueous extracts from twelve native plants of the Yucatan coast.* PLoS One, 2019. **14**(3): p. e0213493.
190. Sundararaman, B. and K.L. Muthuramu, *A comparison of mango seed kernel powder, mango leaf powder and* Manilkara zapota *seed powder for decolorization of methylene blue dye and antimicrobial activity.* J Environ Biol, 2016. **37**(6): pp. 1315–1321.
191. Bedoya, L.M., et al., *Guatemalan plants extracts as virucides against HIV-1 infection.* Phytomedicine, 2008. **15**(6–7): pp. 520–524.

192. Andrade, M.A., et al., *Biological activity of the essential oils from* Cinnamodendron dinisii *and* Siparuna guianensis. Braz J Microbiol, 2015. **46**(1): pp. 189–194.
193. Begum, S., A. Wahab, and B.S. Siddiqui, *Antimycobacterial activity of flavonoids from* Lantana camara *Linn*. Nat Prod Res, 2008. **22**(6): pp. 467–470.
194. Jimenez-Arellanes, A., et al., *Activity against multidrug-resistant* Mycobacterium tuberculosis *in Mexican plants used to treat respiratory diseases*. Phytother Res, 2003. **17**(8): pp. 903–908.
195. Jiménez-Arellanes, A., et al., *Antimycobacterial triterpenoids from* Lantana hispida *(Verbenaceae)*. J Ethnopharmacol, 2007. **111**(2): pp. 202–205.
196. Jiménez-Arellanes, A., et al., *Ursolic and oleanolic acids as antimicrobial and immunomodulatory compounds for tuberculosis treatment*. BMC Complement Altern Med, 2013. **13**: pp. 258.
197. Julião, L.e.S., et al., *Essential oils from two* Lantana *species with antimycobacterial activity*. Nat Prod Commun, 2009. **4**(12): pp. 1733–1736.
198. Kirimuhuzya, C., et al., *The anti-mycobacterial activity of* Lantana camara *a plant traditionally used to treat symptoms of tuberculosis in south-western Uganda*. Afr Health Sci, 2009. **9**(1): pp. 40–45.
199. Andrighetti-Fröhner, C.R., et al., *Antiviral evaluation of plants from Brazilian Atlantic Tropical Forest*. Fitoterapia, 2005. **76**(3–4): pp. 374–378.
200. Bastos, J.F., et al., *Hypotensive and vasorelaxant effects of citronellol, a monoterpene alcohol, in rats*. Basic Clin Pharmacol Toxicol, 2010. **106**(4): pp. 331–337.
201. da Silva, R.E.R., et al., *Vasorelaxant effect of the* Lippia alba *essential oil and its major constituent, citral, on the contractility of isolated rat aorta*. Biomed Pharmacother, 2018. **108**: pp. 792–798.
202. Games, E., et al., *Structurally related monoterpenes p-cymene, Carvacrol and Thymol isolated from essential oil from leaves of* Lippia sidoides *Cham. (Verbenaceae) protect mice against elastase-induced emphysema*. Molecules, 2016. **21**(10): p. 1390.
203. Görnemann, T., et al., *Antispasmodic activity of essential oil from* Lippia dulcis *Trev*. J Ethnopharmacol, 2008. **117**(1): pp. 166–169.
204. Gusman, G.S., et al., *Evaluation of the effects of some Brazilian medicinal plants on the production of TNF- α and CCL2 by THP-1 cells*. Evid Based Complement Alternat Med, 2015. **2015**: p. 497123.
205. Maynard, L.G., et al., *Chemical composition and vasorelaxant effect induced by the essential oil of* Lippia alba *(Mill.) N.E. Brown. (Verbenaceae) in rat mesenteric artery*. Indian J Pharmacol, 2011. **43**(6): pp. 694–698.
206. Menezes, P.M.N., et al., *Relaxant effect of* Lippia origanoides *essential oil in guinea-pig trachea smooth muscle involves potassium channels and soluble guanylyl cyclase*. J Ethnopharmacol, 2018. **220**: pp. 16–25.
207. Pilau, M.R., et al., *Antiviral activity of the* Lippia graveolens *(Mexican oregano) essential oil and its main compound carvacrol against human and animal viruses*. Braz J Microbiol, 2011. **42**(4): pp. 1616–1624.
208. Ruffa, M.J., et al., *Inhibitory effect of medicinal herbs against RNA and DNA viruses*. Antivir Chem Chemother, 2004. **15**(3): pp. 153–159.
209. Simões, E.R., et al., *Biomedical properties and potentiality of* Lippia microphylla *Cham and its essential oils*. J Intercult Ethnopharmacol, 2015. **4**(3): pp. 256–263.
210. Veras, H.N., et al., *Enhancement of the antibiotic activity of erythromycin by volatile compounds of* Lippia alba *(Mill.) N.E. Brown against Staphylococcus aureus*. Pharmacogn Mag, 2011. **7**(28): pp. 334–337.
211. Vilela, D.A.D., et al., Lippia alnifolia *essential oil induces relaxation on Guinea-pig trachea by multiple pathways*. J Ethnopharmacol, 2020. **246**: p. 112162.
212. Elshafie, H.S., et al., *Antimicrobial activity and chemical composition of three essential oils extracted from Mediterranean aromatic plants*. J Med Food, 2016. **19**(11): pp. 1096–1103.

213. Lara-Issasi, G., et al., *Antimicrobial, Antioxidant Activities, and HPLC Determination of the Major Components of* Verbena carolina *(Verbenaceae).* Molecules, 2019. **24**(10): p. 1970.
214. de Oliveira Barddal, H.P., et al., *Anticoagulant activity of native and partially degraded glycoglucuronomannan after chemical sulfation.* Int J Biol Macromol, 2015. **80**: pp. 328–333.
215. Chinsembu, K.C., *Coronaviruses and Nature's Pharmacy for the Relief of Coronavirus Disease 2019.* Revista Brasileira de Farmacognosia, 2020. **30**: pp. 603–621.
216. Carfora, V., et al., *Anticoagulant treatment in COVID-19: A narrative review.* J Thromb Thrombolysis, 2021. **51**(3): pp. 642–648.
217. Tang, N., et al., *Anticoagulant treatment is associated with decreased mortality in severe coronavirus disease 2019 patients with coagulopathy.* J Thromb Haemost, 2020. **18**(5): pp. 1094–1099.
218. Silveira, D., et al., *COVID-19: Is there evidence for the use of herbal medicines as adjuvant symptomatic therapy?* Frontiers in Pharmacology, 2020. **11**: p. 1479.
219. Jose, R.J. and A. Manuel, *COVID-19 cytokine storm: The interplay between inflammation and coagulation.* Lancet Respir Med, 2020. **8**(6): pp. e46–e47.
220. McGonagle, D., et al., *The role of cytokines including interleukin-6 in COVID-19 induced pneumonia and macrophage activation syndrome-like disease.* Autoimmun Rev, 2020. **19**(6): p. 102537.
221. Horby, P., et al., *Dexamethasone in hospitalized patients with Covid-19—Preliminary report.* N Engl J Med, 2021. **384**: pp. 693–704.
222. Johnson, R.M. and J.M. Vinetz, *Dexamethasone in the management of Covid-19.* BMJ, 2020. **370**: p. m2648.
223. Lopes, M.I.F., et al., *Beneficial effects of colchicine for moderate to severe COVID-19: An interim analysis of a randomized, double-blinded, placebo controlled clinical trial.* medRxiv, 2020: p. 2020.08.06.20169573.
224. Antonio, A., L. Wiedemann, and V. Veiga, *Natural products' role against COVID-19.* RSC Advances, 2020. **10**(39): pp. 23379–23393.
225. Orhan, I.E. and F.S. Senol Deniz, *Natural products as potential leads against coronaviruses: Could they be encouraging structural models against SARS-CoV-2?* Nat Prod Bioprospect, 2020. **10**(4): pp. 171–186.
226. Russo, M., et al., *Roles of flavonoids against coronavirus infection.* Chem Biol Interact, 2020. **328**: p. 109211.
227. Hensel, A., et al., *Challenges at the time of COVID-19: Opportunities and innovations in antivirals from nature.* Planta Med, 2020. **86**(10): pp. 659–664.
228. Islam, M.T., et al., *Natural products and their derivatives against coronavirus: A review of the non-clinical and pre-clinical data.* Phytother Res, 2020. **34**(10): pp. 2471–2492.
229. Adhikari, B., et al., *Potential roles of medicinal plants for the treatment of viral diseases focusing on COVID-19: A review.* Phytother Res, 2021. **35**(3): pp. 1298–1312.

Part II

Processing Technologies

3 Drying of Medicinal and Aromatic Plants

Maria do Carmo Ferreira, Fábio Bentes Freire, and José Teixeira Freire

CONTENTS

3.1 Introduction 53
3.2 Drying of Herbs 55
3.3 Applications on Convective Drying of Leaves 66
3.3.1 Drying Basil Leaves in a Vibrofluidized Dryer 67
3.3.1.1 Essential Oils 69
3.3.2 Drying Mint Leaves in a Modified Rotary Dryer 70
3.3.2.1 Color Degradation 73
3.3.3 Drying Olive Leaves in a Conveyor Belt Dryer 75
3.3.3.1 Supercritical Extraction and Bioactive Compounds 77
3.4 Concluding Remarks 78
3.5 Nomenclature 79
References 80

3.1 INTRODUCTION

The use of plants for health and aesthetics purposes has always been popular in Brazilian society. Natural herbs have been regularly marketed at any common Brazilian urban street fair for the most varied purposes, long before the green and ecological waves that recently took off in North America and Europe. Rue (*Ruta graveolens*) leaves for migraines, headache, and colic; aloe (*Aloe vera* L.) leaves for burns and hair loss; and the popular bilberry (*Vaccinium myrtillus* L.) leaves for alcohol abuse, poor digestion, and stomachache are examples of herbal folk medicine.

Brazil, with more than 8.5 million square kilometers of mainly humid tropical and subtropical lands, has over 95% of all the biodiversity on the planet. However, the financial impact of herbaceous and aromatic plants on the market is still irrelevant. According to the Brazilian Association of the Phytoterapic Sector, Food Supplement, and Health Promotion (ABIFISA), despite the phytotherapy market has increased at an average annual rate of 10% in the last 5 years, only 2.2% of the products were herbal medicines that are sold in Brazilian retail in 2018 [1]. This is partly due to inadequate post-harvest handling, which fails to regularly supply good-quality materials to prospective consumers, especially the pharmaceutical, food, and cosmetic industries. Hence, the scenario of small-scale production is not able to efficiently cope with the high demand for large scale industrial production.

DOI: 10.1201/9781003225416-5

Bioactive and aromatic substances might be directly recovered immediately after harvesting, but most local producers have limited knowledge of handling and processing techniques and lack adequate facilities. Fresh herbs have high moisture content and water activity and contain substrates propense to enzymatic reactions. Therefore, they deteriorate very fast. Reducing the moisture content (and the water activity) is a simple alternative to inhibit the enzymatic action and eliminate microorganisms. Hence, drying is a primary and one of the most important post-harvesting processing operations to extend the shelf life of plants on a large-scale basis. In addition, it reduces the volume of products to be handled, and there is evidence that drying treatments contribute to enhancing the concentration of bioactive constituents in extracts or essential oils (EO) [2]. Nonetheless, drying must be performed using techniques and conditions that guarantee the retention of color, volatile compounds associated with aroma and flavor, antioxidant constituents, and so on. Dried herbs have applications in different fields, such as in culinary, medical and toiletry products, food additives, and perfume and cosmetic manufacturing. The quality requirements for dried herbs will depend on their usage, so whereas the content of bioactive compounds is relevant for medicinal use, the color and fresh-like characteristic aroma is most significant for culinary [3].

In a simple definition, bioactive compounds are substances with some kind of biological activity [4]. In fresh herbs, these compounds are secondary metabolites found in the leaves, stems, roots, flowers, or seeds [5]. The biological activity comes from chemical constituents with antioxidant capacity (AC), anti-inflammatory (AI), and antimicrobial (AM) actions, such as phenolic compounds, terpenoids, terpenes, alkaloids among others [6–8]. Such compounds can be recovered in extracts and EOs which are valuable ingredients for many industries. Different methods and techniques have been developed to obtain extracts and EOs from plants, as described by Azmir *et al.* [9].

Herbs can be dried under ambient conditions or in artificially controlled greenhouses, chambers, or dryers. Natural techniques, such as solar or shade drying, result in slow water removal and must take place in a ventilated environment, protected from dust and attack of insects. These methods offer none or limited control of the drying time and temperature. This can compromise the product quality; nevertheless, they are low-cost options and may be appealing for regions of a hot and arid climate. In convective thermal drying, heated air at a low, relative humidity percolates through or over the solid material, and the moisture is effectively removed by evaporation from the leaf surface to the airflow. After all the surface moisture has been removed, the internal moisture gradually moves toward the surface, and from there, it is evaporated to the airflow. The higher is the air temperature and the lower is its relative humidity; the higher will be the drying rate. Under controlled temperatures, drying can be performed at any time of the year regardless of the climate conditions, and the air temperature can be adjusted to minimize degradation of color, aroma, or nutritional value. To reduce the drying time and degradation of bioactive compounds associated with long exposure to hot air flow, alternative heat sources, such as microwave or infrared radiation, can be used to promote the thermal-driven movement of moisture from the leaf to the ambient air [10].

A broad variety of bioactive compounds might be of interest for industrial applications. Although bioactive compounds can be found in all the parts of a plant, this chapter will focus on drying the aerial part—the leaves. It is worth noting that vegetal leaves share peculiar features that offer specific challenges to design, analysis, and modeling drying processes. Typical features are the wide and flat profile, rough surface, and even for samples retrieved from the same specimen, heterogeneous sizes, and shapes. Owing to these morphological characteristics, leaves are prone to agglomerate if processed in fixed beds and do not exhibit good aeration characteristics either. Lowering the water content causes drastic changes in the leaf's size and shape due to shrinkage, bending, and twisting. Hence, all parameters and coefficients related to heat and mass transfer are strongly dependent on the moisture content and change significantly throughout drying.

In this chapter, the most traditional methods to dry aromatic and medicinal leaves will be approached, as well as the advantages and drawbacks of each one concerning processing and energy requirements. Advances and challenges in modeling heat and mass transfer phenomena through a fundamentally based approach will be discussed, with emphasis on convective drying. Some applications on convective drying investigated at the Drying Center at the Department of Chemical Engineering/Federal University of São Carlos (DEQ/UFSCar, Brazil) will be briefly presented to illustrate how we have addressed the drying of different leaf varieties. Finally, comments on recent developments and future perspectives about drying equipment and methods will be presented.

3.2 DRYING OF HERBS

More than 400 types of dryers have been reported in the literature, but the most used equipment sums up the number of 100 [11]. A general search in the Science Direct database with the terms *drying* and *herbs* shows that from 1980 to date approximately 980 research papers have been published. The growing interest in drying operations associated with herbs processing is corroborated by the fact that about 64% of reported research is concentrated in the last 10 years.

Choosing the adequate conditions for drying herbs must contemplate not only the technical aspects such as the volume of leaves to be handled, the desired moisture reduction, energy consumption, safety, space requirement, capital, and operating costs but also the leaf characteristics and product quality. Once a method is picked up, the selection of suitable drying conditions is crucial to ensure a high-quality dried product. The physical structure, morphology, and composition of aromatic herbs differ widely among the specimens. Leaves such as basil (*Ocimum basilicum*) or regular mint (*Mentha* x *villosa* L.), for instance, are extremely fragile and must be delicately handled, whereas eucalyptus (*Corymbia citriodora* H.) or olive (*Olea europaea* L.) leaves are coriaceous and more resistant to harder drying conditions. Quality attributes can be compromised by the collapse of plant tissues because the long exposure to heat might cause chlorophyll degradation and contributes to releasing substrates for undesirable enzymatic browning reactions [3]. Furthermore, the EOs of plants are stored in the structures called trichomes located in the epidermal cells, and preserving such structures upon drying is important to enhance the yield of EOs and the production of extracts [3]. Additionally, many chemical compounds with biological action naturally occurring in plants are heat-sensitive, and the effects of drying on these compounds are not fully assessed so far. The possibility of the production of toxins or undesirable substances due to the degradation of chemical compounds throughout drying is an additional concern [12].

In their review of leaf drying, Babu *et al.* [13] classified the drying techniques for leaves in three main categories, namely *thermal drying*, *chemical drying*, and *special drying*. The *thermal drying* techniques comprise natural and forced convection methods which are based mostly on ambient or heated airflow to remove moisture. The *special drying* techniques include methods based on alternative heat sources (such as the microwave) or other mechanisms to promote water removal (such as press drying, freeze-drying, or carbon dioxide [CO_2] drying). *Chemical drying* is based on using desiccant agents such as glycerin, silica, or calcium chloride. This latter category is mostly applied to preserve a small amount of leaves and will not be discussed here. Further details about these drying methods can be found in Chen and Mujumdar [12]and Babu et al. [13].

Natural methods such as shade or sun drying are attractive due to the low cost and easy setup, but on the other hand, they present drawbacks associated with poor control of temperature and drying time as well as low drying rates that might yield an uneven moisture distribution in the final product. As an alternative to sun drying, the use of solar dryers has emerged as an efficient, affordable, sustainable, and renewable option to dry agricultural products and reduce crop losses [14, 15]. Solar dryers can be classified in passive (direct), active (indirect), and hybrid types. In the direct solar dryers, the material is placed in drying chambers and dried by absorption of solar radiation, while in the indirect ones the air is first heated by solar radiation and then ducted to the drying chamber. In the hybrid types, backup or stored energy is used in the absence of sunlight [14, 15]. Despite the potential of using solar energy for drying herbs, particularly in tropical countries, the adoption of this technology is still limited due to several reasons, such as high costs, lack of information, inadequate regulations, and legislation on renewable energy [15].

The most traditional method for drying herbs is based on convective drying with hot airflow [16]. Forced and natural convection ovens are widely used by academic researchers to investigate the influence of temperature and airflow rate on the drying velocity and quality attributes of herbs. For commercial purposes, large volumes of material can be processed on floor or cabinet tray dryers by spreading layers of herbs over perforated trays and exposing them to heated airflow. The bed depth is a parameter to be carefully evaluated, as the deeper is the layer, the longer is the drying time. Authors who investigated the drying of medicinal herbs in pieces reported an increase of 2.7 times in the drying time by increasing the layer depth from 25 to 50 mm [12]. Floor dryer manufacturers adopt layers up to 40 cm thick [17]. Multi-tray ovens or cabinets can be used to scale up the process according to the required capacity and enhance the thermal efficiency. Nevertheless, drying herbs in fixed beds requires intermittent revolving of material to reduce the drying time and avoid the development of moisture gradients that would lead to uneven moisture profiles in the dried product [13].

Other convective dryers frequently used in leaf processing are the fluidized and vibrofluidized bed dryers [12, 18–20], rotary dryers [21–23], conveyor belt dryers

[24–26], and heat pump dryers [27, 28]. These devices offer flexible and versatile configurations to process materials of different characteristics from a small- to large-scale basis. As the fluidized and rotary dryers operate with moving beds, the contact between the airflow and the leaves is enhanced, and homogeneous products with uniform final moisture are most likely obtained. However, alterations in the design of conventional devices to comply with the particular features of leaves are often reported. Most fresh leaves, for instance, cannot be properly fluidized in conventional equipment, and vibration has been introduced as an alternative to overcome this drawback [19]. Rotary dryers with modified designs have also been proposed to increase the drying rates and enhance homogeneity by providing effective mixing of the material throughout the process [21, 22]. Heat pump dryers operate under low temperatures and are considered appealing to preserve color and bioactive compounds. In such devices, the air is dehumidified, heated, and recirculated back to the dryer. Overall, convective dryers have low maintenance costs, but they also have relevant drawbacks such as high energy consumption and low thermal efficiency [29]. One of the reasons for low thermal efficiency is that a significant part of the energy is lost by the unsaturated outlet air. Recirculation of part of the outlet air has been proposed as an alternative to reduce such energy losses [29].

Microwave dryers are much applied for drying leaves, either alone or combined to hot air or vacuum drying. Microwave drying can speed up the drying velocity considerably, and both the short drying times and the high energy input cause rapid inactivation of color-changing enzymes, resulting in improved color retention [30, 31]. Nevertheless, microwaves interact with polar molecules not only from water but from other compounds as well. Hence, significant losses of volatile compounds such as polar monoterpenes and volatile oils can be observed [31]. The use of industrial microwaves to process medicinal and aromatic herbs has been limited up to now, which is attributed to the incomplete knowledge on how microwave absorption affects the valuable ingredients of plants, the lack of studies on energy evaluations and upscaling calculations, and the high investment costs required for microwave dryers [31].

Freeze-drying is recognized as a suitable method for preservation of color, EO content, and bioactive compounds of herbs [12, 13]. This technique is based on freezing the product at low pressure (typically under 10^4 Pa) and low temperature (less than 0°C). Moisture is turned into ice and further sublimated to the surroundings; hence, there is no thermal degradation, and neither the process allows the action of degradative enzymes [13]. Additionally, this process enhances extraction because the ice crystals formed within the plant matrix can rupture the cell structures and facilitate the solvents assess to cellular components [13]. The high cost, long drying times, and low volume of products restrict this technique to high-value products [13].

The major concerns in drying herbs are to maintain the fresh-like characteristics and to preserve the bioactive compounds; therefore, much research has been conducted to investigate the effects of drying and drying conditions on the quality attributes of dried leaves. A summary of drying research reported for 33 different leaf specimens is shown in Table 3.1. Although these references do not intend to comprise all the published literature in the field, they offer a representative overview of recent research and illustrate a broad variety of dryers and natural techniques used to dry leaves.

TABLE 3.1
A Summary of Research Developed on Medicinal Plant Leaf Drying

Leaf	Drying Method	Analysis	Initial MC (g Water/g Dry Matter)	Final MC (g Water/g Dry Matter)	Air Temperature (°C)/Power (W/g)	Air Velocity (m/s)	Drying Time (min)	RH (%)	Ref.
Basil leaves (*Ocimum basilicum* L.)	Fixed-bed	Essential oil	6.4	0.10	45	0.4	720		[32]
	Vibrated dryer	Essential oil	7.0 ± 0.8	0.19 ± 0.02	30–60	1.0	480		[19]
	Vacuum oven	Methanol extracts	8.62		70		960		[33]
	Shade	Storage			24		30240	10	
	Freeze-drying				−54		4320		
Blueberry leaves (*Vaccinium myrtillus*)	Hot air	Kinetic models	0.78 ± 0.16	0.11–0.18	45–75		20–105		[34]
	Hot air + microwave	Ethanol extracts			45–75/6.25 (max)		10–100		
Bay leaves (*Laurus nobilis* L.)	Shade	Leaf extracts	3–4	0.09	25		30240	39	[35]
	Oven (FC)			0.09	45		840		
	Freeze-drying			0.09	−50.2		1440		
Celak leaves (*Thymus daenensis*)	Shade	Essential oil	1.09	0.062	25				[36]
	Open sun			0.049	30–40		780		
	Oven (FC)			0.014	50 and 70				
	Microwave			0.048	800				
	Freeze-drying			0.024	−15				
Chard leaves (*Beta vulgaris* L.)	Microwave	Kinetic models	9.37 ± 0.06	0.1	14–26		5–9.5		[37]
	Hot air oven	Color change		0.1	50–100		22–195		
	Hot air + microwave	Energy cons.		0.1	50–100/14–26		1.5–7.5		

(Continued)

TABLE 3.1 *(Continued)*
A Summary of Research Developed on Medicinal Plant Leaf Drying

Leaf	Drying Method	Analysis	Initial MC (g Water/g Dry Matter)	Final MC (g Water/g Dry Matter)	Air Temperature (°C)/Power (W/g)	Air Velocity (m/s)	Drying Time (min)	RH (%)	Ref.
Celery leaves (*Apium graveolens*)	Microwave	Kinetic models	6.65	0.1	7.2–36			8–34	[38]
Eucalyptus (*Eucalyptus globulus*)	Solar dryer	Kinetic models	0.9	0.03–0.06	40–60			18–42	[39]
Guaco (*Mikania glomerata S.*)	Tray dryer	Coumarin extracts	4.7	0.02–0.08	40–80	0.473			[40]
Kaffir lime leaves (*Citrus hystrix* DC.)	Tray dryer	Kinetic models	1.15–2.87	0.075	40–60	0.5	165–285	15–32	[27]
	Heat pump	Citronellal Color change			40–60	0.5	50–480	10–19	
Holy basil (*Ocimum sanctum* L.)	Tray dryer	Color change	4.09	0.066	50	1.5	900–960		[41]
	Tray dryer/low humidity air	Extracts & volatiles		0.073	50	1.5	540		
	Infrared dryer			0.074	5		27		
Indian curry (*Murraya koenigii*)	Tray dryer		3		40–60				[42]
	Microwave-vac	Kinetic models			6–12				
	Hot air + microwave	Essential oil			50/9				
	Freeze-drying				–60				
Lemmon balm (*Melissa officinalis* L.)	Hot air through-flow	Color change/ rosmarinic acid			30–90	0.2		2.2–36	[43]
	Oven								
	Shade	Methanol extracts	2.33–5.09		40		2880	60	[44]
			2.33–5.09		26				

(Continued)

TABLE 3.1 *(Continued)*
A Summary of Research Developed on Medicinal Plant Leaf Drying

Leaf	Drying Method	Analysis	Initial MC (g Water/ g Dry Matter)	Final MC (g Water/ g Dry Matter)	Air Temperature (°C)/Power (W/g)	Air Velocity (m/s)	Drying Time (min)	RH (%)	Ref.
Lemon grass *(Cymbopogon citratus)*	Fixed bed	Essential oil		0.124	40–60	0.5/1.0		29–41	[45]
Lemon myrtle *(Backhousia citriodora)*	Fluidized bed	Color and volatiles retention	1.21	0.120–0.127	30–40	2.6	67.2–315	<40	[46]
Lemon verbena *(Lippia citriodora K.)*	Oven	Essential oil	1.64	0.099	40–60		360–1500	38 ± 4	[47]
	Vacuum				40–60		180–780		
	Shade				25 ± 2		3180	22–27	
	Freeze-drying				−52		420		
Mate leaves *(Ilex paraguariensis)*	Fixed bed	Drying model Energy effic.	1.50 ± 0.05		50 & 103	1.04–1.11			[48]
	Conveyor belt		0.48–1.71	0.03–0.04a	55 &133	0.075–0.095			[24]
	Fluidized bed	Drying model	1.50 ± 0.05		52 & 101	0.6–1.0			[18]
Mexican tea leaves *(Chenopodium ambrosioides)*	Solar drying (FC)	Kinetic models	4.16–4.39 ± 0.05	0.102–0.108	45–60	0.05–0.12[b]	50–430	32–52.3 ± 2	[49]

(Continued)

TABLE 3.1 *(Continued)*
A Summary of Research Developed on Medicinal Plant Leaf Drying

Leaf	Drying Method	Analysis	Initial MC (g Water/g Dry Matter)	Final MC (g Water/g Dry Matter)	Air Temperature (°C)/Power (W/g)	Air Velocity (m/s)	Drying Time (min)	RH (%)	Ref.
Mint (*Mentha spicata*)	Oven	Methanol extracts	2.33–5.09		40		2880	60	[44]
	Shade				26				
Mint (*Mentha cordifolia*)	Microwave-vacuum	Kinetic models	9.43 ± 0.02	0.1	8.0; 9.6; 11.2		13; 12; 10		[30]
	Hot air	Color change			60 & 70	1.0	90 & 60		
		Rehydration							
		Structural change							
Mint (*Mentha villosa* H.)	Tunnel	Kinetic, ANN, & RSA models	7.3		36–64	1.0–2.0	100–600		[50] [51] [52]
	Oven	Kinetic & ANN models	6 ± 1		50–70		200–800		
		Color change							
	Rotary drum dryer[a]	Color change	6 ± 1	0.02–0.042	40–60	0.5	540–780		
Mint (*n.i.*)	Open sun	Kinetic models	6.14	0.09	30–46.4		390		[53]
	Solar drying	Energy and exergy analysis		0.05	51.5–66.3		210		
Moringa (*Moringa oleífera* L.)	Tray dryer	Color change	2.45	0.06	40–60	0.5	46–360	12.8–28.5	[54]
	Microwave	Quercetin & kaempferol			12.5–75		5215		
	Heat pump				40–60–85	0.5	40–300	9.2–23.9	
	Freeze-drying	Kinetic models					1440		

(Continued)

TABLE 3.1 *(Continued)*
A Summary of Research Developed on Medicinal Plant Leaf Drying

Leaf	Drying Method	Analysis	Initial MC (g Water/g Dry Matter)	Final MC (g Water/g Dry Matter)	Air Temperature (°C)/Power (W/g)	Air Velocity (m/s)	Drying Time (min)	RH (%)	Ref.
Neem *(Azadirachta indica)*	Oven	Color change		0.06–0.15	45 & 70		900		[55]
	Shade	Methanol extracts			≈27–30		10080		
Olive *(Olea europaea L.)*	Conveyor belt	CO_2 SCE Drying model	1.21 ± 0.03	0.11–0.18	50–70	1.0	60–180		[25]
									[28]
	Heat pump	Essential oil RSA	0.49	<0.10	45–55	0.5–1.5	270–390		
	Rotary drum dryer (FC)	Color change	1.26 ± 0.05	<0.09	40/60	0.5	180/690		[52]
Oregano *(Origanum vulgare)*	Vacuum oven	Methanol extracts			70		960		[33]
	Shade	Storage			24		30240	10	
	Freeze-drying				–54		4320		
Parsley *(Petroselinum crispum)*	Infrareda	Essential oil	7.6	0.13	47.5/50.9	47.5–50.9	180		[56]
	Oven	Essential oil	3.35	<0.11	75		50–70		[57]
	Microwave–vacuum	Color change			642 W[c]				

(Continued)

TABLE 3.1 *(Continued)*
A Summary of Research Developed on Medicinal Plant Leaf Drying

Leaf	Drying Method	Analysis	Initial MC (g Water/g Dry Matter)	Final MC (g Water/g Dry Matter)	Air Temperature (°C)/Power (W/g)	Air Velocity (m/s)	Drying Time (min)	RH (%)	Ref.
Peppermint (*Mentha piperita* L.)	Infrared	Essential oil	8.8	0.12	39.9/45.6	39.9–45.6	135		[56]
	Rotary drum[a] dryer	Essential oil Energy cons. Kinetic models Color change	3.17–6.69	0.10–0.13	25–55[d]		720–900	10–70	[21]
Pitanga leaves (*Eugenia uniflora*)	Conveyor belt	CO_2 SCE drying model	1.22 ± 0.01	0.05–0.15	50–70	1.0	60–120		[26]
Rosemary (*Rosmarinus officinalis*)	Oven (FC)[a]				60	1.2			
	Microwave[a]	Essential oil	3.73	0.01	8				[58]
	Hot air + Microwave[a]				6/8	1.2			
	Oven								
	Sun	Kinetic models		0.02	50		720		
	Microwave	Color change	13.20	1.55	20 to 30		780		[59]
		Mineral cont		0.03	14		3.75		
Sage (*Salvia officinalis*)	Oven	Methanol extracts	2.33–5.09		40		2880	60	[44]
	Shade		2.33–5.09		26				
Spearmint (*Mentha spicata* L.)	Rotary tray (FC)	Essential oil	5.35	0.13	43		300	11–48	[60]
	Vacuum-freeze	Rehydration Kinetic models		0.12	–50		720–900		

(Continued)

TABLE 3.1 *(Continued)*

A Summary of Research Developed on Medicinal Plant Leaf Drying

Leaf	Drying Method	Analysis	Initial MC (g Water/ g Dry Matter)	Final MC (g Water/ g Dry Matter)	Air Temperature (°C)/Power (W/g)	Air Velocity (m/s)	Drying Time (min)	RH (%)	Ref.
Stevia leaves (*Stevia rebaudiana*)	Hot air drying	Aqueous extracts	2.95	0.03	60	1.5	180		[61]
	Vacuum			0.04	60		240		
	Freeze-drying			0.04	−50		600		
	Microwave			0.05	10–16		4–8		
	Infrared			0.07	60		180		
	Shade			0.06	25.5–30.1			32–44.5	
	Sun			0.06	38.5–58.5			11.5–53.5	
Thyme (*n.i.*)	Vacuum oven	Methanol extracts	2.47	70			960		[33]
	Shade	Storage		24			30240	10	
	Freeze-drying			−54			4320		
Thyme (*Thymus officinalis* L.)	Oven (FC)	Essential oil	0.14	45			840		[62]
	Freeze-drying	Storage	0.12	−50					

Abbreviations: FC = forced convection; ANN = artificial neural network; RSA = response surface analysis.

[a] Include leaves and stems.

[b] Estimated value (based on the section area of the drying cabinet).

[c] Mass of leaves not informed.

[d] Intermittent drying.

The initial moisture content of the leaves varies in a wide range, from about 0.48 or 0.49 g water/g dry matter, respectively, for the mate (*Ilex paraguariensis*) and olive (*O. europaea*) leaves, to 13.20 g water/g dry matter for the rosemary leaves (*Rosmarinus officinalis* L.). Because there are relevant differences in the morphological features and composition of each specie, the mechanisms of water removal may vary significantly, and the most suitable drying conditions to preserve the quality attributes have to be identified for each plant. The preservation of bioactive compounds and retention of volatiles in convective drying is strongly correlated to the temperature and time of exposition to hot airflow [46]. Nevertheless, the effects of drying on the composition and concentration of bioactive constituents are not fully assessed so far, mainly because many other factors, such as the geographical origin of the plant, the handling and harvesting procedures, the age of the plant, and the extraction technique, affect the quality attributes of extracts and EOs.

Researchers have investigated in detail the composition and quality of EOs and extracts of leaves dried by different techniques and report quite variable results. There is solid evidence that the chemical constituents responsible for the AC, total phenolics (TP), AM, and AI activities are affected by the drying method and conditions. Overall, the bioactive constituents seem to be best preserved if dehydrated under low temperatures, such as in freeze- or shade drying [33, 36], but there are also reports of higher AC and TP activities observed in extracts obtained from air-dried leaves in comparison to those from freeze-dried samples [61]. Microwave drying, on the other hand, usually provides high color quality and increases the concentration of major compounds in EOs, while oven drying at temperatures over 60°C causes a considerable decrease in the color quality [33]. Authors point out that the drying method must be chosen based on the intended usage for the extracts. Evidence has been found that the characteristic short drying times of microwave dryers favor the retention of color and some volatiles. Researchers [31, 63] emphasize the necessity of additional investigation on the effects of penetration depth and temperature regulation on the quality of dried herbs.

According to Xie *et al.* [63], the combination of two or more techniques to dry herbs can provide a synergistic effect and reduce the energy requirements and the drying time preserving the majority of quality attributes. In hot air drying assisted by microwave, the major portion of water in the initial drying period can be more economically removed by the hot air, while the microwave can be used to speed up the final drying period when the strongly bound water has to be removed [31]. Hybrid techniques have been evaluated by several researchers. Böhm *et al.* [57] evaluated the color, aroma, and off-flavor of parsley (*Petroselinum crispum*) dried by vacuum-microwave and hot air. They observed that the green color and content of EOs were best preserved in the samples processed using the vacuum-microwave compared to those dried with hot air. Alibas [37] tested variable power outputs and air temperatures in combined microwave and hot air drying for drying chard (*Beta vulgaris* L.) leaves. The combination that resulted in minimum drying time and energy consumption with the best color preservation of leaves was achieved at 500 W and 75°C.

3.3 APPLICATIONS ON CONVECTIVE DRYING OF LEAVES

Research carried out in the Drying Center of DEQ/UFSCar investigating the drying of basil leaves, regular mint leaves, and olive leaves, respectively, in a vibrofluidized dryer, a modified rotary dryer, and a conveyor belt dryer will be approached in this section. A brief description of the main characteristics and applications of aforementioned leaves are presented below.

Basil (*O. basilicum* L.) is an annual herb belonging to the *Lamiaceae* family. Species from this family have been traditionally used in natural or complementary medicine against a wide variety of diseases. Research has shown that the EO of basil contains potent anticancer, antiviral, antibacterial, and antioxidant properties [64, 65]. The main phytochemical constituents of the basil's EO include terpenes, monoterpenoids, phenols, and aldehydes.

Regular mint (*Mentha* x *villosa* L.) is a plant from the *Lamiaceae* family that originated from Europe and is widely cultivated throughout Brazil [66]. They have many reported pharmacological actions due to the presence of oxygenated monoterpenes, monoterpenoids, sesquiterpenoids, triterpenoids, and steroids in their EO [67].

The leaves of the olive tree (*O. europaea* L.), a plant from the *Oleaceae* family native from the Mediterranean areas, are recognized as an important source of bioactive compounds. Oleanolic acid, a pentacyclic triterpene found in the olive leaves, as well as its isomer, the ursolic acid, has been reported beneficial effects on the regulation of cardiovascular homeostasis [68].

Despite the obvious challenges involved in measuring the size and describing the shape of leaves, quantitative descriptors are useful for an adequate analysis of the drying processes and modeling purposes as well. The main physical properties and the initial moisture content of the leaves investigated are presented in Table 3.2. The maximum and minimum Feret diameters, the projected area, volume, and thickness of individual leaves are listed in this table. The dimensions were measured in samples from 30 up to 90 leaves, depending on the species. The apparent density and the initial moisture content of the leaves were determined according to the techniques described elsewhere [19, 25, 51].

TABLE 3.2
Physical Properties and Initial Moisture Content of Fresh Leaves [19, 25, 51]

Property	Basil	Mint	Olive
d_{Fmax} (cm)	3.3 ± 0.2	6.1 ± 0.8	6 ± 1
d_{Fmin} (cm)	1.9 ± 0.2	3.5 ± 0.4	1.1 ± 0.2
A_{proj} (cm^2)	4.6 ± 0.7	16 ± 3	3.8 ± 0.7
V_p (cm^3)	0.116	0.29 ± 0.07	0.302
δ (cm)	0.023 ± 0.002	0.018 ± 0.02	0.040 ± 0.004
ϕ (–)	0.16	0.12 ± 0.01	0.126
ρ_p (g/cm^3)	0.87 ± 0.05	0.86 ± 0.02	1.391 ± 0.006
M_i (g/g) d.b.	7.1 ± 0.2	6 ± 1	1.01 ± 0.03

The three leaves have low sphericity (0.16 or lower) and high ratios of the superficial area to volume, which are, in decreasing order, equal to 110 (for the mint leaf), 80 (for the basil), and 21 (for the olive leaf). Fresh basil and mint are delicate herbs with high moisture content and low density, while the olive leaf has lower moisture and is denser and coriaceous.

Some outcomes of studies conducted by our research group on convective drying using different devices will be discussed next.

3.3.1 Drying Basil Leaves in a Vibrofluidized Dryer

Air-fluidized beds appear as a potentially good technique to leaf dehydration and are traditionally used by tea manufacturers to dry fermented tea leaves [12]. However, poor fluidization patterns have been reported on the conventional fluidization of fresh leaves [18, 69]. Morphological features, high moisture content, and rough surface favor the action of attractive forces and might lead to agglomeration and poor air percolation in fluidization. Applying a mechanical vibration to the fluidized bed grid has shown to be effective to improve mixture and enhance the contact between solid and gas phases [12, 19].

Authors who investigated hot air drying of basil leaves found evidence that higher temperatures lead to higher losses in the volatile compounds [10]. Drying at a too low temperature, on the other hand, can cause a considerable loss of chlorophyll pigments because low drying rates favor the browning reactions [70]. Researchers from our group investigated the influence of drying temperature on the composition of the EO extracted from basil dried in a vibrofluidized dryer. Drying was performed at a fixed air velocity (1.0 m/s) under mild temperatures of 30°C, 45°C, and 60°C. The influence of the air temperature on drying kinetics has been previously investigated using the thin-layer drying methodology [69]. Because the temperature and moisture gradients are negligible in thin-layer samples, the results can be extended to moving beds that operate as a well-mixed reactor. The results demonstrated that the moisture removal rate is strongly dependent on the air temperature, and the process is controlled by the internal mass transfer and not by the surface flow conditions [13].

Researchers on plant physiology agree that water in leaf tissues may move through two separate pathways, the symplast and apoplast as a liquid, or through the airspaces as vapor, although the dominant path remains in dispute. The mechanisms involved are quite complex and intimately related to the plant structure, so the overall process has not been fully modeled in terms of experimental variables so far [71]. It is reasonable to assume that the process is controlled by the typical mechanisms of mass transfer in porous media, such as the ordinary vapor and liquid diffusions, liquid capillary flow, Knudsen diffusion, and surface diffusion of water molecules, among others [72], which are all temperature-dependent mechanisms. One must bear in mind that, likely, the cellular tissues are more damaged at higher temperatures, which facilitates moisture flowing out of the cells and enhances the drying rate.

The vibrofluidized drying chamber is a rectangular acrylic column, 30 cm high, with a cross-section of 0.20×0.11 m^2 (Figure 3.1). Air was supplied by a blower and heated in an electric heater connected to a temperature controller. Pressure and temperature sensors were placed at different positions of the line and linked to a data

FIGURE 3.1 Vibrofluidized dryer.

acquisition board. Air entered at the base of the drying chamber, and the vibration amplitude and frequency could be adjusted.

The vibration energy is defined as the dimensionless group:

$$\Gamma = \frac{A(2\pi f)}{g} \tag{3.1}$$

where A and f are the vibration amplitude and frequency, respectively, and g is the gravitational acceleration.

Samples of approximately 180 g of fresh leaves (corresponding to a static height of 10 cm) were inserted into the drying chamber and dried at temperatures ranging from 30°C to 60°C. The vibration was set at $\Gamma = 1$, $A = 0.5$ cm, and U = 1.0 m/s. Under these conditions, the leaves were suspended in the airflow and simultaneously mixed by the imparted vertical vibration. These combined mechanisms prevented channeling/agglomeration and improved gas-solid contact.

It was observed that the dried leaves had uniform color and an even moisture distribution. In drying with air at 45°C and relative humidity of 70%, the final moisture content of leaves sampled from 12 different positions of the drying chamber after drying for 8 h had a mean value of 0.19 ± 0.02 g of water/g dry matter, which was consistent with the estimated equilibrium moisture [19]. Equivalent results have been obtained under the other temperatures, corroborating that the device behaved like a perfectly agitated vessel and was effective to produce a homogeneously dried product with adequate moisture for storage. The leaves underwent significant shrinkage during drying, but they were not damaged or fractured and preserved their integrity.

3.3.1.1 Essential Oils

The influence of drying on the EO composition was evaluated by comparing the chemical profiles of oils extracted from the fresh and dried leaves. The extraction was performed in a Clevenger-type distiller apparatus. The oil was collected with water and separated by liquid-liquid extraction using dichloromethane. The volatile compounds were analyzed using gas chromatography-mass spectrometry (CG-MS) technique, and their identification was based on comparing the retention indices (RI), as well as by computerized matching of the acquired mass spectra with those stored in the NIST library of the CG-MS data system [19].

The chromatographic profiles of oils extracted from leaves dried at 45°C in the vibrofluidized dryer for 2 h and 8 h showed very similar chromatographic profiles [19], corroborating evidence from the literature that alterations in the number and concentration of volatile compounds of the *Lamiaceae* family plants occur in the early drying stages [73, 58].

Forty volatile compounds have been identified in the basil leaves EO, mostly were monoterpenoids, phenylpropanoids, sesquiterpenes, and oxygenated sesquiterpenes. The compounds of higher concentrations in the EO of fresh leaves were eucalyptol, linalool, camphor (monoterpenoids), and eugenol (a phenylpropanoid). The relative percentage area (RPA) of these compounds ranged from 9.4% for camphor to 38.3% for eugenol. Germacrene-D, α-terpineol, and *epi*-α-cadinol were found in relative percentages between 3 and 5%. The other 33 compounds, found in percentages lower than 1%, included pinenes, cadinenes, limonene, and myrcene. Because commercial samples of unknown cultivation practices have been used in the tests, some variability in the oil's profiles was observed. In Table 3.3, the retention times and retention

TABLE 3.3
Main Compounds Identified in the EO Extracted from Fresh Basil Leaves and from Leaves Dried under Different Temperatures [19]

Retention Time (min)	Compound	RI[a] (calc)	RI[b] (lit)	RPA[c] Fresh	30°C	45°C	60°C
9.25	Eucalyptol	1032	1031	14 ± 6	12 ± 5	18 ± 5	27 ± 7
11.34	Linalool	1099	1097	20 ± 3	14 ± 3	24 ± 6	22 ± 5
12.86	Camphor	1148	1146	9.4 ± 0.4	7 ± 2	14 ± 4	17 ± 4
18.94	Eugenol	13533	1359	38 ± 6	49 ± 9	23 ± 2	18 ± 9

[a] RI calculated based on a standard mixture of C1-C-29 hydrocarbons obtained for a DB5-MS column.
[b] RI calculated according to references.
[c] RPA calculated based on the peak areas.

indexes of the four most relevant compounds found in the fresh and dried leaves are compared.

A reduction in the content of eugenol by approximately 37% and 50% is observed in the EO of leaves dried, respectively, at 45°C and 60°C, while no significant change was observed for leaves dried at 30°C as compared to the fresh leaves. The content of linalool was little affected by drying at 30°C and a slight decrease was observed at 45°C and 60°C. Similar results were observed for the content of eucalyptol. In most cases, drying at 30°C preserved better constituents, and a small increase in the content of monoterpenoids was consistently observed when the drying temperature rose. Although researchers agree that the composition of volatile oils is affected by the drying method and drying temperature, assessing how the content of a particular constituent is affected by these factors is still under debate. The results encourage a more in-depth investigation of this drying technique as an alternative to preserve the volatile constituents in the EO of basil leaves.

3.3.2 Drying Mint Leaves in a Modified Rotary Dryer

A modified rotary dryer [22, 52] has been developed to offer an alternative to the vibrated dryer for drying leaves. To operate stably, a vibrated dryer requires a properly sized and well-designed vibration mechanism, and compared to most dryers, it has high capital and operating costs. The purpose was to achieve good mixing of the material using the rotation mechanism instead of the vibration. As illustrated in Figure 3.2(a), the hot air flows perpendicularly to the rotation axis through a perforated wall, which makes it different from a conventional rotary drum, in which the air flows along the axial length [23]. The dryer (Figure 3.2b) is a short drum made of a perforated metal wall 26 cm long and with a diameter of 14.5 cm. It is internally coated with a flexible screen to ensure a uniform air distribution throughout the drum. Acrylic plates closed both ends, so the dynamic patterns of the material could be visually observed during the experiments and a movable port allowed access to the interior. The airflow was supplied by a blower from where it was directed to an

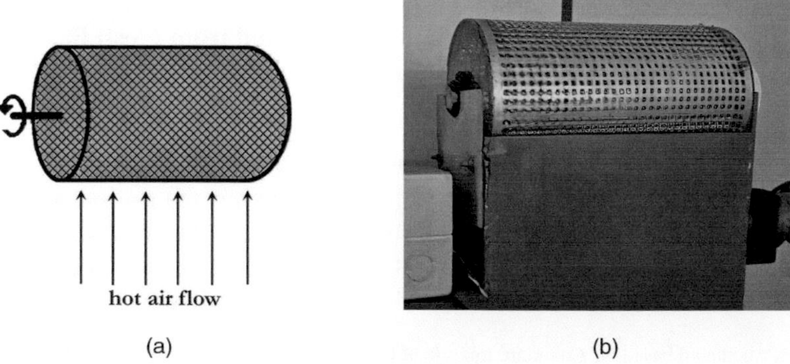

FIGURE 3.2 (a) Schematic illustration of the airflow through a modified rotary dryer for leaves; (b) rotary dryer.

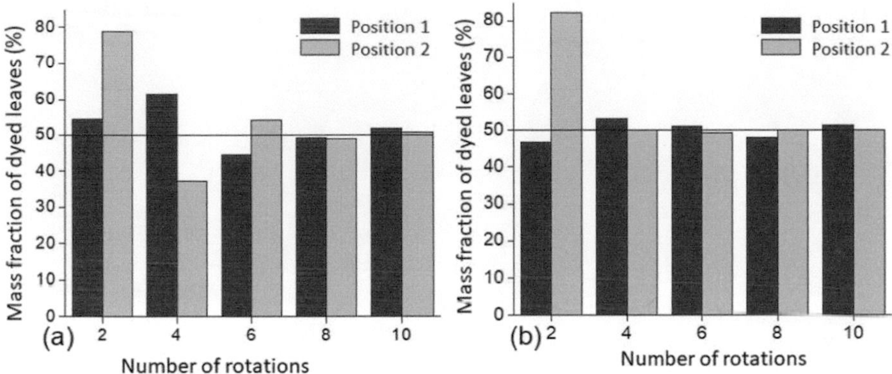

FIGURE 3.3 Mass fraction of dyed branches as a function of the number of rotations, U = 50 cm/s, T = 35°C. (a) M_i = 8.5 ± 0.3 g of water/g of dried material; initial mass = 200 g; (b) M_i = 0.070 ± 0.002 g of water/g of dried material; initial mass = 50 g [52].

electric heater and then toward the drum. An electric motor coupled to a speed variator unit allowed one to set the rotation speed. The airflow rate and temperature could be adjusted and measured at the air inlet section.

Whole branches of fresh regular mint (*Mentha villosa*), composed of about 76% of leaves and 24% of stems on a weight basis were used in the tests [51]. The variations in the moisture content and color were evaluated separately for the leaves and stems because the fractions have different drying rates [22, 51]. Here, we will focus on the analysis of leaves.

An effective mixing of the material inside the rotating drum over the whole drying period was crucial to achieve a final product with a uniform moisture distribution. The mixing patterns were previously checked using a dyed-tracer technique whose detailed description can be found elsewhere [52].

Figure 3.3 shows the mass fraction of dyed branches as a function of the number of rotations for nearly fresh (8.5 g of water/g of dried material) and dried (0.070 g of water/g of dried material) branches. When a mass fraction of 50 ± 5% was found in both positions, it was assumed that full mixing was reached. This happened after 6 rotations for the fresh material and after only 4 rotations for the dried branches. At a rotation speed of 2 rpm, even considering the worst situation (6 rotations), a full homogenization of the material would take about 3 min, which is a short time compared to the usual drying times.

The mint branches shrank significantly in the first hours of drying, with a considerable reduction in the volume of the material (Figure 3.4).

Drying was evaluated under temperatures of 40°C, 50°C, and 60°C based on recommendations suggesting drying under mild temperatures for color preservation [60]. Figure 3.5 shows the moisture reduction ratio, $M(t)/M_i$, versus time obtained under the different air temperatures, where M(t) is the moisture at time t and M_i is the initial moisture content. The absolute ambient temperature varied only 3% throughout the tests. All the assays were replicated, the symbols in Figure 3.5 represent the mean values, and the vertical bars are the standard deviations.

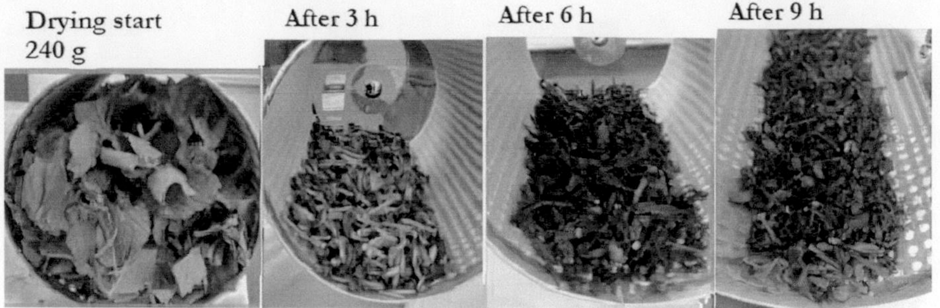

FIGURE 3.4 Rotary drum drying of mint branches, U = 0.5 m/s, 70°C [52].

It took approximately 11 h to reduce the moisture to 10% of the initial value at 40°C, while at 50°C an equivalent reduction was observed after 8 h and at 60°C after less than 6h. Drying was interrupted at t = 15 h when the leaves dried at 40°C attained final moisture of 0.042 g of water/g of dried material. For leaves dried at 50°C and 60°C, this value dropped to 0.020 g of water/g of dried material. The recommended moisture levels for storage range from 0.052 to 0.10 g water/g of dried material [45].

The moisture reduction was slower at 40°C, but the difference in the drying rates observed at 50°C and 60°C was less significant. The temperature of the branches was measured during drying using an infrared thermometer, and it was observed that it remained significantly lower than the air temperature through the whole process.

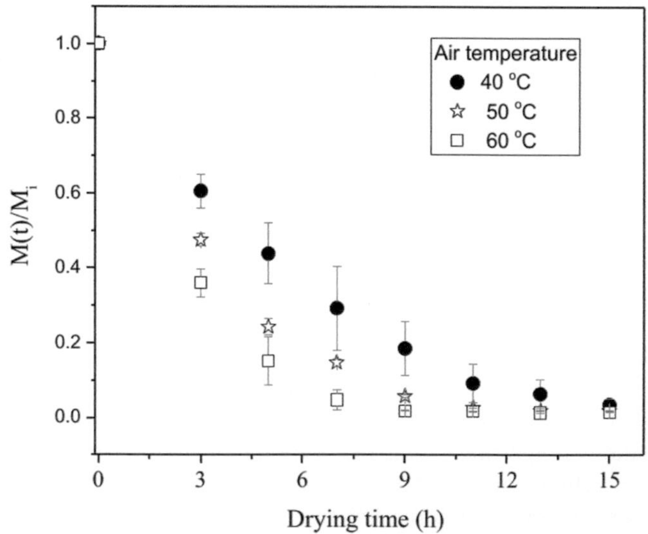

FIGURE 3.5 Moisture reduction ratio of mint leaves in the rotary drum dryer as a function of the time, mass of fresh branches of 750 g.

In the end, the measured temperatures were approximately 8°C, 11°C, and 15°C lower than the air temperature, respectively, for drying at 40°C, 50°C, and 60°C. A thermal equilibrium with the air was not achieved because part of the energy supplied is used to heat the equipment itself and another part is dissipated to the ambient. Since the ambient temperature varied little during the experiments, heat dissipation increases as the air temperature rises, which probably explains why the moisture reduction rates under 50°C and 60°C were not significantly different.

The rotary dryer yielded a homogeneous product with adequate moisture levels for storage. The color change was evaluated as an indicator of product quality, as discussed next.

3.3.2.1 Color Degradation

The leaf color was measured using a CM-5 Konica Minolta spectrophotometer and expressed by the parameters L^*, a^*, and b^* of the CIELAB color space. The parameters L^*, a^*, and b^* in this scale indicate, respectively, the changes in luminosity (which varies from 0 for black to 100 for white color), changes from green ($-a^*$) to red ($+a^*$) color, and from blue ($-b^*$) to yellow ($+b^*$) color. Measurements were carried out in triplicate, and the total color change, ΔE^*, could be estimated by:

$$\Delta E^* = \sqrt{\left(L^*_{in} - L^*_{fin}\right)^2 + \left(a^*_{in} - a^*_{fin}\right)^2 + \left(b^*_{in} - b^*_{fin}\right)^2} \tag{3.2}$$

where the subscripts *in* and *fin* refer to the initial and final values of the parameters. Figure 3.6 shows the values of ΔE^* as a function of the drying time under different temperatures.

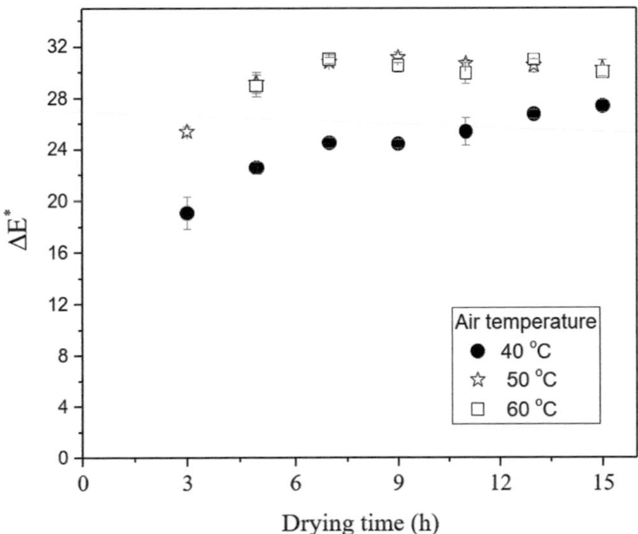

FIGURE 3.6 Color change of mint leaves as a function of the drying time.

TABLE 3.4
Values of Color Parameters of Fresh and Hot Air-Dried Mint Leaves [52]

T_g (°C)	t (h)	Leaf status	L^*	a^*	b^*
—		Fresh	38.4 ± 1.7	−8.56 ± 0.26	18.3 ± 1.4
40	3	Dried	26.5 ± 1.2	0.80 ± 0.12	6.69 ± 0.50
	7		21.0 ± 0.4	0.74 ± 0.08	3.75 ± 0.20
	11		21.0 ± 0.4	0.59 ± 0.16	3.75 ± 0.23
	15		17.7 ± 0.5	1.08 ± 0.16	3.26 ± 0.60
—		Fresh	42.6 ± 2.2	−8.54 ± 0.47	21.7 ± 0.9
50	3	Dried	25.0 ± 0.4	1.36 ± 0.51	6.37 ± 0.64
	7		19.4 ± 0.3	1.29 ± 0.40	4.05 ± 0.40
	11		18.9 ± 0.4	1.56 ± 0.04	4.33 ± 0.33
	15		19.4 ± 0.7	1.72 ± 0.14	5.18 ± 0.61
—		Fresh	42.6 ± 2.2	−8.54 ± 0.47	21.7 ± 0.9
60	3	Dried	22.1 ± 0.8	−0.03 ± 0.09	5.81 ± 0.50
	7		19.0 ± 0.3	0.83 ± 0.03	4.09 ± 0.07
	11		19.5 ± 0.5	0.88 ± 0.12	4.13 ± 0.31
	15		19.6 ± 0.5	0.85 ± 0.08	4.99 ± 0.28

Drying caused considerable changes in the leaf color. The lowest values of ΔE^* were observed in drying at 40°C, while no significant differences were observed in drying under 50°C and 60°C. It is agreed in the literature that hot air drying did not preserve the original color of aromatic and medicinal plants [37, 59]. Both the temperature level and the length of time the herbs are exposed to the hot air as well as mechanical damage caused by mixing contribute to darkening [21].

Table 3.4 shows the values of L^*, a^*, and b^* for the fresh leaves and for leaves dried over different times and temperatures. The darkening is evidenced by the significant drop observed in the L^* values as compared to those of the fresh leaves. The changes of a^* from negative to positive values indicate a deterioration in the green color, and the decrease of b^* indicates a reduction of the yellow component. It is seen that major changes occur in the first 3 h of drying and after 15 h the extent of leaf color deterioration is similar regardless of the air temperature, confirming the effect of long drying time on darkening. The values of L^* obtained in our study are compatible with those reported by Tarhan *et al.* [21] in hot air drying of peppermint leaves under constant or wave-shaped temperature profiles. Researchers pointed out that color might be best preserved by fast dehydration of the surface of a product when color-changing enzymes like chlorophyllase would be rapidly inactivated [30, 31]. This is why microwave drying is considered effective for color preservation. Associating hot air drying with other drying techniques [10, 42] or using high temperatures with intermittent heating [21] has been attempted aiming to reduce the drying times and minimize the color deterioration but with limited success so far.

3.3.3 Drying Olive Leaves in a Conveyor Belt Dryer

In a conveyor belt dryer, the product is layered over a perforated screen, and hot air flow is forced through the material as the screen is slowly pulled up. Possible configurations include the single pass/multiple stage dryers or the multiple pass dryers [74], and a broad variety of products can be handled in either batch or continuous operation modes. They are used in the Brazilian South region and Argentina to process mate (*I. paraguariensis*) leaves on a commercial scale [25, 75].

The performance of a conveyor belt on drying olive leaves (*O. europaea* L.) has been investigated by our research group, and the effects of the drying conditions on the bioactive compounds of supercritical extracts recovered from the dried leaves have been assessed [25]. Drying is a required pretreatment for supercritical extraction because the high moisture levels of fresh leaves can work as a barrier for mass transfer and might reduce the extraction yields (EY) [76]. According to the literature, EYs in supercritical extraction are enhanced by operating with moisture levels from 7 to 23% [77].

To evaluate the effect of the air temperature and residence time on the moisture reduction of the olive leaves, drying kinetic curves under different air temperatures were first obtained. After, a theoretical model based on mass and energy conservation balances was implemented to estimate the moisture content of the leaves at the conveyor belt discharge and establish the drying conditions aimed at supercritical extraction.

The olive leaves used in this study were cultivated in Baependi, Minas Gerais, Brazil. The conveyor belt dryer (Figure 3.7) is a rectangular chamber (0.7 m high, 0.1 m wide, and 0.6 m long) that supports a stainless-steel perforated conveyor belt, whose velocity (u_c) could be conveniently adjusted. The air supplied by a blower is heated and divided into equal parts before entering the plenum by two opposite-sided orifices. The assays were performed under temperatures of 50°C, 60°, and

FIGURE 3.7 Conveyor belt dryer.

70°C. A constant mass of leaves was distributed as a uniform layer over the conveyor belt, and the air velocity through the bed of leaves was 1.0 m/s.

Canabarro *et al.* [25] reported that the time to reduce the leaf moisture content to the equilibrium moisture was reduced from 350 min at 50°C to about 60 min at 70°C. The steep increase in the drying rates observed at 70°C was attributed to the collapse of the leaf structure. Fresh olive leaves possess overlapping peltate trichomes on their surfaces, structures that, among other functions, help to prevent evaporative water loss under dry weather conditions [78]. Canabarro *et al.* [79] evaluated the surface morphology of the dried olive leaves by a scanning electron microscopy technique and observed that in the leaves dried at 70°C the trichomes were more damaged, probably facilitating the water removal.

Differently from basil and mint leaves that shrunk uniformly in all directions during drying, the olive leaves shrunk in a pattern known as rolling deformation, which is induced by the shrink difference along with leaf thickness [80]. Overall, the results corroborate the strong influence of the leaf's morphological characteristics and composition on the drying rates and quality attributes.

To predict the moisture reduction and the leaf temperature throughout the conveyor dryer length, a pseudo-homogeneous model [24, 81] was adapted and implemented by Canabarro *et al.* [25]. The mass and energy conservation balances (Table 3.5) were applied over a representative volume element which was supposed to comprise the solid and gas phases. The model assumes that both phases (the leaves and the air) constitute a homogeneous porous media whose characteristics remain unaltered throughout drying. Besides, moisture was assumed to be present in both phases either as vapor or liquid, and the moisture and temperature gradients across the leaf layer were considered negligible. Thermodynamic properties of the water (c_{ps}, c_{pw}, and λ) were obtained from the literature, and the specific heat of fresh leaves was measured by differential scanning calorimetry technique [25]. The mass transfer coefficient k_m was estimated by fitting experimental data of moisture versus time to Eqn. (3.3), in which the term axial moisture gradient was omitted because the data were obtained at $u_c = 0$ m/s. Then, the convective heat coefficient h_m was estimated

TABLE 3.5
Modeling Conveyor Belt Drying of Olive Leaves: Mass and Energy Balances, Initial and Boundary Conditions

Water Mass Balance:

$$\frac{\partial M}{\partial t} = -u_c \frac{\partial M}{\partial x} - k_m \left(M - M_{eq}\right) \quad (3.3)$$

Energy Balance:

$$\frac{\partial T_s}{\partial t} = -u_c \frac{\partial T_s}{\partial x} - \frac{k_m \left(M - M_{eq}\right)}{\left(c_{ps} + c_{pw} M\right)} \left[c_{pv}\left(T_g - T_s\right) + \lambda + c_{pw} T_s\right] + \frac{h_m \left(T_g - T_s\right)}{\left(c_{ps} + c_{pw} M\right)} \quad (3.4)$$

Initial and Boundary Conditions:

$$t = 0 \rightarrow M = M_i \; ; T_s = T_{si} \quad (3.5)$$

$$x = 0 \rightarrow M = M_0 \; ; T_s = T_{so} \quad (3.6)$$

TABLE 3.6
Drying Conditions of Samples for Supercritical Extractions

Sample	T(°C)	τ (min)/ No. Passes	$M_{out\ exp}$ (w/w)	$M_{out\ pred}$ (w/w)
1	50	180/3	0.18 ± 0.01	0.18
2	60	120/2	0.18 ± 0.01	0.18
3	70	60/1	0.11 ± 0.01	0.13

by fitting experimental temperature profiles to Eqns. (3.3) and (3.4). The initial values of moisture and temperature were determined experimentally. The model was solved by the numerical method of lines as described elsewhere [25].

Based on the conveyor belt length and conveyor velocity, a single pass of leaves through the chamber took approximately 60 min. The model was used to predict the discharge moisture of the leaves under residence times ranging from 60 min (single-pass drying) to 180 min (three passes). Three combinations of air temperature and residence time (τ) that met the requirements of moisture content range for supercritical extraction (<20%) were selected to dry the samples. The drying conditions and the comparison between the discharge moistures obtained experimentally and predicted by the model can be seen in Table 3.6. The accurate model predictions suggest that this simplified model might be useful for monitoring or controlling drying processes in conveyor belts.

3.3.3.1 Supercritical Extraction and Bioactive Compounds

The samples described in Table 3.6 were ground using a knife mill, resulting in powders with a mean diameter of 274 μm and a real density of 1.51 ± 0.05 g/cm^3 [25]. The extractions were carried out with supercritical CO_2 at 250 bar and 80°C in a laboratory-scale unit [26]. The solvent flow rate set at 6 g/min and the extraction time was 80 min. The EY was calculated by:

$$EY(\%) = \frac{\text{extract mass}}{\text{mass of fresh leaves}} \times 100 \tag{3.7}$$

The extracts were characterized concerning their chemical composition, antioxidant activity (AA), and total phenolic content (TPC). The chemical profiles were analyzed by the CG-MS technique, the TPC was quantified using the Folin-Ciocalteu reagent, and the AA was evaluated toward the DPPH radical methodology and expressed in terms of the effective concentration EC_{50}. Fresh olive leaf extracts were obtained by the Soxhlet technique to serve as a reference to compare the EYs. Details of the procedures can be found elsewhere [25]. Table 3.7 shows the EYs, as well as the values of EC_{50}, and TPC found in the extracts recovered from different samples (conditions given in Table 3.6).

Table 3.7 shows that the highest EY (3.50 ± 0.02%) was found in the sample dried for 180 min at 50°C. The AA and TPC were higher in the sample dried at 60°C for 120 min. Sample #3, dried at 70°C for 60 min showed the poorest results for

TABLE 3.7
Extraction Yield, Antioxidant Capacity, EC_{50}, and TPC Values of Supercritical Extracts of Olive Leaves Dried under Different Conditions [25]

Sample	EY (% wt)	AA (%)	EC_{50} (μg/mL)	TPC (mgGAE/g Dry Leaf)
1	3.50 ± 0.02^a	64 ± 1^a	1.2 ± 0.1^a	32.2 ± 0.1^a
2	3.00 ± 0.01^b	73 ± 2^b	1.1 ± 0.1^b	36.1 ± 0.2^b
3	2.80 ± 0.01^c	48 ± 1^c	2.1 ± 0.1^c	30.2 ± 0.1^c

[a,b,c] Different letters in the columns indicate statistically different means at 5% significance level.

EY, AA, and TPC. The air temperature, drying time, and the moisture level of the vegetal matrices affect the bioactive constituents. As samples 1 and 2 have similar moistures, the results suggest that the longer drying time of sample 1 was responsible for the drop in the AA and TPC. As for sample 3, the short residence time was insufficient to compensate for the degradation of bioactive compounds caused by drying at 70°C. The low values of EC_{50} indicate that the olive leaves have high AA. Goulas *et al.* [82] investigated the AA of olive leaf extracts obtained from lyophilized leaves of different cultivars using polar solvents. They found values of AA ranging from 21 ± 1% to 73 ± 1%, which are compatible with ours, despite the differences of leaf cultivars, drying technique, and extraction methods. On the other hand, they found much higher TPC values corroborating that lyophilization contributes to preserving more phenolic constituents than convective drying.

The compounds of major concentrations identified in the extracts were uvaol and oleanolic acid [25], both are pentacyclic triterpenes with reported AI and antidiabetic pharmacological activities [83]. In minor concentrations, stigmasterol, γ-sitosterol, and γ-tocopherol were identified. Compounds such as oleuropein, luteolin, and rutin, which have been found in extracts recovered using polar solvents [84], have not been detected in our extracts, as supercritical CO_2 is a nonpolar solvent and has affinity for different compounds.

The conveyor belt appears as a robust and reliable equipment to dry olive leaves and relevant bioactive constituents can be preserved by choosing adequate drying conditions. Aspects such as thermal efficiency and processing costs need to be further investigated to assess the feasibility of scale up.

3.4 CONCLUDING REMARKS

Standardization and quality optimization are the main aspects to be sought in drying leaves and medicinal plants. Because the leaves might vary widely in shape, size, texture, and composition, each drying method has to be studied for each type of herb, and choosing an adequate dryer is a challenging task. The studies approached in Section 3.3

cover a few examples of the many possible configurations for drying leaves. Although all the devices discussed were based on convective hot air drying, the contact between air and leaves in each one was provided through distinct modes. In the vibrofluidized dryer, a combination of mechanical vibration and ascending airflow was responsible for the effective interphase contact and good mixing, assuring a homogeneously dried product. In the perforated drum, an equivalent outcome was obtained by combining the airflow and the drum's rotation. The action of gravitational force contributed to mixing the leaves and enhancing the contact. As for the conveyor belt, hot airflow percolated through a single layer of material, providing effective contact and uniform drying. A future challenge in drying herbs is to develop equipment and technologies to enhance the interphase contact and increase the drying rates without compromising quality. Making robust and cost-effective continuous dryers easily accessible to small producers would be quite useful to improve the production chain of herbal and medicinal plants in developing countries like Brazil. Alternative heating methods are appealing options to reduce the energy requirements and optimize the process. Solar energy, infrared, or microwave radiations emerge as alternative sources for heating the product, so the air could work preferentially as a carrier media for moisture removal to the outer environment. Current research dedicated to investigate the use of pretreatments and hybrid technologies, as well as incorporating advanced techniques, such as nanotechnology, is expected to be deepened, bringing important contributions toward these goals. In short term, the advances in numerical methods and increase in the computing processing capacity will allow the design of large-scale dryers without the need of making tests in experimental prototypes. Besides, automation and online control tools are becoming more accessible and effective and will significantly contribute to improving the herb's processing technology and the quality of dried products.

3.5 NOMENCLATURE

$\mathbf{d_{Fmax}}$	Maximum Feret diameter (cm)
$\mathbf{d_{Fmin}}$	Minimum Feret diameter (cm)
$\mathbf{a^*}$	Parameter defined in Eqn. (3.2)
A	Vibration amplitude (cm)
AA	Antioxidant activity (%)
$\mathbf{A_{proj}}$	Projected area of a leaf (cm^2)
$\mathbf{b^*}$	Parameter defined in Eqn. (3.2)
D	Diameter (cm)
EY	Extraction yield (%)
f	Vibration frequency (Hz)
g	Gravitational acceleration ($cm.s^{-2}$)
$\mathbf{L^*}$	Parameter defined in Eqn. (3.2)
M	Moisture content ($g.g^{-1}$)
$\mathbf{M_{eq}}$	Equilibrium moisture content ($g.g^{-1}$)
$\mathbf{M_i}$	Initial moisture content of leaves ($g.g^{-1}$)
$\mathbf{M_{out}}$	Discharge moisture content of leaves ($g.g^{-1}$)
t	Drying time (min)
$\mathbf{T_g}$	Drying air temperature (°C)

$\mathbf{u_c}$ Conveyor belt velocity ($m.s^{-1}$)
$\mathbf{U}$ Superficial air velocity ($m.s^{-1}$)
$\mathbf{V_p}$ Volume of a leaf (cm^3)
$\mathbf{x}$ Axial direction in conveyor belt dryer (cm)
δ Thickness of a leaf (cm)
$\Delta \mathbf{E}^*$ Total color variation defined in Eqn. (3.2)
ρ_p Bulk density of a bed of leaves ($g.cm^{-3}$)
ϕ Leaf sphericity
Γ Vibration number

REFERENCES

1. Jornal O Estado de São Paulo. SP amplia uso de planta medicinal e distribui 6,7 milhões de fitoterápicos, published in 20/01/2020. Available at https://saude.estadao.com.br/noticias/geral,70003165326 (accessed in 17/06/2020).
2. Chan, E.W.C.; Lye, P.Y.; Eng, S.Y, Tan, Y.P. Antioxidant properties of herbs with enhancement effects of drying treatments: a synopsis. Free Radicals and Antioxidants 2013, 3, 2–6.
3. Thamkaew, G.; Sjöholm, I.; Galindo, F.G. A review of drying methods for improving the quality of dried herbs. Critical Reviews in Food Science and Nutrition 2020, DOI: 10.1080/10408398.2020.1765309.
4. Dictionary of Food Science and Technology. Compiled and edited by the International Food Information Service, 2nd ed., John Wiley & Sons, 458 p., 2009.
5. Rocha, R.P.; Melo, E.C.; Radünz, L.L. Influence of drying process on the quality of medicinal plants: a review. Journal of Medicinal Plants Research 2011, 5(33), 7076–7084.
6. Calixto, J.B.; Scheidt, C.; Otuki, M.; Santos, A.R.S. Biological activity of plant extracts: novel analgesic drugs. Expert Opinion on Emerging Drugs 2001, 6(2), 261–279.
7. Nakatsu, T.; Lupo Jr., A.T.; Chinn, J.W.; Kang, R.K.L. Biological activity of essential oils and their constituents. Atta-ur-Rahman (Ed.). Studies in Natural Products Chemistry 2000, 21, 571–631.
8. Rates, S.M.K. Plants as source of drugs. Toxicon 2001, 39, 603–613.
9. Azmir, J.; Zaidul, I.S.M.; Rahman, M.M.; Sharif, K.M.; Mohamed, A.; Sahena, F.; Jahurul, M.H.A.; Ghafoor, K.; Norulaini, N.A.N.; Omar, A.K.M. Techniques for extraction of bioactive compounds from plant materials: a review. Journal of Food Engineering 2013, 117, 426–436.
10. Calín-Sanchez, A.; Lech, K.; Szumny, A.; Figiel, A.; Carbonell-Barrachina, A.A. Volatile composition of sweet basil essential oil (*Ocimum basiculum* L.) as affected by drying method. Food Research International 2012, 48, 217–225.
11. Mujumdar, A.S. Principles, classification, and selection of dryers. Ch. 1, pp. 4–28. In: Handbook of Industrial Drying, Ed. A.S. Mujumdar, 4th ed., CRC Press/Taylor and Francis Group, 2015.
12. Chen, G.; Mujumdar, A.S. Drying of herbal medicines and tea. Ch. 30, pp. 637–646. In: Handbook of Industrial Drying, Ed. A.S. Mujumdar, 4th ed., CRC Press/Taylor and Francis Group, 2015.
13. Babu, A.K.; Kumaresan, G.; Antony Aroul Raj, V.; Velraj, R. Review of leaf drying: mechanism and influencing parameters, drying methods, nutrient preservation, and mathematical models. Renewable and Sustainable Energy Reviews 2018, 90, 536–556.
14. El-Sebaii, A.A.; Shalaby, S.M. Solar drying of agricultural products: a review. Renewable and Sustainable Energy Reviews 2012, 16, 37–43.

15. Udomkum, P.; Romuli, S.; Schock, S.; Mahayothee, B.; Sartas, M.; Wossen, T.; Njukwe, M.; Vanlauwe, B; Müller, J. Review of solar dryers for agricultural products in Asia and Africa: an innovation landscape approach. Journal of Environmental Management 2020, 268, 110730.
16. Erbay, Z.; Icier, F. A review of thin layer drying of foods: theory, modelling, and experimental results. Critical Reviews in Food Science and Nutrition 2010, 50, 441–464.
17. Herbas d.o.o. Manufacturer of agricultural and tobacco processing machinery and equipment for medicinal plant processing. Croatia. Available at: http://herbas.hr/susara-podna2/?lang=en. Accessed in July 5, 2020.
18. Zanoelo, E.F. A theoretical and experimental study of simultaneous heat and mass transport resistances in a shallow fluidized bed dryer of mate leaves. Chemical and Engineering Processing 2007, 46, 1365–1375.
19. Lima-Corrêa, R.A.B.; Andrade, M.S.; Fernandes da Silva, M.F.G.; Freire, J.T.; Ferreira, M.C. Thin-layer and vibrofluidized drying of basil leaves (*Ocimum basilicum* L.). Journal of Applied Research on Medicinal and Aromatic Plants 2017, 7, 54–63.
20. Temple, S.J.; van Boxtel, A.J.B. A comparison of dryer types used for tea drying. Journal of Agricultural Engineering Research 2000, 77(4), 401–407.
21. Tarhan, S.; Telci, I.; Taner Tuncay, M.; Polatci, H.; Product quality and energy consumption when drying peppermint by rotary drum dryer. Industrial Crops and Products 2010, 32, 420–427.
22. Rosanova, A.H.; Ferreira, M.C. Analysis of drying basil leaves and stems in a basket-type rotary dryer. In: Proc. of ENEMP 2015, v. 2, São Carlos-SP, Brazil, 2015 (in Portuguese), 1444–1453. DOI: 10.5151/ENEMP2015-SE-343.
23. Delele, M.A.; Weigler, F.; Mellman, J. Advances in the application of a rotary dryer for drying of agricultural products: a review. Drying Technology 2015, 33(5), 541–558.
24. Tussolini, L.; Oliveira, J.S.; Freire, F.B.; Freire, J.T.; Zanoelo, E.F. Thin-layer drying of mate leaves (*Ilex paraguariensis*) in a conveyor-belt dryer: a semi-automatic control strategy based on a dynamic model. Drying Technology 2014, 32, 1457–1465.
25. Canabarro, N.I.; Mazutti, M.A.; Ferreira, M.C. Drying of olive (*Olea europaea*) leaves on a conveyor belt for supercritical extraction of bioactive compounds: mathematical modelling of drying/extraction operations and analysis of extracts. Industrial Crops and Products 2019, 136, 140–151.
26. Canabarro, N.I.; Ugalde, G.A.; Mazutti, M.A.; Ferreira, M.C. Conveyor-belt drying of *Eugenia uniflora* L. leaves: influence of drying conditions on the yield, composition, antioxidant activity and total phenolic content of supercritical CO_2 extracts. Food and Bioproducts Processing 2019, 116, 140–149.
27. Phoungchandang, S.; Srinukroh, W.; Leenanon, B. Kaffir lime leaf (*Citrus hysteric* DC.) drying using tray and heat pump dehumidified drying. Drying Technology 2008, 26(12), 1602–1609.
28. Erbay, Z.; Icier, F. Optimization of drying of olive leaves in a pilot-scale heat pump dryer. Drying Technology 2009, 27(3), 416–427.
29. Kudra, T. Energy performance of convective dryers. Drying Technology 2012, 30(11&12), 1190–1198.
30. Therdthai, N.; Zhou, W. Characterization of microwave vacuum drying and hot air drying of mint leaves (*Mentha cordifolia* Opiz ex Frezen). Journal of Food Technology 2009, 91, 482–489.
31. Heindl, A.G.W.; Müller, J. Microwave drying of medicinal and aromatic plants. Stewart Postharvest Review 2007, 4(5), 1–6.
32. Baritaux, O.; Richard, H.; Touche, J.; Derbesy, M. Effects of drying and storage of herbs and spices on the essential oil. Part 1. Basil, *Ocimum basilicum* L. Flavour and Fragrance Journal 1992, 7, 267–271.

33. Rahimalek, M.; Goli, A.A.H. Evaluation of six drying treatments with respect to essential oil yield, composition and color characteristics of *Thymys daenensis* subsp. *Daenensis*, Celak leaves. Industrial Crops and Products 2013, 42, 613–619.
34. Routray, W.; Orsat, V.; Gariepy, Y. Effect of different drying methods on the microwave extraction of phenolic components and antioxidant activity of highbush blueberry leaves. Drying Technology 2014, 32(16), 1888–1904.
35. Diaz-Maroto, M.C.; Pérez-Coello, M.S.; Cabezudo, M.D. Effect of drying method on the volatiles in bay leaf (*Laurus nobilis* L.). Journal of Agricultural Food Chemistry 2002, 50, 4520–4524.
36. Lemus-Mondaca, R.; Vega-Gálvez, A.; Rojas, P.; Stucken, K.; Delporte, C.; Valenzuela-Barra, G.; Jagus, R.J.; Agüero, M.V.; Pasten, A. Antioxidant, antimicrobial and anti-inflammatory potential of *Stevia rebaudiana* leaves: effect of different drying methods. Journal of Applied Research on Medicinal and Aromatic Plants 2018, 11, 37–46.
37. Alibas, I. Characteristics of chard leaves during microwave, convective, and combined microwave-convective drying. Drying Technology 2006, 24, 1425–1435.
38. Deminhan, E.; Özbek, B. Thin-layer drying characteristics and modeling of celery leaves undergoing microwave treatment. Chemical Engineering Communications 2011, 198(7), 957–975.
39. Kouhila, M.; Kechaou, N.; Otmani, M.; Fliyou, M.; Lahsasni, S. Experimental study of sorption isotherms and drying kinetics of Moroccan *Eucalyptus globulus*. Drying Technology 2002, 20(10), 2027–2039.
40. Radünz, L.L.; Melo, E.C.; Barbosa, L.C.A.; Rocha, R.P.; Berbert, P.A. Coumarin extraction yield from guaco *(Mikania glomerata Sprengel)* leaves submitted to different drying temperatures. Revista Brasileira de Plantas Medicinais 2012, 14(33), 453–457.
41. Raksakantong, P.; Siriamompun, S.; Ratseewo, J.; Meeso, N. Optimized drying of Kaprow leaves for industrial production of holy basil spice powder. Drying Technology 2011, 29(8), 974–983.
42. Choo, C.O.; Chua, B.L.; Figiel, A.; Jaloszynski, K.; Wojdylo, A.; Szumny, A.; Lyczko, J.; Chong, C.H. Hybrid drying of *Murraya koenigii* leaves: energy consumption, antioxidant capacity, profiling of volatile compounds and quality studies. Process 2020, 8, 240.
43. Argyropoulos, D.; Müller, J. Kinetics of change in color and rosmarinic acid equivalents during convective drying of lemon balm (*Melissa officinalis* L.). Journal of Applied Research on Medicinal and Aromatic Plants 2014, 1, e15–e22.
44. Rababah, T.M.; Al-u'datt, M.; Alhamad, M.; Al-Mahasneh, M.; Ereifej, K.; Andrade, J.; Altarifi, B.; Almajwal, A.; Yang, W. Effects of drying process on total phenolics, antioxidant activity and flavonoid contents of common Mediterranean herbs. International Journal of Agricultural and Biological Engineering 2015, 8, 145–150.
45. Martins, P.M.; Melo, E.C.; Barbosa, L.C.A.; Santos, R.H.S.; Machado, M.C. Influence of the temperature and velocity of the drying air in the content and composition of essential oil of lemon grass (in Portuguese), 155–161 pp. In: Proc. of 1st Latin American Symposium on Medicinal and Aromatic Plants, Eds. L.C. Ming *et al.*, Acta Hort 569, International Society for Horticultural Science, 2002.
46. Buchaillot, A.; Caffin, N.; Bhandari, B. Drying of lemon myrtle (*Backhousia citriodora*) leave retention of volatiles and color. Drying Technology 2009, 27, 445–450.
47. Ebadi, M.T.; Azizi, M.; Sefidkon, F.; Ahmadi, N. Influence of different drying methods on drying period, essential oil content and composition of *Lippia citriodora* Kunth. Journal of Applied Research on Medicinal and Aromatic Plants 2015, 2, 182–187.
48. Zanoelo, E.F.; di Celso, G.M.; Kaskantzis, G.; Drying kinetics of mate leaves in a packed bed dryer. Biosystems Engineering 2007, 96(4), 487–494.
49. Ethmane Kane, C.S.; Jamali, A.; Kouhila, M.; Mimet, A.; Ahachad, M. Single-layer drying behavior of Mexican tea leaves (*Chenopodium ambrosioides*) in a convective

solar dryer and mathematical modeling. Chemical Engineering Communications 2008, 195(7), 787–802.

50. Costa, A.B.S.; Freire, F.B.; Ferreira, M.C.; Freire, J.T. Convective drying of regular mint leaves: analysis based on fitting empirical correlations, response surface methodology and neural networks. Acta Scientiarum 2014, 36(2), 271–278.
51. Rosanova, A.H.; Maia, G.D.; Freire, F.B.; Ferreira, M.C. A neural based modeling approach for drying kinetics analysis of mint branches and their fractions (leaves and stems). Advances in Chemical Engineering and Science 2017, 7, 154–174.
52. Rosanova, A.H. Development of a rotary drum dryer for dehydration of condiment and phytotherapic leaves. Ph.D. Thesis, Graduate Program of Chemical Engineering, Federal University of São Carlos, 136 p., 2017 (in Portuguese).
53. Akpinar, E.K. Drying of mint leaves in a solar dryer and open sun: modelling performance analyses. Energy Conversion and Management 2010, 51, 2407–2418.
54. Potisate, Y.; Phoungchandang, S.; Kerr, W.L. The effects of predrying treatments and different drying methods on phytochemical compound retention and drying characteristics of moringa leaves (*Moringa oleifera* Lam.). Drying Technology 2014, 32(16), 1970–1985.
55. Sejali, S.N.F.; Anuar, M.S. Effect of drying methods on phenolic contents of Neem (*Azadirachta indica*) leaf powder. Journal of Herbs, Spices and Medicinal Plants 2011, 17(2), 119–131.
56. Pääkkönen, K.; Havento, J.; Galambosi, B.; Pyykkönen, M. Infrared drying of herbs. Agricultural and Food Science in Finland 1999, 8, 19–27.
57. Böhm, M.E.; Bade, M.; Kunz, B. Quality stabilization of fresh herbs using a combined vacuum-microwave drying process. Advances in Food Science 2002, 2, 55–61.
58. Szumny, A.; Figiel, A.; Gutiérrez-Ortíz, A.; Carbonell-Barrachina, A.A. Composition of rosemary essential oil (*Rosmarinus officinalis*) as affected by drying method. Journal of Food Engineering 2010, 97, 253–260.
59. Arslan, D.; Özkan, M.M. Evaluation of drying methods with respect to drying kinetics, mineral content and colour characteristics of rosemary leaves. Energy Conversion and Management 2008, 49, 1258–1264.
60. Antal, T.; Figiel, A.; Kerekes, B.; Sikolya, L. Effect of drying methods on the quality of the essential oil of spearming leaves (*Mentha spicata* L.). Drying Technology 2011, 29, 1836–1844.
61. Hossain, M.B.; Barry-Ryan, C.; Martin-Diana, A.B.; Brunton, N.P. Effect of drying method on the antioxidant capacity of six *Lamiaceae* herbs. Food Chemistry 2010, 123, 85–91.
62. Usai, M.; Marchetti, M.; Foddai, M.; Del Caro, A.; Desogus, R.; Sann, I.; Piga, A. Influence of different stabilizing operations and storage time on the composition of essential oil of thyme (*Thymus officinalis* L.) and rosemary (*Rosmarinus officinalis* L.). LWT– Food Science and Technology 2011, 44, 244–249.
63. Xie, L.; Mujumdar, A.S.; Xiao, H.W.; Gao, Z.J. Recent technologies and trends in medicinal herb drying, 2015. Available at: http://www.Academia.edu/download/41682412/Chapter_4 _/Recent_technologies_andtrends_in_medicinal_herb_drying-revised_5_December_2015.pdf
64. Tilebeni, H.G. Review to basil medicinal plant. International Journal of Agronomy and Plant Production 2011, 2, 5–9.
65. Bassolé, I.H.N.; Lamien-Meda, A.; Bayala, B.; Tirogo, S.; Franz, C.; Novak, J.; Nebié, C.; Dicko, M.H. Composition and antimicrobial activities of *Lippia multilflora* Moldenke, *Mentha* x *piperita* L. and *Ocimum basilicum* L. essential oils and their major monoterpene alcohols alone and in combination. Molecules 2010, 15, 7825–7839.
66. Sousa, P.J.C.; Linard, C.F.B.M.; Azevedo-Batista, A.; Oliveira, A.C.; Coelho-de-Souza, A.N.; Leal-Cardoso, J.H. Antinociceptive effects of the essential oil of *Mentha x villosa* leaf and its major constituent piperitenone oxice in mice. Brazilian Journal of Medical and Biological Research 2009, 42, 655–659.

67. Martins, A.P.; Craveiro, A.A.; Machado, M.I.L.; Raffin, F.N.; Moura, T.F.; Novák, Cs.; Éhen, A. Preparation and characterization of *Mentha* x *villosa* Hudson oil-β-cyclodextrin complex. Journal of Thermal Analysis and Calorimetry 2007, 88(2), 363–371.
68. Ahn, Y.M; Choi, Y.H.; Yoon, J.J.; Lee, Y.J.; Cho, K.W.; Kang, D.G.; Lee, H.S. Oleanolic acid modulates the renin-angiotensin system and cardiac natriuretic hormone concomitantly with volume and pressure balance in rats. European Journal of Pharmacology 2017, 809, 231–241.
69. Lima, R.A.B.; Ferreira, M.C. Fluidized and vibrofluidized shallow beds of fresh leaves. Particuology 2011, 9, 139–147.
70. Rocha, T.; Lebert, A.; Marty-Audotin, C. Effect of pretreatments and drying conditions on drying rate and color retention of basil (*Ocimum basilicum*). LWT—Food Science and Technology 1993, 26(5), 456–463.
71. Rockwell, F.E.; Holbrook, N.M.; Strook, A.D. Leaf hydraulics I: scaling transport properties from single cells to tissues. Journal of Theoretical Biology 2014, 251–266.
72. Freire, J.T.; Freire, F.B.; Perazzini, H. On the influence of particles characteristics on moisture diffusivity during drying of granular porous media. Advances in Chemical Engineering and Science 2014, 4, 7–16.
73. Figiel, A.; Gutiérrez-Ortíz, A.; Carbonell-Barrachina, A.A. Composition of oregano essential oil (*Origanum vulgare*) as affected by drying method. Journal of Food Engineering 2010, 98, 240–247.
74. Poirier, D. Conveyor dryers. Ch. 18, pp. 393–403. In: Handbook of Industrial Drying, Ed. A.S. Mujumdar, 4th ed., CRC Press/Taylor and Francis Group, 2015.
75. Schimalko, M.E.; Peralta, J.M.; Alzamora, S.M. Modeling the drying of a deep bed of *Ilex paraguariensis* in an industrial belt conveyor dryer. Drying Technol 2007, 25(12), 1967–1975.
76. Casas, L.; Mantell, C.; Rodriguez, M.; Gordillo, M.; Torrres, A.; Macias, F.; Martinez de la Ossa, E. Effect of the pre-treatment of the samples on the natural substances extraction from *Helianthus annuus* L. using supercritical carbon dioxide. Talanta 2005, 67, 175–181.
77. Nagy, B.; Simándi, B. Effects of particle size distribution, moisture content, and initial oil content on the supercritical extraction of paprika. Journal of Supercritical Fluids 2008, 46, 293–298.
78. Urban, J.; Ingwers, M.; McGuire, M.A.; Teskey, R.O. Stomatal conductance increases with rising temperature. Plant Signaling and Behavior 2017, 12(8), e1335653334.
79. Canabarro, N.I.; Mazutti, M.; Ferreira, M.C. Convective drying of aromatic and medicinal leaves: influence of physical and morphological properties on the drying rates. In: Proc. of ENEMP 2019, Belém-PA, 2019 (in Portuguese). Available at: https://proceedings.science/enemp-2019/papers/secagem-convectiva-de-folhas-aromaticas-e-medicinais–influencia-das-propriedades-fisicas-e-morfologicas-nas-taxas-de-se.
80. Liu, C.; Guo, X.; Wang, L. Experiment on and simulation of moisture transfer and rolling deformation during leaf drying. Drying Technology 2018, 36(14), 1653–1661.
81. Kiranoudis, C.T.; Maroulis, Z.B.; Marinos-Kouris, D. Dynamic simulation and control of conveyor belt dryers. Drying Technology 1994, 12(7), 1575–1603.
82. Goulas, V.; Pappoti, V.; Exarchou, V.; Tsimidou, M.; Gerothanassis, I. Contribution of flavonoids to the overall radical scavenginng activity of olive (*Olea europaea* L.) leaf polar extracts. Journal of Agricultural and Food Chemistry 2010, 58, 3303–3308.
83. Pollier, J.; Goossens, A. Oleanolic acid. Phytochemistry 2012, 77, 10–15.
84. Bilgin, M.; Şahin, S. Effects of geographical origin and extraction methods on total phenolic yield of olive tree (*Olive europea*) leaves. Journal of the Taiwan Institute of Chemical Engineers 2013, 44, 8–12.

4 Extraction, Isolation, and Identification of Phytopharmaceuticals

João Carlos Palazzo de Mello and Larissa Valone

CONTENTS

4.1 Introduction 85
4.2 Extraction of Biomolecules from Raw Plant Materials 87
4.2.1 Ultrasound Extraction Method 89
4.2.2 Turbolysis Extraction 89
4.2.3 Maceration 90
4.2.4 Soxhlet Extraction 90
4.2.5 Extraction by Steam Drag 91
4.2.6 Pressing Extraction 91
4.2.7 Percolation 92
4.2.8 Supercritical Fluid Extraction (SFE) 92
4.3 Fractionation and Isolation 96
4.3.1 Liquid-Liquid Partition 97
4.3.2 Precipitation 97
4.3.3 Dialysis 97
4.3.4 Thin-Layer Chromatography (TLC) 97
4.3.5 Column Liquid Chromatography 99
4.3.6 High-Pressure Liquid Chromatography (HPLC) 99
4.3.7 Supercritical Fluid Chromatography (SFC) 100
4.4 Identification of Biomolecules 101
4.4.1 Identification by Chemical Reactions 101
4.4.2 Analytical Chromatography 101
4.5 Final Remarks 103
References 103

4.1 INTRODUCTION

Since the dawn of humankind, human beings use plants in their routine, whether to eat, dress, build houses, among others. Knowledge of the use of plants in the treatment of various diseases has been accumulated over time, and with the advancement of modern science, it has been possible to understand the relationship between the structure-activity of various phytochemical compounds. Knowledge of the use of plants in the treatment of various diseases has been accumulated over time, and with

DOI: 10.1201/9781003225416-6

TABLE 4.1
Examples of Drugs Obtained from Plant Extracts

Drug	Therapeutic Action	Species
Atropine	Anticholinergic	*Atropa belladonna* L.
Caffeine	Central stimulant	*Coffea* species
Colchicine	Antirheumatic	*Colchicum autumnale* L.
Digoxin, digitoxin	Cardiotonic	*Digitalis purpurea* L.
Scopolamine	Antiparkinsonian	*Datura* species
Ephedrine	Antiasthmatic	*Ephedra* species
Morphine, codeine	Analgesic, antitussive	*Papaver somniferum* L.
Quinine, quinidine	Antimalarial, antiarrhythmic	*Cinchona* species

Source: Simões et al. [1].

the advancement of modern science, it has been possible to understand the relationship between the structure-activity of various phytochemical compounds. Classic examples of therapeutic agents derived from plants, such as atropine, caffeine, scopolamine, among others (in parts), are described in Table 4.1. Currently, research for a new biomolecule is usually based on the purification of chemical constituents of plants, organic substances called phytochemicals. Hence, understanding the processes of extraction, isolation, and identification of these compounds is the initial stage in the search for new drugs and improving production processes for biomolecules already known.

Plants have a complex mixture of organic substances, which constitute their primary and secondary metabolites. Primary metabolites are those involved in the metabolic pathways essential for plant survival, such as sugars, amino acids, and fatty acids. Although secondary metabolites come from modifying the primary metabolism, they are not involved in the essential plant metabolism but play varied roles such as the attraction of pollinators and plant defence against predators and insects. Often, secondary metabolites are synthesised only in the face of a specific stimulus, such as water shortage or excess, flowering, or infection by some microorganism and can be stored in reservoirs as a form of protection. The classification of the secondary metabolites is mainly based on their structural backbone, and important classes are the polyphenols, terpenoids, esters, aldehydes, alkaloids, among many others. Each plant species has specific biosynthetic routes for its secondary metabolism, and therefore, different species may produce similar molecules although with different functions. They are found in low concentrations when we consider the plant as a whole. Most substances can play an active role in the metabolism of other organisms, including humans and animals; therefore, they have a high potential to be used in pharmaceutical products [2].

Considering the potential of secondary metabolism to be used in the research and development of new drugs, their isolation from the plant in natura and subsequent identification is paramount. Notwithstanding, the concentrations of each specific metabolic in a plant are usually minimal, so several techniques are needed to enable their purification. Initially, an extraction technique is used to obtain the extract, which consists of a complex biological matrix that is difficult to characterise. Afterwards, purification techniques are used for fractionation until it is possible to isolate the biomolecules to start the identification studies. Different techniques can be applied in each stage, and their peculiarities will be addressed shortly in the next sections. However, the most used techniques involve using organic solvents, which are not sustainable and cause damage to the environment [3].

With the industrial booming, the impacts on the environment such as global warming, acid rain, and thermal inversion have become a cause for concern. Thus, sustainable processing is on the agenda of society and industry. Safer alternatives to humans and the environment have been the subject of research in recent decades in the expectation of developing new processes that value green chemistry, such as the supercritical fluid extraction (SFE) technology.

4.2 EXTRACTION OF BIOMOLECULES FROM RAW PLANT MATERIALS

The first step in investigating plant biomolecules is extraction, in which several techniques can be performed. The extraction consists of transferring a mixture of molecules from the plant to the extractor solvent. Usually, complex mixtures of substances are obtained, consisting of different classes of biomolecules having very distinct functional groups. The extraction techniques may be divided into those that employ heat to improve the solvation power of solvents and those in the cold that value the stability of plant substances. We can also group the methods for the solvent renewal or not and for the extraction efficiency, such as total exhaustion of the plant or partial exhaustion. The mechanisms by which biomolecules are extracted from the plant matrix consist of leaching and diffusion (Figure 4.1). Leaching represents the washing of cell content free from walls and membranes. Diffusion refers to transport through cell protection layers where the solute migrates by a difference in concentration gradient. Methods that mainly use diffusion and do not have solvent renewal usually perform an extraction without exhaustion of the plant drug since the

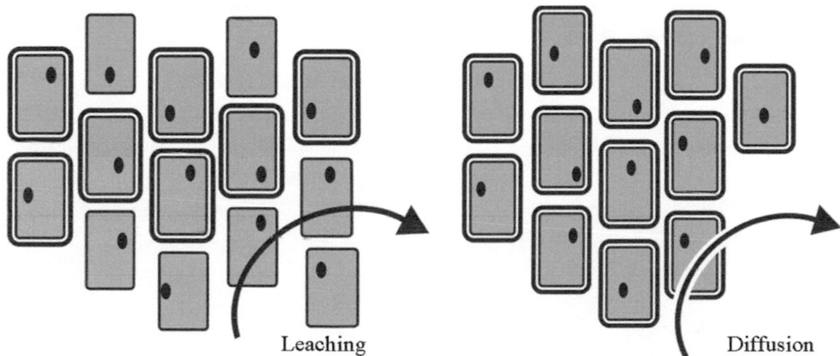

FIGURE 4.1 Representation of the extraction mechanisms of the vegetable drug.

solvent reaches a saturation point, where the diffusion equilibrium occurs. On the other hand, the methods that use solvent renewal allow the maintenance of a concentration gradient, enabling the flow of biomolecules.

Organic solvents are usually used in the extraction processes. The solvents are chosen based on the polarity of the desired biomolecules; thus, molecules of the chosen class of compounds can be extracted preferentially. The use of mixtures of solvents and methods is usually performed to achieve the best recovery of biomolecules. Since an immense variety of substances are extracted from raw plant material, subsequent techniques must be used to isolate specific biomolecules. The end of the extractive process is the drying, which consists of removing the solvent system used to enable the use of the extract and prolong its stability. Table 4.2 provides some examples of the solvents used to extract plant phytochemicals [4]. The obtained extract usually has a complex biomolecule matrix that can act in a complementary or antagonistic biological way, requiring the fractionation to separate the desired substances.

The extraction efficiency can be improved by heating, increasing the extraction time, agitation, solvent renewal, pH changes, and others. The overall objective is to promote a high transference of the desired biomolecules to the extractor solvent. However, for each plant and desired biomolecule, the best parameters for each extractive method employed must be evaluated experimentally, taking into account the lowest cost and highest efficiency, selectivity, and molecule stability.

TABLE 4.2
Main Characteristics of Liquid Solvents Used in the Extraction of Biomolecules

Solvent	Molecular Mass	Ebullition Point (°C)	Examples of Biomolecules Class Extracted
n-Hexane	86.17	68.7	Lipids, waxes, pigments, furanocoumarins
Toluene	92.14	110.6	Alkali-free bases, free anthraquinones, volatile oils, cardiotonic glycosides
Dichloromethane	84.94	39.9	
Chloroform	119.38	61.2	
n-Butanol	74.12	117.7	
Ethanol	46.09	78.3	Heterosides in general
Methanol	32.04	64.5	
Ethyl acetate	74.12	34.5	Aglycones, flavonoids, coumarins, waxes, sapogenins, iridoids, and sesquiterpenes
Hydroalcoholic mixtures	—	—	Saponins, tannins
Water	18.02	100	
Acidified water	—	—	Alkaloids
Alkalised water	—	—	Saponins

Source: Bassani [4].

Traditional extraction methods generally involve the use of organic solvents with low selectivity and are very time-consuming, generate solvent residues that are often prohibited in food, and promote the molecule oxidative transformation during solvent removal [5]. Organic solvents can oxidise by free radicals, leading to the formation of low-level ozone and air pollution. In addition, the effects of conjunctival irritation, discomfort in the nose and throat, headache, allergic skin reaction, dyspnoea, declines in serum cholinesterase levels, nausea, fatigue, and dizziness are attributed to the presence of vapours from these solvents [3].

For this reason, new methodologies have been developed to reduce the generation of harmful contaminants to the environment and improve extraction efficiency. Supercritical extraction, assumed to be an efficient and green method, is one of the extraction technologies currently investigated by both academia and industry.

The specificities of some extraction methods, fractionation, isolation, and identification of biomolecules from the benchtop—used at the research level—to the industrial ones, and ending with supercritical technology, will be addressed in the next sections.

4.2.1 Ultrasound Extraction Method

The ultrasound extraction method (UEM) is based on the pressure variations inside the extracting liquids, resulting from waves between 20 and 40 kHz, which generate acoustic cavitations in the herbal drug. Cavitations cause disruption of plant structures and release of cell content, thus promoting high mass transfer of biomolecules from herbal matrix to the extractor solvent. In addition, the high increase of the solvent movement also enhances its solubility and penetration power in the plant matrix.

Among the advantages of the UEM are its high reproducibility, the possibility of using it for a wide range of sample sizes, processing speed, and low cost. The extraction efficiency using the ultrasound technique has been cited as equal to or higher than the one obtained by Soxhlet [1]. Its disadvantages are linked to heat release during the technique that can hinder some molecule stability, causing their degradation.

4.2.2 Turbolysis Extraction

The process occurs with the reduction of plant material resulting from the rotation of slides from an ultra-turrax (Figure 4.2) that break the cells and release the cell content into the solvent. With the constant movement of the solvent and continuous reduction of the herbal drug, the process happens very quickly and almost depletes the material. In addition, the high shear rates release heat, and therefore, the technique is more applied to materials that are difficult for the solvent to penetrate. Intermittent processing is usual during the extraction to avoid the sample overheating. Temperatures below 40 °C are most suitable.

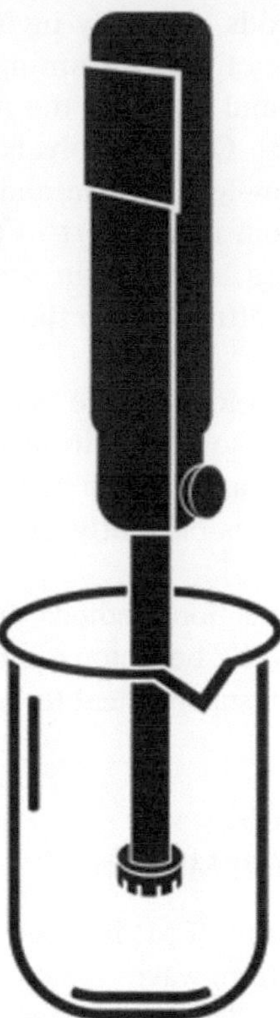

FIGURE 4.2 Representative schema of the ultra-turrax.

4.2.3 Maceration

Maceration consists of prolonged contact of the reduced herbal drug with the solvent in a closed container and without solvent renewal. It can happen for days, and at the end, there is the separation of the extract from the residue. If there is only occasional agitation during the process, it is called static; if constant, it is called dynamic (Figure 4.3). In these processes, saturation and equilibrium between the solvent and the cell's interior may occur, with no complete drug depletion.

4.2.4 Soxhlet Extraction

The method uses continuous solid-liquid extraction with a small amount of solvent passing through the same sample several times through evaporation and condensation. The equipment consists of a heated solvent container equipped with a condenser that drips the solvent into the herbal drug until it reaches the siphon. When it is filled, the solvent flows with the extracted material into the heated container. The solvent continues to heat, evaporating, condensing, extracting, and returning to the initial container as many times as necessary until total exhaustion. Its disadvantage

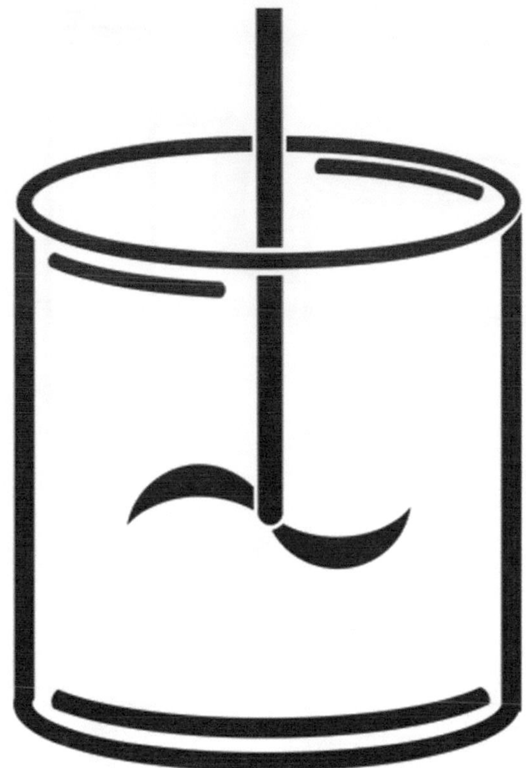

FIGURE 4.3 Representative scheme of an agitated tank used for dynamic macerations on an industrial scale.

consists in heating the extracted material, and therefore, it cannot be used for substances that degrade at high temperatures (thermolabile compounds).

4.2.5 Extraction by Steam Drag

This technique is based on the dragging of the desired biomolecules from the plant drug by water vapour. The system consists of a boiler that heats the water (solvent), and the steam is directed to the column containing the pulverised herbal drug, taking volatile biomolecules to the collection system (Figure 4.4). This process is generally applied to extract volatile oils and allows the total exhaustion of the drug.

4.2.6 Pressing Extraction

The process occurs with mechanical compression and release of oils from the herbal drug, which may occur continuously or discontinuously. The continuous technique has the disadvantage of releasing heat inherent to the process, which can cause changes in biomolecules. However, it is usually used to obtain large volumes.

FIGURE 4.4 Representative scheme of a steam puller.

In small volumes or thermosensitive materials, discontinuous pressing is more suitable. Both processes do not allow depletion of oils, and if necessary, more methodologies are applied in sequence in the obtained residue. Additional processes involve pretreatment of the sample such as decortication, grinding, and heating; the waste treatments using heating or extraction with organic solvents.

4.2.7 Percolation

This technique continuously drags the biomolecules by the extraction solvent and solvent renewal (Figure 4.5). Usually, the solvent is kept in contact with the herbal drug for a period, and then, the flow of the obtained extract is promoted. Then, a new amount of solvent is added, and the process is repeated until the herbal drug is exhausted.

4.2.8 Supercritical Fluid Extraction (SFE)

Supercritical fluids are substances subjected to supercritical conditions of temperature (T_c) and pressure (P_c), where liquids and gases are indistinguishable from each other. The substance that reaches this condition has compressibility and diffusivity of gas, but density and viscosity as a liquid, making them excellent solvents [6].

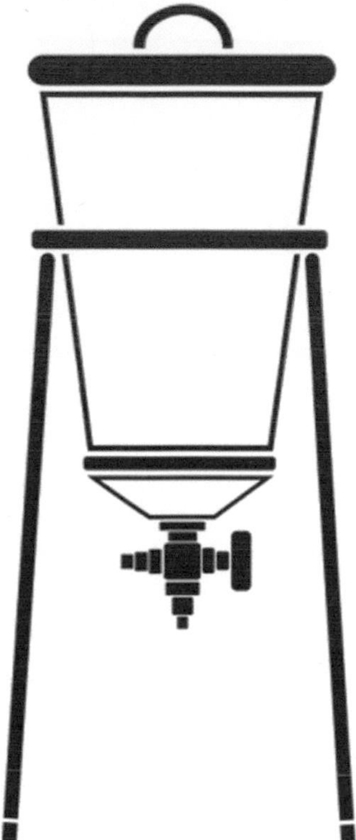

FIGURE 4.5 Schematic representation of a percolator.

Figure 4.6 shows a typical phase diagram of a substance illustrating the molecular interaction in the solid, liquid, gaseous, and supercritical regions (▲: triple point; ♦: supercritical point).

Supercritical fluids are charming alternatives in terms of extraction, as they have great potential to change solubility by modifying the pressure and temperature of the system. In addition, they have high penetrating power in plant material due to low viscosity and high diffusivity, leading to faster extraction processes. Therefore, SFE can be considered a green extraction technology [3].

The benefits to the environment can be attributed to reduced time, increased selectivity and specificity, and the use of non-toxic solvents. However, if organic solvents are used, the benefits to nature are unlikely to outweigh traditional extraction methods due to the use of high energy involved in the process. Therefore, the use of water and supercritical carbon dioxide ($scCO_2$) is preferred [3]. However, water has a critical temperature of 374 °C and a supercritical pressure of 22.0 MPa, requiring a more sophisticated experimental apparatus to work at these extreme conditions. On the other hand, carbon dioxide presents supercritical conditions of 31.2 °C and 7.3 MPa, temperatures close to that of the environment and milder pressure. In addition to involving most often the use of solvents recognised as safe, the supercritical extractor allows direct coupling with fractionation and identification techniques.

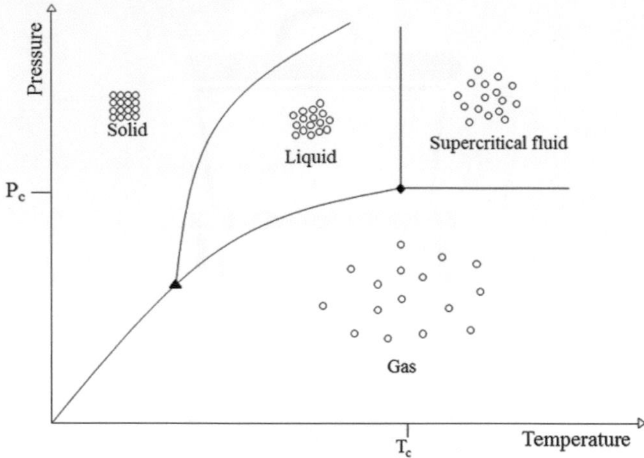

FIGURE 4.6 Phase diagram illustrating the molecular interaction in each region (▲: triple point; ◆: supercritical point).

Carbon dioxide is the main solvent used in the SFE of biomolecules from plants due to its critical temperature and pressure being easy to reach, absence of toxicity, non-corrosive, non-flammable, do not produce residues to the environment, being able to be recycled and reused, low cost, and compatible with most detectors. It is found as a gas at room temperature, so after depressurising the system, it separates from the extract, making it dry without the need for a drying process. This energy-saving obtained with the absence of additional drying steps is another point favouring the green chemistry of supercritical fluids. $scCO_2$ has a low polarity, and modifiers can assign more polar characteristics to the system and enable better extraction of polar substances. Modifiers are polar solvents used in low concentrations, for example, water and ethanol.

The extraction system (Figure 4.7) consists of the CO_2 reservoir, a pump coupled to a temperature-controlled thermostatic bath, connected in series to a temperature-controlled extraction cell, and may contain a second similar system for pumping the modifiers. There is a pressure regulator at the outlet of the extraction cell and may contain a fractionation system coupled to a depressuriser, but the extract can be released in collectors without depressurisation systems. It may also contain collection systems for solvent recycling. After extraction and depressurisation of the system, the solvent evaporates and separates easily, resulting in a dry extract.

Due to the great diversity of classes of biomolecules from plants (phytocomplex), different T_c, P_c, and modifiers are used to select the type of molecular structure desired. For example, milder conditions are used for smaller and volatile substances, while extraction of carotenoids and phenolics requires higher temperature and pressure, as shown in Table 4.3 [7]. There is also the possibility of changing parameters during extraction to produce different extract's compositions in the same SFE process, known as fractional extraction.

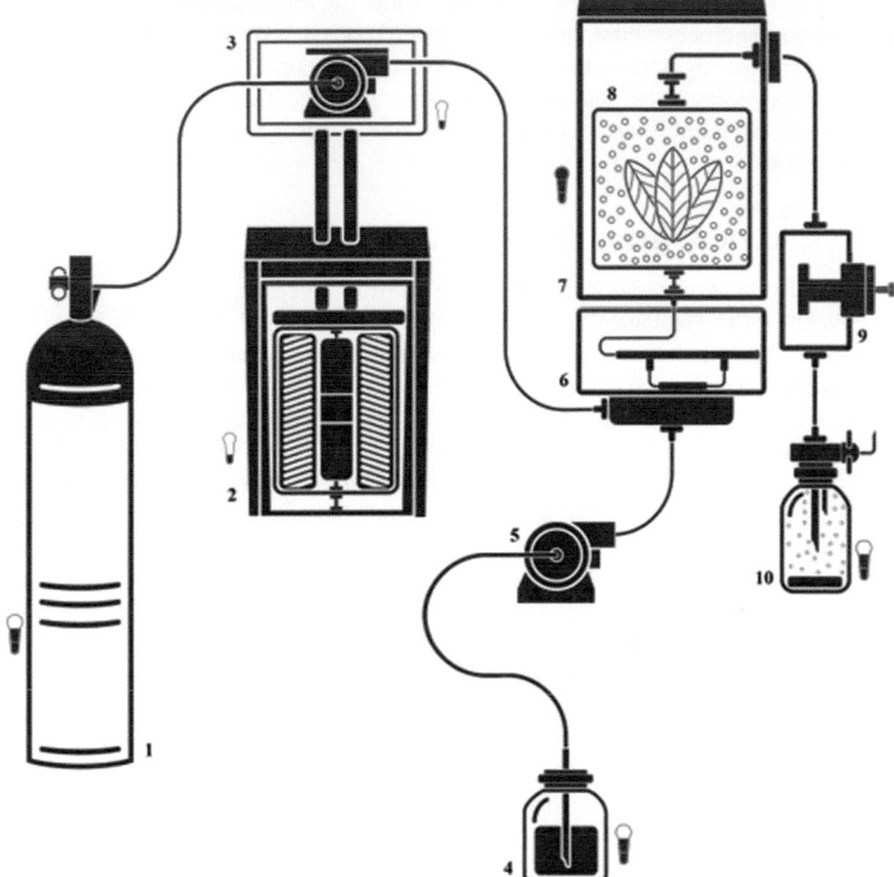

FIGURE 4.7 Schematic representation of an SFE, where (1) carbon dioxide cylinder; (2) water bath; (3) CO_2 pump; (4) modifier; (5) modifier pump; (6) accumulator; (7) oven; (8) extraction cell; (9) backpressure; (10) sample collector.

TABLE 4.3
Conditions Usually Used to Extract Some Classes of Biomolecules from Plants by SFE

	Temperature (°C)	Pressure (MPa)	Cosolvent (%)
Volatile molecules	30–50	8–25	—
Carotenoids	40–50	U50	—
Phenolic molecules	35–60	20–40	Ethanol: 0–25

Source: Souza et al. [7].

One of the classic applications of supercritical carbon dioxide is in the coffee decaffeination process. First, the ground coffee beans and $scCO_2$ are fed in countercurrent, and $scCO_2$ extracts the caffeine. Next, the obtained extract is washed with water and collected later, and the caffeine-free $scCO_2$ is then recycled back to the extraction cell. Finally, water containing caffeine is dried, and powdered caffeine is obtained [3].

4.3 FRACTIONATION AND ISOLATION

The development of research involving plant extracts presents challenges due to the complexity of the biological matrices of plants (phytocomplex). Each fraction can exhibit different activities and act on different targets (see Table 4.1) [8]. Thus, it is necessary to separate the substances of interest, maintaining those that can enhance the activities of each other due to synergism. These objectives can be reached through biomolecule fractionation and isolation processes.

The fractionation process can be done by several technologies involving pre- and post-processing steps. The most used methodology begins with the liquid-liquid partition with solvents of different polarities and immiscible. Hence, the extract can be fractionated based on the polarity of its phytochemical constituents. This procedure aims to separate the molecules of interest in a given fraction, reduce the proportion of unwanted substances, or facilitate the next steps of isolation.

The substance isolation process usually involves more than one step. Since the complexity of substances in a plant extract is huge, separation in several stages is usually employed. Subsequent steps may involve other partitions of increasing polarity, precipitation by changes in temperature or pH, and chromatographic processes.

Precipitation consists of the differences in solubility between the substances present in the extract. When dissolving it in a solvent that does not solubilise part of the biomolecules, the precipitate can be separated by filtration from the rest of the extract, generating two fractions.

The fractionation process is probably more complex and allows (if well executed) a wider separation of the extract components using chromatographic methods with several variations. Several chromatographic techniques can be employed, such as thin-layer chromatography (TLC), countercurrent chromatography, liquid chromatography, capillary electrophoresis (CE), high-performance liquid chromatography, and supercritical fluid chromatography (SFC). Each type has its particularity, depending on the technique and separation mechanism chosen.

Classically, sequential fractionations are used until an isolated substance is obtained. Liquid-liquid partitions, liquid chromatography, and TLC, among others, can be used to perform each fractionation step [1]. However, this process is time-consuming and generates organic wastes—sometimes toxic as explained by Lancaster [3]—solvents, therefore, having a high environmental impact. Some kinds of chromatographic methods like high-speed countercurrent, flash, and vacuum liquid chromatography are possibilities or alternatives to lower solvents consumption and time. However, it would be ideal for developing a single methodology capable of isolating a particular substance from an extract, and supercritical chromatography (SCC) has proved to be a viable and promising alternative.

SCC using $scCO_2$ does not generate organic waste and also allows the recovery and reuse of CO_2. By coupling chromatographic columns and detectors, isolating and identifying substances from a plant matrix using a single method is possible. Several detectors can be coupled to the SCC, such as Photo Diode Array, Mass Spectrometer, and Circular Dichroism, allowing the data comparison with known patterns of biomolecules, identifying functional groups, and elucidating the molecular structure of new substances.

An overview of the methods usually used for extract fractionation and isolation is presented here.

4.3.1 Liquid-Liquid Partition

In this process, two immiscible solvents are used. Initially, the extract/fraction is solubilised in one of them and transferred to a separating funnel. Then, when adding the second solvent and promoting agitation, part of the biomolecules is transferred by affinity to it, thus separating the biomolecules into two phases.

4.3.2 Precipitation

When the biomolecules to be separated have different solubility from the others in a certain solvent, this feature can perform a simple and low-cost procedure. First, the extract/fraction is solubilised in the solvent. Then, after the precipitation of desired substances, a simple filtration is carried out, separating the compounds of interest from the rest of the matrix due to the difference in particle size. This technique can be used only when the biomolecules of interest are the ones that precipitate or when it is needed to separate some compounds from the rest of the matrix because they have undesirable characteristics.

4.3.3 Dialysis

A semi-permeable cellulose membrane with a defined porosity in the shape of a bag is used (Figure 4.8). The sample is placed inside, and the bag is put in a container with plenty of solvents. The separation, in this case, occurs due to differences in molecular size. The smaller molecules pass to the outside of the bag while the larger molecules remain.

4.3.4 Thin-Layer Chromatography (TLC)

TLC uses the differential adsorption of the sample substances in their stationary phase and migration through a mobile phase flow. The stationary phase consists of a thin layer of adsorbent material—the most used are silica and alumina—retained on a backing plate (Figure 4.9). The mobile phase consists of a pure solvent, or mixture of them, which allows the solubilisation of the sample to be separated. When applying the sample to the base of the mobile phase plate, the plate is accommodated in a saturated solvent tank and keeps it in contact with its base, and the solvent elutes the plate above, dragging the sample; due to the difference in the interaction between the phase mobile and stationary phase, it drags the biomolecules at different speeds. At the end of the process, specific regions with different biomolecules will be formed. Then, the

FIGURE 4.8 Representation of a dialysis separation.

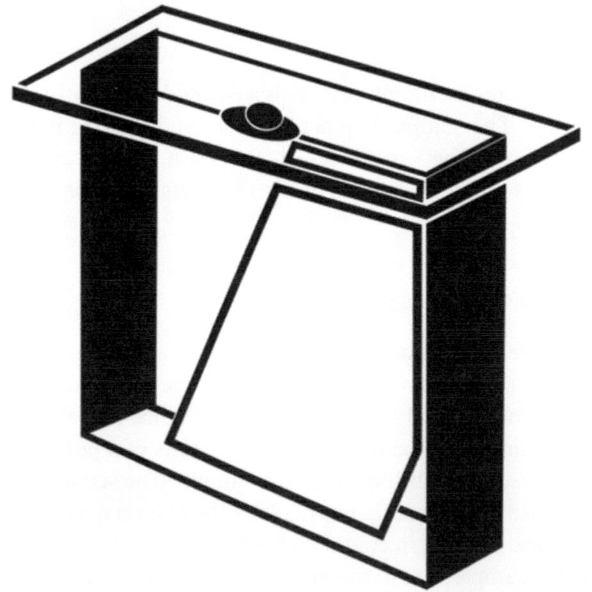

FIGURE 4.9 Schematic representation of thin-layer chromatography.

stationary phase containing the fraction or compound of interest is separated and is performed a simple extraction, with subsequent filtering and separation of the mobile phase. The method requires little instrumentation and is easy to reproduce.

4.3.5 Column Liquid Chromatography

Column liquid chromatography is also based on differential migration of the plant constituents, in this case through a glass column filled with the stationary phase. The sample and the mobile phase are added at the top of the column, crossing the entire column through the continuous flow of the mobile phase. Interactions of biomolecules and stationary phase reduce their speed. So, at the end of the column, they are collected at different times, in a collection point regulated by a valve (Figure 4.10). Advantages of the method consist of simple instrumentation, the possibility of separating large amounts of sample and reusing the column.

4.3.6 High-Pressure Liquid Chromatography (HPLC)

This technique consists of specialisation of the previous method since it uses packed columns and mobile phase under high pressure, with automated instrumentation, allowing high-resolution efficiency and reproducibility. The process also includes

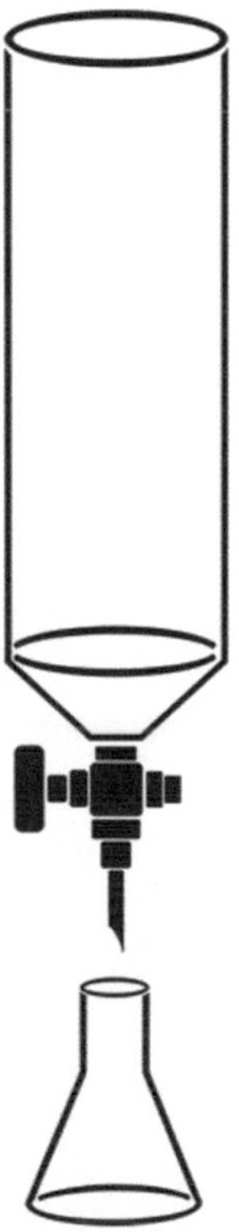

FIGURE 4.10 Schematic representation of column chromatography.

the coupling of detectors that allow the identification of the biomolecules that are being eluted. A recent variation of the method is the ultra-high-pressure liquid chromatography (UHPLC), which operates with small columns packed with stationary phase particles with a size smaller than 2 μm, which gives a higher particle density. For this reason, UHPLC systems normally operate at pressures significantly higher than the normal HPLC (~1000 bars × ~200 bar). Operating at higher pressures and small and more dense columns leads to better resolutions and reduced retention times than conventional HPLC.

4.3.7 Supercritical Fluid Chromatography (SFC)

The chromatographic process and instrumentation of SFC (Figure 4.11) are similar to the HPLC system, but with the advantages of extremely high speed, reduced use

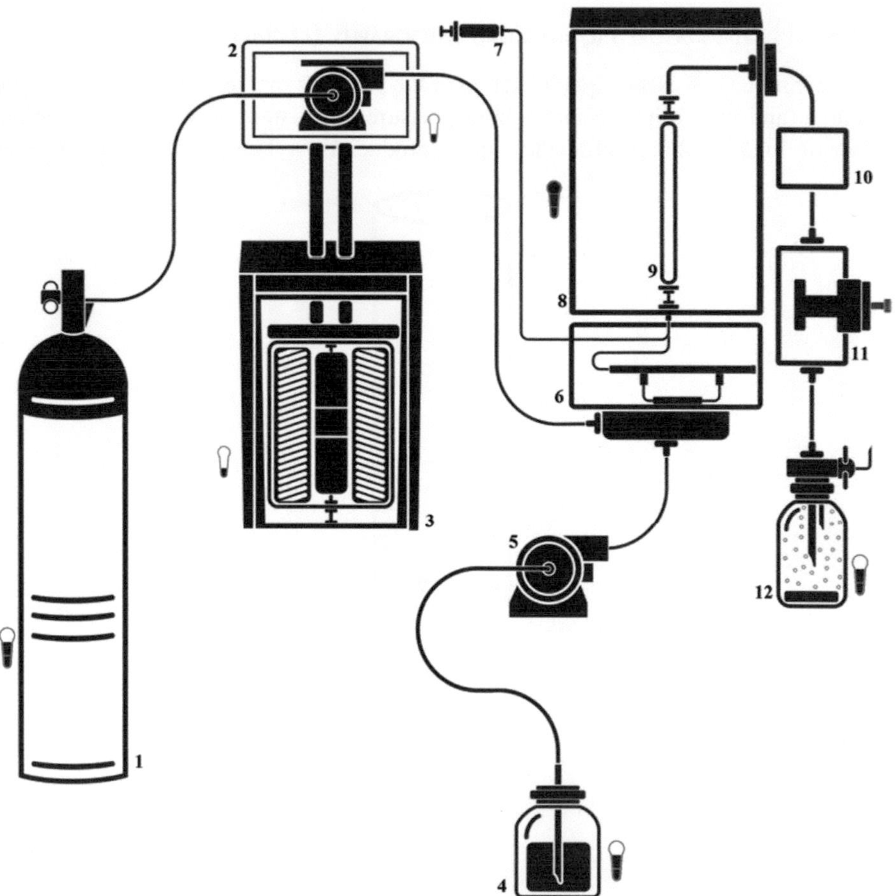

FIGURE 4.11 Schematic representation of an SFC, where (1) carbon dioxide cylinder; (2) CO_2 pump; (3) water bath; (4) modifier; (5) modifier pump; (6) accumulator; (7) sampler; (8) oven; (9) chromatographic column; (10) detector; (11) backpressure; (12) collector.

of organic solvents, high reproducibility, efficiency, and resolution supercritical fluid provides. The system operates at high pressures and temperatures so that the mobile phase remains in a supercritical state. Similar to SFE, the SFC can also use modifiers that increase the polarity of the mobile phase when $scCO_2$ is used. In addition, it has one or more detectors in series to allow the identification of biomolecules eluting from the column.

It is also possible to change the pressure and temperature along the chromatographic run to produce a gradient of the $scCO_2$ properties. At higher pressures and temperatures, $scCO_2$ can acquire a greater quadrupolar moment and thus present a better interaction with polar molecules [3]. The proportion of modifiers can also be changed throughout the chromatographic run for the same purpose.

An excellent isolation capacity of molecules with different characteristics can be reached by using polar modifiers. The chromatographic run starts with small amounts of modifiers, which can increase throughout the run. In this way, biomolecules of lower polarity are obtained first, followed by those with increasing polarity. The eluted biomolecules pass through the available detectors—Photo Diode Array, Circular Dichroism, among others—allowing comparison with known standards. Structural elucidation of new substances can also be done by coupling the SFC to a Mass Spectrometer. In addition, the process also allows for the collection of selectively eluted substances when connected to a fractionator and a sample collector. SFC also has the advantage of automatic solvent evaporation when subjected to ambient temperature and pressure.

4.4 IDENTIFICATION OF BIOMOLECULES

During the fractionation process, identification techniques guide the process towards a specific group of biomolecules or one in particular. The processes used include known chemical reactions with a consequent colour change, precipitation, or chromatographic methods.

4.4.1 Identification by Chemical Reactions

The methods are based on colour changes or precipitate formation to indicate molecules in the phytocomplex of a certain group of secondary metabolites. Those based on colour formation may be suitable in addition to qualitative or quantitative analysis, as well (Table 4.4).

4.4.2 Analytical Chromatography

Chromatographic methods are based on comparison with a reference standard of the desired substance. Chromatographic techniques are the most used procedure for analyzing biomolecules from plants due to separating them from complex matrix, versatility, specificity, selectivity, and a wide variety of available methods. Among the separation processes, TLC, CE, gas chromatography (GC), HPLC, and SFC can be used, some of which are described in item 4.3 (Isolation). In addition to the separation, it is necessary to use methods to identify the eluted substances. In TLC,

TABLE 4.4
Classic Examples of Reactions Used to Identify Groups of Biomolecules

Metabolic Group	Chemical Reaction	Positive Feature
Alkaloids	Bertrand, Dragendorff	Turbidity or precipitate
Anthraquinones	Bornträger	Red colour
Steroids	Liebermann-Burchard	Blue-green colour
Triterpenes	Liebermann-Burchard	Pink/violet colour
Flavonoids	Shinoda	Red colour
Tannins	Ferric chloride	Dark blue colour

Source: Simões et al. [1].

revealers are used to make it possible to visualise different colours for different molecules and to compare the Rf value (migration distance of the substance under study/ migration distance of solvent front), with the reference standard. The most varied revealers can be used in column chromatography techniques, depending on the technique and molecule of interest. The revealers used in the TLC can be based on the excitability of the biomolecules in ultraviolet light, allowing the visualisation of a fluorescent stain. For example, the iodine reveals a brown colour.

Several detectors may be used in column chromatography, selected based on the chromatographic method and the sample to be analised (Table 4.5). Some methods are destructive, such as flame ionisation, and are not used in processes where the objective is to collect the sample at the end of the separation. Some detectors are not destructive (e.g. absorption detectors) and can be used in preparative systems to collect biomolecules fractions.

TABLE 4.5
Examples of Detectors Used in Column Chromatography

Chromatography	Detector	Principle of Technique
Thermal conductivity	GC	Differential speed of heat loss
Flame ionisation	GC, SFC	Ions formed after contact with flame
Photometric, Spectrophotometer, and Diode arrangement	HPLC, SFC, CE	Light absorbance
Fluorescence	HPLC, CE	Excitability and light emission
Mass spectrometry	TLC, HPLC, SFC, CE	Molecular weight of ions generated after contact with flame
Circular dichroism	HPLC, SFC	Differentiated absorption of polarised light

4.5 FINAL REMARKS

The therapeutic knowledge of plants has been transmitted and improved from generations since ancient times. With the advancement of science, efforts have been directed towards identifying molecules or classes of substances present in herbal medicine associated with an assigned biological activity. This study involves different stages, which include extraction, isolation, and identification/structural elucidation of phytochemicals. These steps are of fundamental importance in the process of discovering new drugs from plants. Several technologies can be used at each stage, and their advantages and disadvantages must be taken into account, such as the use of organic solvents, efficiency, speed, execution, cost, environmental impact, among others. Preliminary studies by statistical analysis are generally used to guide the best methodological conditions. With this, it is possible to improve the characteristics of the processes and reduce time, cost, and the use of organic solvents and increase efficiency, selectivity, and operational performance, for example. Among the techniques presented in this chapter, SFE and SFC stand out for employing the principles of green chemistry and can be used together, allowing all stages of the development of a phytopharmaceutical to be carried out in a single step.

Highlights

- Constitutive complexity of plants requires several steps to isolate a molecule of interest.
- The steps consist of extraction, isolation, and identification.
- The extraction processes allow a mixture separation of phytocomplexes from the plant matrix.
- Isolation generally occurs through the use of different fractionation and purification techniques.
- Classic colourimetric tests or chromatographic methods can carry out the identification.
- Supercritical technology can be used in all stages of research of phytopharmaceuticals, adding green chemistry with reduced impact on the environment and facilitating processes with reduced steps and increased efficiency.

REFERENCES

1. Simões, C. M. O.; Schenkel, E. P.; Mello, J. C. P.; Mentz, L. *Farmacognosia - Do Produto Natural Ao Medicamento*; Artmed:Porto Alegre, 2017.
2. Newman, D. J.; Cragg, G. M. Natural Products as Sources of New Drugs from 1981 to 2014. *J. Nat. Prod.*, **2016**, *79* (3), 629–661.
3. Lancaster, M. Organic Solvents: Environmentally Benign Solutions. In *Green Chemistry, An Introductory Text. 1*; Lancaster, M., Ed.; Royal Society of Chemistry: United Kingdom, 2007; pp. 130–165.
4. Bassani, V. L. Desenvolvimento Tecnológico e Produção de Fitoterápicos. In *Farmacognosia: Da Planta Ao Medicamento*; Simões, C. M. O., Schenkel, E. P., Gosmann, G., Mello, J. C. P., Mentz, L. A., Petrovick, P. R., Eds.; Ed. da UFRGS: Porto Alegre; Ed. da UFSC: Florianópolis, 2003; pp. 289–326.
5. López-Sebastián, S.; Ramos, E.; Ibáñez, E.; Bueno, J. M.; Ballester, L.; Tabera, J.; Reglero, G. Dearomatization of Antioxidant Rosemary Extracts by Treatment with Supercritical Carbon Dioxide. *J. Agric. Food Chem.*, **1998**, *46* (1), 13–19.

6. Leitner, W.; Jessop, P. G. Volume 4: Green Solvents, Supercritical Solvents. In *Handbook of Green Chemistry*; Anastas, P. T., Ed.; WILEY-VCH Verlag GmbH & Co. KGaA: Weinheim, 2014.
7. Souza, G. H. B.; Mello, J. C. P.; Lopes, N. P. *Revisões Em Processos e Técnicas Avançadas de Isolamento e Determinação Estrutural de Ativos de Plantas Medicinais*. UFOP: Ouro Preto, Brazil 2011, p. 252.
8. Heinrich, M. Ethnopharmacology in the 21st Century—Grand Challenges. *Front. Pharmacol.*, 2010, *1*, 8.

5 Standardisation of Herbal Extracts by Drying Technologies

Wanderley Pereira Oliveira

CONTENTS

5.1 Introduction 105
5.2 Phytochemicals 106
5.2.1 Factors Affecting the Concentration of Phytochemicals on Herbal Materials 108
5.2.2 Applications of Phytochemicals 108
5.3 Standardisation of Herbal Medicinal Products 109
5.3.1 Technological Development of Herbal Medicinal Products 110
5.3.2 Unit Operations Used in Processing Herbal Medicinal Products 111
5.3.2.1 Primary Operations 113
5.3.2.2 Extraction of the Bioactive Compounds 116
5.3.2.3 Concentration of the Extractive Solution 117
5.4 Standardisation of Herbal Extracts by Drying Technologies 117
5.4.1 Spray Drying 117
5.4.1.1 Spray Drying of Herbal Extracts 119
5.4.2 Freeze-Drying 126
5.4.2.1 Freeze-Drying of Herbal Products 130
5.5 Stability Testing 131
5.6 Challenges and Prospects 132
5.7 Concluding Remarks 133
Acknowledgements 133
References 134

5.1 INTRODUCTION

Since ancient times, medicinal plants have been used to treat human illnesses, being the basis of millenary systems of traditional medicine such as Ayurvedic, Chinese, and Unani. Medicinal plants are also used to produce fine chemicals, herbal remedies, standardised extracts, nutraceuticals, colourants, cosmetics, essential oils, fragrances, and pesticides. The world trade in medicinal plants and extracts is growing continuously and exceeds dozens of billions of US dollars [1, 2].

DOI: 10.1201/9781003225416-7

Until the beginning of the 19th century, medicinal plants were the main source of products used for human healing. However, with the strong evolution of organic synthesis, synthetic drugs predominated, and traditional medicine was neglected, especially in developed Western nations.

The herbal medicine has remerged over the last 40 years, partly due to proof of its effectiveness and safety, cultural reasons, low cost, self-medication, and the disbelief and inefficacy of some allopathic treatments. The World Health Organization (WHO) incentives for the developing countries to use traditional plant medicine to fulfil needs unmet by modern health care systems also contributed to this growth [3, 4]. Currently, about 70–80% of the world population in developing countries rely essentially on non-conventional medicine in their primary healthcare [5].

Traditional medicine is widely based on medicinal plant and their derivatives, which receive various denominations, such as botanicals, herbal medicines, or phytomedicines [6]. It has been reported that between 35,000 and 70,000 plant species are used to treat diseases worldwide, but only a few have been scientifically studied to assess their quality, safety, and efficacy [6, 7]. Since the development of standardised herbal remedies demands significantly lower investment and technology needs than a new synthesised medicine, they are fully feasible for underdeveloped and developing nations.

Regulations for phytomedicines have been implemented by several countries, including Brazil, establishing instruments to guide their production and guaranteeing their safety, effectiveness, and quality [6, 8]. The evolution of legal requirements for the registration of phytomedicines is covered comprehensively in Chapter 12.

5.2 PHYTOCHEMICALS

Phytochemicals are organic substances synthesised by plants. They comprise the primary and secondary metabolites, although, in recent years, the term 'phytochemical' has been associated with the secondary metabolites [9]. Secondary metabolites have a complex and diversified chemical structure, which can incorporate primary metabolites.

Secondary metabolites may be classified based on pharmacological activity, chemical structures, and functional groups. They can be classified into major categories such as glycosides, carotenoids, phenolics, alkaloids, terpenes, sterols, saponins, nitrogen-containing compounds, and organosulfur compounds [10, 11]. Fruits, vegetables, grains, and other dietary and medicinal plants are rich sources of phytochemicals. The continuous intact of them can proportionate significant health benefits, contributing to reduce the risk of major chronic diseases, such as dementia, diabetes, atherosclerosis, osteoporosis, stroke, hypertension, rheumatoid arthritis, and so on [7, 12]. Figure 5.1 shows few examples of important phytochemicals and their sources: lycopene from tomatoes; apigenin from parsley; curcumin from turmeric; diallyl sulphide from garlic; genistein from soybean; gingerol from gingers; epigallocatechin-3-gallate from green tea; resveratrol from grapes; rosmarinic acid from rosemary; sulforaphane from broccoli; silymarin from milk thistle; capsaicin from chilli peppers; and indole-3-carbinol from cabbage [7, 13].

Although not directly involved in the essential biochemical plant metabolism, phytochemicals can perform useful functions for them, such as protection against

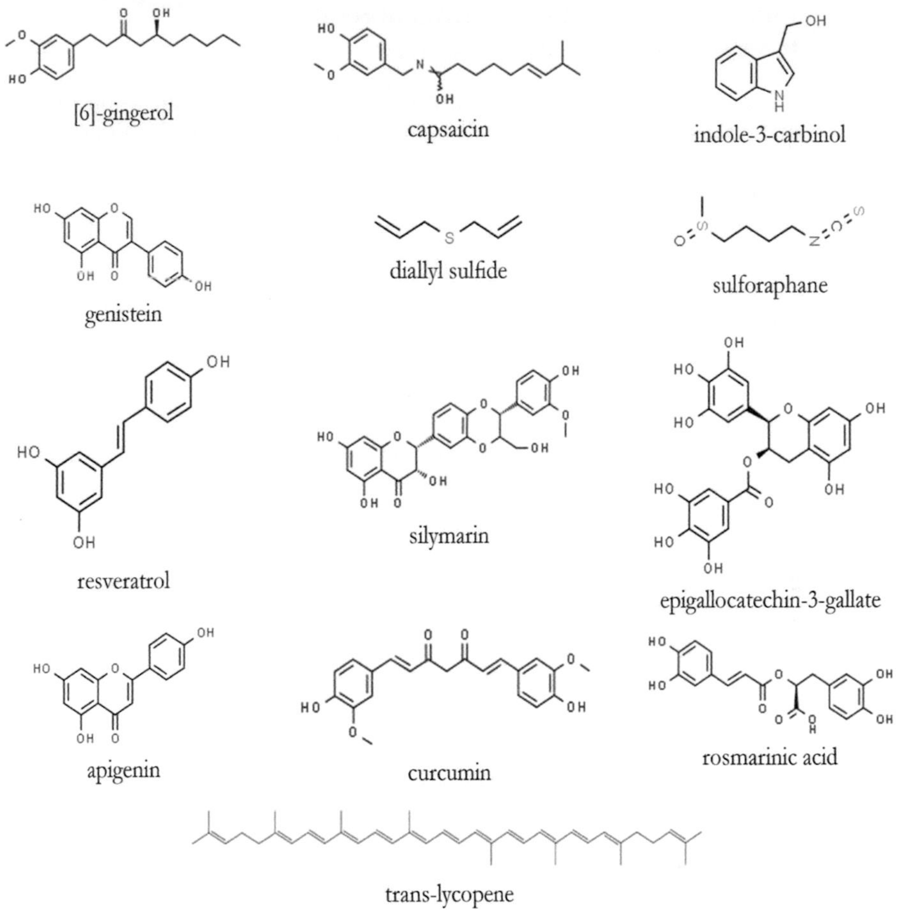

[6]-gingerol

capsaicin

indole-3-carbinol

genistein

diallyl sulfide

sulforaphane

resveratrol

silymarin

epigallocatechin-3-gallate

apigenin

curcumin

rosmarinic acid

trans-lycopene

FIGURE 5.1 Chemical structures of relevant phytochemicals. (From: www.Chemspider.com.)

pests and pathogens, the attraction of pollinators, and chemical signalling [14]. Flavonoids, for example, can protect the plant against reactive oxygen species abundantly generated during photosynthetic pathways, while alkaloids generally repel herbivorous animals or insect attacks (phytoalexins). Terpenoids can attract pollinators or seed dispersers or inhibit competing plants. Phenolics and carotenoids are the most studied phytochemicals and involve substances as phenolic acids, flavonoids, stilbenes, coumarins, tannins, lycopene, curcumin, β-carotene, lutein, and so on. These compounds can exhibit potent biological properties, such as antioxidant, antimicrobial, anti-inflammatory, and antitumor, with enormous potential to be explored by the pharmaceutical, food, cosmetic, agricultural, and veterinary industries. Relevant information on important classes of secondary metabolites, including chemical structures, biosynthesis, and physicochemical properties, can be found in Simões et al. [15] and Crozier et al. [16].

5.2.1 Factors Affecting the Concentration of Phytochemicals on Herbal Materials

Phytochemicals are produced by the plant's secondary metabolism using distinct biosynthetic routes. The production is affected by available resources and environmental demands. In most situations, there are variations in the abundance and phytochemical profiles over time, which may significantly affect the biological activity of the medicinal plant. The production of metabolites may be influenced by several factors, like seasonality, circadian rhythm, age and stage of plant development, temperature, water availability, the incidence of ultraviolet radiation, soil type, altitude, atmosphere composition, and damage to plant tissues. Seasonality is a key factor. It interrelates with most of the factors listed, such as the circadian cycle, water stress, and sun exposure. Therefore, one of the decisive requirements for the development and registration of herbal products (e.g. phytomedicines) is the knowledge of the variations of the chemical constituents of the selected plant species (wild or cultivated) over a certain period of the day or year [17, 18]. Hence, studies must be carried out to determine the proper conditions for planting, soil, harvest, and daytime period that provide a vegetable raw material with optimum composition and concentration of the metabolites of interest. Comprehensive reviews of the effects of seasonality and other factors such as plant age and stage of development, temperature, water availability, and incidence of radiation can be found in the literature [17, 19].

5.2.2 Applications of Phytochemicals

Medicinal and aromatic herbs are a rich source of bioactive organic substances (some unknown), and most of them are specific for a determined plant species. These substances have very diversified chemical structures, most of which exhibit potent biological effects in humans and animals. For example, terpenoids have antibacterial, antiviral, and anti-inflammatory activities, alkaloids have anaesthetic properties, and polyphenols and flavonoids exhibit antioxidant, antitumor, and antimicrobial activities [20–22].

The biodiversity of the flora is enormous, with a large number of species still unknown or not scientifically studied. Therefore, a plethora of phytochemicals with diversified biological activities remains unidentified. The biodiversity of the tropical and equatorial environments has a huge potential in biologically active compounds that can be used as models for medicinal chemistry and drug discovery [23]. Therefore, the search for molecules from plant species to be used as new molecular models for medicinal chemistry, for the development of new drugs, agrochemicals, fragrances, cosmetics, and food supplements is an exciting research subject [24]. Currently, it is estimated that more than 25% of the drugs that are available come from tropical plants. For example, artemisinin and quinine, two effective drugs widely used to treat malaria, are derived from natural sources based on traditional medicine [25]. Figure 5.2 presents the usual steps involved in the search of new drugs from herbal material.

The phytochemical chemical structures vary widely. Many of them are too complicated or uneconomical to be fully synthesised in the laboratory. Hence, various

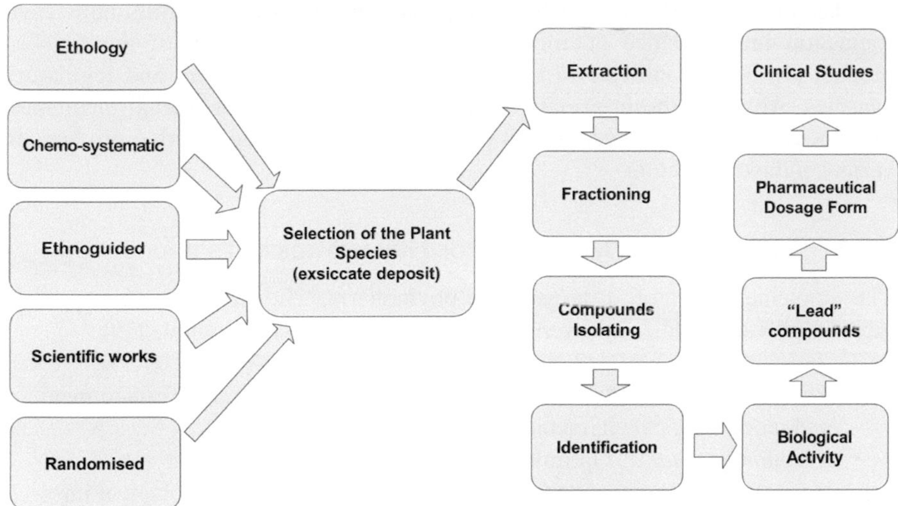

FIGURE 5.2 Usual steps involved in the search of new drugs from herbal material.

complex substances or precursors are extracted from natural sources when needed for industrial or pharmaceutical uses. For example, paclitaxel production still uses plant sources in either semisynthetic or culture-based formats [26].

Herbal materials are also used to extract essential oils, aromas, fragrances, functional additives, natural antioxidants, dyes and preservatives, natural herbicides and pesticides, among others, with applications in various sectors, such as chemical, food, pharmaceutical, agricultural, and veterinary. Various extracts and phytochemicals from medicinal, dietary, and aromatic plants are currently marketed as herbal medicines, dietary supplements, and food and cosmetics ingredients [27].

5.3 STANDARDISATION OF HERBAL MEDICINAL PRODUCTS

The increasing production and marketing of herbal products have been accompanied by a significant increase in the requirements regarding their quality control. To be used in speciality applications, such as herbal medicines and food ingredients, these products must be presented in standardised forms, with the qualitative and quantitative characterisation of their main active constituents. However, the biological activity of herbal products is generally superior to those observed for the main isolated compounds, which is attributed to synergistic interactions acting on multiple targets simultaneously (multiple mechanisms of action).

The production of a standardised product involves numerous sequential steps, namely obtaining a high-quality vegetable raw material (wildcrafting or cultivation), pre-processing and characterisation of the raw material (primary treatment), exhaustive extraction of the bioactive constituents, the guarantee of stability of these substances throughout the production and storage process, and the elaboration of the final pharmaceutical form, with adequate physicochemical characteristics [28].

All the processing steps must be carried out sustainably, with minimum environmental impact, since obtaining the raw herbal material until the finished product [1]. Sustainability is a current demand from consumers and regulatory agencies. Although the information presented here focuses on herbal medicines, the processing steps are general and can be applied to finished herbal products in various industrial sectors.

5.3.1 Technological Development of Herbal Medicinal Products

The implementation of a large-scale phytopharmaceutical production process includes previous studies in several knowledgeable fields, for example [29]:

- *Botanical studies*: Identification of plant species, analysis of anatomical, and morphological characteristics
- *Agronomic studies*: Optimisation of biomass production and active constituents, micropropagation studies, genetic improvement, ecological interrelationships, primary processing, and storage
- *Chemical studies*: Identification and characterisation of plant species regarding their main chemical constituents, purification and isolation of phytochemicals, structural elucidation, and identification of chemical markers to be used in the planning and monitoring of technological transformation actions and to evaluate the stability of intermediate and final products [30]
- *Biological activity studies*: *In vitro* and *in vivo* studies of the pharmacological activity and toxicity of extracts, fractions, or isolated constituents. Relevant questions to be answered in this step are what or which pharmacological actions are attributed to the plant? What is the pharmacological activity to be explored? What is the pharmacogen? Which or which substances are responsible for the activity? What is the concentration and the potency of the active substance in the plant? Are there toxic substances in the fraction of interest?
- *Development of analytical methodologies*: Evaluation of the quality of the herbal product in the stages of the production cycle (from plant to medicine), chemistry, and development of physical–chemical and technological protocols (from pharmacopoeia and technical-scientific literature)
- *Formulation studies*: Selection of technological excipients, production of the pharmaceutical form, experimental designs; accompanying the requirements of the technical standards of Good Manufacturing Practices (GMP) and Quality Control, the correct choice of equipment according to the production scale and objectives of the transformation operations

The transformation of the vegetable raw material into an herbal product is carried out by sequential transformation actions, where each action generates an intermediate product. All production stages must be strictly controlled and monitored, as they may cause specific changes in product quality. The final product quality is dictated by the sum of the quality obtained in each stage. The key point in obtaining good-quality herbal products is standardisation. Standardisation can be considered a condition in which the product's effectiveness is guaranteed by consistency in the content of the main active constituents. Standardisation involves establishing quality control parameters with strict control of all stages involved in the phytopharmaceutical processing [31–33]. The process's complexity and the number of operations depend on the degree of technological transformation required. It can be minimal, as is the case of scraped, crushed, or pulverised plants for the preparation of teas, or much more complex, when the objective is to obtain purified fractions or even a solid coated pharmaceutical dosage form. The choice of a specific unit operation is guided by the physical and physical–chemical characteristics specified for the product, the nature of the plant raw material to be processed, and the production capacity [28, 29].

The processing operations must be carried out following the current GMP (cGMP), which provide guidelines of the minimum requirements that the producer must follow to guarantee from batch to batch, a consistent high-quality product for the use intended [34]. The GMP version proposed by the WHO [35] is followed by several nations, mainly in the developing world. Similar rules are enforced by the health regulatory agencies of several countries/regions, such as the European Medicines Agency (EMA), the US Food and Drug Administration (USFDA), and the Brazilian Health Surveillance Agency (ANVISA, Brazil).

The processing starts with obtaining good-quality herbal material, which can be collected directly from nature (wildcrafting) or cultivated in controlled conditions. The cultivation and collection of plant material must be sustainable and follow the Good Agricultural and Collection Practices (GACP) of medicinal plants. These guidelines concern the cultivation and collection of medicinal plants and include certain post-harvest operations [35].

Adulteration is a critical point when working with plant materials. Hence, the validation of commercial sources is mandatory. Cases of poisoning due to the confusion or exchange of plant materials are routinely reported. The exclusion or limitation of impurities and other parts of the plant or foreign matter, of microorganisms and their metabolites (aflatoxins), and the presence of pesticide residues and heavy metals are also important factors to be evaluated.

Due to the complex chemical composition of the plant materials, processing is crucial in maintaining quality constancy. Variations due to several factors such as temperature, sun exposure, availability of water and nutrients, period, time and method of harvest, age and part of the plant used, drying, storage, and transportation conditions generally affect the quality of the raw plant material and, consequently, the quality and therapeutic value of the final herbal products. Figure 5.3 shows a diagram of factors that can affect the quality of the herbal drug.

5.3.2 Unit Operations Used in Processing Herbal Medicinal Products

Herbal medicinal products (HMPs) must be produced from exclusively active plant raw materials. They can be classified as: *Herbal Drug*—the whole, scraped, crushed, or pulverised medicinal plant, after collection, stabilisation, and drying; *Herbal Drug*

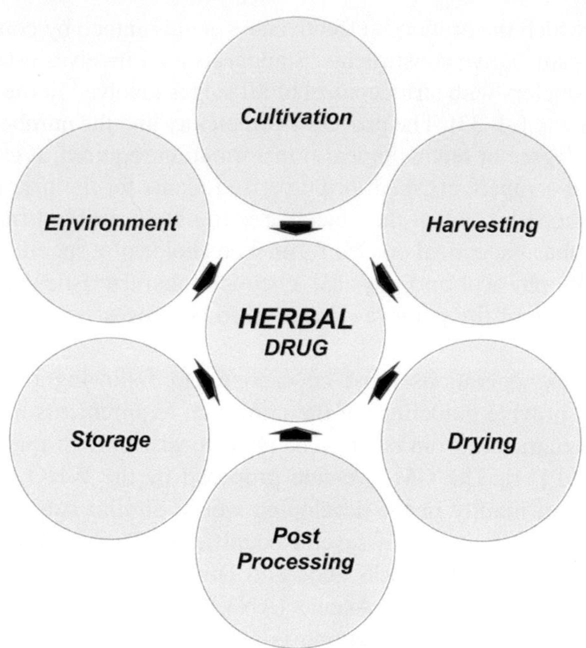

FIGURE 5.3 Factors affecting the quality of herbal drugs.

Derivative—products of the extraction of vegetable raw material: extract, tincture, oil, wax, exudate, juice, among others; *Phytomedicine*—medicine produced from exclusively active plant raw materials, characterised by the knowledge of its effectiveness and risks, with reproducibility and constancy of its quality batch to batch.

HMPs are usually marketed as tinctures, syrups, fluid, and dry extracts. However, the phytopharmaceutical processing industry's current tendency is to replace the traditional fluid forms with the more stable standardised dried extracts, a dried product manufactured to the specified concentration of marker compounds. Standardised dried extracts show several advantages compared to fluid forms, such as the high concentrations of the phytoconstituents, high stability, and ease of standardisation of the bioactive compounds; ease of transportation; reduced space required for product storage; and lower risk of microbial contamination. These characteristics significantly increase the value of the processed product. Figure 5.4 shows the increment in the market value of herbal-derived products caused by technological processing [28, 36].

The development and production of a standardised dry extract is not a simple task. Some key parameters such as the part of the plant to be used (leaves, roots, flowers); harvesting of the herbal material; extraction method and additional purification steps; type of solvent system; the proportion of plant material to the solvent system; concentration of active ingredients; and selection of the most appropriate drying method and drying adjuvants must be optimised to achieve a final product

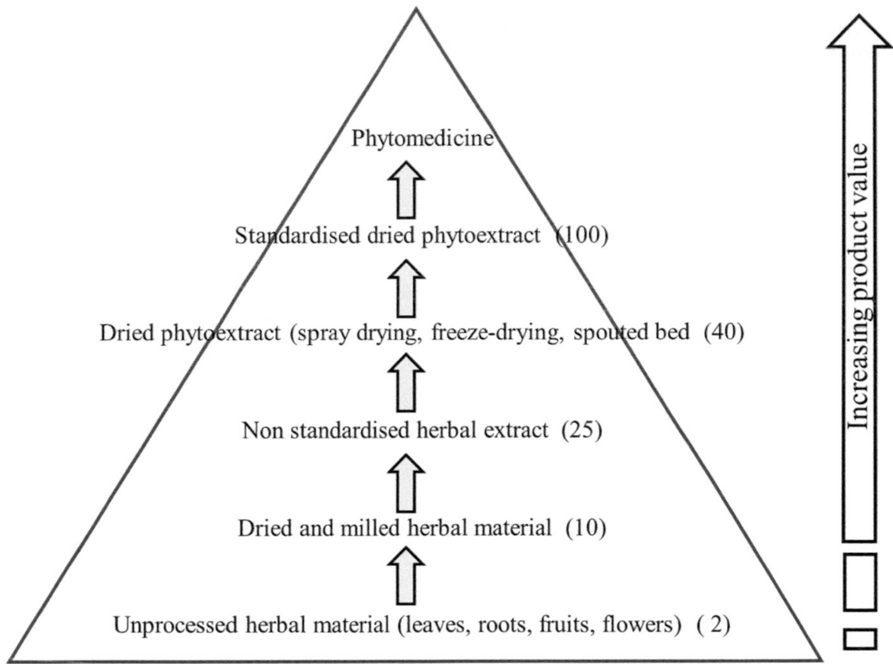

FIGURE 5.4 Market value added to the herbal-derived products due to processing and standardisation. (Adapted from Aziz et al. [36].)

with the desired quality and therapeutic value [6, 7, 28, 37, 38]. Figure 5.5 presents a schematic diagram showing the various processing steps involved in the standardisation of plant extracts by drying technologies.

The processing steps must follow the guidelines on good herbal processing practices for herbal medicines proposed by the WHO [39]. Studies related to the large-scale production of the active raw materials, aspects related to pharmaceutical technology (pre-formulation studies, formulation, and stability tests), clinical trials, and regulatory and registration aspects complete the development cycle of a phytomedicine.

5.3.2.1 Primary Operations

Immediately after harvesting, the fresh vegetable raw material must be submitted to some primary processing to guarantee its quality. The primary processing usually includes the macroscopic analysis, cleaning, drying of herbal material (unless fresh material is required), comminution to reach a size suitable for extraction and subsequent steps to prepare the standardised extract or the pharmaceutical dosage form. In some situations, the herbal material can also be submitted to other primary operations such as fumigation with sulphur dioxide (for preserving or improving the product colour and preventing insects and moulds growth) and ultraviolet light irradiation (to reduce the microbial load).

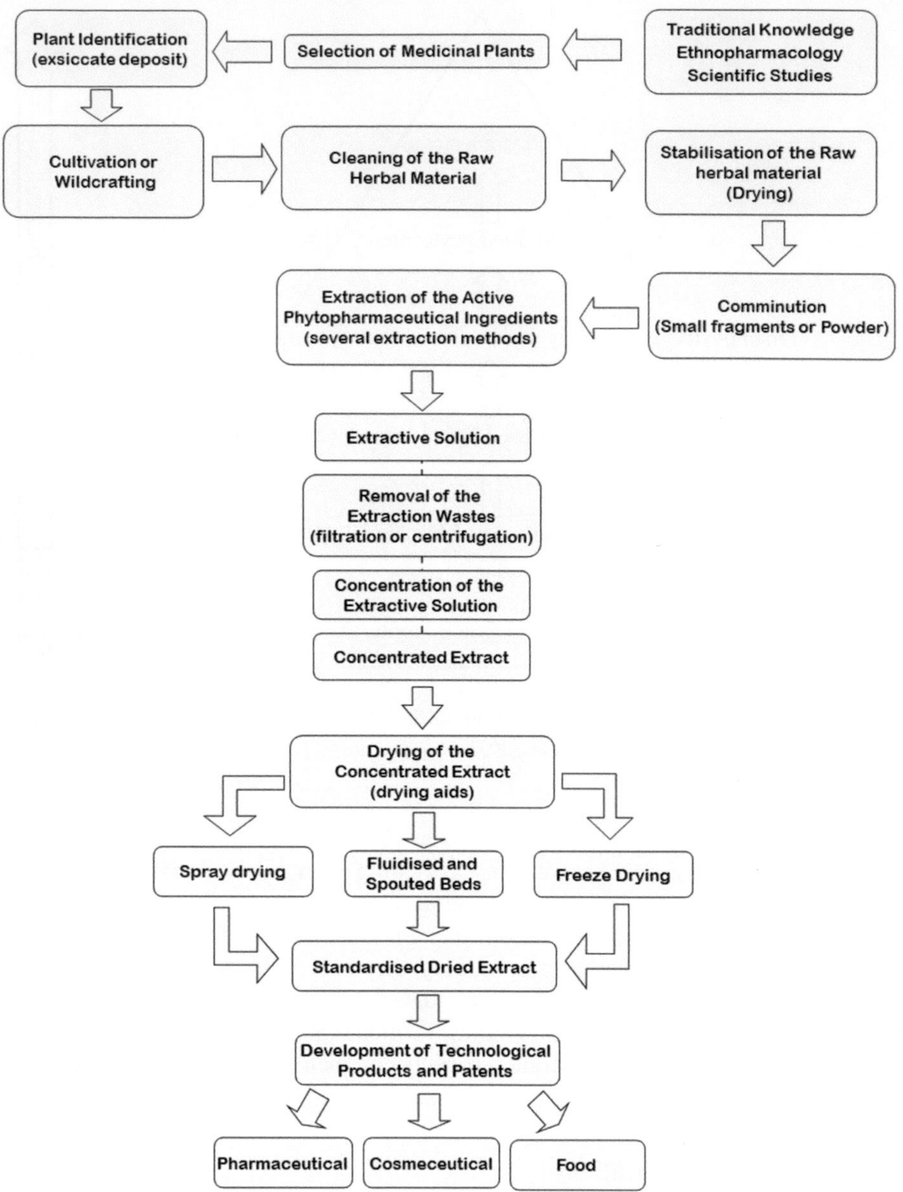

FIGURE 5.5 Schematic flowsheet of the main steps involved in the standardisation of herbal extracts by drying technologies.

5.3.2.1.1 Macroscopic Analysis—Cleaning

A macroscopic evaluation is generally used to clean the plant raw material. It should be carried out almost immediately after harvesting to eliminate the presence of some possible contaminants, such as foreign plant species, and unwanted materials, or parts of the plant (e.g. gravel, sand, branches, and seeds) [33].

5.3.2.1.2 *Drying of the Herbal Material*

After harvesting and cleaning, the vegetable raw material must be dried. If the fresh raw material is required, it should be delivered to the processing facility and used as soon as possible to minimise the spoilage by microorganisms, or endogenous enzymes. Drying is a critical step having a significant impact on the final quality of the herbal product. The main objective of drying is to remove large amounts of free water present in plant cells and tissues, minimising hydrolysis reactions, microbial growth, and enzymatic degradation processes, allowing the maintenance of the quality and chemical profile of the herbal material for a long time. However, in most situations, the quality of dried herbs is lower than that of fresh herbs. The herbal material's drying can be carried out simply by exposing the material outdoors, at shade or under direct sunlight (natural drying). The material must be rotated intermittently for the best result. The operation can also occur using heated gas, in simple greenhouses or in air circulation dryers, such as drying ovens with forced airflow (convective drying) that allows more precise control of the drying and product quality. Placing the herbal material in thin layers leads to more efficient drying and a uniform product. The drying of herbs must be done at temperatures below 60°C, better in the range of 40–45°C, to avoid the loss of thermosensitive constituents. Natural drying is usually more economical but requires more attention to guarantee the quality of the product concerning uniformity and absence of contamination. In many situations, solar radiation can also cause changes in chemical composition of the herbal product. In these cases, drying in the shade is recommended [40]. The drying time and the quality of the dry product obtained by convective drying depend on the processing conditions. Factors such as the thermal sensitivity of the herbal constituents have a strong influence on the selection of the drying system, processing conditions (temperature, flow rate, and temperature of the drying gas), and storage conditions for the dried medicinal and aromatic plants. Sometimes the pretreatment of the herbal material (e.g. blanching, ultrasound, and so on) enhances the quality of the dried herb [15, 41–43]. In recent decades, several novelty herbs drying techniques have been introduced, aiming to generate a product of better quality at a lower cost. Examples of these novel systems are solar-assisted dryers, microwave drying, and hybrid technologies, combining the advantages of two or more specific processes.

An excellent review of drying methods to improve the quality of dried herbs, including hybrid systems, was reported by Thamkaew et al. [43]. A more comprehensive description of important aspects of medicinal and aromatic plant drying, covering some processing variables and case studies is the subject of Chapter 3.

5.3.2.1.3 *Comminution, Fragmentation, Grinding, or Milling*

The reduction of the dried herbal material to size near 30–40 mesh sieves (or another dimension if necessary) is generally conducted before extracting the desired bioactive compounds. When the extraction is carried out with fresh plant material, it must be carried out as soon as possible after wildcrafting or harvesting to reduce the risk of degradation of the product due to enzymatic reactions or microbial contamination [39]. The comminution of the herbal material in small particles causes the rupture of plant tissues and cells and increases the extraction of the chemical constituents, due to the higher product surface area exposed to the extraction solvent system. Examples of mills widely used for the processing of plant-based materials include the knife mill (leaves and flowers, stems, bark, and roots), ball mills (combined impact and friction—hard, brittle, and friable materials), hammer mills (coarse grinding of leaves, bark, and roots, friable, and resins containing materials), and disc mill (for dry extracts, desiccant fruits and seeds, hard, brittle, and friable materials—generate a very fine powder) [39].

5.3.2.2 Extraction of the Bioactive Compounds

The herbal extract consists of a mixture of phytochemicals extracted from fresh or dried whole plants or parts of the plants (leaves, flowers, seeds, roots, or barks). The objectives of a well-planned extractive process are the more selective and complete removal of the phytochemicals of interest (or an active fraction of the plant raw material) to obtain a final product with a high content of bioactive substances. Toxicologically safe and sustainable (green) solvents or solvent mixtures are desired. Besides water, ethanol, and CO_2, only ethyl acetate and acetone, and the gases propane, butane, and nitrous oxide are generally recognised as safe solvents. Single solvents as hexane are allowed for special purposes [1].

After the extraction period, the mixture is filtered, generating the extractive solution. This solution can be subjected to liquid–liquid extraction to obtain fractions enriched with some compounds or even purified substances.

Infusion, digestion, and decoction are methods of extraction commonly used in the domestic extraction routine. Maceration, percolation, Soxhlet extraction, and solid–liquid extraction are classical processes. Recent systems include turbolysis, dynamic maceration, micellar, ultrasound-assisted, microwave-assisted, and supercritical fluid extraction. An excellent review of sustainable and intensified techniques for the extraction of food and natural products, including innovative methods, was present by Chemat et al. [44].

There are also techniques applied to the extraction of volatile compounds, which are extraction by organic solvents, pressing, enfleurage, hydrodistillation, vapour entrainment, and supercritical fluids extraction [7, 15, 45, 46].

Several factors influence extractive processes: the degree of division of the plant raw material, agitation, the temperature, the solubility of the bioactive principles in solvent systems, pH, and extraction time [15, 47, 48]. Since extraction is a multivariate process, determining the ideal extraction conditions is tricky. It involves the simultaneous assessment of the influence of key processing variables on the quality of the extract and extraction yield, in addition to other factors, such as process complexity and costs involved. Using statistical tools, such as experimental designs, in conjunction with regression and multiresponse analyses are highly recommended. They allow simultaneous evaluation and, with less experimental effort, the effects of a set of process variables on the responses of interest. A good description of the statistical design of experiments (DoE) and multiresponse analyses to select the extraction method and optimise the processing conditions applied to the extraction of flavonoid compounds from plant-based materials can be found in Souza et al. [49].

5.3.2.3 Concentration of the Extractive Solution

The extractive solution or the concentrated extract can be the final form of the herbal medicine, or it can be subjected to other processing steps, such as drying. Although it is possible to carry out the direct drying of the extractive solution, from an economic point of view, it is recommended to concentrate it before to remove organic extraction solvents and increase the energetic efficiency of the evaporation process. The concentration reduces the amount of moisture to be removed by the dryer, increasing drying efficiency and reducing processing costs. Concentration operation is usually performed in evaporators, such as rotary evaporation system (common in the laboratory practice), thin-film evaporators, wiped film evaporators, and multiple effect evaporators [45].

5.4 STANDARDISATION OF HERBAL EXTRACTS BY DRYING TECHNOLOGIES

Drying consists of the removal of the moisture present in a wet product through heating. The heat transfer to the wet body may occur by conduction, convection, or radiation. The drying process may also be classified according to the type of equipment used, such as spray drying (SD), freeze-drying (FD), fluidised bed drying, and microwave drying. Excellent works regarding drying fundaments and applications to pharmaceutical products have been reported by Kemp [50], and by Oliveira et al. [51]

The production of standardised dry extracts is an important operation in the herbal medicine production chain. The dry extract has high chemical and microbiological stability, lower volume, and allows the easy manufacture of solid dosage forms, like tablets and capsules. Drying system and operating conditions have a significant impact on the physical and chemical product properties (e.g. concentration of the major constituents, powder size, loss on drying, water content, water activity, hygroscopicity, flow properties, density, and morphology) and on product costs [52–55].

Dried extracts can be obtained through various drying technologies, including FD, SD, spouted, and fluidised beds. SD is most commonly used in the herbal processing industries, while FD is common in research studies. However, there are various FD herbal extracts on the market. Spouted bed drying (SBD) has also been investigated as an innovative alternative to SD for drying herbal extracts [56–58].

Some important aspects of SD and FD of phytochemical compositions are presented in the next sections. SBD is the subject of Chapter 6.

5.4.1 Spray Drying

SD is widely used in several industrial sectors, such as pharmaceutical, chemical, ceramic, polymer, dyestuffs and pigments, fertilisers, detergents, enzymes, among others, when the objective is to generate powdered products from liquid feeds. SD products are common in our daily lives, such as powdered milk, dehydrated soups, and powdered coffee. Dry powders, granules, or fine agglomerates can be produced continuously by drying solutions, emulsions, or suspensions. An important advantage attributed to SD is its potential to generate a product with preset physicochemical properties (e.g. moisture content, water activity, wettability, solubility, redispersion capacity, powder size, apparent density, fluidity, and compactability), by defining the equipment configuration, processing variables, and operating conditions [59]. Conceptually, SD is a simple process and consists of the atomisation of a solid–fluid mixture diluted in a heated gas stream, promoting the evaporation of the solvent and generating a dry product. The feed is atomised as very fine droplets by the atomisation system, as centrifugal (high-speed rotating wheels), pneumatic or double fluid atomisers. Centrifugal atomisers are the most used model in production equipment, while double fluid atomisers are more common in laboratory practice. The liquid feed and the drying gas can occur concurrently, counter-currently, or in a mixed flow. The drying gas carries the dried product, and at gas exiting, a cyclone removes the fine powders. At the same time, the coarse particles are usually collected at the conical bottom of the drying chamber [59, 60]. Figure 5.6 shows a schematic diagram of the SD.

SD is a process of simultaneous heat and mass transfer between hot gas and wet droplets. The driving force of the SD is the difference in the vapour pressure of the liquid on the droplet surface and its partial pressure in the hot gas. The gas temperature decreases rapidly during its journey through the SD chamber due to the transfer of the latent heat necessary for liquid evaporation (evaporative cooling). The process is very fast, and the product residence time in the dryer is short. The surface of the atomised droplet remains saturated with the liquid, keeping it at a low temperature, allowing the drying of thermosensitive products [61, 62]. The droplets dry from their surface inward, and an outer layer of concentrated solids is formed. The rapid removal of the liquid strongly increased the viscosity on the surface of the droplets, causing their vitrification (glassy state) before the occurrence of collisions between

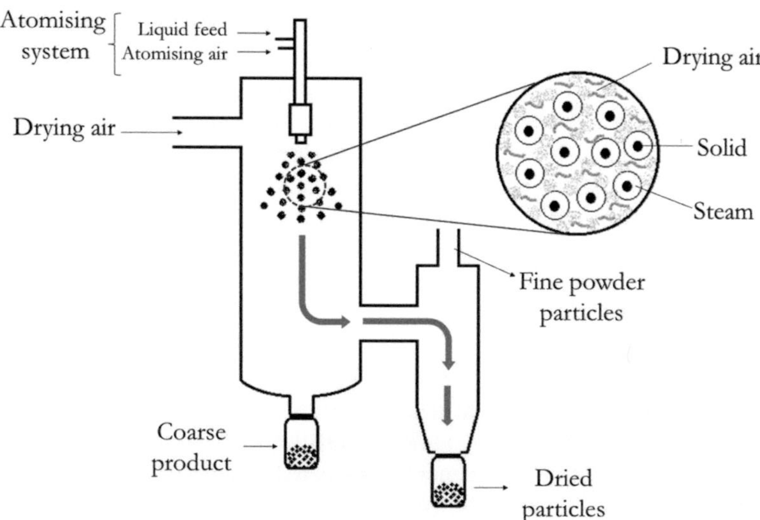

FIGURE 5.6 Schematic diagram of spray drying.

them or with the drying chamber wall. The droplets vitrification during SD reduces their stickiness on the SD wall, thus allowing their free flow. For a successful SD operation, the temperature and water content of the particles should support the solid glassy state [63, 64].

In addition to physical transformations, other types of chemical, biological, and enzymatic transformations can also occur during SD, which depends on the property of the product to be dried and on the processing conditions. Some transformations are desired since they enhance the product's characteristics, such as increasing the product's solubility and reducing the microbial load (caused by heating). Undesirable effects can also occur, such as the degradation of the substances of interest and the loss of volatile compounds [65].

The product properties are linked to the properties of the feed composition and the SD operational parameters [59–61, 65]. Important properties of the feed composition are rheology, solids content, density, surface tension, type, and concentration of drying excipients added [51, 66]. The main SD variables are the temperature and humidity of the drying gas, the temperature of the gas at the outlet, type of flow between the drying gas and the atomised material (concurrent, counter-current, and mixed flow), flow rate and pressure of the atomising gas, the atomisation system, and the feed flow rate of the composition to be dried [51, 59].

Therefore, several variables must be identified, optimised, and controlled to engineer a stable product with pre-defined physicochemical properties, combined with a high drying yield, with minimum product adhesion on the drying chamber wall (sticking).

5.4.1.1 Spray Drying of Herbal Extracts

SD is the technology most used to produce standardised dry plant extracts. SD of herbal extracts is a very active research topic, with numerous published works [67–70]. A search on Web of Science (https://webofknowledge.com/) from 2000 to 2020, using the phrases "spray drying of plant extracts" or "spray drying of herbal extracts", shows the continuous increase in the number of publications and citations in referred documents over time, reaching a total of 4,560 documents with 16,211 citations (excluding self-citation—Figure 5.7). These results give evidence of the significant scientific importance of this knowledge field.

The concentration of the dried product's main bioactive substances and stability is of paramount importance during the drying of herbal extracts [58, 65]. Each plant extract has its own chemical identity (chemical constituents, carbohydrates, reducing sugars, lipids, organic acids, proteins, among others); therefore, there are no universal equipment configuration and processing conditions valid for all products. Thus, the specification of the drying system and the definition of processing conditions are mainly based on theoretical and experimental works, which must be carried out for each plant species under study, taking into account the desired product properties. So, the physical and chemical product properties (e.g. loss on drying, degradation of active ingredients, particle size distribution, chromatographic profile, X-ray diffraction, thermal behaviour) and the dryer performance's parameters (e.g. drying yield, powder production, thermal efficiency, energy consumption) are monitored under various processing conditions during the development stage of a productive process.

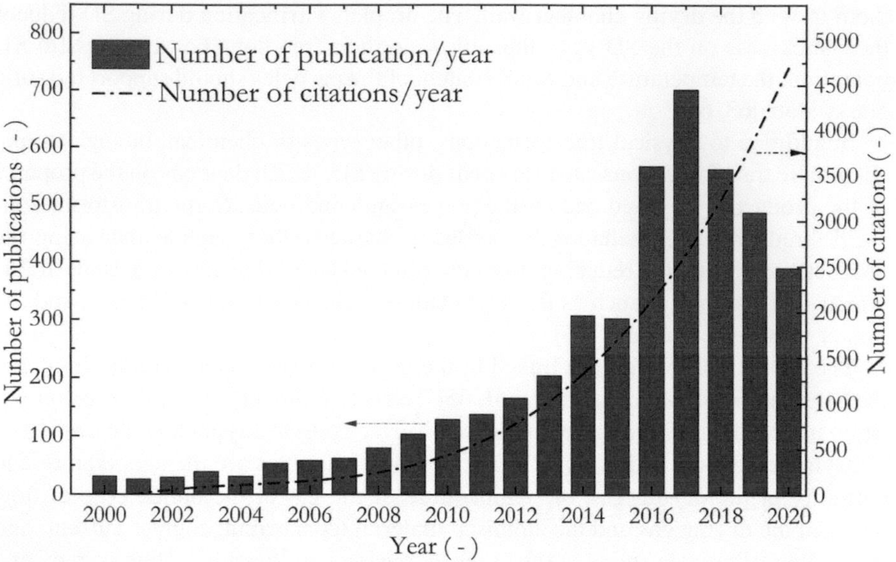

FIGURE 5.7 Number of documents and citations found on the Web of Science website by searching the phrases "spray drying plant extracts" and "spray drying herbal extracts".

The methods used to determine the properties of the dried product and parameters of system performance can be found in Souza [28], WHO [33], and Sampaio et al. [71].

A common problem during SD of herbal extracts is the stickiness phenomenon (adhesion or cohesion). This issue has been extensively investigated for foodstuffs and occurs more frequently for sugar-rich materials [72]. Since plant extracts may contain higher amounts of reducing and non-reducing sugars, carbohydrates, and organic acids [73], the occurrence of stickiness during SD is a reality. Hence, it is almost mandatory to add drying adjuvants to the extractive solution before SD, to improve the product properties and system performance.

5.4.1.1.1 Drying Adjuvants

Drying adjuvants are also called *drying aids* or *drying carrier*, and these terms will be used here interchangeably to express the same thing. The correct selection of drying adjuvants is a fundamental step in producing dry extracts with a strong influence on the quality, stability, and bioavailability of the bioactive constituents in the final product. Drying aids must be chemically inert, harmless, and thermally stable [52, 74]. Polymers, carbohydrates, and gums are typical classes of materials widely used as drying aids. Some of these adjuvants are also used for encapsulation purposes to protect the sensitive compounds against adverse conditions, increase their stability, or promote the controlled release of bioactive substances. In these applications, the drying aids are normally called wall material [64, 75]. Drying aids may be used alone or mixed in appropriate proportions. The ideal proportions should be established for each specific situation, both in terms of the extract composition and processing conditions used [51, 65, 75]. One of the main functions of the drying aids is to increase the glass transition temperature of the material being dried, thus promoting a reduction in product stickiness during drying and storage, forming a stable product [63, 64, 76]. Examples of drying adjuvants widely used during drying of herbal extracts include the colloidal silicon dioxide (SiO_2; CAS: 7631-86-9), Maltodextrins ($[C_6H_{10}O_5]\ nH_2O$) of various dextrose equivalent, gum Arabic (also known as gum acacia), cyclodextrins (CDs) and CD derivatives (e.g. α-CD, β-CD, γ-CD, dimethyl-β-CD, 2-hydroxyethyl-β-CD, trimethyl-β-CD), starch and modified starches, and microcrystalline cellulose (MCC) [52, 65, 77]. Information concerning the main characteristics and properties of these and others adjuvants can be found in Sheskey et al. [78].

5.4.1.1.2 Experimental Studies

SD is a widely used method for producing dry microparticles from vegetable extracts and other bioactive compounds from natural sources. The process is also widely used in the food industry (e.g. milk, fruit pulps and juices, soups, and so on) and in microencapsulation processes of essential oils, flavours, and other bioactive compounds [71, 79–82]. The low temperature reached by the atomised droplet and the short residence time of the product through the dryer makes SD an optimum process for drying plant extracts, with minimal degradation of bioactive compounds, preserving in most cases the extract chemical composition and its bioactivity. The product's properties and the dryer performance depend on the formulation of the feed composition and operating dryer conditions. The feed composition's rheology, pH, surface tension, solids content, and glass transition temperature can be properly planned by adding suitable drying adjuvants to the extractive solution (see Sections 5.4.1 and 5.4.1.1.1).

An evaluation of the dryer performance and product properties during SD of *Bauhinia forficata* (*Bf*) Link extracts in presence of the drying adjuvant colloidal SiO_2 was reported by Souza and Oliveira [83]. The extractive solution was obtained by dynamic maceration from dried and milled *Bf* leaves placed in contact with ethanol:water solution (70:30 w:w) at a temperature of 50°C. The extract was filtered under vacuum and concentrated 3 times in a rotary evaporator, and its density, solids concentration, alcohol, and total flavonoid content (TFC) were determined. Colloidal SiO_2 (Tixosil® 333) at a ratio extract:adjuvant of 1:0.8 (dry basis) was thoroughly mixed with the concentrated extractive solution and submitted to drying in a benchtop Lab-Plant SD-05 spray dryer. The SD variables were the inlet gas temperature (T_{in} = 80 and 150°C), the ratio of the mass feed flow rate of the concentrated extract to the water evaporation capacity of the dryer ($\dot{m}_{feed}/\dot{m}_{max}$ = 15, 45, 75, and 100%), and the feed flow rate of the drying gas ($\dot{m}_{air}$ = 0.0118, 0.0168, and 0.0227 kg/s). The feed flow rate of the atomising air ($\dot{V}_{at}$) was fixed at 15 L/min at a pressure (P_{at}) of 100. kPa. Data of water evaporation capacity of the SD was reported by Souza and Oliveira [84]. The results obtained confirm the significant impact of the drying conditions on product properties and dryer performance during the production of standardised dried extract of *Bf*. In general, the drying conditions that give an end product with the desired specification are not linked with the best dryer performance. Therefore, during optimisation of processing conditions for the production of SD extracts of medicinal plants, the product quality and system behaviour should be taken into account simultaneously.

Oliveira et al. [85] evaluated the production of SD extracts of leaves of three Brazilian medicinal plants, namely *Passiflora alata* (*Pa*), *Maytenus ilicifolia* (*Mi*), and *Bf*. The drying runs were carried out in the spray dryer SD-05 Lab-Plant using similar drying conditions for the three plant species (T_{in} = 150°C, $\dot{m}_{feed}/\dot{m}_{max}$ = 15 %, and $\dot{m}_{air}$ = 0.0227 kg/s, $\dot{V}_{at}$ = 15 L/min at P_{at} of 100 kPa). Colloidal SiO_2 (Tixosil 333) at concentrations of 40% for *Pa* and *Mi* and 80% for *Bf* (dry basis) was used as drying adjuvant. Processing conditions were efficient for producing dry leaf extracts of *Pa*, *Bf*, and *Mi*. The yields of the dried powders for *Pa* and *Mi* were around 70% and only 62.5% for *Bf* (even using higher amount of the drying adjuvant). These results were attributed to the differences in the chemical constituents of the extractive solutions. A good-quality powder product, with low moisture content (≤4.6%) and relatively small degradations of the TFC (8.7% w/w for *Pa* and 13.6% w/w for *Bf*), and total tannins (3.2% w/w for *Mi*) were generated. The particle sizes have a polydisperse distribution (~3.0 to 23.0 μm), with average diameters around 13.0 μm, and were almost independent of the properties of the feed composition. The authors compared the experimental data with those obtained by SBD and found similar results, but with negligible marker compound degradation. This result was related to the differences in the drying mechanism of the drying systems.

Gallo et al. [86] compared the process yield and product properties during SD of extracts from various medicinal plants, namely *Rhamnus purshiana* (bark—maceration and percolation), *Hamamelis virginiana* L. (leaves—decoction), *Peumus boldus* Mol. (leaves—infusion), *Centella Asiatica* L. (aerial parts—infusion), *Valeriana officinalis* L. (rhizomes, roots, and stolons—infusion), *Hypericum perforatum* L. (aerial parts—infusion), and *Cynara scolymus* L. (leaves—infusion). Colloidal SiO_2 (Aerosil® 200 at a ratio of 1:1, dry base) was used as drying adjuvant for all extractive solutions. The extracts were dried in a Büchi B-290 benchtop SD, using the same SD operating conditions for all extractive solutions (T_{in} = 130°C, $\dot{V}_{at}$ = 400 L/h), feed flow rate of the extract's compositions, $\dot{V}_{feed}$ = 3 mL/min, and gas flow rate of the drying air $\dot{V}_g$ = 35–38 m^3/h. The unique SD operating conditions allowed the production of dry extracts of distinct medicinal herbs, with good flow and compaction properties. The characterisation of the different SD extracts and their produced compacts revealed the effect of the herbs' chemical nature on the products' physical behaviour. The influence of composition on dry extract physical and chemical properties, such as particle size and morphology, loss on drying, hygroscopicity, and flow properties, was negligible.

On the other hand, the process yields and some powder and compact properties (e.g. glass transition temperature, particle and bulk densities, powder composition, compact porosity, wetting and disintegration times) evidenced differences among the tested SD extracts. Process yields ranged from 46 to 94%. The lower values were exhibited by the *P. boldus* and *C. Asiatica*, which was attributed to sticky problems, perhaps caused by the inherent differences of the chemical constituents.

In general, the product properties are strongly affected by the drying systems, as can be seen in the comparative study of the processes performance and the product properties during the manufacture of *Rosmarinus officinalis*–dried extracts by SD and SBD [54]. The extractive solution was prepared by dynamic maceration using ethanol at 70% v/v as solvent, extraction time of 1 hour, extraction temperature of 50°C, and a plant-to-solvent mass ratio of 0.2. Colloidal SiO_2 (Tixosil 333) and maltodextrin DE 14 blends, at concentrations of 40 and 20% w/w of the extract (dry basis) were the drying adjuvants. The product was characterised by determining the loss on drying, size distribution, morphology, flow properties, and concentration and degradation of the total polyphenol (TPC) and TFC contents. The SD and SBD performance were assessed by estimating thermal efficiency, product accumulation, and product recovery. The drying conditions studied were T_{in} = 80 and 150°C, $\dot{m}_{feed}/\dot{m}_{max}$ = 15, 45, and 75%, $\dot{m}_{air}$ = 0.0340 kg/s—SBD and 0.0118—SD, $\dot{V}_{at}$ = 20 L/min at P_{at} of 196.1 kPa. The SB was loaded with 14.0 cm of concave-cylinder Teflon beads with a mean diameter of 5.45 mm (inert bodies). Data of water evaporation capacity of the SD and SBD were presented by Souza and Oliveira [84, 87]. Both processes generated irregular, polydisperse and agglomerated particles with average diameters ranging from 7 to 22 μm. The powdered *R. officinalis* extracts did not present good flow properties, exhibiting high Hausner ratios and compressibility indices, indicating a cohesive or fairly free-flowing tendency and poor compression characteristics. Higher losses of TPC (45–53%) and TFC (13.1–49.9%) were observed for both the SD- and the SBD-dried extract. In general, the TFC degradation ratio tended to increase with $\dot{m}_{feed}/\dot{m}_{max}$ and T_{in}. The increase in T_{in} resulted in a reduction of TPC. Under the conditions studied, it was concluded that the performance of the SD and SBD of *rosemary* extract was poor, and both processes and the compositions of the feed need be improved significantly to be industrially feasible.

On the other hand, some authors report the successful production of SD-dried extracts of *R. officinalis* without the addition of drying adjuvants [88, 89]. Couto and coworkers [88] evaluated the effects of processing factors on the chemical marker contents and *in vitro* antioxidant activities of SD rosemary extracts using the design of experiments (DoE). The extractive solution was prepared by percolation using ethanol:water solution (80:20 v/v) as solvent system. The extractive solution was concentrated until it reaches a solid content of 9.66% ± 0.07 (% w/w) before submission to SD. The drying runs were carried out in a bench-top SD (MSD 1.0; Labmaq do Brasil Ltda., Ribeirão Preto, SP, Brazil), with a concurrent flow regime and a two-fluid spray nozzle with an inlet orifice diameter of 1.2 mm. The authors evaluate the effects of $\dot{V}_{feed}$ = 2, 4, and 6 mL/min; T_{in} = 80, 110, and 140°C, and of $\dot{V}_{at}$ = 30, 40, and 50 L/min, while the other set of factors was kept constant: P_{at} = 4.0 bar, the total mass of extract fed to the dryer 300 g, and $\dot{V}_g$ = 1.0 m^3/min. The results showed that the product exhibited antioxidant with IC_{50} (concentration needed to reduce the DPPH radical in 50%) ranging from 17.6 to 24.8 μg/mL, even with the dry products losing some of their polyphenols. All factors studied showed significant effects on most of the quality parameters analysed (e.g. concentration of the marker contents and antioxidant activity [AA]). The best combination of processing conditions to produce dry rosemary extracts with good physicochemical and functional properties proposed by the authors was extract feed rate of 6 mL/min, drying air inlet temperature of 140°C, and an atomiser airflow rate of 50 L/min.

The experimental results of the physicochemical properties of the dried extracts (moisture content, water activity, Hausner Ratio, Carr's Index, angle of repose, and the mean powder particles size) and of the process yield (powder recovery) were then submitted to statistical analyses to determine the significant effects of the processing factors [89]. The process yield ranged from 17.1 to 74.96%, and the product moisture content and water activity were below 5 and 0.5, respectively. The inlet temperature of the drying air (T_{in}) was recognised as the main factor affecting the product properties. Low levels of moisture content and water activity was associated with high process yield. In contrast, a low level of $\dot{V}_{feed}$ (2 mL/min), and of T_{in} (80°C), and an intermediate value of $\dot{V}_{at}$ (40 L/min) are required to form a product with the flowability and compression properties adequate for pharmaceutical applications [89]. However, the proposed conditions differs significantly from those reported in previous work [88], although distinct aspects were analysed.

The comparison of the results of Couto et al. [88] with those reported by Souza and coworkers [54] shows some disagreements, mainly concerning the need for drying adjuvants to engineer SD *R. officinalis* extracts with acceptable quality and good dryer performance. The conflicting results reported by the distinct research groups can be linked, for example, to the different sources of the herbal material, extraction methods, and solvent system used (1 = Ribeirão Preto/SP, dynamic maceration, ethanol:water at 70% v/v at 50°C [54], and 2 = Goiania/GO-Brazil, percolation, ethanol:water at 80:20 v/v at room temperature [88]). Different processes and extraction conditions may produce extracts with distinct composition and other properties which, certainly, will behave differently during the SD. These results reinforce the importance of the experimental studies for the development of high-quality standardised dry plant extracts.

De Paula et al. [90] evaluated three distinct drying adjuvants, namely colloidal SiO_2 pure and its blend with MCC and β-CD at 1:1 ratio during the production of SD extracts of *Achyrocline satureioides* (Marcela). The extractive solution was prepared by maceration of 7.5% inflorescences (w/v) in ethanol 80% (v/v). Twenty percent of the polysorbate 80 and 80% of the drying adjuvants (relative to extract solid contents) were placed to 80 mL of water and maintained under magnetic stirring. Then, 100 g of extractive solution was added to the drying adjuvants mixture. The resulting formulations were concentrated under reduced pressure at a temperature lower than 50°C until 40% of the initial mass of the extractive solution. The mass of the concentrated extracts was completed to 50 g with distilled water and SD in a Büchi 190 mini SD at a $\dot{V}_{feed}$ of 3.0 mL/min, and T_{in} and T_{out} of 150–160°C and 95–96°C, respectively. The powdered extracts were incorporated in an ointment base. The spreadability, oiliness index, viscosity, and pH of the ointments were determined to evaluate the effects of drying adjuvants on them. Although all compositions evaluated maintained their plastic behaviour, the drying adjuvants showed effects on the physical parameters at different levels. The use of colloidal SiO_2 alone promoted a small oiliness index and an intermediary spreadability. The substitution of part of the colloidal SiO_2 by MCC or β-CD increased the oiliness index and improved the ointment spreadability.

GA and Aerosil 200 were evaluated as drying adjuvants during SD extracts of *Fraxinus excelsior* [91]. The liquid extracts were obtained by steeping 570 g of dried leaves in 10 L of boiling water (E1) or 710 g of dried leaves in 10 L of boiling 70% ethyl alcohol (E2) for 1 h, followed by filtration. The aqueous extract was SD with 88 g (dry weight) of GA and the hydroethanolic extract with 80 g (dry weight) of Aerosil 200. SD was carried out in a Niro Atomiser (type Minor), with turbine drive and countercurrent flow regime at T_{in} of 130–140°C and T_{out} of 65–70°C. The physicochemical, organoleptic, and pharmacological properties of the dry extracts qualified them for medicinal preparations. The product obtained from the hydroalcoholic extract appeared to be superior compared to that originated from the aqueous extract. Thin-layer chromatograms showed no effect of the SD on marker compounds compared to the extractive solutions. The addition of drying adjuvants improved the product shelf life.

Cortés-Rojas and Oliveira [52] investigated the drying aid's effects on system performance, and the physicochemical properties of *Bidens pilosa*'s SD extracts. Extracts were prepared using dynamic maceration at optimised extraction conditions, namely extraction temperature of 66.2°C, ethanol:water at 62.7% (v/v), plant-to-solvent ratio of 1:10 (w/v), and extraction time of 30 min [92]. The extractive solution was filtered and concentrated by rotary evaporation until a dry residue of 8.4% w/w. The drying adjuvants used were β-CD, colloidal SiO_2 (Aerosil 200), and blends of Aerosil 200 with MCC or MD DE10 at a ratio of 1:3. The ratio between the extract and the drying adjuvants was maintained at 1:1 (dry basis). The final solid content of the drying compositions was set to 16.7% w/w, except for the composition containing Aerosil 200. Solid concentrations higher than 13% resulted in a thick, paste-like material difficult to atomise, when Aerosil 200 was used as drying adjuvant. The SD runs were carried out in Lab-Plant SD-05 equipment at preset operating conditions: T_{in} of 150°C, $\dot{m}_{feed}$ of 240 g/h (≈15% of SD evaporative capacity), $\dot{V}_g$ of 60 m^3/h, P_{at} and $\dot{V}_{at}$ of 196.1 kPa and 15. L/min, respectively. The physical–chemical properties and the content of the marker compounds (rutin, hyperoside, 4,5-Dicafeoylquinic acid, and an isolated polyacetylene compound) of the dry extracts, as well as the dryer performance, were affected by the adjuvants used. The dry extract containing Aerosil 200 showed better flow properties. However, the lowest degradation of total flavonoids (8.6%) and the highest concentration of marker compounds have been obtained using β-CD as the drying adjuvant, which generates a product with good solubility and with the water activity below 0.5. The mixture of Aerosil 200 with MCC generates a powder with a higher average particle size (34.0 ± 35.3), with the better SD process yield (~87%).

Fernandes et al. [93] analyzed the effects of pure β-CD, and of mixtures of the drying adjuvants MD DE10, Aerosil 200, and GA (Encapsia®) on the AA of SD extracts of *Psidium guajava* leaves. The extractive solution of *P. guajava* leaves was obtained by dynamic maceration, using ethanol:water at 70% v/v and plant/solvent ratio of 1:10 (w/v), maintained under constant stirring for 60 min at 50°C. The extractive solution was concentrated in a rotary evaporator until it reaches 12% w/w of solids content. The concentrated extract was submitted to SD in the presence of the drying adjuvants: MD DE10:Aerosil—ratio 7:1, MD DE10:Encapsia:Aerosil—ratio 5:2:1, or pure β-CD, at a proportion of 8% (wet base). SD runs were carried out in Lab-Plant SD-05 equipment at preset operating conditions: T_{in} of 150°C, $\dot{m}_{feed}$ of 240 g/h, $\dot{V}_g$ of 60 m^3/h, P_{at} and $\dot{V}_{at}$ of 147.1 kPa and 15 L/min, respectively. SD extracts with high TPC and TFC were generated at processing conditions used, with slight differences caused by the drying adjuvants employed. The antioxidant activities of the concentrated extract and SD powders were assessed by four antioxidant assays, namely the

2,2-Diphenyl-1-picrylhydrazyl [DPPH] radical scavenging, 2,2'-azinobis (3-ethylb enzthiazoline-6-sulfonic acid) [ABTS] radical scavenging, ferric reducing antioxidant power (FRAP), and oxygen radical absorption capacity (ORAC). SD powders exhibited strong AA showing IC_{50} from 7.96 to 9.76 μg/mL—DPPH method; 3,125.1–3,406.0 μM Trolox Equivalent (TE)/g dry weight—ABTS method; 4,210–4,540 μM FeSO4 E/g—FRAP method; and from 1,820 to 2,020 μM TE/g—ORAC method. The drying adjuvants did not cause significant influence on the AA of the SD extracts, regardless of the antioxidant assay used. The AA of the concentrated and SD extracts of *P. guajava* was similar to that exhibited by commercial synthetic antioxidants (e.g. BHT). Therefore, the SD extracts of *P. guajava* have a high potential to be used as a natural antioxidant for food, pharmaceutical, and cosmeceutical products.

An interesting study of the influence of different drying adjuvants on antimalarial activity of SD extracts of *B. pilosa* roots was reported by Cortés-Rojas et al. [77]. *B. pilosa* root extract was produced by dynamic maceration at optimum conditions determined previously [92]. The adjuvants used were a mixture of colloidal SiO_2 (Aerosil 200) and MCC (MCC-102) at a ratio 13:37 and pure β-CD. The relation between the concentrated extract and Aerosil 200:MCC-102 was 2:1 and 1:1 for β-CD (dry basis). The compositions were concentrated until a solid content of 11.4% w/w submitted to SD at previously optimised conditions [94]. A lyophilised sample of the crude extractive composition (without adjuvants) was also prepared and used as a control in the biological assays. The qualitative HPLC profiles of the SD *B. pilosa* extracts did not evidence degradation of the extract constituents. The dry SD products have a moisture content of 5.6 ± 0.4 and 6.4 ± 0.1% w/w, and water activity of 0.2524 ± 0.0133 and 0.2353 ± 0.004, respectively, for products with Aerosil 200:MCC-102 and β-CD. The TPC and TFC of the SD *B. pilosa* extracts were lower than those for the lyophilised control sample (dilution effect). The SD *B. pilosa* extracts showed enhanced antimalarial activity (*in vivo* tests) compared to the lyophilised, inhibiting up to 71% of the growth of the parasite *Plasmodium berghei* (in infected mice) even at the lowest tested dose. The dry extracts did not show any signs of toxicity (*in vitro* and *in vivo* assays—OECD 425 and MTT protocols) at the concentrations assayed [95]. The authors concluded that the dry root extract of *B. pilosa* co-SD with the selected drying adjuvants can stabilise the bioactive compounds and enhance their antimalarial activity compared to the control sample.

There are many other examples of SD herbal extracts from various plant species. A brief review of some other studies is shown in Table 5.1 [55, 68, 96–99].

5.4.2 Freeze-Drying

FD is also known as lyophilisation or cryodesiccation. It occurs under very specific conditions, below the triple point of a substance, conditions in which the direct passage of the water from the solid phase to the gas phase occurs (sublimation). This point can be easily determined in a pressure–temperature phase diagram, being the temperature and pressure conditions where the solid, liquid, and vapour phases coexist in thermodynamic equilibrium. The triple point occurs at a temperature of 273.16 K (0.01°C) and a pressure of 610.62 Pa (4.58 torr) for water. The lyophilisation cycle involves freezing the material at low temperatures and reducing the pressure

TABLE 5.1
Brief Overview of Some Other Studies Reported in the Scientific Literature on Spray Drying of Plant Extracts

Plant Extract	Spray Drying Parameters	Drying Carriers	Main Findings	Ref.
Glycine max (beans)	**Lab-Plant SD-05** T_{in} = 80, 115, and 150°C; $\dot{m}_{feed}$= 240 g/h $\dot{m}_{air}$ = 0.0227 kg/s $\dot{V}_{at}$ = 0.90 m³/h P_{at} = 1 bar C_s = 25.0% w/w	Colloidal SiO_2 (Tixosil 333®), MD DE 10, and starch, 2.5% relative to the solids content in the extract.	The drying adjuvant shown significant impact on spray-dried soybean extract properties. The product with colloidal SiO_2 showed high contents of polyphenol and genistein, and antioxidant activity. The chemical and antioxidant activities of spray-dried product showed to be affected by the drying temperature. It was observed high losses of TPC (67%) and genistein (75%) during spray drying.	[55]
Salvia miltiorrhiza (radix)	**Büchi B-290 mini-SD** T_{in} = 70, 80, and 90°C T_{out} = 44–62°C $\dot{V}_{feed}$ = 3.0, 3.5, and 4.0 mL/min	Gelatin and sodium salt of carboxy-methyl-cellulose at different proportions. Relation between core and wall material varied from 1/2 to 1/6.	The spray-dried microcapsules had a regular spherical shape, but the majority presented rough surfaces or invaginations with a diameter of 2–5 μm. Roots of *S. miltiorrhiza* nanoparticles were embedded in the wall system consisting of gelatin and CMC-Na. Higher encapsulation yield and encapsulation efficiency were obtained under T_{in} of 80°C and the ratio between core:wall material of 1/4. *S. miltiorrhiza* microcapsules could regulate the release of bioactive compounds.	[97]
Ananas comosus (stem)	**Lab-Plant SD-05** T_{in} = 70, 110, and 150°C $\dot{m}_{feed}/\dot{m}_{max}$ = 24, 36, and 48% $\dot{m}_{air}$ = 0.0227 kg/s P_{at} = 2 kgf/cm² $\dot{V}_{at}$ = 1.20 m³/h C_s = 11.46% w/w	MD (DE14) at proportions of 60 to 100% relative to solids content in the extract of *A. comosus* stem.	Significant effects of the processing parameters on the retention of the proteolytic activity of the SD extracts were observed. High drying temperatures reduced the product moisture content, particle size, and agglomerating tendency. A product with insignificant losses of the proteolytic activity (≈ 10%) and low moisture content (less than 6.5%) was engineered at selected drying conditions.	[98]

(Continued)

TABLE 5.1 ***(Continued)***
Brief Overview of Some Other Studies Reported in the Scientific Literature on Spray Drying of Plant Extracts

Plant Extract	Spray Drying Parameters	Drying Carriers	Main Findings	Ref.
Lippia sidoides (aerial parts)	**Lab-Plant SD-05** T_{in} = 140–160°C P_{at} = 5 kgf/cm^2 $\dot{V}_{feed}$ = 240 mL/h C_s = 20% w/w T_{feed} = 50°C	MD DE10 and GA in different proportions (4:1, 3:2, 2:3, 0:1) (w/w)	SD products show average particle sizes from 7.8 to 10.6 µm, regular and spherical morphology and moisture content between 7.8 and 9.4%, and thymol retentions from 70.2 to 84.2% (in relation to liquid extract). Thymol retention tended to the increase of GA ratio. *L. sidoides* extractive solutions and SD extracts showed antifungal activity against fungal strains of *Candida albicans*—ATCC 64548, *Candida glabrata*—ATCC 90030, *Candida krusei*—ATCC 6258, and *Candida parapsilosis*—ATCC 22019), evidencing their potential as a natural antifungal agent for medicinal, food, and cosmeceutical purposes.	[96]
Cymbopogon citratus	**Lab-Plant SD-06** T_{in} = 150°C T_{out} = 107°C P_{at} = 2 kgf/cm^2 $\dot{V}_{feed}$ = 240 mL/h C_s = 7.32% w/w $\dot{m}_{air}$ = 0.0227 kg/s P_{at} = 2 kgf/cm^2 $\dot{V}_{at}$ = 0.90 m^3/h	GA, MD, or MD:GA (7:3). The relation between the extract and drying adjuvants was maintained at 3:1 (dry basis).	SD product with GA has higher loose density, although the differences did not show statistical significance. SD GA powder product also shown a slightly higher moisture content, followed by the MD and MD: GA mixture. The authors associated these differences with the product hygroscopicity. "Differences in the encapsulation efficiency of volatile constituents by the different carrier systems studied may had affected these results, since actually the authors determine the Loss on drying, instead of the real moisture content value". The powdered product MD exhibited the highest aqueous solubility, followed by the mixture MD: GA and pure GA, which was attributed to differences in the physicochemical properties of SD powders, such as moisture content, particle microstructure, particle size, and so on. The carrier systems caused slight differences in the concentrations of TPC, TFC, and AA of the SD powder, and the authors suggest MD as the best carrier for the production of dry leaf extract of *C. citratus*.	[68]

(Continued)

TABLE 5.1 ***(Continued)***
Brief Overview of Some Other Studies Reported in the Scientific Literature on Spray Drying of Plant Extracts

Plant Extract	Spray Drying Parameters	Drying Carriers	Main Findings	Ref.
Euphorbia hirta L. (whole plant without roots)	**Lab-Plant SD-06** T_{in} = 180°C $\dot{V}_{feed}$ = pump set at 15 rpm C_s = ~27.3% w/w Other conditions not informed	Aqueous solution of MD at 20%. The relation evaporated ethyl acetate fraction of *E. hirta* L. extract:MD solution was 1:10.	The SD product shows higher contents of TPF and TFC, compared to the values of the crude extract, and the petroleum ether, and chloroform fractions. The dried extract showed moisture content, bulk density, colour characteristics, solubility, and hygroscopicity of 4.9567 ± 0.00577%, w/w 0.3715 ± 0.01286 g/mL, 3.7367 ± 0.1424 Hue, 95.83 ± 1.44 % w/w, and 9.9890 ± 1.4538 g H_2O/100 g, respectively. The effects of the dried extract on Diabetes Mellitus parameters were evaluated. The results show that the spray-dried powder inhibited 51.19% α-amylase at 10 mg/mL and reduced 51% in fast blood glucose after 4-h treatment. The administration of SD powder for 15 days significantly lowered the fast blood glucose level in streptozotocin-diabetic mice by 23.32%, lower than the standard antidiabetic drug (acarbose—30.87%), plus higher than distilled water (control—16.89%). According to the authors, the results evidenced a potential antidiabetic activity of *E. hirta* L. SD powders developed.	[99]

around the sample at a very low level, making the frozen sample sublime in the gas phase. These conditions make lyophilisation an ideal drying method for perishable, thermosensitive, or easily oxidisable materials, including plant extracts. Physical and chemical degradation reactions, such as protein denaturation, oxidation, hydrolysis, enzymatic reactions, and losses of volatile compounds, are also minimised [51].

Dehydration during FD is slow and increases with pressure reduction, but there is a minimum value. It is also necessary to keep the temperature of the solvent collector at least 15–20°C below the solvent's freezing temperature [100]. Another disadvantage attributed to lyophilisation refers to the high costs for its implementation, operation, and maintenance. However, the high quality of the FD product seems to overcome the disadvantages of high costs and long processing times.

The FD operation occurs in three stages. The freezing of the material is a decisive step for the quality of the lyophilised product since the freezing speed defines the pore distribution, sizes, and connectivity between them. The second stage, also known as primary drying, occurs at low temperatures under a vacuum and involves removing frozen water by sublimation. In the third stage, called secondary drying or desorption, the moisture is removed by evaporation of thawed water bind to the material structure at a higher temperature to increase the drying rate [51, 101].

Examples of products successfully FD include enzymes, proteins, microorganisms, antibiotics, vaccines and serums, herbal foods (e.g. coffee, tea, maple syrup), herbal extracts, and microcapsules. In many situations, the product quality may be unsatisfactory [102, 103]. Generally, stabilising and structuring agents are added to the initial liquid mixture to protect their constituents and generate a product with an elegant aspect and adequate solubility. These excipients can be classified by molecular weight (low, medium or high), by function in the composition (cryoprotectants, structuring agents, antioxidants, buffering agent) or material type. Saccharides (lactose, maltose, trehalose, sucrose), polysaccharides (cellulose, dextran), polyols (mannitol, sorbitol, xylitol), amino acids (glycine, histidine and arginine), surfactants, and salts are typical FD excipients [104, 105].

5.4.2.1 Freeze-Drying of Herbal Products

FD of herbal products is more common in research and development studies, but there are several examples of lyophilised plant-based products in the market [103, 106].

Abascal et al. [106] present a review on the FD effects and implications on the constituents of medicinal plants. The authors show that there is not enough information to conclude that FD causes some unforeseen and potentially significant effects in some classes of medicinal plant phytochemicals, such as changes in the concentrations of phenolics, carotenoids, and volatile substances. The authors emphasise the need for systematic research on the possible effects of FD on phytochemical profiles of herbal materials compared to other sample preparation methods, such as alcohol extractions from fresh plant material. These changes can affect the biological activity tests (pharmacological studies). Some information on the effects of drying methods, including FD, on some quality aspects of medicinal and aromatic plants is covered in Chapter 3.

The sample composition will affect the FD operation and the product quality for herbal extracts. Thus, experimental work is strongly needed to determine the lyophilisation conditions and properties of the initial composition (e.g. solids content, type, and concentration of stabilising agents), which generate lyophilised extracts with minimal phytochemical profiles variation and acceptable quality and shelf life. The lyophilisation conditions and initial composition properties must be set case to case due to the diversified chemical constitution of herbal materials.

The stabilising agents also have a significant impact on the product quality of FD products. Pudziuvelyte et al. [102] encapsulated ethanolic extract and the essential oil of *Elsholtzia ciliata* by FD. They evaluated six different stabilising agents: skim milk, sodium caseinate, gum Arabic, maltodextrin, β-maltodextrin, and resistant-maltodextrin, alone, in binary and quaternary mixtures (total concentration of 20% w/w). Ethanolic *E. ciliata* extract was prepared by the ultrasound-assisted extraction method and the essential oil by hydrodistillation. The authors determined the encapsulation efficiency of TPC and the physicochemical properties of the product. Results showed that the FD powders produced using binary mixtures have a lower moisture content and higher solubility, Carr index, and Hausner ratio than those produced with the adjuvant alone. The adjuvant systems also affected the microencapsulation efficiencies. The worst result (21.17%) was exhibited by maltodextrin, while the sodium caseinate showed the highest (83.02%). The results showed that FD is a suitable method for encapsulating *E. ciliata* ethanolic extract, generating dried products with high polyphenols content, depending on the properties of the type of adjuvant system used.

Pop et al. [107] evaluated three drying technologies (SD, fluid bed [FB], and FD) for encapsulation of bioactive constituents of watery extracts of leaves of Persian walnut (*Juglans regia*), European Mistletoe (*Viscum album*), and White willow bark (*Salix alba*) in natural agents. The extracts were prepared by maceration for 48 hours in water acidulated with HCl 1%. The concentration of the raw dried herbal material was maintained at 15% w/w. The extracts were filtered and mixed with three types of matrices (maltodextrin, lactose, and salt) added to plant extract at a ratio 10:90 and then submitted to drying at specific conditions (SD: T_{in} = 190°C, T_{out} = 45°C; FB: T_{in} = 80°C, T_{out} = 40°C; FD: –55°C, 0.12 mbar for 7 h—primary drying, and –5°C, 0.12 mbar for 3 hours—final drying). The physical and chemical properties of the dried extracts were influenced by the drying methods and adjuvant system used. For example, the best results were obtained by SD and FD for the willow extract, preferentially with lactose. Good retention of TPC was exhibited by nut extract produced by FB (with salt or lactose). For mistletoe extract, SD reached the highest retention of TPC (82%). Hence, it can be concluded that the adjuvants behaved according to the extract composition and drying method used, which also affects the physicochemical product properties. These findings justify the relevance of the experimental works in the development of FD extracts of suitable quality.

5.5 STABILITY TESTING

Evaluation of the stability of a pharmaceutical product is the final step of the development before it can be launched to the market. This evaluation is essential to guarantee the pharmaceutical product's safety, effectiveness, and quality until the shelf-life expiration. The stability testing is conducted under preset storage conditions according to the type of assay and climatic zone [108], with the product in the final recipient to be marketed. The minimum requirements of the stability testing should be conducted according to guidelines enforced by the health regulatory agencies of several countries, such as the EMA, the USFDA, and the Brazilian Health Surveillance Agency (ANVISA, Brazil). Most of the guidelines have been harmonised for the uniformisation of product registration in different countries. General recommendations have been proposed by International Conference on Harmonisation [109] and by the WHO [110].

Herbal-derived products (including the standardised dried extracts and phytomedicines) are prone to degradation, caused by variations in the storage temperature, time, humidity, light intensity, partial vapour pressure, and so on. Hence, stability testing for active phytopharmaceutical ingredients (APIs) or HMPs is mandatory to ensure the quality, safety, and efficacy of the finished product. The product's colour variation, consistency, moisture uptake, particle size and morphology, flow properties, crystalline state, thermal properties, solubility, water redispersion, solubility, wettability, the content of the marker compounds, presence of toxic artefacts, and microbiological assays must be monitored periodically. From the results, an expiration date can be proposed.

However, the stability evaluation for APIs/HMPs is more complicated than for regular pharmaceuticals. If the standardisation is based on the phytochemicals responsible for the biological activity, it is common to monitor their contents during the stability test. Nevertheless, this procedure may furnish disappointing results in most situations due to degradation or loss of extracts constituents present at very low concentrations, which may act in close synergy with the major constituents. In more complex scenarios, the whole herbal drug or herbal drug preparations (which may result from an herbal mixture) are regarded as active and may contain dozens of different substances. The appearance of new chemical entities (sometimes toxic), the increase of determined constituents, or degradations of marker compounds by different mechanisms may also occur during the stability testing of HMPs. Typical degradation pathways include hydrolysis, dehydrogenation, epoxidation, racemisation, double bond cleavage, allyl oxidations, and enzymatic browning (Maillard reactions). Sometimes they occurred without noticeable physical changes in the product [33, 111, 112].

The high temperature and the moisture uptake during the stability tests can also cause undesirable effects on the API/HMP's physical properties. Alteration of the crystalline state, thermal properties, colour, flow properties, solubility, wettability and redispersion capacity, and product caking are common. The caking is usually caused by the wetting of the particle surface, which causes plasticity and sometimes even the dissolution of substances present in that zone, causing an instantaneous agglomeration phenomenon, being more frequent with amorphous powders. Due to these considerations, it can be concluded that the stability testing of herbal-derived products is a very challenging task. Sometimes, it is appropriate to accomplish biological activity assays as a part of the stability testing protocol since biological activity may depend on various substances acting in synergism instead of only the major constituents [43, 47, 48].

Excellent works dealing with important quality attributes and instability testing guidelines for pharmaceutical products, some of which address HMPs, can be found in the literature [38, 112, 113–117].

5.6 CHALLENGES AND PROSPECTS

Although herbal medicines and herbal extracts are widely accepted as important therapeutic tools for treating various ailments, several challenges need to be overcome. The biological activity of phytochemicals depends on the amount administered and their bioavailability. However, in many cases, the bioactivity of an herbal product is drastically reduced or lost after oral use, caused by low solubility in aqueous or lipid systems, high molecular weight, or degradation during gastrointestinal transit. Thus, phytochemical pharmacokinetics and systemic bioavailability are usually not dose-dependent [118–121]. In practice, the theoretical dosages needed to produce the observed *in vitro* activity are often impractical due to acute toxicity problems [122]. Therefore, there is an urgent need to develop novel delivery systems for herbal products that protect, maintain the phytochemicals active, and deliver them to a specific physiological target [59]. Various technologies used for encapsulation of pharmaceuticals can be easily transferred to herbal products [123]. This research topic has high growth potential, allowing the development of innovative products for application in several industrial sectors, including the pharmaceutical, food, cosmetics, veterinary, and agroindustry. This subject is covered with more details in Chapters 7 and 8.

5.7 CONCLUDING REMARKS

Phytotechnology, also named as phytopharmaceutical technology or phytochemical technology can be defined as using science and engineering to produce innovative bioactive products from plants. These products have applications in several sectors, including pharmaceutical, cosmeceutical, food, chemical, veterinary, and agro-industrial. Noteworthy applications of medicinal and aromatic plants include the production of fine chemicals, herbal remedies, standardised phytoextracts, nutraceuticals, colourants, antioxidants, essential oils, fragrances, and pesticides.

The market and consumer demand for these products are significant and continue to grow steadily. This growth has been accompanied by a significant increase in quality control requirements. However, the technological development of herbal products is a multidisciplinary and multitasking subject, using know-how from different areas of knowledge. All processing steps must be done accurately, as the final product quality is dictated by the sum of the quality achieved in each processing step. Standardisation and optimisation of quality are key factors in developing high value-added products with reproducible batch-to-batch quality.

This chapter covered various topics and factors involved in standardising phytoextracts using drying technologies. Several processing factors that influence product quality are addressed, including obtaining a high-quality vegetable raw material (wildcrafting or cultivation), primary treatment and pre-processing operations, main unit operations, emphasising standardisation of phytoextracts by drying, stability tests, challenges, and prospects. All processing steps must be carried out sustainably with minimal environmental impact, from the supply chain of vegetable raw material to the product on the market, being a current exigence of consumers and regulatory agencies. Although the information presented here is more focused on herbal medicines, the processing steps are general and can be applied to prepare innovative products in various industrial sectors. Due to the complexity of the subject, the topics have not been thoroughly explored here. Readers with a greater interest in this fascinating subject are advised to consult the references and other chapters in the book.

ACKNOWLEDGEMENTS

I acknowledge all current and former researchers of LAPROFAR/USP Group (undergraduate and graduate students, post-doc researchers) and other collaborators, which direct or indirectly contributed to the development of this research subject. I also acknowledge the Foundation of the Research Support of the Sao Paulo State

(FAPESP), Brazilian National Council of the Research and Development (CNPq), and Coordination for the Improvement of Higher Education Personnel (CAPES), for the continuous financial aids and fellowships given along the years.

REFERENCES

1. Ditz, R.; Gerard, D.; Hagels, H. J.; Igl, N. Phytoextracts—Proposal towards a New Comprehensive Research Focus. *ProcessNet Subject Division Plant Based Extracts Products and Processes*; DECHEMA: Frankfurt, DE, 2017; p 33.
2. Vasisht, K.; Sharma, N.; Karan, M. Current Perspective in the International Trade of Medicinal Plants Material: An Update. *Curr. Pharm. Des.*, **2016**, *22* (27), 4288–4336.
3. Ekor, M.; Pistelli, L. The Growing Use of Herbal Medicines: Issues Relating to Adverse Reactions and Challenges in Monitoring Safety. *Front. Pharmacol.*, **2014**, 4, article 177.
4. Bandaranayake, W. M. Quality Control, Screening, Toxicity, and Regulation of Herbal Drugs. In Modern Phytomedicine: Turning Medicinal Plants into Drugs; I. Ahmad, I. Aqil, M. Owais, (Eds.); WILEY-VCH, Weinheim, DE, **2006**.
5. Sasidharan, S.; Chen, Y.; Saravanan, D.; Sundram, K. M.; Yoga Latha, L. Extraction, Isolation and Characterization of Bioactive Compounds from Plants' Extracts. *African J. Tradit. Complement. Altern. Med.*, **2011**, *8* (1), 1–10.
6. Calixto, J. B. Efficacy, Safety, Quality Control, Marketing and Regulatory Guidelines for Herbal Medicines (Phytotherapeutic Agents). *Brazilian J. Med. Biol. Res.*, **2000**, *33* (2), 179–189.
7. Alamgir, A. N. M. *Therapeutic Use of Medicinal Plants and Their Extracts: Volume 1: Pharmacognosy.* Springer International Publishing AG: Cham, Switzerland, **2017**, pp. 546.
8. Carvalho, A. C. B.; Perfeito, J. P. S.; Silva, L. V. C.; Ramalho, L. S.; Marques, R. F. de O.; Silveira, D. Regulation of Herbal Medicines in Brazil: Advances and Perspectives. *Brazilian J. Pharm. Sci.*, **2011**, *47* (3), 467–473.
9. Huang, Y.; Xiao, D.; Burton-Freeman, B. M.; Edirisinghe, I. *Chemical Changes of Bioactive Phytochemicals during Thermal Processing.* Reference Module in Food Science, Elsevier, 2016, 1–9.
10. Velu, G.; Palanichamy, V.; Rajan, A. P. Phytochemical and Pharmacological Importance of Plant Secondary Metabolites in Modern Medicine. In *Bioorganic Phase in Natural Food: An Overview*; S. Mohana Roopan, G. Madhumitha (Eds.); Springer International Publishing AG: Cham, Switzerland, **2018**; pp 135–156.
11. Cacace, J. E.; Mazza, G. Pressurized Low Polarity Water Extraction of Biologically Active Compounds from Plant Products. In *Functional Food Ingredients and Nutraceuticals: Processing Technologies.* J. Shi (Ed); 2nd Ed., CRC Press: Boca Raton, FL, **2015**; pp. 177–198.
12. Boeing, H.; Bechthold, A.; Bub, A.; Ellinger, S.; Haller, D.; Kroke, A.; Leschik-Bonnet, E.; Müller, M. J.; Oberritter, H.; Schulze, M.; et al. Critical Review: Vegetables and Fruit in the Prevention of Chronic Diseases. *Eur. J. Nutr.*, **2012**, *51* (6), 637–663.
13. Surh, Y. J. Cancer Chemoprevention with Dietary Phytochemicals. *Nat. Rev. Cancer*, **2003**, *3* (10), 768–780.
14. Wink, M. Plant Secondary Metabolites Modulate Insect Behavior-Steps toward Addiction? *Front. Physiol.*, **2018**, *9*, 1–9.
15. Simões, C. M. O.; Schenkel, E. P.; Mello, J. C. P.; Mentz, L. *Farmacognosia—Do Produto Natural Ao Medicamento*; Artmed: Porto Alegre, Brazil, **2017**.
16. Crozier, A.; Clifford, M. N.; Ashihara, H. *Plant Secondary Metabolites*; Blackwell Publishing Ltd: Oxford, 2006.
17. Liebelt, D. J.; Jordan, J. T.; Doherty, C. J. Only a Matter of Time: The Impact of Daily and Seasonal Rhythms on Phytochemicals. *Phytochem. Rev.*, **2019**, *18* (6), 1409–1433.

18. Gobbo-Neto, L.; Lopes, N. P. Plantas Medicinais: Fatores de Influência No Conteúdo de Metabólitos Secundários. *Quim. Nova*, **2007**, *30* (2), 374–381.
19. Mohiuddin, A. Effect of Environment on Secondary Metabolism of Medicinal Plants. *Open Access J. Environ. Soil Sci.*, **2019**, *2* (1), 145–155.
20. Sayhan, H.; Beyaz, S. G.; Çeliktaş, A. The Local Anesthetic and Pain Relief Activity of Alkaloids. In *Alkaloids—Alternatives in Synthesis, Modification and Application*, A. Pavlov, V. Georgiev (Eds)., IntechOpen, **2017**; p. 57–84.
21. Górniak, I.; Bartoszewski, R.; Króliczewski, J. Comprehensive Review of Antimicrobial Activities of Plant Flavonoids. *Phytochem. Rev.*, **2019**, 18 (1), 241–272.
22. Proshkina, E.; Plyusnin, S.; Babak, T.; Lashmanova, E.; Maganova, F.; Koval, L.; Platonova, E.; Shaposhnikov, M.; Moskalev, A. Terpenoids as Potential Geroprotectors. *Antioxidants*, **2020**, *9* (6), 529.
23. Bolzani, V. da S.; Valli, M.; Pivatto, M.; Viegas, C. Natural Products from Brazilian Biodiversity as a Source of New Models for Medicinal Chemistry. *Pure Appl. Chem.*, **2012**, *84* (9), 1837–1846.
24. Valli, M.; Bolzani, V. S. Natural Products: Perspectives and Challenges for Use of Brazilian Plant Species in the Bioeconomy. *An. Acad. Bras. Cienc.*, **2019**, *91* (suppl 3), e20190208.
25. Ginsburg, H.; Deharo, E. A Call for Using Natural Compounds in the Development of New Antimalarial Treatments—An Introduction. *Malar J.*, **2011**, *10*, S1.
26. Li, Y.; Zhang, G.; Pfeifer, B. A. Current and Emerging Options for Taxol Production. *Adv. Biochem. Eng. Biotechnol.*, **2015**, *148*, 405–425.
27. Neacsu, M.; Vaughan, N.; Raikos, V.; Multari, S.; Duncan, G. J.; Duthie, G. G.; Russell, W. R. Phytochemical Profile of Commercially Available Food Plant Powders: Their Potential Role in Healthier Food Reformulations. *Food Chem.*, **2015**, *179*, 159–169.
28. Souza, C. R. F. *Produção de Extratos Secos Padronizados de Plantas Medicinais Brasileiras: Estudo da Viabilidade Técnica e Econômica do Processo em Leito de Jorro*. PPGCF-FCFRP/USP: Ribeirão Preto, 2007; p. 219.
29. Toledo, A. C. O.; Hirata, L. L.; Buffon, M. C. M.; Miguel, M. D.; Miguel, O. G. Fitoterápicos: Uma Abordagem Farmacotécnica. *Lecta*, **2014**, *21*, 7–13.
30. WHO. WHO Guidelines for Selecting Marker Substances of Herbal. *WHO Tech. Rep. Ser. No. 1003*, **2017**, 71–86.
31. Kroll, U. Ã.; Cordes, C. Pharmaceutical Prerequisites for a Multi-Target Therapy. *Phytomedicine,* **2006**, *13*, 12–19.
32. Djordjevic, S. M. From Medicinal Plant Raw Material to Herbal Remedies. In *Aromatic and Medicinal Plants—Back to Nature*; H. El-Shemy (Ed.); BoD–Books on Demand, **2017**.
33. WHO. Quality Control Methods for Medicinal Plant Materials World Health Organization Geneva. *WHO*, 1998.
34. WHO. WHO Guidelines on Good Manufacturing Practices (GMP) for Herbal Medicines; WHO, **2007**.
35. WHO. WHO Guidelines on Good Agricultural and Collection Practices (GACP) for Medicinal Plants; *WHO*, **2003**.
36. Aziz, R. A.; Sarmidi, M. R.; Kumaresan, S.; Taher, Z. M.; Foo, D. C. Y. Phytochemical Processing: The Next Emerging Field in Chemical Engineering—Aspects and Opportunities. *J. Kejuruter. Kim. Malaysia*, **2003**, *3* (November 2014), 45–60.
37. Mosihuzzaman, M.; Choudhary, M. I. Protocols on safety, efficacy, standardization, and documentation of herbal medicine (IUPAC Technical Report). *Pure Appl. Chem.*, 2008, 80 (10), 2195–2230.
38. Bauer, R. Quality Criteria and Standardization of Phytopharmaceuticals: Can Acceptable Drug Standards Be Achieved? *Ther. Innov. Regul. Sci.*, **1997**, *32* (1), 101–110.

39. WHO. WHO Guidelines on Good Herbal Processing Practices for Herbal Medicines; **2018**.
40 Simoes, C. M. O.; Schenkel, E. P.; Gosmann, G.; Mello, J. C. P.; Mentz, L. A.; Petrovick, P. R. *Famacognosia, Da Planta Ao Medicamento*; 6th Ed.; UFSC/UFRGS: Porto Alegre, Brazil, **2007**; p. 1102.
41. WHO. WHO Guidelines on Good Manufacturing Practices (GMP) for Herbal Medicines—Annex 2. 2007, 153–177.
42. Müller, J.; Heindl, A. Drying of Medicinal Plants. In *Medicinal and Aromatic Plants*; R. J. Bogers, L. E. Craker, D. Lange (Eds.); Springer: Netherlands, 2006; pp 237–252.
43. Thamkaew, G.; Sjöholm, I.; Galindo, F. G. A Review of Drying Methods for Improving the Quality of Dried Herbs. *Crit. Rev. Food Sci. Nutr.*, **2020**, *61* (11), 1763–1786.
44. Chemat, F.; Abert Vian, M.; Fabiano-Tixier, A. S.; Nutrizio, M.; Režek Jambrak, A.; Munekata, P. E. S.; Lorenzo, J. M.; Barba, F. J.; Binello, A.; Cravotto, G. A Review of Sustainable and Intensified Techniques for Extraction of Food and Natural Products. *Green Chem.*, **2020**, *22* (8), 2325–2353.
45. Zhang, Q. W.; Lin, L. G.; Ye, W. C. Techniques for Extraction and Isolation of Natural Products: A Comprehensive Review. *Chin. Med.* , **2018**, 13 (1), 1–26.
46. Handa, S. S.; Khanuja, S. P. S.; Longo, G.; Rakesh, D. D. *Extraction Technologies for Medicinal and Aromatic Plants*; United Nations Industrial Development Organization and the International Centre for Science and High Technology: Trieste, 2008.
47. Azmir, J.; Zaidul, I. S. M.; Rahman, M. M.; Sharif, K. M.; Mohamed, A.; Sahena, F.; Jahurul, M. H. A.; Ghafoor, K.; Norulaini, N. A. N.; Omar, A. K. M. Techniques for Extraction of Bioactive Compounds from Plant Materials: A Review. *J. Food Eng.*, **2013**, *117* (4), 426–436.
48. Abubakar, A. R.; Haque, M. Preparation of Medicinal Plants: Basic Extraction and Fractionation Procedures for Experimental Purposes. *J. Pharm. Bioallied Sci.*, **2020**, 12 (1), 1–10.
49. Souza, C. R. F.; Bott, R. F.; Oliveira, W. P. Optimization of the Extraction of Flavonoids Compounds from Herbal Material Using Experimental Design and Multi-Response Analysis. *Lat. Am. J. Pharm.*, **2007**, *26* (5), 682–690.
50. Kemp, I. C. Drying of Pharmaceuticals in Theory and Practice. *Dry. Technol.*, **2017**, *35* (8), 918–924.
51. Oliveira, W.P.; Freitas, L. A. P.; Freire, J. T. Drying of Pharmaceutical Products. In *Transport Phenomena in Particulate Systems*; J. T. Freire, A. M. Silveira, M. C. Ferreira (Eds.); Bentham Science Publishers, Oak Park, IL, **2012**; pp 148–171.
52. Cortés-Rojas, D. F.; Oliveira, W. P. Physicochemical Properties of Phytopharmaceutical Preparations as Affected by Drying Methods and Carriers. *Dry. Technol.*, **2012**, *30* (9), 921–934.
53. Souza, C. R. F.; Oliveira, W. P. Spouted Bed Drying of *Bauhinia forficata* Link Extract: The Effects of Feed Atomizer Position and Operating Conditions on Equipment Performance and Product Properties. *Braz. J. Chem. Eng.*, **2005**, *22* (2), 239–247.
54. Souza, C. R. F.; Schiavetto, I. A.; Thomazini, F. C. F.; Oliveira, W. P. Processing of *Rosmarinus officinalis* Linne Extract on Spray and Spouted Bed Dryers. *Braz. J. Chem. Eng.*, **2008**, *25* (1), 59–69.
55. Georgetti, S. R.; Casagrande, R.; Souza, C. R. F.; Oliveira, W. P.; Fonseca, M. J. V. Spray Drying of the Soybean Extract: Effects on Chemical Properties and Antioxidant Activity. *LWT—Food Sci. Technol.*, **2008**, *41* (8), 1521–1527.
56. Benelli, L.; Oliveira, W. P. Fluidized Bed Coating of Inert Cores with a Lipid-Based System Loaded with a Polyphenol-Rich *Rosmarinus officinalis* Extract. *Food Bioprod. Process.*, **2019**, 114, 216-226.
57. Benelli, L.; Souza, C. R. F.; Oliveira, W. P. Quality Changes during Spouted Bed Drying of Pepper-Rosmarin Extract. *Can. J. Chem. Eng.*, **2013**, *91* (11), 1837–1846.

58. Souza, C. R. F.; Oliveira, W. P. Drying of Phytochemical Preparations in a Spouted Bed: Perspectives and Challenges. *Dry. Technol.*, **2012**, *30* (11–12), 1209–1226.
59. Çelic, M.; Wendel, S. Spray Drying and Pharmaceutical Applications. In *Handbook of Pharmaceutical Granulation Technology*; D. M. Parikh (Ed.); Informa Health Care USA, Inc.: New York, NY,, **2009;** pp 98–125.
60. Masters, K. *Spray Drying Handbook*, 5th Ed.; Longman Scientific & Technical. Wiley: New York, NY, 1991.
61. Santos, D.; Maurício, A. C.; Sencadas, V.; Santos, J. D.; Fernandes, M. H.; Gomes, P. S. Spray Drying: An Overview. In *Biomaterials—Physics and Chemistry—New Edition*; R. Pignatello, T. Musumeci (Eds.); InTech, 2018.
62. Vehring, R.; Foss, W. R.; Lechuga-Ballesteros, D. Particle Formation in Spray Drying. *J. Aerosol Sci.*, **2007**, *38* (7), 728–746.
63. Roos, Y. H. Importance of Glass Transition and Water Activity to Spray Drying and Stability of Dairy Powders. *Lait*, **2002**, *82* (4), 475–484.
64. Bhandari, B.; Hartel, R. Phase Transitions during Food Powder Production and Powder Stability. In *Encapsulated and Powdered Foods*; C. Onwulata (Ed.), CRC Press, Boca Raton, FL, **2005,** pp. 273–304.
65. Oliveira, O. W.; Petrovick, P. R. Secagem Por Aspersão (Spray Drying) de Extratos Vegetais: Bases e Aplicações. *Rev. Bras. Farmacogn.*, **2010**, *20* (4), 641–650.
66. Sollohub, K.; Cal, K. Spray Drying Technique: II. Current Applications in Pharmaceutical Technology. *J. Pharm. Sci.*, **2010**, *99* (2), 587–597.
67. Cortés-Rojas, D. F.; Souza, C. R. F.; Oliveira, W. P. Assessment of Stability of a Spray Dried Extract from the Medicinal Plant *Bidens pilosa* L. *J. King Saud Univ.—Eng. Sci.*, **2016**, *28* (2), 141–146.
68. Tran, T. T. A.; Nguyen, H. V. H. Effects of Spray-Drying Temperatures and Carriers on Physical and Antioxidant Properties of Lemongrass Leaf Extract Powder. *Beverages*, **2018**, *4* (4), 84.
69. Tengse, D. D.; Priya, B.; Kumar, P. A. R. Optimization for Encapsulation of Green Tea (*Camellia sinensis* L.) Extract by Spray Drying Technology. *J. Food Meas. Charact.*, **2017**, *11* (1), 85–92.
70. Fenoglio, D.; Soto Madrid, D.; Alarcón Moyano, J.; Ferrario, M.; Guerrero, S.; Matiacevich, S. Active Food Additive Based on Encapsulated Yerba Mate (*Ilex paraguariensis*) Extract: Effect of Drying Methods on the Oxidative Stability of a Real Food Matrix (Mayonnaise). *J. Food Sci. Technol.*, **2021**, 58 (4), 1574–1584.
71. Sampaio, R. C. A.; Costa, R. S.; Souza, C. R. F.; Duarte Júnior, A. P.; Ribeiro-Costa, R. M.; Costa, C. E. F.; Oliveira, W. P.; Converti, A.; Silva Júnior, J. O. C. Thermal Characterization of *Arrabidaea chica* (Humb. & Bonpl.) B. Verl. Dry Extracts Obtained by Spray Dryer. *J. Therm. Anal. Calorim.*, **2016**, *123* (3), 2469–2475.
72. Padukka, I.; Bhandari, B.; D'arcy, B. Evaluation of Various Extraction Methods of Encapsulated Oil from β-Cyclodextrin-Lemon Oil Complex Powder. *J. Food Compos. Anal.*, **2000**, 13 (1), 59–70.
73. Chu, K. K. W.; Chow, A. H. L. Impact of Carbohydrate Constituents on Moisture Sorption of Herbal Extracts. *Pharm. Res.*, **2000**, 17 (9), 1133–1137.
74. Teixeira, H. F. *Avaliação Da Influência de Adjuvantes Farmacêuticos Sobre as Características Físicas, Químicas, Tecnológicas e Farmacológicas de Extratos Secos Nebulizados de Achyrocline Satureioides*; PPGCF/UFRGS: Porto Alegre, **1996**.
75. Anandharamakrishnan, C.; Ishwarya, S. P. Selection of Wall Material for Encapsulation by Spray Drying. In *Spray Drying Techniques for Food Ingredient Encapsulation*; C. Anandharamakrishnan (Ed.); John Wiley & Sons, Ltd: Chichester, **2015**; pp 77–100.
76. Muzaffar, K.; Nayik, G. A.; Kumar, P. Stickiness Problem Associated with Spray Drying of Sugar and Acid Rich Foods: A Mini Review. *J. Nutr. Food Sci.*, **2015**, *s12*, 11–13.

77. Cortés-Rojas, D. F.; Medeiros, T. L.; Oliveira, C. B. S.; Meurer, Y. da S. R.; Andrade-Neto, V. F.; Oliveira, W. P. Antimalarial Activity of *Bidens pilosa* Root Extract Co-Spray Dried in Presence of β-Cyclodextrin or Aerosil®: Microcrystalline Cellulose Blend. *Planta Medica Int. Open*, **2021**, *8* (01), e1–e9.
78. Sheskey, P. J.; Hancock, B. C.; Moss, G. P.; Goldfarb, D. J. *Handbook of Pharmaceutical Excipients*, 9th Ed.; Pharmaceutical Press and American Pharmacists Association: London, **2020**, p. 1296.
79. Bott, R. F.; Labuza, T. P.; Oliveira, W. P. Stability Testing of Spray- and Spouted Bed–Dried Extracts of *Passiflora alata. Dry. Technol.*, **2010**, *28* (11), 1255–1265.
80. Gallo, L. C.; Bucalá, V.; Ramírez Rigo, M. V. R.; Piña, J. Herbal Medicine: Dry Extracts Production and Applications. In *Plant Extracts: Role in Agriculture, Health Effects and Medical Applications*; A. Giordano, A. Costs (Ed.); Nova Science Pub Inc., Hauppauge, NY, 2013.
81. Bankole, V. O.; Osungunna, M. O.; Souza, C. R. F.; Salvador, S. L.; Oliveira, W. P. Spray-Dried Proliposomes: An Innovative Method for Encapsulation of *Rosmarinus officinalis* L. Polyphenols. *AAPS PharmSciTech*, **2020**, *21* (5), 143.
82. Fernandes, L. P.; Oliveira, W. P.; Sztatisz, J.; Szilágyi, I. M.; Novák, C. Solid State Studies on Molecular Inclusions of *Lippia sidoides* Essential Oil Obtained by Spray Drying. *J. Therm. Anal. Calorim.*, **2009**, *95* (3), 855–863.
83. Souza, C. R. F.; Oliveira, W. P. Powder Properties and System Behavior during Spray Drying of *Bauhinia forficata* Link Extract. *Dry. Technol.*, **2006**, *24* (6), 735–749.
84. Souza, C. R. F.; Oliveira, W. P. Extratos Secos de *Bauhinia forficata* Link Obtidos por Spray Drying: Efeito de Parâmetros Operacionais na Degradação Térmica de Princípios Ativos e nas Propriedades Físicas do Produto. In *Anais do XV Congresso Brasileiro de Engenharia Química—COBEQ*; Curitiba, UFPR/ABEQ, 2004; pp 1–8 CD-Rom.
85. Oliveira, W. P.; Bott, R. F.; Souza, C. R. F. Manufacture of Standardized Dried Extracts from Medicinal Brazilian Plants. *Dry. Technol.*, **2006**, *24* (4), 523–533.
86. Gallo, L.; Ramírez-Rigo, M. V.; Piña, J.; Bucalá, V. A Comparative Study of Spray-Dried Medicinal Plant Aqueous Extracts. Drying Performance and Product Quality. *Chem. Eng. Res. Des.*, **2015**, *104*, 681–694.
87. Souza, C. R. F.; Oliveira, W. P. Comparative Study of the Evaporation Capacity of the Conventional and Jet Spouted Bed Dryers for Liquid Materials. In *13th International Drying Symposium*; Beijing, CN, 2002; pp 808–816.
88. Couto, R. O.; Conceição, E. C.; Chaul, L. T.; Oliveira, E. M. S.; Martins, F. S.; Bara, M. T. F.; Rezende, K. R.; Alves, S. F.; Paula, J. R. Spray-Dried Rosemary Extracts: Physicochemical and Antioxidant Properties. *Food Chem.*, **2012**, *131* (1), 99–105.
89. Chaul, L. T.; Conceição, E. C.; Bara, M. T. F.; Paula, J. R.; Couto, R. O. Engineering Spray-Dried Rosemary Extracts with Improved Physicomechanical Properties: A Design of Experiments Issue. *Braz. J. Pharmacogn.*, **2017**, *27* (2), 236–244.
90. De Paula, I. C.; González Ortega, G.; Bassani, V. L.; Petrovick, P. R. Development of Ointment Formulations Prepared with *Achyrocline satureioides* Spray-Dried Extracts. *Drug Dev. Ind. Pharm.*, **1998**, *24* (3), 235–241.
91. Casadebaig, J.; Jacob, M.; Cassanas, G.; Gaudy, D.; Baylac, G.; Puech, A. Physicochemical and Pharmacological Properties of Spray-Dried Powders from *Fraxinus excelsior* Leaf Extracts. *J. Ethnopharmacol.*, **1989**, *26* (2), 211–216.
92. Cortés-Rojas, D. F.; Souza, C. R. F.; Oliveira, W. P. Optimisation of the Extraction of Phenolic Compounds and Antioxidant Activity from Aerial Parts of *Bidens pilosa* L. Using Response Surface Methodology. *Int. J. Food Sci. Technol.*, **2011**, *46* (11), 2420–2427.
93. Fernandes, M. R. V.; Kabeya, L. M.; Souza, C. R. F.; Massarioli, A. P.; Alencar, S. M.; Oliveira, W. P. Antioxidant Activity of Spray-Dried Extracts of *Psidium guajava* Leaves. *J. Food Res.*, **2018**, *7* (4), 141–148.

94. Cortés-Rojas, D. F.; Souza, C. R. F.; Oliveira, W. P. Optimization of Spray Drying Conditions for Production of *Bidens pilosa* L. Dried Extract. *Chem. Eng. Res. Des.*, **2015**, *93*, 366–376.
95. OECD. *OECD Guidelines for the Testing of Chemicals, Section 4. Test No. 425: Acute Oral Toxicity—Up-and-Down Procedure*; OECD Publishing, Paris, **2001**; pp. 1–27. Available at: https://doi.org/10.1787/9789264071049-en
96. Fernandes, L. P.; Candido, R. C.; Oliveira, W. P. Spray Drying Microencapsulation of *Lippia sidoides* Extracts in Carbohydrate Blends. *Food Bioprod. Process.*, **2012**, *90* (3), 425–432.
97. Su, Y. L.; Fu, Z. Y.; Zhang, J. Y.; Wang, W. M.; Wang, H.; Wang, Y. C.; Zhang, Q. J. Microencapsulation of Radix *Salvia miltiorrhiza* Nanoparticles by Spray-Drying. *Powder Technol.*, **2008**, *184* (1), 114–121.
98. Cabral, A. C. S.; Said, S.; Oliveira, W. P. Retention of the Enzymatic Activity and Product Properties During Spray Drying of Pineapple Stem Extract in Presence of Maltodextrin. *Int. J. Food Prop.*, **2009**, *12* (3), 536–548.
99. Tran, N.; Tran, M.; Truong, H.; Le, L. Spray-Drying Microencapsulation of High Concentration of Bioactive Compounds Fragments from *Euphorbia hirta* L. Extract and Their Effect on Diabetes Mellitus. *Foods*, **2020**, *9* (7), 881.
100. Matejtschuk, P. Lyophilization of Proteins. *Methods in Mol. Biol. (Clifton,* NJ*)*, **2007**, *368*; 59–72.
101. Hua, T.; Liu, B.; Zhang, H. *Freeze-Drying of Pharmaceutical and Food Products*; Woodhead Pub. Ltd., Cambridge, 2010, p. 257.
102. Pudziuvelyte, L.; Marksa, M.; Sosnowska, K.; Winnicka, K.; Morkuniene, R.; Bernatoniene, J. Freeze-Drying Technique for Microencapsulation of *Elsholtzia ciliata* Ethanolic Extract Using Different Coating Materials. *Molecules*, **2020**, *25* (9), 2237.
103. Bhatta, S.; Janezic, T. S.; Ratti, C. Freeze-Drying of Plant-Based Foods. *Foods*, **2020**, *9* (1), 1–22.
104. Bjelošević, M.; Zvonar Pobirk, A.; Planinšek, O.; Ahlin Grabnar, P. Excipients in Freeze-Dried Biopharmaceuticals: Contributions toward Formulation Stability and Lyophilisation Cycle Optimisation. *Int. J. Pharm.*, **2020**, *576*, 119029.
105. Hua, T.-C.; Liu, B.-L.; Zhang, H. Protective Agents and Additives for Freeze-Drying of Pharmaceutical Products. In *Freeze-Drying of Pharmaceutical and Food Products*; Woodhead Pub. Ltd., Cambridge, 2010; pp 170–186.
106. Abascal, K.; Ganora, L.; Yarnell, E. The Effect of Freeze-Drying and Its Implications for Botanical Medicine: A Review. *Phyther. Res.*, **2005**, *19* (8), 655–660.
107. Pop, C.; Ranga, F. Ń.; Fetea, F.; Socaciu, C. Application of Three Alternative Technologies (Spray Drying, Fluid Bed Drying and Freeze Drying) to Obtain Powdered Formulas from Plants with Antimicrobial Potential. *Bull. Univ. Agric. Sci. Vet. Med. Cluj-Napoca—Anim. Sci. Biotechnol.*, **2013**, *70* (1), 95–103.
108. Bott, R. F.; Oliveira, W. P. Storage Conditions for Stability Testing of Pharmaceuticals in Hot and Humid Regions. *Drug Dev. Ind. Pharm.*, **2007**, *33* (4), 393–401.
109. ICH. ICH Q1A (R2) Stability Testing of New Drug Substances and Drug Products. *Curr. Step*, **2003**, 4, 1–24.
110. WHO. Annex 2 Stability Testing of Active Pharmaceutical Ingredients and Finished Pharmaceutical Products. *WHO Technical Report Series*, **2009**, 87–130.
111. Lund, M. N.; Ray, C. A. Control of Maillard Reactions in Foods: Strategies and Chemical Mechanisms. *J. Agric. Food Chem.*, **2017**, *65* (23), 4537–4552.
112. Thakur, L.; Ghodasra, U.; Patel, N.; Dabhi, M. Novel Approaches for Stability Improvement in Natural Medicines. *Pharmacogn. Rev.*, **2011**, *5* (9), 48–54.
113. Bhandari, B. R.; Howes, T. Implication of Glass Transition for the Drying and Stability of Dried Foods. *J. Food Eng.*, **1999**, *40* (1), 71–79.

114. Bansal, G.; Kaur, J.; Suthar, N.; Kaur, S.; Negi, R. S. Stability Testing Issues and Test Parameters for Herbal Medicinal Products. In *Methods for Stability Testing of Pharmaceuticals*; S. Bajaj, S. Singh (Eds.); Humana Press: New York, NY, **2018**; pp 307–333.
115. Gafner, S.; Bergeron, C. The Challenges of Chemical Stability Testing of Herbal Extracts in Finished Products Using State-of-the-Art Analytical Methodologies. *Curr. Pharm. Anal.*, **2005**, *1* (2), 203–215.
116. Bajaj, S.; Singla, D.; Sakhuja, N. Stability Testing of Pharmaceutical Products. *J. Appl. Pharm. Sci.* **2012**, *02* (03), 129–138.
117. Bhagyashree, P.; Karishma, G.; Sampada, A.; Ankita, P.; Pratibha, C.; Kailash, V. Recent Trends in Stability Testing of Pharmaceutical Products: A Review. *Res. J. Pharm. Biol. Chem. Sci.*, **2015**, *6* (1), 1557–1569.
118. Rodríguez, G. R. V.; Blancas-benítez, F. J.; Wall-medrano, A.; Sáyago-ayerdi, G.; González-aguilar, G. A. Bioaccessibility and Bioavailability of Phenolic Compounds from Tropical Fruits 8. 2 Bioaccessibility : First Barrier Prior to Absorption 8. 3 Bioavailability of Tropical Fruits Polyphenols. **2018**, *I*, 155–164.
119. Manach, C.; Scalbert, A.; Morand, C.; Rémésy, C.; Jiménez, L. Polyphenols: Food Sources and Bioavailability. *Am. J. Clin. Nutr.*, **2004**, *79* (5), 727–747.
120. Williamson, G.; Manach, C. Bioavailability and Bioefficacy of Polyphenols in Humans. II. Review of 93 Intervention Studies. *Am. J. Clin. Nutr.*, **2005**, 81 (1), 243S–255S.
121. Manach, C.; Williamson, G.; Morand, C.; Scalbert, A.; Rémésy, C. Bioavailability and Bioefficacy of Polyphenols in Humans. I. Review of 97 Bioavailability Studies. *Am. J. Clin. Nutr.*, **2005**, 81 (1), 230S–242S.
122. Holst, B.; Williamson, G. Nutrients and Phytochemicals: From Bioavailability to Bioefficacy beyond Antioxidants. *Curr. Opin. Biotechnol.*, **2008**, *19* (2), 73–82.
123. Fang, Z.; Bhandari, B. Encapsulation of Polyphenols—a Review. *Trends Food Sci. Technol.*, **2010**, *21* (10), 510–523.

6 Drying of Phytochemical Compositions by Spouted Bed

An Update[1]

Cláudia Regina Fernandes Souza and Wanderley Pereira Oliveira

CONTENTS

6.1 Introduction 142
6.2 General Aspects of Spouted Bed Technology 142
6.3 Spouted Bed Drying of Liquid Feeds: Technical Considerations 145
6.4 Stickiness Issues during Drying 146
  6.4.1 Typical Instability Issues during Spouted Bed Drying of Sticky Compositions 148
6.5 Spouted Bed Drying of Phytochemical Preparations 150
  6.5.1 Effects of Processing Conditions on Spouted Bed Behaviour and Product Properties 151
  6.5.2 Evaluation of Experimental Studies 151
6.6 Key Product Properties 162
  6.6.1 Loss on Drying and Water Activity 162
  6.6.2 Particle Size and Size Distribution 163
  6.6.3 Product Morphology 163
  6.6.4 Flow Properties 163
  6.6.5 X-Ray Diffraction 164
  6.6.6 Product Solubility 164
6.7 Product Stability during Storage 165
6.8 Concluding Remarks 165
Acknowledgements 166
Nomenclature 166
References 167

[1] This chapter is an update of the article published by Taylor & Francis Group in *Drying Technology* on 17 Aug 2012, available at: https://www.tandfonline.com/doi/full/10.1080/07373937.2012.692746 (Permission P112019-05/LDRT).

DOI: 10.1201/9781003225416-8

6.1 INTRODUCTION

Phytochemicals are secondary metabolites synthesised by plants and include the carotenoids, phenolics, alkaloids, terpenes, sterols, saponins, nitrogen-containing compounds, and organosulfur compounds [1, 2]. Secondary metabolites are organic substances not directly essential for normal plant life but can have some useful functions for the plant. Phenolics and carotenoids are the most studied phytochemicals and involve substances as phenolic acids, flavonoids, stilbenes, coumarins, tannins, lycopene, curcumin, β-carotene, and lutein. In addition, several phytochemicals can exhibit potent biological properties such as antioxidant, antimicrobial, anti-inflammatory, and anti-tumoral, promising to be exploited in the pharmaceutical, food, and cosmetics industries [3–5]. Examples of important industrial uses of phytochemicals include natural colourants (e.g. bixin, curcumin, anthocyanins, and betaine), natural antioxidants (e.g. carnosic acid, tea catechins, flavonoids, and chlorogenic acid), natural preservatives (e.g. thymol, carvacrol, and eugenol), and herbal medicines. In general, many dietary plants, including fruits, vegetables, beverages, herbs, and spices, are rich sources of bioactive compounds [6, 7].

The demand for herbal products has increased continuously, forcing the industry to develop standardised methods for their production to guarantee their quality, safety, and efficacy. Dry phytochemical preparations (or phytoextracts) are technologically viable for large-scale production due to greater physical, chemical, and microbiological stability as well as the possibility of standardising the major bioactive compounds. Standardised dried phytoextracts can be manufactured from the dehydration of concentrated extractive solutions from herbal materials (leaves, roots, seeds, fruit peels, bark, whole plant, inflorescence, fruits, and so on), resulting in a dried powder product. Dry extracts can be produced by several techniques, including freeze-drying, spray drying, and spouted bed (SB) drying [8–10].

The application of SB drying for the manufacture of dry herbal extracts has been proposed as an innovative alternative to spray drying, the method most used in the phytopharmaceutical processing industries [8, 11–21]. The SB dryer has shown good performance in the production of dried phytoextracts at laboratory scale (small scale); however, studies concerning scaling up, modelling, and simulation of these systems are still scarce.

The purpose of this chapter is to present an overview of the drying of phytochemical preparations by the SB technology, focusing on the effects of feed composition and processing variables on the system performance and product quality.

6.2 GENERAL ASPECTS OF SPOUTED BED TECHNOLOGY

The SB was originally developed in 1954 as an alternative method for drying moist wheat particles [22]. The original SB configuration consisted of a cylindrical column connected to a conical base with a small inlet orifice at the bottom. The spout regime is established in a bed of solid particles loaded in the system by injecting a fluid (generally a gas) vertically upwards through the inlet orifice. If the fluid injection flow rate is high enough, its resulting velocity causes a stream of particles to rise very fast in a hollowed central core within the bed of solids. After reaching somewhat

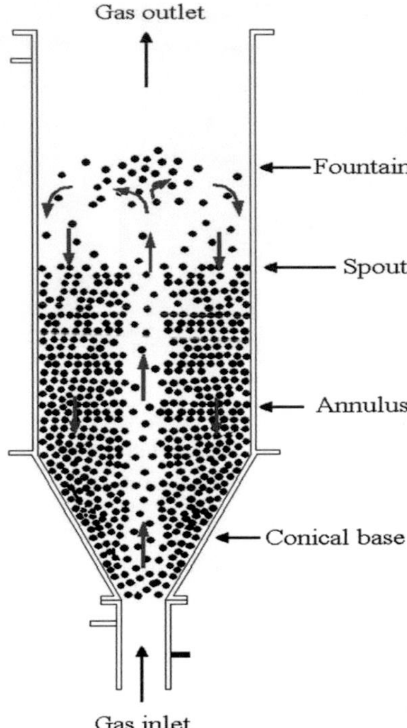

FIGURE 6.1 Schematic diagram of a typical spouted bed system.

above the peripheral bed level, the particles decelerate and fall onto an annular zone formed between the central core and equipment wall. This zone is denser than the central region, and the particles tend to move slowly downwards and radially to some extent. As a result, a cyclic solids flow pattern is established, creating a unique solid–fluid contacting system. In the central core, the solid particles flow upwards concurrent with the spouting fluid and downwards and countercurrent with fluid in the annular zone. In general, SBs work better with particles ≥1.0 mm while fluidised beds ≤1.0 mm. Figure 6.1 shows a schematic diagram of the conventional SB system.

From a hydrodynamic point of view, the main parameters related to the SB design are the minimum spouting velocity, U_{ms}, the maximum pressure drop, ΔP_m, and the pressure drop of stable spouting, ΔP_s, which are linked to the lower gas velocity needed for the spout phenomenon, the minimum potency of the blower, and the energy consumption during stable spouting, respectively. These parameters can be obtained from the characteristic fluid dynamic curve of the SB, which relates the bed pressure drop as a function of the gas velocity fed into the system. Increasing the gas velocity fed to the SB changes the solid–fluid flow patterns significantly, as shown in the pictures presented in Figure 6.2 (a–e) [23]. Figure 6.3 shows typical fluid dynamic graphs obtained for a conical–cylindrical SB, having a conical angle base of 40°, column diameter of 150 mm and inlet orifice diameter of 33 mm, loaded with nearly spherical glass beads with a diameter of 2.8 mm (static bed heights, H_0, of 7.0, 10.5, and 14.0 cm).

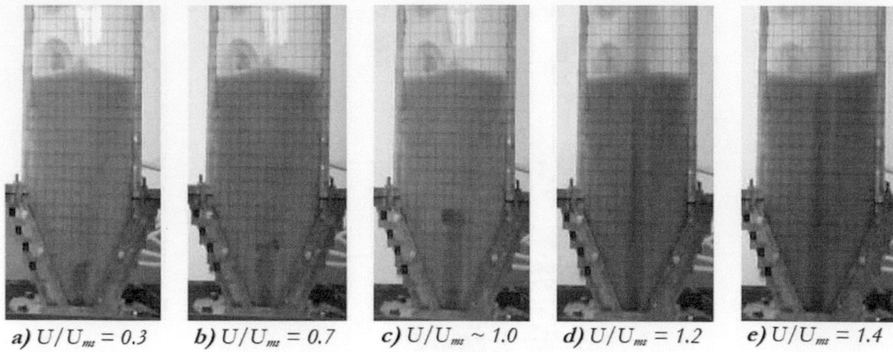

FIGURE 6.2 Typical SB solid–fluid flow patterns with the increase in gas velocity fed to the system ($H_0 = 250$ mm, $d_p = 1.2$ mm, $U_{ms} = 0.459$ m/s). (Reproduced with permission from Oliveira et al. (2009) © John Wiley & Sons [23].)

At low gas velocities, the gas percolates through the voids between the bed particles, and the system behaves as a fixed bed. With the increment of the gas flow, the particles near the inlet orifice begin to move upwards, creating a small cavity surrounded by a compact layer of particles (Figure 6.2 a), causing an increase in the bed pressure drop. The size of the cavity tends to expand with the increase of the gas flow, leading to the formation of an internal spouting (Figure 6.2 b). The pressure drop continues to rise until it reaches a peak value (maximum pressure drop, ΔP_m). After this point, the size of the internal spouting exceeds that of the solid layer that limits the internal cavity, and consequently, there is a gradual decrease in the bed pressure drop. After a determined point in the descending curve, called incipient spouting, any increment of the gas velocity causes an abrupt fall in the bed

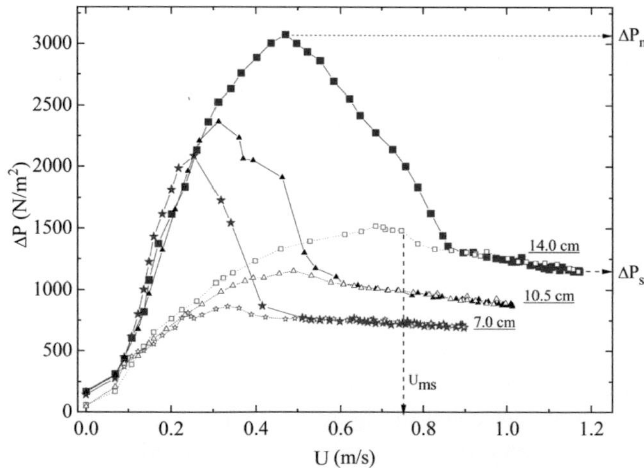

FIGURE 6.3 Typical fluid dynamic curves of the spouted bed [20]. Solid symbols: spout development with the increasing gas flow rate. Open symbols: describe the inverse process.

pressure drop until a point where the spout bursts through the bed particles surface (Figure 6.2c), and the spouting flow patterns begin. This gas velocity is defined as the minimum spouting velocity, U_{ms}. The bed pressure drop remains practically constant after this point (pressure drop of stable spouting, ΔP_s), and a further increase in the gas velocity only increases the fountain height [Figures 6.2 (d and e)] [22–24].

However, due to the instabilities generated by the rupture of the bed particles, the gas velocity of the minimum spout is not exactly reproducible, being better determined by the reverse process. With the reduction of the spouting gas velocity, the bed pressure drop remained constant until the point corresponding to minimum spouting, when a small increment is observed. A maximum value of bed pressure drop is reached with a further reduction of the spouting gas velocity; however, the value is significantly lower than that determined with the flow increment since, in the reverse process, the bed pressure drop is only the result of the gas–solid interaction. From this maximum value, the pressure drop continuously decreases with gas velocity [24, 25].

The stable spouting phenomenon is limited by a maximum static bed height (H_m), beyond which bed instabilities occur, in the form of fluidisation or as a piston-like motion of the bed particles. The maximum static bed height depends on the properties and dimensions of the bed particles and the SB design parameters, such as the angle of the conical base, ratio between column and inlet orifice diameters, and chamber diameter among others. Furthermore, to understand the various transport phenomena that occur simultaneously in the SB operation, it is also desirable to know the profiles of the gas velocity and bed porosity, the dimensions of the SB zones, the solids circulation patterns, and also the heat and mass transfer coefficients [22].

6.3 SPOUTED BED DRYING OF LIQUID FEEDS: TECHNICAL CONSIDERATIONS

SBs have been used for several applications, including coal combustion, chemical reactions, drying of solids, drying of solutions and suspensions, granulation, blending, grinding, and particle coating [26, 27]. During the continuous SB drying of herbal extracts, a concentrate extractive solution is sprayed on the top or below a bed of inert particles suspended by a hot gas flow. The atomised droplets coat the inert bodies with a thin layer of the liquid feed, which dries by the heat transferred by inert particles (conduction) and hot gas (convection). It is expected that the coated layer will become friable with the drying course, fracture due to attrition caused by the particle–particle and particle–wall collisions. The fractured film leaves with the exit air and is collected as the product. The film-free inert bodies are recycled by the SB to be recoated. Figure 6.4 shows a schematic of the drying of liquid materials on the surface of inert bodies in an SB. Therefore, the process has two components: drying the liquid material layer and removing the dry film. The cyclic process of deposition, drying, and removal of the drying layer occurs continuously given that the bed temperature for a specified feed flow rate remains high enough to maintain the proportion of wet particles under the steady-state condition at a low level to avoid

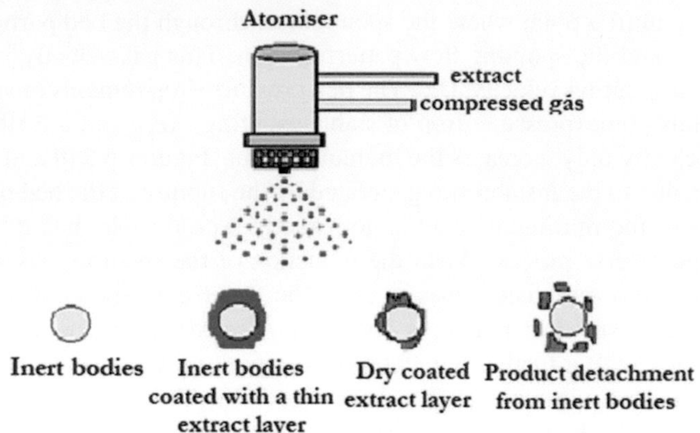

FIGURE 6.4 Scheme of the drying of liquid materials on the surface of inert bodies in an SB.

the cessation of the spout movement due to the wet agglomeration. Under normal operation, the coating of inert material, drying of wet layer, and removal rate of the dry product occur simultaneously, and dynamic equilibrium in the system is established, resulting in a uniform temperature of the dried material and the exhaust gas. The stable operation of the dryer is reached when the rate of the removal of the dried layer is at least equal to the feed flow rate of liquid material [25, 28]. The adhesion of the wet material onto surfaces of thc bed particles and to the equipment wall might lead to a low layer removal rate causing the process malfunctioning, evidenced by the product accumulation in the dryer and perhaps the immediate spout cessation and system collapse [13, 29–31].

Glass, Teflon, polyethene, and polypropylene beads are typical examples of inert materials utilised. Teflon is suitable for food and pharmaceutical applications due to its inert nature, high thermal stability, low coefficient of friction, insolubility, and absence of toxicological effects [32]. Teflon beads have been used in SB drying of biological products, including herbal extracts [8, 15]. On the other hand, glass particles are not indicated for the SB drying of food and pharmaceutical products. The high particle–particle and particle–wall friction during the spouting can produce material fractures, contaminating the dry product and causing harmful effects to the consumer's health.

The advantages of SB are its simplicity and low cost, and with proper selection of operating conditions, they can provide high-quality products with low losses of bioactive compounds [8]. There are various SB configurations such as the conical SB, jet SB, bi-dimensional SB, and hybrid systems as the spout-fluidised beds and microwave SBs [33–35].

6.4 STICKINESS ISSUES DURING DRYING

Adhesion is a time- and temperature-dependent phenomenon during manufacturing (drying) and storage of dry products. The term cohesion is used to describe the adherence between similar materials (e.g. particle–particle attraction) and the term adhesion between different materials (e.g. between the extract with the inert particles/equipment wall surfaces) [36]. In a general way, products to be submitted to drying can be classified into two categories: products of elevated adhesivity or sticky products and product with low adhesion tendency or non-sticky products [36, 37]. Sticky products can remain in the form of a high-viscosity syrup tending to adhere on the dryer surfaces, leading to critical operating problems and a considerable reduction in product yield (recovery).

The adhesion problem may be associated with a high concentration of sugar (sucrose, maltose, glucose, fructose) and organic acids (e.g. tartaric acid, citric acid, malic acid, and lactic acid). Products having a high concentration of these compounds exhibit not only sticky problems during the drying (adhesion on the equipment surfaces, drying interruption, among others) but are also susceptible to agglomeration and caking during storage. Powdered fruit juices, powdered honey, powdered amorphous lactose and herbal extracts are typical products that exhibit stickiness problems. In addition, the fast drying of atomised drops in some drying systems can cause a sudden rise of the product viscosity, increasing the time necessary to realign the molecules, generating amorphous solid [37–40].

Hygroscopicity, solubility, melting point, sticky point, and glass transition temperature, T_g, are properties usually linked to the occurrence of adhesion during drying [39]. The glass transition temperature, a specific property of amorphous materials, has been used as a fundamental indicator of the sticky behaviour of some sugar-rich products. The problem of powder stickiness is mainly due to the low glass transition temperature of the composition constituents with low molecular weight (MW), such as some sugar products (glucose, fructose, sucrose) and organic acids. The glass transition temperature is defined as the temperature at which an amorphous system changes from the glassy to the rubbery state. Molecular mobility in the glassy state is extremely slow due to the high viscosity of the matrix (about 10^{12} Pa.s). Usually, T_g can be taken as a reference parameter for the drying systems project and characterise the product properties, quality, stability, and safety of food and pharmaceutical systems. Several methods can be used for experimental determination of T_g, including the differential scanning calorimetry (DSC), which permits detecting a characteristic change in the specific heat of the material at T_g [37]. Additional difficulties arise in multi-component systems, where several constituents can undergo many small thermal transitions at the same temperature interval [39, 41–43].

Structural changes, such as stickiness, agglomeration, caking, and crystallisation, may also occur in amorphous food powders when stored and processed at temperatures above the T_g. Since glass transition temperature increases with the material's MW, the addition of drying adjuvants (drying aids) has been commonly used to produce food and pharmaceutical powders to reduce the product stickiness and wall deposition [37, 42, 44]. In the pharmaceutical industry, the correct use of adjuvants during the drying of phytochemical preparations plays a key role in the stability and quality of the finished product. One of the main functions of the drying aids is to increase the glass transition temperature of the composition to be dried, thus reducing its tendency to agglomerate during drying and storage, allowing longer shelf life for the dry product.

Drying adjuvants with wide use in the dehydration of herbal extracts include corn, cassava and rice starches, modified starches, maltodextrins, microcrystalline cellulose, colloidal silicon dioxide, gum Arabic, and cyclodextrins (see Section 5.4.1.1.1 for more details). They can be used alone or mixed, and the ideal proportions should be established for each specific case in terms of the extract to be dried, the drying method, and the operating conditions used. The effects of the addition of the drying adjuvants are relatively well-known for spray drying, with numerous scientific works available in the literature [29, 44–48]. This information, however, is not directly applicable to SB drying due to the distinct drying mechanisms [26].

The thermal sensibility of the product is another important characteristic during the drying of biological materials (e.g. herbal extracts, enzymes, biologicals), which leads to restrictions on drying operating conditions [29]. Thus, three factors are of primordial importance for selecting a drying method and operating conditions: the initial moisture content of the material, the evaporation rate needed, and the velocity of undesirable product transformations during drying.

Rocha and coworkers have developed several fundamental studies aiming to link the physical properties of the feed composition and of contacting materials (surface tension, rheological properties, density, pH, and contact angle between them) with the performance of the SB drying/coating [13, 30, 49]. Their findings suggest that it is possible to predict the SB drying/coating performance based on the knowledge of the physicochemical properties of the feed composition and the inert material used.

6.4.1 Typical Instability Issues during Spouted Bed Drying of Sticky Compositions

When applied for drying liquid feeds, the SB is subjected to several technical difficulties, which can be resolved through careful selection of processing conditions. Factors such as the chemical composition of the feed, physical properties of the inert material (e.g. density, sphericity, repose angle), and dryer wall material exert direct influence on the powder removal rate and consequently on product accumulation into the SB dryer. Compositions presenting high viscosity or adhesive properties can cause agglomeration of the inert material, leading to dryer malfunctioning. Various problems concerning product accumulation in the dryer, impairing the fluid dynamic and bed stability, have been reported [13, 30, 50].

The unstable SB behaviour can be evidenced by a sudden reduction of the pressure drop when the extract (liquid material) is fed. This reduction can be explained by increasing the viscosity of the feed composition due to liquid evaporation during drying, increasing its tendency to stickiness. This viscosity change can cause adhesion between the inert materials, changing the solids' circulation and the gas flow through the bed and increasing the fraction of the gas flowing through the spout zone [51]. Some authors have attributed the changes in the SB dynamics to the powder accumulation inside the drying chamber [40]. Depending on the SB drying conditions, distinct spouting states can occur, as Oliveira et al. [52] identified during SB drying of sucrose solutions with different concentrations (see Figure 6.5). Figure 6.6 a,b shows a scheme of solids flow pattern changes during SB drying of *Bauhinia forficata* leaf extract [25].

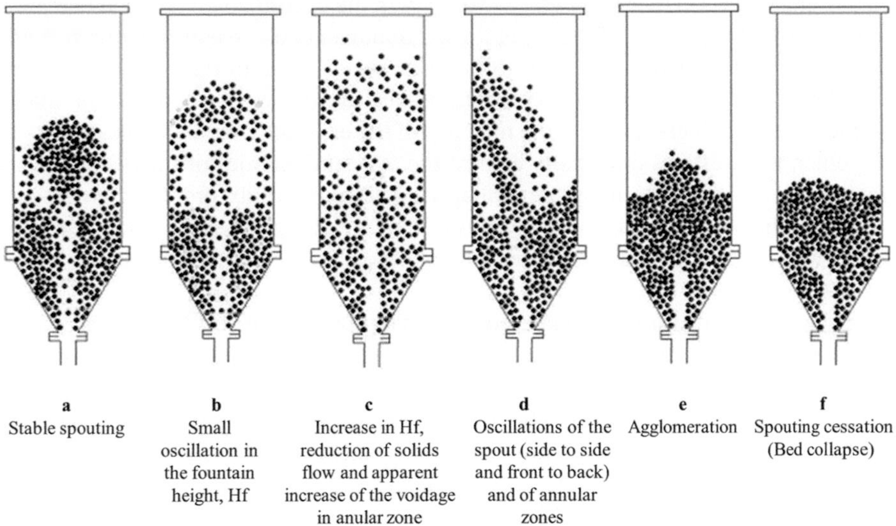

FIGURE 6.5 Scheme of major changes of the spouting regimes caused by the feeding of sucrose solutions. (Reproduced with permission from Oliveira et al. (2009) © John Wiley & Sons [52].)

When operating outside of the stable operating zone, the instabilities arise when the liquid material is atomised into the bed. The cohesion/adhesion of the particles causes the formation of preferential channels in the central zone. As a result, the high flow of gas through the spout zone causes an increase in the fountain height. However, due to particle agglomeration, the fountain's solids concentration decreases, as shown in Figure 6.6 b. Simultaneous changes in the gas and solids flow patterns

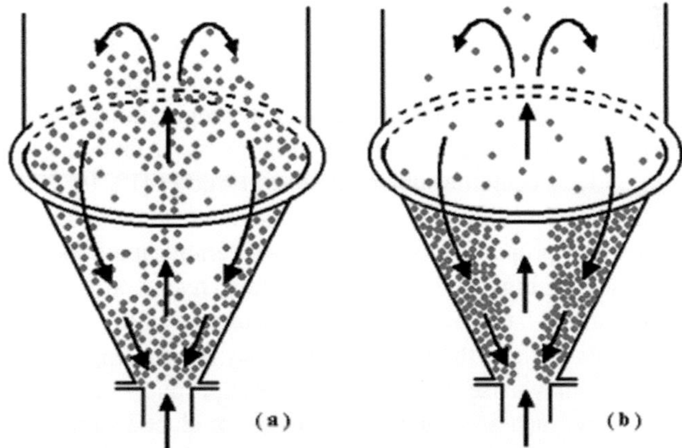

FIGURE 6.6 Scheme of the solids' flow during spouted bed drying of *Bauhinia forficata* leaf extract: (a) normal dynamics and (b) change in bed dynamics caused by the packaging of particles in the annular zone and development of preferential channel in the central core [25].

occur, characterised by increased gas velocity in the central zone, reduced bed pressure drop, and expansion of the fountain and annular zones. In addition, the size and weight of the bed particles tended to increase steadily due to the continuous accumulation of a dry product layer on the inert material surface. Also, the accumulated product tends to degrade due to the increase of its residence time in the heated dryer. Together, these effects drastically change the overall dynamics of the SB dryer and may cause spout cessation (system collapse). These instability problems are associated with the physicochemical properties of the feed composition, the inert particles, dryer wall surface, the SB configuration, and the operating conditions used [13, 15, 18, 19, 30, 40, 49].

Souza and Oliveira [53] compared the drying of *B. forficata* leaf extract in SB with and without a draft tube installed. Colloidal silicon dioxide (Tixosil® 333) was used as a drying adjuvant. It was found that the occurrence of instabilities was more significant in the draft tube SB, where it was observed the packing of the inert bodies in the annular zone and the spouting cessation (bed collapse) in several drying runs. The particle concentrations in the spout zone decreased drastically with poor solids circulation, and the gas flowed freely. The drying in the SB without a draft tube, system instabilities, or bed collapse was also observed in 31% of the experimental runs. The instabilities were associated with the pulsation of the bed particles; in all cases (31%), the presence of large agglomerates of the inert particles inside the bed was verified, which can be a factor responsible for the irregular solids flow of the inert particles inside the dryer [25].

6.5 SPOUTED BED DRYING OF PHYTOCHEMICAL PREPARATIONS

Drying implies significant physical and chemical changes of the product in complex media. These transformations, which cannot be described thoroughly, may persist during product storage [54, 55]. The drying of extractive solutions from herbal material consists of solvent removal (by evaporation, sublimation, or vaporisation), generating a stable solid product at ambient temperature. In phytopharmaceutical technology, the higher stability, easy handling and transport, and standardised concentration of the bioactive compounds are the main factors responsible for the increasing interest in the use of dry phytochemical preparations [10, 26].

SB drying is a versatile and promising technology for producing dry phytochemical preparations and has been the subject of several studies [15, 16, 27, 56]. However, the herbal extracts are constituted by several substances (some unknown) with diversified physicochemical properties, presenting considerable amounts of organic acids, lipids, carbohydrates of high and low MW, protein, resins, among others [57, 58]. Most of these substances have low glass transition temperature and are highly hygroscopic and thermoplastic, and their dehydrating may be challenging (see Chapter 5). Numerous problems may arise during drying these products on moving beds, such as the SB technology, such as system instabilities, product accumulation inside the dryer, coating of the inert bodies, agglomeration, and system collapse. Significant losses of bioactive constituents might also occur due to processing conditions, which are frequently associated with degradation of thermosensitive substances, oxidation, and the losses of volatile compounds due to the action of various factors, including processing temperature, pH, and oxygen. The proper selection of drying adjuvants (drying aids) during SB drying of phytoextracts plays a vital role in improving process performance and product quality (see Sections 6.4 and 5.4.1.1.1).

6.5.1 Effects of Processing Conditions on Spouted Bed Behaviour and Product Properties

An overview in the scientific literature shows several studies aiming to correlate the thermal degradation of bioactive compounds and the SB drying performance (production yield, product accumulation, residence time, among others) to the material's intrinsic properties to be dried with processing conditions.

Table 6.1 presents a summary of several studies of drying of herbal extracts by the SB. It can be seen in Table 6.1 that the physicochemical properties of the dried product depend on the drying conditions as well as the composition of the plant extract. Due to the complex composition of herbal extracts, the theoretical prediction of the behaviour of these products during drying is very challenging, and experimental work is almost unavoidable during the development of standardised dry phytochemical preparations by SB technology. Therefore, an outlook of important studies regarding system performance and product quality affected by feed composition properties and SB operating conditions will be presented.

6.5.2 Evaluation of Experimental Studies

An evaluation of the effects of position of the feed atomiser and operating conditions on the dryer performance (product recovery, accumulation ratio, elutriation, and thermal efficiency) and product properties (moisture content, size distribution, thermal degradation of the bioactive compounds, and flow properties of the powder product) during SB drying of *B. forficata* was reported by Souza and Oliveira [62]. The extraction of the bioactive constituents was carried out by dynamic maceration by placing one part of milled *B. forficata* leaves in contact with 5 parts of ethanol:water at 70% v/v at 50°C, being maintained under stirring for 1 h. Then, the extractive mixture was vacuum-filtered and -concentrated. Colloidal SiO_2 (Tixosil® 333) at a concentration of 80% w/w of the concentrated extract (dry basis) was used as a drying adjuvant. The drying runs were performed in a conical–cylindrical SB with 150 mm of column diameter, 33 mm of inlet orifice diameter, and conical base angle of 40°. Rounded Teflon beads with a diameter of 5.45 mm were used as inert material, and the static bed height (H_0) was maintained at 140 mm.

The processing parameters investigated were the position of the feed atomiser (top spray or bottom spray), the inlet drying gas temperature, T_{in} (80–150°C), and the feed flow rate of extract related to the evaporation capacity of the system $\dot{m}_{feed}/\dot{m}_{max}$ (15–100%). Data on the evaporative capacity of the SB dryer was presented by Souza and Oliveira [63]. The feed flow rate of spouting gas was maintained at 0.0340 kg/s ($Q/Q_{ms} = 1.4$). The atomising air feed flow rate was fixed at 0.90 m^3/h at a pressure of 147.1 kPa. The study showed that the SB drying of thermosensitive materials with a high content of reducing sugar and organic acids, such as the phytochemical preparations, may be technologically feasible. However, depending

TABLE 6.1
Summary of Recent Studies on Drying of Phytochemical Preparations by Spouted Bed Technology

Herbal Material	Operating Conditions	Feed Composition	Main Findings	Ref.
Passiflora alata **Dryander** (**Passion flower**: anti-spasmodic, anti-inflammatory, tranquiliser, analgesic, antipyretic, and so on)	d_c = 15.0 cm; γ = 60°; H_0 = 14 cm; T_{in} = 80–150°C; $\dot{m}_{feed}$ = 4.8 and 12.0 g/min; $\dot{m}_{air}$ = 0.014 kg/s; Q_{at} = 0.90 m^3/h; P_{at} = 147.1 kPa; Cs = 15.8% w/w; Q/Q_{ms} = 1.4; glass beads (2.8 mm)	Ethanol:water (1:1) extract with Colloidal SiO_2 (Tixosil 333®) at 40% and Tween 80® at 2% w/w relative to the solids content in the extract.	Powdered product, with particle sizes almost independent of drying conditions; moisture content between 3.4 and 7.7%; degradation of the total flavonoid content (TFC) between 25.8 and 44%; HPLC profiles did not change with drying; better process performance at intermediate drying temperature (T_{in} = 115°C), independent of the $\dot{m}_{feed}$.	[59]
Paullinia cupana HBK (**Guarana**: stimulants, aphrodisiacs, antidiarrheals, antiaging agents, weight loss)	LabMaq 1.0 SBD; M_0 = 600 g; T_{in} = 60–180°C; $\dot{m}_{feed}$ = 3.0–7.0 g/min, by dropping; Q_{at} = 0.42–0.57 m^3/min; Q/Q_{ms} = 1.2–1.6; Cs = 4.08% w/w	20% w/v of the seed powder in ethanol:water 7:3 w/w at 40°C for 2 h. No adjuvant added.	Fine powder, low caffeine degradation at selected operating condition, moisture content between below 3.0% at drying temperatures above 120°C, drying feasible without drying aid.	[60]
Bixa orellana L. (**Urucum**: natural colour, condiment, hypotensive, expectorant, antibiotic)	d_c = 9.3 cm; γ = 63°; M_0 = 300 g; T_{in} = 60–120°C; Q = 0.5 m^3/min; Q/ Q_{ms} = 1.6; $\dot{V}_{feed}$ = 1 to 4 mL/min, dropping; glass beads (2.6 mm)	Urucum seeds washed 5× with NaOH basified water (1:1). No adjuvant added.	Product with dark red colour, good flow properties, bixin content comparable to commercial powders. It was verified a sharp decrease in pigment content at T_{in} above 80°C.	[61]

(Continued)

TABLE 6.1 *(Continued)*
Summary of Recent Studies on Drying of Phytochemical Preparations by Spouted Bed Technology

Herbal Material	Operating Conditions	Feed Composition	Main Findings	Ref.
Rosmarinus officinalis L. (**Rosemary**: antioxidant, antispasmodic, respiratory disorders, hair growth; choleretic, hepatoprotective and antitumerogenic)	d_c = 15 cm; γ = 40°; H_0 = 14 cm; T_{in} = 80 and 150°C; $\dot{m}_{feed}/\dot{m}_{max}$ = 15–75%; $\dot{m}_{air}$ = 0.034 kg/s; $\dot{V}_{at}$ = 1.2 m³/h; P_{at} = 196.1 kPa; Q/Q_{ms} = 1.4; Cs = 7.32% w/w; Teflon beads (5.45 mm)	Extraction by dynamic maceration, milled rosemary leaves, and ethanol:water (1:5, 70% v/v) at 50°C. Colloidal SiO_2 and maltodextrin at a 40:20% w/w of the extract (dry basis) was used as drying adjuvant.	Product with poor flow and compression properties, with the presence of irregular and polydisperse agglomerated particles (mean diameters varying from 7 to 22 μm); higher losses of total polyphenols content (TPC - 45–53%) and TFC (13.1–49.9%); and stickiness and agglomeration problems during drying	[50]
Hymenaea courbaril L. (**Jatobá:** Hypoglycemic, asthma, bronchitis treatment, antiseptic, wound healing, kidney problems, anti-inflammatory activity, rheumatism)	d_c = 15 cm; γ = 40°; H_0 = 7 cm; T_{in} = 80, 115 and 150 °C; $\dot{m}_{feed}/\dot{m}_{max}$ = 15 to 45 %; Q_{at} = 0.9 m³/h; P_{at} = 147.1 kPa; Q/Q_{ms} = 1.4 and 1.85; Cs 10.0% w/w; Top feeding; Teflon beads (5.45 mm)	Dynamic maceration, milled *H. courbaril* stem bark, 50 °C, ethanol:water at 70% v/v, plant:solvent of 1:10 w/v), 60 min. Colloidal SiO_2:extract of 1:2 (dry basis) was used as drying adjuvant.	Dried product of high quality: TPC (25.1 ± 0.8 to 27.3 ± 0.5% w/w); total tannins (10.1 ± 0.5 to 16.7 ± 0.6% w/w); high antioxidant activity; particle diameter (10.1 ± 9.6 to 17.0 ± 15.8 ± μm); low moisture content (4.3 ± 0.1 to 9.5 ± 0.3% w/w); and water activity (0.073 ± 0.027 to 0.398 ± 0.002). Good spouted bed drying performance. Optimum drying conditions were: T_{in} = 150 °C; $\dot{m}_{feed}/\dot{m}_{max}$ = 45%; and Q/Q_{ms} = 1.85.	[19]
B. forficata Link (**Cow's hoof**: hypoglycemic, antidiabetic, antiinfection, pain, and anti-inflammatory activities)	d_c = 15 cm; γ = 40°; H_0 = 14 cm; T_{in} = 80 and 150°C; $\dot{m}_{feed}/\dot{m}_{max}$ = 15–100%; $\dot{m}_{air}$ = 0.034 kg/s; Q_{at} = 0.9 m³/h; P_{at} = 147.1 kPa; Q/Q_{ms} = 1.4; Cs = 8.05% w/w; top and bottom feeding; Teflon beads (5.45 mm)	Extraction by dynamic maceration, milled *B. forficata* leaves and ethanol:water (1:5, ~70%) v/v at 50°C, 1 h. Colloidal SiO_2 at a 80% w/w of the extract (dry basis) was used as drying adjuvant.	Product of low-density, high-compressibility indexes; good flow properties; TFC degradation between 0.2 and 48.0%; particle diameter of 6.8 ± 5.0 to 22.3 ± 15.9 μm; moisture content between 1.62 and 10.6%. Better dryer performance with top feeding.	[62]

(Continued)

TABLE 6.1 ***(Continued)***
Summary of Recent Studies on Drying of Phytochemical Preparations by Spouted Bed Technology

Herbal Material	Operating Conditions	Feed Composition	Main Findings	Ref.
Bidens pilosa (**Spanish needles**: antimalarial, anticancer, antimicrobial, immunosuppressive, anti-inflammatory, and antioxidant properties)	d_c = 15 cm; γ = 40°; H_0 = 7 cm; T_{in} = 80 and 150°C; Q = 1.2 m^3/min; $\dot{m}_{feed}$ = 8.1 g/min; Q_{at} = 0.9 m^3/h; P_{at} = 147.1 kPa; Q/Q_{ms}= 1.85; Cs = 17.6% w/w, 13% w/w for adj. Aerosil® 200; Teflon beads (5.45 mm)	Dynamic maceration (milled dry aerial parts), 66.2°C, ethanol:water at 62.7% (v/v), plant-to-solvent ratio of 1:10 (w/v), 30 min. Adjuvants: β-CD; colloidal SiO_2 (Aerosil® 200), and blends of Aerosil 200 with MCC or MD DE10 (1:3 ratio), added to the extract at a 1:1 ratio (dry basis).	Degradation of the marker compounds, particle size, and powder morphology depend on the adj. β-cyclodextrin product showed the lowest losses of TFC and the marker compounds.	[18]
Lippia sidoides Cham. (**Pepper-rosmarin**: aromatic herb from northeast of Brazil, antimicrobial, larvicidal, molluscicides, and antioxidant activities)	d_c = 15 cm; γ = 40°; H_0 = 7 cm; T_{in} = 80–150°C; Q = 1.2 m^3/min; $\dot{m}_{feed}/\dot{m}_{max}$ = 15–75% Q_{at} = 0.9 m^3/h; P_{at} = 1.5 kgf/cm^2; Q/Q_{ms} ≅ 1.8; Cs = 12.7% w/w; Teflon beads (5.45 mm)	Dynamic maceration (milled dry leaves), 50°C, ethanol:water (2:1 v/v), plant-to-solvent ratio 0.131 (kg/L), 30 min. Adjuvant was added to extract at concentrations ranging from 5.5 to 16.5% w/w (wet basis) and consisted of a mixture of Arabic gum (20%), plus Aerosil® 200 (0, 40, or 80%), and MCC-102 (0, 40, or 80%).	Concentration and type of drying adjuvant show a significant effect on physicochemical product properties. The dry extract shows high antioxidant activity but significant losses (from 31% to 97%) of the marker compound thymol was observed. The highest thymol retention was obtained for the composition with the lower amount of Adj, with the highest percent of Aerosil 200, dried under $\dot{m}_{feed}/\dot{m}_{max}$ set at 30% and T_{in} of 115°C.	[15]

(Continued)

TABLE 6.1 ***(Continued)***
Summary of Recent Studies on Drying of Phytochemical Preparations by Spouted Bed Technology

Herbal Material	Operating Conditions	Feed Composition	Main Findings	Ref.
Maytenus ilicifolia Martius (**Espinheira santa**: treatment of gastric ulcers, indigestion, chronic gastritis, dyspepsia, analgesic, disinfectant, tonic, and wound healing)	(d_s = 34 cm; γ = 38°; T_{in} = 80–150°C; $\dot{m}_{feed}/\dot{m}_{air}$ = 0.0056–0.0119; Q/Q_{ms} = 1.4 and 1.85; Q_{ms} = 0.9 and 1.4 m^3/min (H_0 = 7 and 14 cm); Q_{at} = 0.9 m^3/h; P_{at} = 147.1 kPa; Cs = 15.82% w/w; Teflon beads (5.45 mm)	Dynamic maceration (milled dry leaves), 60.2°C, ethanol:water (2:1 v/v), plant-to-solvent ratio 0.16 (kg/L), 120 min. Adjuvant colloidal SiO_2 (Tixosil® 333) added to the extract at concentration of 40% relative to solids content of the extractive solution.	Dry extract with good flow properties, dark beige colour, TFC degradation between 5.0 and 30.0%, moisture content from 0.30 to 14.8%; preservation of the organoleptic properties. The product showed anti-ulcer activity	[35]

on the composition properties, adhesion problems are likely to occur, which may cause product degradation, loss of volatile substances, poor product recovery, and dryer malfunctioning. The use of drying adjuvants may contribute to minimising the adhesion problems. The performance of the SB dryer with the atomisation at the top of the spout (top spray feed system) was superior to the bottom spray feed system, showing a small product accumulation into the dryer. The drying at the inlet temperature of 150°C, $\dot{m}_{feed}/\dot{m}_{max}$ of 45%, and top spray feeding showed the best drying performance, generating a dried product with residual moisture content lower than 4% (dry basis) and reduced thermal degradation of bioactive compounds.

Similar instability problems can occur on SB drying of fruit pulps and juices, as demonstrated by Medeiros and coworkers [40], which studied the effects of the physical properties of the feed composition on the SB performance during the drying of tropical fruits. Pulp of "Espada" mango (*Mangifera indica*) was used as a model fruit pulp, and its composition was changed by adding sugar, fibres, starch, pectin, olive oil, and citric acid. Drying runs were carried out in a cone cylindrical SB, made of stainless steel, with acrylic windows. The angle of the conical base has 60° and the column diameter 18 cm. A load of 2.5 kg of high-density polyethene beads (950 kg/m³), with a diameter of 3 mm, was selected as the inert material; T_{in} was set at 70°C, Q/Q_{ms} at 1.25 and 40 minutes of processing time. Fifty grams of the modified pulps were fed in the fountain region through 25-mL syringes. The experimental results showed that the physical properties and the feed composition did not affect the evaporation rate of the system.

Regarding the fluid system dynamics, there was no significant effect of the feed compositions on the flow rate of minimum spouting, while the sugar and starch concentrations changed the pressure drop of stable spouting. Pulps with high sugar concentrations caused system instabilities, while high pectin and starch concentrations promote superior SB drying performance. The drying of the pulps occurred in the first minutes of processing, and the variations observed in the bed dynamics were associated with the dry powder present in the bed. However, the powder production (product recovery) was very low, with significant product retention within the system (dispersed or adhered to the inert particles or the equipment wall). Compositions containing lipids, starch, and pectin showed positive effects, while reducing sugar has significant detrimental effects on powder production.

In another study, the same group investigated the effects of pulp composition during SB drying of tropical fruits, relating important results of the effects caused by different concentrations of reducer sugar, fat, fibres, starch, and pectin on drying behaviour [64]. Mango pulp (*Espada* variety) and preparations of mango modified with different concentrations of glucose, fructose, soluble starch, citric pectin, citric acid, olive oil, and distilled water were also used as fruit pulp models. The effects of feed composition were evaluated with the aid of a 2^4 factorial planning. The same SB configuration and operating conditions described in the previous work was used [40]. The system was monitored through inlet and outlet drying gas temperatures and the SB pressure drop. An empirical model for the prediction of the efficiency of powder production was fitted to experimental data. The model optimisation permitted the estimation of the pulp composition, presenting the maximum efficiency of powder production (80.73%), namely 5.52% of sugar, 14.69% of fat, 4.93% of starch, and 2.78% of citric pectin. An experimental run at the optimised composition furnished an efficiency of powder production of nearly 70%, showing the potential of the proposed model to predict the SB performance during drying of tropical fruit pulps. Hence, the SB performance during dehydration of fruit pulps can be improved by changing the properties of the feed. These changes, however, are subjected to restrictions considering the desirable organoleptic and nutritional properties of food powders.

The specific system performance observed during the SB drying of the liquid feeds, such as phytochemical preparations and fruit pulps and juices, may be linked to the properties at the liquid (feed composition) and the solid (inert material) contact (e.g. contact angle, surface tension, work of adhesion, among others), as reported by Donida et al. [65]. The authors investigated the fluid dynamic behaviour of a conventional SB during drying/coating of two polymeric compositions (based on hydroxyethyl cellulose), using 4 different inert particles (acrylonitrile butadiene styrene—ABS, polypropylene, polystyrene, and glass spheres). The study was carried out in a conventional cone cylinder SB with a column diameter of 20 cm and a cone angle of 60°. The parameters analysed were the spouting gas flow rate, the bed pressure drop, the inlet and outlet temperature and humidity of the drying gas, the solids temperature in the annular region, the increase in the fountain and annular zone heights, and the solids circulation at the SB wall. The adhesion of the feed material to inert particles was quantified by determining the work of adhesion. The performance of the coating process (coating efficiency, particles growth, and elutriation losses) and the drying (product recovery) were investigated. The results showed that for high values of the work of adhesion at liquid–solid contacting surfaces (for glass spheres and ABS), and for contact angle lower than 70°, the coating process predominates. The drying was more evident for the polystyrene and polypropylene particles, which exhibit weak adhesion at liquid/particle surface, and contact angles higher than 76°. Distinct fluid dynamic behaviours were identified for each process (coating and drying). During the coating, the velocity of the solids circulation and the bed pressure drop increased with the spouting gas ratio. For drying, the velocity of solids circulation decreases with the retention of solids in the system, while the stable spouting pressure drop remained nearly constant. In some situations, it is recommended to increase the spouting gas flow rate during the drying/coating operation to avoid the system collapse due to the changes in the fluid dynamic behaviour caused by the powder accumulation inside the dryer or increase in the size of inert particles. The powder accumulation inside the bed reduces the annulus porosity, diminishes the particle circulation, and causes a lateral displacement of the fountain.

The influence of the addition of several drying adjuvants on the enhancement of the performance of the SB drying of hydroalcoholic extract of *B. forficata* Link was investigated by Souza and coworkers [13, 25]. Experimental runs were carried out in a conical–cylindrical SB with 150 mm of column diameter, 33 mm of inlet orifice diameter, and conical base angle of 40°. Rounded Teflon beads with a diameter of 5.45 mm were used as inert material, and the static bed height was maintained at 140 mm. Several preliminary drying tests were carried out to evaluate the effect of different drying adjuvants on drying performance, namely cornstarch, manioc starch, maltodextrins DE 10 and 20, and colloidal silicon dioxide (colloidal SiO_2). The drying adjuvants used resulted in low product recovery mainly due to adherence of the product to the surface of inert particles and drying chamber walls, which lead to particle agglomeration and spout collapse in a relatively short processing time. An exception was observed for the colloidal silicon dioxide (Tixosil® 333), which improved the drying behaviour significantly. This behaviour may be linked to the anti-caking and free-flowing donating characteristics of the colloidal SiO_2 [32]. The enhancing effects of this drying adjuvant were associated with the formation of a monolayer around the herbal extract atomised droplets, which may keep the particles apart, reducing to a minimum the Van der Waals adhesion forces between the surfaces.

Detachment tests of the feed compositions (extract plus Tixosil® 333) were performed on the surface of small Teflon and stainless-steel plates. The plates were previously submitted to heat treatment at 105°C for 1 h to remove residual water from the surface, and then they were placed in support. A thin layer of the concentrated *B. forficata* extract and compositions containing the Tixosil® 333 were uniformly spread (≅0.10 mm) over the surfaces and placed in a circulation oven at 75.0 ± 0.5°C. The drying and the film detachment were visually monitored and registered by digital pictures, following the

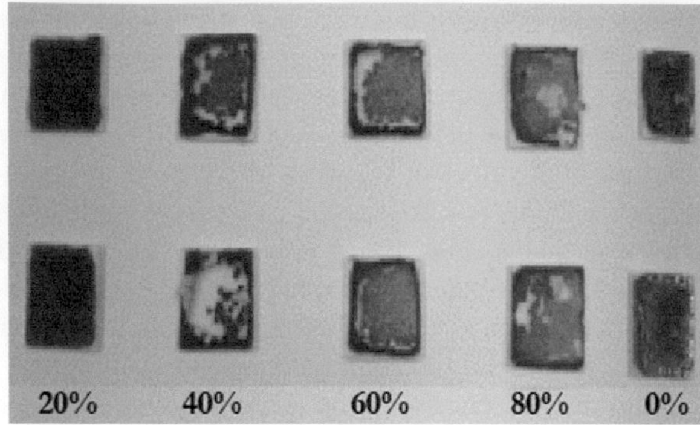

FIGURE 6.7 Detachment of thin layers of herbal compositions from Teflon surfaces as a function of the concentration of colloidal SiO_2 (Tixosil® 333—dry basis) [25].

procedure presented in Collares et al. [41]. Figures 6.7 and 6.8 show the images of the detachment of thin layers of herbal compositions from the Teflon and the stainless-steel surfaces as a function of the concentration of colloidal SiO_2 (Tixosil® 333) added.

The resulting compositions were characterised by determining the surface tension, rheology, density, pH, and contact angle between extract and inert material. The detachment of the extract layer from the Teflon surfaces occurred almost spontaneously and showed dependence on the concentration of Tixosil® 333 added. However, for the stainless-steel surfaces, the extract layer remained adhered to the surface, perhaps due to the low contact angle and consequently high work of adhesion of the herbal extract composition on this material. These results corroborate the significant effects of the physicochemical properties of the composition of the feed and its adhesive behaviour with the drying surfaces on the rate of product removal during SB drying. In practical situations, the impact and the friction forces within the solid particles and the dryer wall will enhance the removal rate of the dried product.

Drying runs were also carried out to investigate the role of the colloidal SiO_2 (Tixosil® 333) on the SB drying performance. The processing parameters investigated

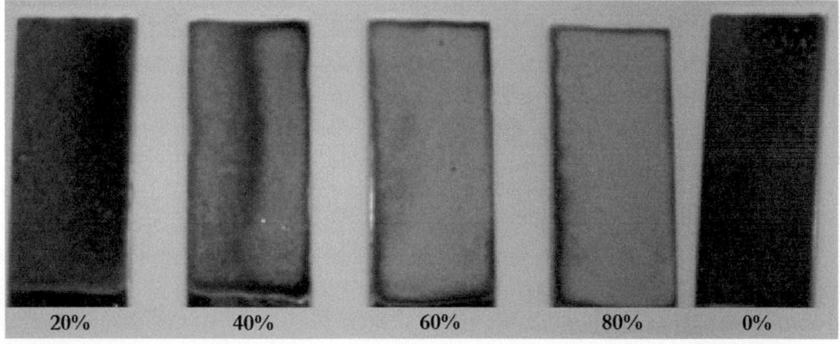

FIGURE 6.8 Detachment of thin layers of herbal compositions from stainless-steel surfaces as a function of the concentration of colloidal SiO2 (Tixosil® 333—dry basis) [25].

were the feed flow rate of extract related to the evaporation capacity of the dryer ($\dot{m}_{feed}/\dot{m}_{max}$ = 15 and 45%) and the concentration of Tixosil® 333 added to the *B. forficata* extract (20–80% w/w of the solids content of the extract). This drying adjuvant was added in two different ways: before extract concentration and after extract concentration. Then, the compositions were submitted to the SB drying. The feed flow rate of the spouting gas was maintained at Q/Q_{ms} = 1.4 and 1.8, respectively, for static bed heights, H_0, of 140 and 70 mm. The inlet drying gas temperature was set at 150°C.

The experimental results showed that the drying conditions and the concentration of the drying adjuvant used have a significant impact on the SB drying behaviour. The increase in the concentration of the colloidal silicon dioxide improved the drying performance, reducing the product accumulation significantly in the bed. The extract compositions with 60 and 80% of drying adjuvant, added before the concentration stage, showed a small increase in the product recovery (drying yield), although the observed differences did not show statistical significance. Figure 6.9 shows the

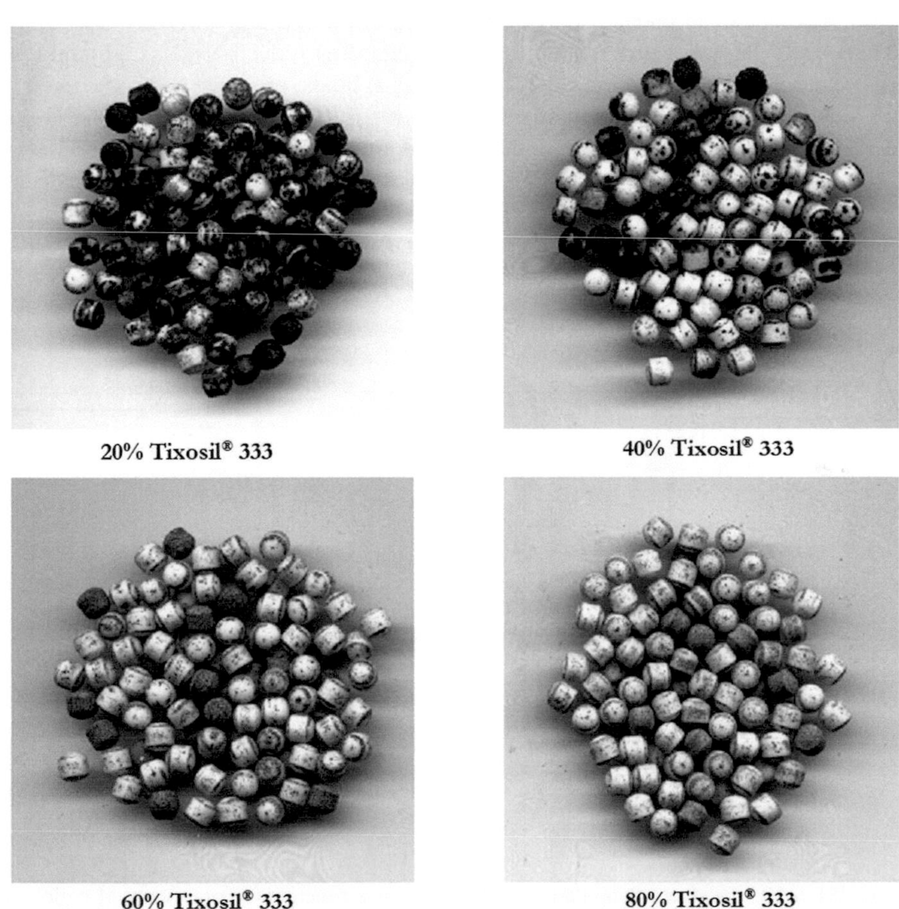

FIGURE 6.9 Pictures of the Teflon beads just after spouted bed drying runs for several concentrations of colloidal SiO_2 (Tixosil® 333) added to the concentrated extract of *B. forficata*.

pictures of the Teflon beads obtained just after the drying runs, as a function of the amount of colloidal SiO_2 added to the concentrated *B. forficata* extract ($H_0 = 70$ mm; $\dot{m}_{feed}/\dot{m}_{max} = 15\%$, $Q/Q_{ms} = 1.8$, $T_{in} = 150°C$).

The increase in the concentration of the drying adjuvant also showed a protective effect on the content of the bioactive substances, reducing their degradation during drying. In the same way, the product moisture content (loss on drying) shows a tendency to decrease conversely with the amount of the colloidal silicon dioxide added. Thus, the experimental results confirmed that the rheological properties of the feed compositions, the contact angle with the inert particles and dryer wall, the resulting work of adhesion, together with the drying conditions play important roles in the SB performance during drying of phytopharmaceutical compositions, in close agreement with previous studies [13, 30, 38, 49, 65].

Figures 6.10 and 6.11 show, respectively, graphs of the product accumulation and product recovery of the SB dryer as a function of the amount of the drying adjuvant (Tixosil® 333) added to the concentrated extracts of dry leaves of three Brazilian medicinal plants (*B. forficata, Passiflora alata,* and *Maytenus ilicifolia*). These extracts have a different composition regarding reducer sugar, high and low MW carbohydrates, organic acids, reducer sugar, lipids, proteins, and some chemical constituents, as shown in Table 6.2. Figures 6.10 and 6.11 show, respectively, a significant reduction of the product accumulation in the SB dryer and a rise in product recovery by increasing the amount of colloidal SiO_2 (Tixosil® 333) added; behaviour is also dependent on the extract constitution. Hence, the correct selection of the type and amount of the drying adjuvant, the inert material, and drying conditions are specific to each phytochemical preparation.

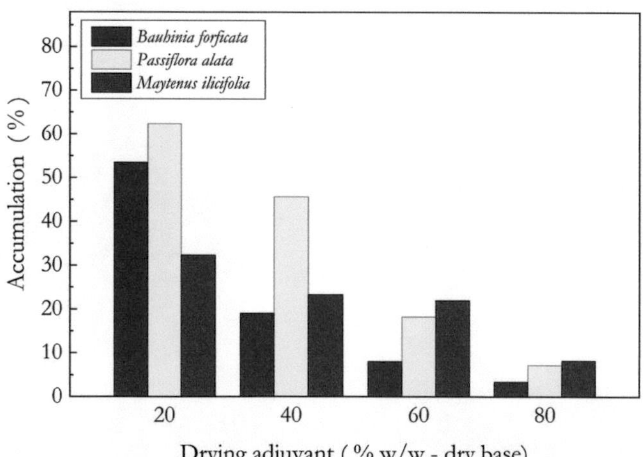

FIGURE 6.10 Product accumulation in the dryer as a function of the amount of colloidal SiO_2 (Tixosil® 333) added to the concentrated extracts of three Brazilian medicinal plants (*Bauhinia forficata*, *Passiflora alata*, and *Maytenus ilicifolia*) during SB drying.

TABLE 6.2
Results of the Characterisation of the Concentrated Extractive Solutions of Dry Leaves of *Bauhinia forficata, Passiflora alata,* and *Maytenus ilicifolia* [66]

Assay	*B. forficata*	*M. ilicifolia*	*P. alata*	Ref.
TFC (mg/g)	8.24 ± 0.20	—	11.75 ± 0.11	[67]
Total tannins (mg/g)	—	148.2 ± 1.2	—	[67]
Solid contents (% w/w)	9.82 ± 0.06	8.07 ± 0.05	8.85 ± 0.06	[67]
Titratable acidity (% v/w)	0.92 ± 0.01	0.95 ± 0.12	1.11 ± 0.11	[68] Method 13.6.2
Carbohydrate HMWC (mg/g) LMWC	0.25 ± 0.01	0.40 ± 0.01	0.21 ± 0.01	[58]
	14.34 ± 0.07	13.23 ± 0.10	16.21 ± 0.42	
Reducing sugar (% w/w)	4.82 ± 0.18	6.18 ± 0.04	4.40 ± 0.03	[68] Method 4.13.2
Lipids (% w/w)	14.66 ± 0.51	4.27 ± 0.31	0.14 ± 0.02	[68] Method 4.10
Protein (mg/mL)	15.83 ± 0.23	8.71 ± 0.09	7.69 ± 0.15	[69]

Abbreviations: HMWC = High molecular weight carbohydrates; LMWC = low molecular weight carbohydrates.

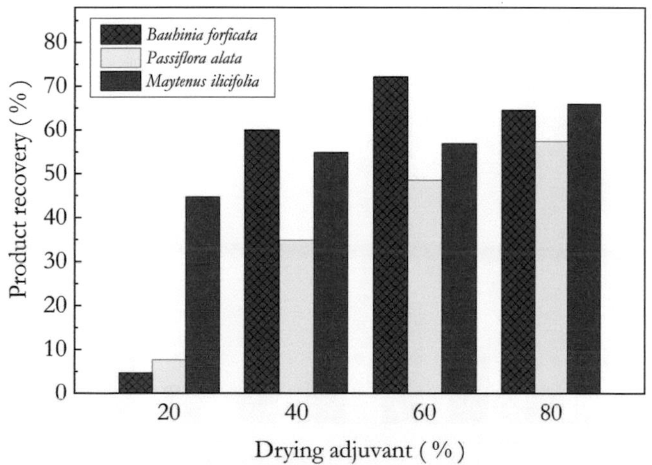

FIGURE 6.11 Product recovery as a function of the amount of colloidal SiO_2 (Tixosil® 333) added to the concentrated extracts of three Brazilian medicinal plants (*Bauhinia forficata, Passiflora alata,* and *Maytenus ilicifolia*) during SB drying.

6.6 KEY PRODUCT PROPERTIES

Product properties generally used to characterise dried phytochemical preparations include the loss on drying (≈moisture content), water activity, product size distribution, product morphology, flow properties, solubility, wettability, the content of marker compounds, thermal properties, product crystallinity, among others. The physical and chemical properties of the dried product depend on the operating parameters, initial extract constituents, and type and amount of the drying adjuvant. In general, the combination of processing and composition variables affects the physicochemical properties in a complex way.

6.6.1 Loss on Drying and Water Activity

The loss on drying (= moisture content plus volatiles) and the water activity of dry phytochemical preparations are very important properties since biological materials are subjected to spoilage due to degradation reactions (e.g. enzymatic hydrolysis, Maillard reaction, oxidation) and also by microbial growth. Thus, the moisture content and the water activity of the dry product should be maintained at safe levels, which will significantly reduce the occurrence of chemically or biochemically degrading reactions and microbial growth. Below the water activity value corresponding to the monolayer moisture content, degradation reactions, and microorganism growth, such as fungus and bacteria, are drastically reduced. Water activity ≤0.5 is usually considered a safe limit to avoid microbial growth [70, 71]. The water activity of the dried products depends on the feed composition properties and drying conditions. These properties may also influence other product properties, such as size distribution, agglomeration tendency, and flow properties [25, 70, 72]. Figure 6.12 presents

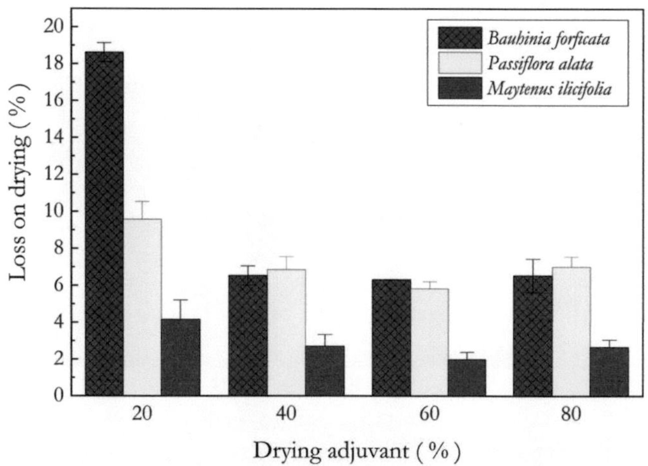

FIGURE 6.12 Product loss on drying as a function of the amount of colloidal SiO_2 (Tixosil® 333) added to the concentrated extracts of three Brazilian medicinal plants (*Bauhinia forficata*, *Passiflora alata*, and *Maytenus ilicifolia*) during SB drying.

experimental results of the loss on drying of SB-dried concentrated extracts from dry leaves of three Brazilian medicinal plants (*B. forficata*, *P. alata*, and *M. ilicifolia*) as a function of the colloidal SiO_2 (Tixosil® 333) added.

The results show that the increase in the concentration of the drying adjuvant from 20 to 40% w/w causes a remarkable decrease in the loss on drying of the dry extracts, reaching an almost constant value beyond 40%, specific for each extract composition (see Table 6.2). The behaviour observed may be also associated with the absorptive properties of the colloidal SiO_2 [73].

6.6.2 Particle Size and Size Distribution

Particle size is a very important property of the powders. Product solubility, wettability, and flow properties, factors of fundamental importance in pharmaceutical processing (e.g. powder mixtures, granulation, encapsulation, and compression), are affected by the particle size and size distribution. Examples of methods commonly used to determine the particle size of dry phytochemical preparations are optical microscopy and light scattering methods [26]. Fine particles with a polydisperse particle size distribution are generally generated during SB drying of herbal preparations. The mean size diameter depends on the type and concentration of drying adjuvant used and the drying and atomising conditions [18].

6.6.3 Product Morphology

Important properties of the powdered pharmaceutical solids, such as the surface area, flow properties, and compactability are intrinsically associated with their morphology. The SB drying mechanism and the properties of the feed composition have a significant impact on the product morphology. More irregular particles are expected during the SB drying of phytochemical preparations, some with flakes shape, compared with spray drying [8, 18]. The morphology and microstructure of powders are usually characterised by microscopic techniques, which can be categorised into three main groups [74], namely: (i) optical microcopy (e.g. bright field microscopy, phase contrast microscopy, Confocal Laser Scanning Microscopy [CLSM], fluorescent microscopy); (ii) Electron microscopy (e.g. Scanning Electron Microscopy [SEM], Transmission Electron Microscopy [TEM); and (iii) scanning probe microscopy techniques (e.g. Scanning Tunneling Microscopy [STM], Atomic Force Microscopy [AFM]).

6.6.4 Flow Properties

To some extent, the particle size and particle morphology affect the flow properties of the dry product. Free-flowing powders are desirable for the industrial processing of solid products. The repose angle, Hausner ratio, and Carr's Index are parameters commonly used to characterise the powders flow properties and are determined according to pharmacopeial recommendations [75–78]. Hausner found that the ratio of tapped to untapped (bulk) powder densities is related to the friction between the particles. Powders with low friction values, such as large particles, have Hausner factors ≤1.2, whereas smaller and cohesive particles with restricted flow present Hausner factors higher than 1.6. Carr's Index is also an indirect measure of the resistance of a powder to flow. Lower the Carr's Index, better flowability. The SB-dried phytochemical preparations usually exhibit poor flow properties in parts due to the small diameters of the product particles. The amount and type of drying aids added to the feed composition can change the product's flow properties [18].

6.6.5 X-Ray Diffraction

Amorphous solids are more likely to be formed during the drying of complex mixtures, such as phytochemical preparations, since some constituents would hinder the occurrence of crystallisation [79]. However, the drying conditions and properties of the feed composition might affect the crystallisation degree of the dry extract. Several studies have tried to correlate the crystallisation degree (during spray drying) with the glass transition temperature of some constituents of the feed. Products with a low glass transition temperature will present a high-temperature gradient relative to the drying gas temperature, affecting the product crystallisation. For example, Cortés-Rojas and Oliveira [18] used two nearly amorphous (colloidal silicon dioxide and maltodextrin) and two almost crystalline adjuvants (microcrystalline cellulose and β-cyclodextrin) as drying adjuvant during spray and SB drying of phytochemical preparations of *Bidens pilosa*. The MW, glass transition temperature (T_g), solubility, and crystalline degree of the carriers used significantly differ [32, 80–82]. According to the authors, the differences in the crystallinity degree of the dry extracts, evidenced in the X-ray diffractograms, show a strong influence of the drying adjuvant, independent of the drying process. As expected, the dry products generated from compositions containing colloidal SiO_2 as a single drying adjuvant and their mixture with Maltodextrin DE 10 exhibit X-ray diffractograms with large, non-defined peaks with abundant noises, a typical amorphous "halo" pattern. On the other hand, an increase in the crystallinity degree of the spray- and spouted-dried powders was observed for the dry extracts containing β-cyclodextrin or microcrystalline cellulose, showing the presence of some sharp and defined peaks, indicative of the presence of material in a highly ordered state.

6.6.6 Product Solubility

Solubility is an important property of pharmaceutical powders. The solubility of the dry product is intrinsically linked to its physicochemical properties, such as particle size, porosity, wettability, crystalline state, among others. In addition, factors such as the solvent system used to extract the bioactive compounds from the herbal material, the properties of the drying adjuvants used (e.g. water solubility, emulsifying properties), and the drying conditions affect the product properties and consequently its aqueous solubility [83, 84]. Generally, amorphous powders have increased aqueous solubility compared to the equivalent crystalline form [85].

6.7 PRODUCT STABILITY DURING STORAGE

Although the protocols for stability testing and routes of chemical degradation are well-known for most of the chemical substances, there is a lack of information regarding the stability of phytochemical preparations [86–89]. The stability of extracts made from plant material is essential to ensure the quality, safety, and efficacy of the finished product on the market. However, in most cases, the whole herbal drug or phytopharmaceutical preparations are regarded as the active substance. Since it may contain thousands of different substances, regardless of whether constituents with defined therapeutic activity are known, its stability measurement and shelf-life determination are demanding [88, 90]. An exception can be made for products where the substances responsible for the desired effect are fully known. Stability testing using different stressing storage conditions, especially temperature, relative humidity, luminosity, and oxygen, is usually employed to access quality changes as a function of time. Stressing storage conditions accelerate the degradation reactions and predict product shelf life [91, 92]. Physical and chemical analysis, including X-ray diffraction, thermal calorimetry, infrared spectrometry, UV-spectrophotometry, and chromatographic methods, can monitor physical and chemical product changes as a function of time and storage conditions [57, 86].

Evaluations of stability of spouted and spray-dried extracts of *P. alata* containing colloidal SiO_2 as drying adjuvant were presented by Bott et al. [57]. Samples of spray and SB extracts of *P. alata* were stored for 28 days, at 2 different temperatures (34 and 45°C) and 2 different relative humidities (52 and 63% RH for 34°C; 52 and 60% RH for 45°C), being analysed every 4 days. The flavonoid vitexin was used as the marker compound, assayed during the storage period by high-performance liquid chromatography. The results showed that the dry extracts were very hygroscopic. The high propensity to absorb water may be one of the key factors responsible for the high degradation of the marker compound vitexin and the short shelf life determined, ranging from 9 to 184 days (depending on the drying process and storage conditions). The authors were concerned with their finding since the dry herbal preparations, in general, are used as the active ingredient for the development of phytopharmaceutical dosage forms (solid and liquid preparations). However, the shelf life of dry *P. alata* extracts can be extended beyond 2 years if stored at lower storage temperatures and in packages with low permeability to water vapour, for example, aluminium laminated film.

6.8 CONCLUDING REMARKS

As stated in previous sections, the successful application of SBs for drying phytoextracts depends on several factors related to the feed composition properties, system configuration, and operating conditions. The system performance and product properties are directly linked to the correct selection of the processing conditions.

Factors such as physical properties of the feed composition and inert particles (e.g. surface tension, rheological properties, density, pH, and contact angle between them) may affect the SB dryer performance. The properties of the feed composition can be modified by adding the drying adjuvants [83], which is important for the drying process due to their influence on system behaviour, powders properties, and product stability. One of the main functions of the drying adjuvants is to increase the product's glass transition temperature, reducing its stickiness and wall deposition in the drying and agglomeration in storage, producing a stable product [42, 44, 72].

In summary, fundamental aspects related to the SB drying of phytochemical compositions were presented in this work, for example, the need for the correct selection of drying adjuvants, effects of drying adjuvant on product properties and system performance, the importance of stability testing of the finished product, among others. From the information presented, it can be affirmed that the SB technology can be used to produce high-quality dry phytochemical preparations adequate for food and pharmaceutical purposes, attending to the needs of product safety, quality, and efficacy. Nevertheless, it should be emphasised that, at this moment, the proposed technology is suitable only for small scale production, mainly due to the difficulties of scale-up, modelling and simulation of SB drying systems, chemical complexity of phytopharmaceutical compositions, and difficulties to predict product properties and system behaviour during operation.

ACKNOWLEDGEMENTS

The authors thank the São Paulo Research Foundation—FAPESP for the continuous financial support as scholarships and research grants.

NOMENCLATURE

$\mathbf{C_s}$	solids content [M M^{-1}]
$\mathbf{d_c}$	column diameter of the SB [L]
$\mathbf{H_0}$	static bed height [L]
$\mathbf{H_m}$	maximum static bed height [L]
$\mathbf{M_0}$	initial load of inert material [M]
$\dot{m}_{air}$	mass flow rate of the spouting gas [M T^{-1}]
$\dot{\mathbf{m}}_{\mathbf{feed}}$	mass flow rate of the feed composition [M]
$\dot{\mathbf{m}}_{\mathbf{max}}$	evaporation capacity of the dryer [M L^{-1} T^{-2}]
$\mathbf{P_{at}}$	pressure of the atomising gas [M L^{-1} T^{-2}]
$\mathbf{Q}$	flow rate of the spouting gas [L^3 T^{-1}]
$\mathbf{Q_{at}}$	flow rate of the atomising gas [L^3 T^{-1}]
$\mathbf{Q_{feed}}$	flow rate of the feed composition [L^3 T^{-1}]
$\mathbf{Q_{ms}}$	flow rate of the gas at minimum spouting [L^3 T^{-1}]
$\mathbf{T_g}$	glass transition temperature [θ]
$\mathbf{T_{in}}$	inlet gas temperature [θ]
$\mathbf{U}$	spouting gas velocity [L T^{-1}]
$\mathbf{U_{ms}}$	minimum spouting velocity [L T^{-1}]
$\mathbf{\Delta P_m}$	maximum pressure drop [M L^{-1} T^{-2}]
$\mathbf{\Delta P_s}$	pressure drop of stable spouting [M L^{-1} T^{-2}]
$\boldsymbol{\gamma}$	conical base angle °

REFERENCES

1. Cacace, J. E.; Mazza, G. Pressurized Low Polarity Water Extraction of Biologically Active Compounds from Plant Products. In *Functional Food Ingredients and Nutraceuticals Processing Technologies*; 2nd Ed; Shi, J., Ed.; CRC Press: Boca Raton, FL; 2015; pp. 177–198.
2. Pietta, P.; Minoggio, M.; Bramati, L. Plant Polyphenols: Structure, Occurrence and Bioactivity. In Studies in Natural Products Chemistry; Vol. 28, Bioactive Nat. Products (Part I), Rahman, A., Ed.; Elsevier: Amsterdam, The Netherland; 2003; pp. 257–312.
3. Ditz, R.; Gerard, D.; Hagels, H. J.; Igl, N. *Phytoextracts Proposal towards a New Comprehensive Research Focus*. DECHEMA: Frankfurt am Main, DE; 2017; p. 33.
4. Djordjevic, S. M. From Medicinal Plant Raw Material to Herbal Remedies. In *Aromatic and Medicinal Plants—Back to Nature*; El-Shemy, H. (Ed.), IntechOpen; 2017; pp. 269–288.
5. Alamgir, A. N. M. Therapeutic Use of Medicinal Plants and Their Extracts: Volume 1 Pharmacognosy; Springer International Publishing AG, Cham, Switzerland; 2017; p. 546.
6. Manach, C.; Scalbert, A.; Morand, C.; Rémésy, C.; Jiménez, L. Polyphenols: Food Sources and Bioavailability. *Am. J. Clin. Nutr.*, **2004**, *79* (5), 727–747.
7. Yoon, J.-H.; Baek, S. J. Molecular Targets of Dietary Polyphenols with Anti-Inflammatory Properties. *Yonsei Med. J.*, **2005**, *46* (5), 585–596.
8. Oliveira, W. P.; Bott, R. F.; Souza, C. R. F. Manufacture of Standardized Dried Extracts from Medicinal Brazilian Plants. *Dry. Technol.*, **2006**, *24* (4), 523–533.
9. Teixeira, C. C. C.; Cabral, T. P. F.; Tacon, L. A.; Villardi, I. L.; Lanchote, A. D.; Freitas, L. A. P. Solid State Stability of Polyphenols from a Plant Extract after Fluid Bed Atmospheric Spray-Freeze-Drying. *Powder Technol.*, **2017**, *319*, 494–504.
10. Oliveira, O. W.; Petrovick, P. R. Secagem Por Aspersão (Spray Drying) de Extratos Vegetais: Bases e Aplicações. *Rev. Bras. Farmacogn.*, **2010**, *20* (4), 641–650.
11. Benelli, L.; Oliveira, W. P. Fluidized Bed Coating of Inert Cores with a Lipid-Based System Loaded with a Polyphenol-Rich *Rosmarinus Officinalis* Extract. *Food Bioprod. Process.*, **2019**, *114*, 216–226.
12. Souza, C. R. F.; Oliveira, W. P. Drying of Phytochemical Preparations in a Spouted Bed: Perspectives and Challenges. *Dry. Technol.*, **2012**, *30* (11–12), 1209–1226.
13. Souza, C. R. F.; Donida, M. W.; Rocha, S. C. S.; Oliveira, W. P. The Role of Colloidal Silicon Dioxide in the Enhancement of the Drying of Herbal Preparations in Suspended State. *Chem. Eng. Commun.*, **2008**, *196* (3), 391–405.
14. Benelli, L.; Cortés-Rojas, D. F.; Souza, C. R. F.; Oliveira, W. P. Fluid Bed Drying and Agglomeration of Phytopharmaceutical Compositions. *Powder Technol.*, **2015**, *273*, 145–153.
15. Benelli, L.; Souza, C. R. F.; Oliveira, W. P. Quality Changes during Spouted Bed Drying of Pepper-Rosmarin Extract. *Can. J. Chem. Eng.*, **2013**, *91* (11), 1837–1846.
16. Souza, C. R. F.; Oliveira, W. P. Drying of Herbal Extract in a Draft-Tube Spouted Bed. *Can. J. Chem. Eng.*, **2009**, *87* (2), 279–288.
17. Souza, C. R. F.; Baldim, I.; Bankole, V. O.; Ana, R. da; Durazzo, A.; Lucarini, M.; Cicero, N.; Santini, A.; Souto, E. B.; Oliveira, W. P. Spouted Bed Dried *Rosmarinus officinalis* Extract: A Novel Approach for Physicochemical Properties and Antioxidant Activity. *Agric.*, **2020**, *10* (8), 1–16.
18. Cortés-Rojas, D. F.; Oliveira, W. P. Physicochemical Properties of Phytopharmaceutical Preparations as Affected by Drying Methods and Carriers. *Dry. Technol.*, **2012**, *30* (9), 921–934.
19. Souza, C.R.F.; Fregonesi, F.; Cortes-Rojas, D.F.; Oliveira, W.P. Parâmetros de produção e caracterização de sistemas micro-particulados contendo polifenois. In *XXXV Congresso Brasileiro de Sistemas Particulados (XXXV ENEMP)*; Vassouras, RJ, 2012, p.601-610 (Anais CD-Rom, Ed. UFRRJ).

20. Souza, C. R. F. Estudo Comparativo Da Produção de Extrato Seco de *Bauhinia forficata* Link Pelos Processos Spray-Dryer e Leito de Jorro Estudo Comparativo Da Produção de Extrato Seco de *Bauhinia forficata* Link Pelos Processos Spray-Dryer e Leito de Jorro. PPGCF-FCFRP/USP: Ribeirão Preto 2003, p. 180.
21. Souza, C. R. F.; Oliveira, W. P. Powder Properties and System Behavior during Spray Drying of *Bauhinia forficata* Link Extract. *Dry. Technol.*, **2006**, *24* (6), 735–749.
22. Epstein, N.; Grace, J. R. Introduction. In *Spouted and Spout-Fluid Beds: Fundamentals and Applications*; Epstein, N., Grace, J. R., Eds.; Cambridge University Press: Cambridge; 2011; pp. 1–16.
23. Oliveira, W. P.; Souza, C. R. F.; Lim, C. J.; Grace, J. R. Evaluation of Flow Regimes in a Semi-Cylindrical Spouted Bed through Statistical, Mutual Information, Spectral and Hurst's Analysis., *Can. J. Chem. Eng.*, **2008**, *86* (3), 582–597.
24. Bi, X. Initiation of Spouting. In *Spouted and Spout-Fluid Beds*; Epstein, N., Grace, J. R., Eds.; Cambridge University Press: Cambridge; 2010; pp. 17–28.
25. Souza, C. R. F. *Standardized Dried Extracts of Brazilian Medicinal Plants: Assessment of Technical and Economical Feasibility of the Spouted Bed Drying*. PPGCF-FCFRP/USP: Ribeirão Preto; 2007; p 219.
26. Oliveira, W. P.; Freitas, L. A. P.; Freire, J. T. Drying of Pharmaceutical Products. In *Transport Phenomena in Particulate Systems*; Freire, J. T., Silveira, A. M., Maria do Carmo Ferreira, Eds.; Bentham Science Publishers Ltd.; Oak Park, IL; 2012; pp. 148–171.
27. Freitas, L. A. P. Pharmaceutical Applications of Spouted Beds: A Review on Solid Dosage Forms. *Particuology*, **2019**, *42*, 126–136.
28. Passos, M. L.; Massarani, G.; Freire, J. T.; Mujumdar, A. S. Drying of Pastes in Spouted Beds of Inert Particles: Design Criteria and Modeling. *Dry. Technol.*, **1997**, *15* (2), 605–624.
29. Benali, M.; Amazouz, M. Effect of Drying-Aid Agents on Processing of Sticky Materials. *Dev. Chem. Eng. Miner. Process.*, **2008**, *10* (3–4), 401–414.
30. Rocha, S. C. S.; Donida, M. W.; Marques, A. M. M. Liquid-Particle Surface Properties on Spouted Bed Coating and Drying Performance. *Can. J. Chem. Eng.*, **2009**, *87* (5), 695–703.
31. Markowski, A. S. Quality Interaction in a Jet Spouted Bed Dryer for Bio-Products. *Dry. Technol.*, **1993**, *11* (2), 369–387.
32. Rowe, R. C.; Sheskey, P. J.; Quinn, M. E. *Handbook of Pharmaceutical Excipients*, 6th ed.; Pharmaceutical Press: London; 2009.
33. Epstein, N.; Grace, J. R., Eds. *Spouted and Spout-Fluid Beds: Fundamentals and Applications*; Cambridge University Press: Cambridge; 2011.
34. Karim, M. A.; Law, C.-L.; Wang, Y.; Mujumdar, A. S.; Zhang, M. Microwave-Assisted Pulsed Fluidized and Spouted Bed Drying. In *Intermittent and Nonstationary Drying Technologies Principles and Applications*; Karim, M. A., Law, C.-L., Eds.; CRC Press, Boca Raton, FL, 2017; pp. 139–162.
35. Cordeiro, D. S.; Oliveira, W. P. Technical Aspects of the Production of Dried Extract of *Maytenus ilicifolia* Leaves by Jet Spouted Bed Drying. *Int. J. Pharm.*, **2005**, *299* (1–2), 115–126.
36. Jaya, S.; Sudhagar, M.; Das, H. Stickiness of Food Powders and Related Physico-Chemical Properties of Food Components. *J. Food Sci. Technol.*, 2002, 1–7.
37. Bhandari, B. R.; Datta, N.; Howes, T. Problems Associated with Spray Drying of Sugar-Rich Foods. *Dry. Technol.*, **1997**, *15* (2), 671–684.
38. Souza, C. R. F.; Bott, R. F.; Donida, M. W.; Rocha, S. C. S.; Oliveira, W. P. Stickiness on Drying of Herbal Extracts in Suspended State: Requisites of the Substrate and Feed Composition. In *Proceedings of 15th International Drying Symposium*; Farkas, I., Ed.; University Publisher, Gödöllő, HU; 2006; pp. 700–707.

39. Bhandari, B. R.; Howes, T. Implication of Glass Transition for the Drying and Stability of Dried Foods. *J. Food Eng.*, **1999**, *40* (1), 71–79.
40. Medeiros, M. F. D.; Rocha, S. C. S.; Alsina, O. L. S.; Jerônimo, C. E. M.; Medeiros, U. K. L.; da Mata, A. L. M. L. Drying of Pulps of Tropical Fruits in Spouted Bed: Effect of Composition on Dryer Performance. *Dry. Technol.*, **2002**, *20* (4–5), 855–881.
41. Collares, F.; Finzer, J. R.; Kieckbusch, T. Glass Transition Control of the Detachment of Food Pastes Dried over Glass Plates. *J. Food Eng.*, **2004**, *61* (2), 261–267.
42. Li, R.; Lin, D.; Roos, Y. H.; Miao, S. Glass Transition, Structural Relaxation and Stability of Spray-Dried Amorphous Food Solids: A Review. *Dry. Technol.*, **2019**, *37* (3), 287–300.
43. Abiad, M. G.; Carvajal, M. T.; Campanella, O. H. A Review on Methods and Theories to Describe the Glass Transition Phenomenon: Applications in Food and Pharmaceutical Products. *Food Eng. Rev.*, **2009**, *1* (2), 105–132.
44. Muzaffar, K. Stickiness Problem Associated with Spray Drying of Sugar and Acid Rich Foods: A Mini Review. *J. Nutr. Food Sci.*, **2015**, *s12*, 11–13.
45. Fazaeli, M.; Emam-Djomeh, Z.; Kalbasi Ashtari, A.; Omid, M. Effect of Spray Drying Conditions and Feed Composition on the Physical Properties of Black Mulberry Juice Powder. *Food Bioprod. Process.*, **2012**, *90* (4), 667–675.
46. Samborska, K. Powdered Honey—Drying Methods and Parameters, Types of Carriers and Drying Aids, Physicochemical Properties and Storage Stability. *Trends Food Sci. Technol.*, **2019**, *88*, 133–142.
47. Chaul, L. T.; Conceição, E. C.; Bara, M. T. F.; Paula, J. R.; Couto, R. O. Engineering Spray-Dried Rosemary Extracts with Improved Physicomechanical Properties: A Design of Experiments Issue. *Brazilian J. Pharmacogn.*, **2017**, *27* (2), 236–244.
48. Bhandari, B.; Howes, T. Relating the Stickiness Property of Foods Undergoing Drying and Dried Products to Their Surface Energetics. *Dry. Technol.*, **2005**, *23* (4), 781–797.
49. Vieira, M. G. A.; Donida, M. W.; Rocha, S. C. S. Adhesion of an Aqueous Polymeric Suspension to Inert Particles in a Spouted Bed. *Dry. Technol.*, **2004**, *22* (5), 1069–1085.
50. Souza, C. R. F.; Schiavetto, I. A.; Thomazini, F. C. F.; Oliveira, W. P. Processing of *Rosmarinus officinalis* Linne Extract on Spray and Spouted Bed Dryers. *Brazilian J. Chem. Eng.*, **2008**, *25* (1), 59–69.
51. Bacelos, M. S.; Neto, P. I. S.; Silveira, A. M.; Freire, J. T. Analysis of Fluid Dynamics Behavior of Conical Spouted Bed in Presence of Pastes. *Dry. Technol.*, **2005**, *23* (3), 427–453.
52. Oliveira, W. P.; Souza, C. R. F.; Lim, C. J.; Grace, J. R. Identification of the State of a Wet Spouted Bed through Time-Frequency Analysis of Pressure Fluctuation Time Series. *Can. J. Chem. Eng.*, **2009**, *87* (2), 289–297.
53. Souza, C. R. F.; Oliveira, W. P. Influence of Spouted Bed Design on Dryer Throughput and Product Quality. In *Proceedings of 16th International Drying Symposium*; Thorat, B. N., Ed.; University of Mumbai, Mumbai; 2008; pp. 667–675.
54. Bonazzi, C.; Dumoulin, E. Quality Changes in Food Materials as Influenced by Drying Processes. In *Modern Drying Technology*; Tsotsas, E., Mujumdar, A. S., Eds.; Wiley-VCH Verlag GmbH & Co. KGaA: Weinheim, Germany; 2011; Vol. 3–4, pp. 1–20.
55. Bhandari, B.; Hartel, R. Phase Transitions during Food Powder Production and Powder Stability. In *Encapsulated and Powdered Foods*, Onwulata, C., Ed.; CRC Press, Boca Raton, FL, 2005; pp. 261–292.
56. Souza, C. R. F.; Baldim, I.; Bankole, V. O.; Ana, R.; Durazzo, A.; Lucarini, M.; Cicero, N.; Santini, A.; Souto, E. B.; Oliveira, W. P. Spouted Bed Dried *Rosmarinus officinalis* Extract: A Novel Approach for Physicochemical Properties and Antioxidant Activity. *Agriculture*, **2020**, *10* (8), 1–16.
57. Bott, R. F.; Labuza, T. P.; Oliveira, W. P. Stability Testing of Spray- and Spouted Bed–Dried Extracts of *Passiflora alata*. *Dry. Technol.*, **2010**, *28* (11), 1255–1265.

58. Chu, K. K. W.; Chow, A. H. L. Impact of Carbohydrate Constituents on Moisture Sorption of Herbal Extracts. *Pharm. Res.*, **2000**, *17*, 1133–1137.
59. Runha, F. P.; Cordeiro, D. S.; Pereira, C. A. M.; Vilegas, J.; Oliveira, W. P. Production of Dry Extracts of Medicinal Brazilian Plants by Spouted Bed Process. *Food Bioprod. Process.*, **2001**, *79* (3), 160–168.
60. Pagliarussi, R. S.; Bastos, J. K.; Freitas, L. A. P. Fluid Bed Drying of Guarana (*Paullinia cupana* HBK) Extract: Effect of Process Factors on Caffeine Content. *AAPS PharmSciTech*, **2006**, *7* (2), 1–7.
61. Shuhama, I. K.; Aguiar, M. L.; Oliveira, W. P.; Freitas, L. A. P. Experimental Production of Annatto Powders in Spouted Bed Dryer. *J. Food Eng.*, **2003**, *59* (1), 93–97.
62. Souza, C. R. F. R. F.; Oliveira, W. P. P. Spouted Bed Drying of *Bauhinia forficata* Link Extract: The Effects of Feed Atomizer Position and Operating Conditions on Equipment Performance and Product Properties. *Brazilian J. Chem. Eng.*, **2005**, *22* (2), 239–247.
63. Souza, C. R. F.; Oliveira, W. P. Comparative Study of the Evaporation Capacity of the Conventional and Jet Spouted Bed Dryers for Liquid Materials. In *Proceedings of 13th International Drying Symposium*, Cao, C.W.; Pan, Y.K.; Liu, X.D.;Qu, Y.X., Eds., Pub. Online, Beijing, CN,2002; pp. 808–816.
64. Medeiros, M. F. D.; Rocha, S. C. S.; Alsina, O. L. S.; Lima, L. M. O.; Lima, C. A. C. Efeito da Composição Sobre o Desempenho da Secagem de Polpas de Frutas em Leito de Jorro: Validação de Modelos Empíricos e Otimização. In *XIV Congresso Brasileiro de Engenharia Química (XIV COBEQ)*; Curitiba, 2004; p. Anais CD-Rom.
65. Donida, M. W.; Rocha, S. C. S.; Castro, B. D.; Marques, A. M. M. Coating and Drying in Spouted Bed: Influence of the Liquid-Particle Work of Adhesion. *Dry. Technol.*, **2007**, *25* (2), 319–326.
66. Oliveira, W. P.; Bott, R. F.; Souza, C. R. F. Sorption Isotherms of Spray and Spouted Bed Dried Herbal Extracts. In *Proceedings of 17th International Drying Symposium*; Tsotsas, E.; Metzger,T.; Peglow, M., DECHEMA, Magdeburg, 2010; pp. 990–997.
67. Bott, R. F. *Influence of the Production Process, Storage Conditions and Physical and Chemical Properties on the Stability of Standardised Dried Extracts of Medicinal Plants*; PPGCF-FCFRP/USP: Ribeirão Preto, BR; 2008; p. 182.
68. Instituto Adolfo Lutz. *Analytical Methods of Institute Adolfo Lutz—Chemical and Physical Methods for Food Analysis*, 3rd ed; IMESP: São Paulo; 1985.
69. Bradford, M. M. A Rapid and Sensitive Method for the Quantitation of Microgram Quantities of Protein Utilising the Principle of Protein-Dye Binding. *Anal. Biochem.*, **1976**, *72* (1–2), 248–254.
70. Labuza, T.; Shafiur Rahman, M. Water Activity and Food Preservation. In *Handbook of Food Preservation*; Rahman, M. S., Ed.; CRC Press: Boca Raton, FL, 2007; pp. 447–476.
71. Maltini, E.; Torreggiani, D.; Venir, E.; Bertolo, G. Water Activity and the Preservation of Plant Foods. *Food Chem.*, **2003**, *82* (1), 79–86.
72. Roos, Y. H. Importance of Glass Transition and Water Activity to Spray Drying and Stability of Dairy Powders. *Lait*, **2002**, *82* (4), 475–484.
73. Wang, J.; Trinkle, D.; Derbin, G.; Martin, K.; Sharif, S.; Timmins, P.; Desai, D. Moisture Adsorption and Desorption Properties of Colloidal Silicon Dioxide and Its Impact on Layer Adhesion of a Bilayer Tablet Formulation. *J. Excipients Food Chem.*, **2014**, *5* (1), 21–31.
74. Burgain, J.; Petit, J.; Scher, J.; Rasch, R.; Bhandari, B.; Gaiani, C. Surface Chemistry and Microscopy of Food Powders. *Prog. Surf. Sci.*, **2017**, *92* (4), 409–429.
75. Sarraguça, M. C.; Cruz, A. V.; Soares, S. O.; Amaral, H. R.; Costa, P. C.; Lopes, J. A. Determination of Flow Properties of Pharmaceutical Powders by Near Infrared Spectroscopy. *J. Pharm. Biomed. Anal.*, **2010**, *52* (4), 484–492.

76. ICH, I. C. on H. Guidance on Q4B Evaluation and Recommendation of Pharmacopoeial Texts for Use in the International Conference on Harmonisation Regions; Annex 13 on Bulk Density and Tapped Density of Powders General Chapter; Availability. Notice. *Fed Regist.*, **2013**, *78* (102), 6.
77. Silva, J. S.; Splendor, D.; Gonçalves, I. M. B.; Costa, P.; Lobo, J. S. Note on the Measurement of Bulk Density and Tapped Density of Powders According to the European Pharmacopeia. *AAPSPharmscitech*, **2013**, 14 (3), 1098–1100.
78. Moondra, S.; Maheshwari, R.; Taneja, N.; Tekade, M.; Tekadle, R. K. Bulk Level Properties and Its Role in Formulation Development and Processing. In *Dosage Form Design Parameters*, Vol 2; Tekade, R. K., Ed.; Academic Press: London, UK; 2018; pp. 221–256.
79. Langrish, T. A. G.; Wang, S. Crystallization Rates for Amorphous Sucrose and Lactose Powders from Spray Drying: A Comparison. *Dry. Technol.*, **2009**, *27* (4), 606–614.
80. Islam, M. I. U.; Langrish, T. A. G.; Chiou, D. Particle Crystallization during Spray Drying in Humid Air. *J. Food Eng.*, **2010**, *99* (1), 55–62.
81. Tabary, N.; Mahieu, A.; Willart, J. F.; Dudognon, E.; Dande, F.; Descamps, M.; Bacquet, M.; Martel, B. Characterization of the Hidden Glass Transition of Amorphous Cyclomaltoheptaose. *Carbohydr. Res.*, **2011**, *346* (14), 2193–2199.
82. Terinte, N.; Ibbett, R.; Schuster, K. C. Overview on Native Cellulose and Microcrystalline Cellulose I Structure Studied By X-Ray Diffraction (Waxd): Comparison Between Measurement Techniques. *Lenzinger Berichte*, **2011**, *89* (1), 118–131.
83. Lee, J. K. M.; Taip, F. S.; Abdullah, Z. Effectiveness of Additives in Spray Drying Performance: A Review. *Food Res.*, **2018**, *2* (6), 486–499.
84. Cortés-Rojas, D. F.; Souza, C. R. F.; Oliveira, W. P. Optimization of Spray Drying Conditions for Production of *Bidens pilosa* L. Dried Extract. *Chem. Eng. Res. Des.*, **2015**, *93*, 366–376.
85. Cano-Chauca, M.; Stringheta, P. C.; Ramos, A. M.; Cal-Vidal, J. Effect of the Carriers on the Microstructure of Mango Powder Obtained by Spray Drying and Its Functional Characterisation. *Innov. Food Sci. Emerg. Technol.*, **2005**, *6* (4), 420–428.
86. Gafner, S.; Bergeron, C. The Challenges of Chemical Stability Testing of Herbal Extracts in Finished Products Using State-of-the-Art Analytical Methodologies. *Curr. Pharm. Anal.*, **2005**, *1* (2), 203–215.
87. Cortés-Rojas, D. F.; Souza, C. R. F.; Oliveira, W. P. Assessment of Stability of a Spray Dried Extract from the Medicinal Plant *Bidens pilosa* L. *J. King Saud Univ.—Eng. Sci.*, **2016**, *28* (2), 141–146.
88. Bansal, G.; Suthar, N.; Kaur, J.; Jain, A. Stability Testing of Herbal Drugs: Challenges, Regulatory Compliance and Perspectives. *Phytother. Res.*, **2016**,30 (7), 1046–1058.
89. Thakur, L.; Ghodasra, U.; Patel, N.; Dabhi, M. Novel Approaches for Stability Improvement in Natural Medicines. *Pharmacogn. Rev.*, **2011**, *5* (9), 48–54.
90. Bauer, R. Quality Criteria and Standardization of Phytopharmaceuticals: Can Acceptable Drug Standards Be Achieved? *Ther. Innov. Regul. Sci.*, **1997**, *32* (1), 101–110.
91. Gil-Alegre, M.; Bernabeu, J.; Camacho, M.; Torres-Suarez, A. Statistical Evaluation for Stability Studies under Stress Storage Conditions. *Il Farmaco*, **2001**, *56* (11), 877–883.
92. Bhagyashree, P.; Karishma, G.; Sampada, A.; Ankita, P.; Pratibha, C.; Kailash, V. Recent Trends in Stability Testing of Pharmaceutical Products: A Review. *Res. J. Pharm. Biol. Chem. Sci.*, **2015**, *6* (1), 1557–1569.

7 Drying of Lipid Systems Loaded with Phytochemicals

Elizabeth Céspedes-Gutiérrez and Diego Francisco Cortés-Rojas

CONTENTS

7.1 Introduction ... 173
7.2 Lipid Formulation Design Oriented towards a Drying Process ... 174
 7.2.1 Wall Materials ... 175
7.3 Methods to Prepare Lipid-Based Formulations ... 176
 7.3.1 High-Pressure Homogenisation (HPH) ... 177
 7.3.2 Ultrasonic Homogenising ... 178
 7.3.3 Solvent Injection ... 178
 7.3.4 Microemulsion-Based Method ... 178
 7.3.5 Melt Emulsification ... 179
7.4 Physicochemical Characterisation of Lipid Systems ... 179
7.5 Stability of Lipid-Based Formulations ... 180
7.6 Drying of Lipid-Based Formulations ... 182
7.7 Case Study: Spray Drying of *Syzygium aromaticum* Lipidic Emulsions ... 185
7.8 Final Remarks ... 190
References ... 190

7.1 INTRODUCTION

Lipid-based formulations are important delivery systems for active phytopharmaceutical ingredients (API). Volatile, non-polar, or heat-sensitive compounds could be encapsulated and protected by using this technique. Emulsions and liquid lipid formulations are effective delivery systems for API that are poorly soluble in water, enhancing their absorption and bioavailability. Lipidic systems delivered by the oral route might increase the solubility of the active ingredient in the intestinal tract, reducing the first-pass effect by promoting intestinal lymphatic transport and facilitating enterocyte-mediated transport [1]. Topically, lipid nanoparticles allow greater contact of the drug with the stratum corneum associated with the increased surface area, produce a hydration effect due to lipid occlusive properties, which increase the chemical stability of compounds sensitive to light, oxidation, and hydrolysis [2].

Lipid-based formulations cover basic lipid solutions to advanced self-emulsifying delivery systems [3]. Oil and water are immiscible phases and, consequently,

DOI: 10.1201/9781003225416-9

thermodynamically unstable systems, and the stability of liquid emulsions decreases with storage time. Drying lipid-based systems is a strategy to improve stability and facilitate handling, transportation, and storage [4]. Powdered formulations can be easily reconstituted at the time of use [5]. Freeze-drying, spray freeze-drying, spray congealing, or spray drying can convert the liquid lipid formulations into powdered forms. However, spray drying is one of the most suitable techniques due to the easy scaling-up, simplicity, and low cost [4].

7.2 LIPID FORMULATION DESIGN ORIENTED TOWARDS A DRYING PROCESS

A proper formulation should be designed to protect the API during the drying process. Factors such as the type of lipid, the emulsifiers, wall material, and the emulsification process are very important, directly influencing the physical–chemical properties of the product and therefore on the protection of the API [6]. The formulation components must be selected carefully to achieve maximum encapsulation efficiency, prevent or minimise degradation of the API, and maximise its absorption and stability. The high energy at the oil–water interphase could be reduced by adding surface-active compounds by reducing droplet size or modifying the flow and electrical properties of the interfacial layer [7]. Reduction of the interfacial tension and coalescence depends on the ability of surface-active compounds to cover the oil–water interface quickly [8].

The API to be encapsulated is usually dispersed in the lipid phase, which must be compatible. The biocompatibility and biodegradability of the employed lipids are linked to the bioaccessibility and bioavailability of the incorporated drug [3]. The first step to develop a lipid formulation is lipid screening. It can be performed by mixing the API with the melted lipid phase and checking its solubility. A novel approach for lipid screening has been proposed based on the determination of the Hansen solubility parameters. The affinity of the API with the lipid is estimated through theoretical calculations taking into account the dispersion forces between molecules (van der Waals), polarity (related to dipolar intermolecular force between molecules), and hydrogen bonding [9]. Commonly, lipids of natural origin are used because they are considered safe for human consumption and are easily digested and absorbed [10]. However, chemically modified lipids, such as propylene glycol (PEG) units, are also widely used. Lipids are composed of mixtures of triglycerides of long-chain fatty acids with varying degrees of unsaturation. The melting point of the lipids is directly related to their chemical composition; the smaller the fatty acid chain and the fewer number of unsaturation, the lower the melting point [10]. Depending on the application of the final product, the lipid phase can be solid or liquid at room temperature. Other factors must also be considered in selecting the appropriate lipid, such as its subsequent application, route of administration, and the temperatures at which the formulation must be stable. For example, in topical application, the melting point of the composition must be above 45°C. The formulations to be subjected to spray drying should preferably be composed of lipids with a high melting point, minimising the stickiness problems on the equipment walls and allowing viable drying temperatures. The stickiness phenomena during spray drying are related to the softening and the glass transition temperature of the processed material [11, 12].

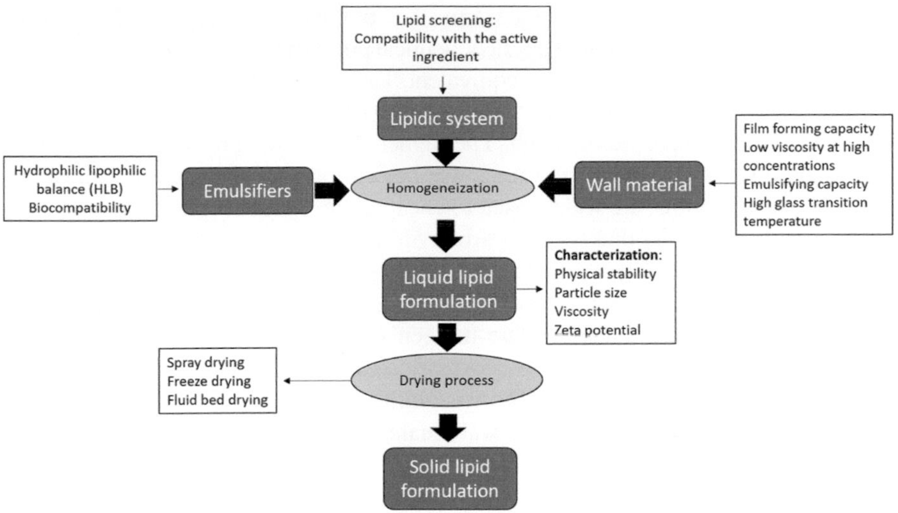

FIGURE 7.1 Schematic diagram of the main steps needed for the preparation of dry lipid systems.

After selecting the lipid system, it is required to choose the surfactants to promote the dispersion of the lipid and aqueous phases by reducing surface tension and forming micelles of proper size and physical stability. Factors such as the API site of action, toxicity, and biocompatibility should be considered. The most widely used surfactants are hydrophilic with Hydrophilic Lipophilic Balance (HLB) greater than 10, which form (oil-in-water [O/W]) emulsions, e.g., polysorbate 80 (Tween® 80), polyoxyethylene-polyoxypropylene (Poloxamer® 188, Pluronic® F68, Lutrol® F68, Kolliphor® 188), sodium cocoamphoacetate (Miranol Ultra C32), and polyethoxylated castor oil (Chremophor®) [13]. Ionic emulsifiers are employed to obtain multilayer-based emulsions adding oppositely charged polyelectrolytes improving the emulsion stability against environmental stresses due to the increment of thickness interface [14]. Solid surfactants at room temperature could facilitate the drying process; however, the lipid melting is an additional operation. Figure 7.1 shows the schematic diagram of the main steps required for the preparation of dry lipid systems.

7.2.1 Wall Materials

A fundamental step in the drying and encapsulation of lipidic formulations is selecting the wall material (carrier) based on the product's end use, the type of material to be encapsulated, and cost [15]. The wall material must have the necessary characteristics: the film-forming capacity, low viscosity at high concentrations, emulsifying capacity, non-reactivity with the material to be encapsulated, high glass transition temperature, and low cost [16]. Wall materials can be classified by their chemical composition, with carbohydrates, gums, and proteins being widely used.

Carbohydrates are commonly used in the encapsulation of food compounds due to their low cost, good solubility, and excellent degree of protection that they can provide.

Maltodextrins, starches, and β-cyclodextrin stand out in this group. Maltodextrins are hydrolysed starches with different physicochemical properties, depending on the degree of hydrolysis, given by their dextrose equivalent. The increase in the degree of dextrose equivalent gives maltodextrin properties similar to dextrose, while the decrease in DE approximates the properties of starch. The higher the DE, the greater the hygroscopicity, solubility and sweetness, and the lower the viscosity. Maltodextrins, pure or in combination with gums, are widely used to encapsulate volatile compounds [17].

Cyclodextrins are another type of carbohydrate with a cyclic structure composed of 6 (α-cyclodextrin), 7 (β-cyclodextrin), or 8 (γ-cyclodextrin) glucose monomers and are produced by enzymatic degradation of starch by the enzyme cyclodextrin glucanotransferase (EC 2.4.1.19). The molecular structure of cyclodextrins has a hydrophobic cavity that facilitates the formation of inclusion complexes with different molecules, improving their solubility, stability, and bioavailability [18].

Starch and modified starches are wall materials widely used for encapsulation purposes. Starches are modified through an esterification process with n-octenyl succinyl anhydride (OSA) to render an amphiphilic hydrocolloid with improved emulsification and encapsulation properties. Modified corn starches such as Capsul® and Hi-Cap® 100 have shown good results in encapsulating different volatile compounds such as cafestol and kahweol from green coffee oil or lemon myrtle oil [14, 19].

Concerning gums, Arabic gum is the most used and consists of a polymer composed of D-glucuronic acid, L-rhamnose, D-galactose, and L-arabinose with approximately 2% of proteins which are responsible for the emulsifying properties [16]. It is a natural soluble fibre obtained from the *Acacia senegal* and *Acacia seyal* tree exudates, native from Africa. Arabic gum has shown excellent results in the encapsulation of volatile compounds [20]. Among the disadvantages of using Arabic gum are its relatively high cost, limited availability, and possible variations in its quality [11]. Gum arabic is a natural soluble fibre extracted from the exudates of the *A. senegal* and *A. seyal* plants (Leguminosae family), which normally grow in several countries in the sub-Saharan Africa region.

Proteins, such as gelatin, caseinates, soy, or whey proteins, are also widely used as wall material, as they have an amphiphilic character, offering the physical–chemical and functional properties required to encapsulate hydrophobic materials. Proteins have been successfully used to encapsulate various phytoconstituents such as essential oils, lycopene-rich tomato extract, polyunsaturated fatty acid–rich sunflower oil, curcumin, lutein, and phenolic extracts [21–25]. Factors such as pH and ionic strength must be considered when using proteins to avoid changes in their properties [11]. For example, the protein-API interaction changes with the isoelectric point of the protein and the medium pH [26].

7.3 METHODS TO PREPARE LIPID-BASED FORMULATIONS

The method used to prepare lipid-based formulations has a direct impact on product stability and encapsulation efficiency. Factors such as the easiness of scale-up, the cost, production time, and the use of organic solvents should be considered previously in selecting the preparation method. Table 7.1 presents the main techniques usually employed to prepare the lipid particles reported in the literature with

TABLE 7.1
Preparation Methods of Lipid-Based Formulations Loaded with Active Phytopharmaceutical Ingredients (API)

Method	API	Oily Phase	Surfactants	Reference
High-pressure homogenisation	Eugenol	Stearic and oleic acid	Cremophor® RH40, Pluronic® F68, Tween® 20	[27]
	Lutein	Cutina® CP, Dynasan® 116, Carnauba wax, Mygliol® 812	Plantacare® 810	[28]
Ultrasonic homogenisation	Psoralens	Precirol® ATO 5	Pluronic® F68, Tween® 80, soy phosphatidylcholine, Myverol® 18-04K	[29]
	Lutein	Precirol® ATO 5	Myverol® 18-04K Pluronic® F68	[30]
	Scutellaria baicalensis flavonoid	Tripalmitin, phosphatidylcholine, vitamin E	Gelucire® 49/8, Gelucire® 62/5	[31]
Solvent injection	Simvastatin	Glycerol monostearate and oleic acid	Poloxamer® 407	[32]
Solvent evaporation	Apocynin	Glyceryl tristearate, sucrose ester 15, sucrose monopalmitate	Polyvinyl alcohol (PVA)	[33]
	Rosemary polyphenols	Cholesterol	Phospholipon® 90H	[34]
Microemulsion	Oridonin, *Rabdosia rubescens* diterpenoid	Glycerol monostearate, medium-chain triglyceride	Pluronic® F68, PEG2000-stearate	[35]
Melt-emulsification	*Pterodon pubescens* fruit oil	Compritol® 888 ATO, Precirol® ATO 5, Phospholipon® 90H	Tween® 80, PEG-40	[36]
	Tetrandrine	Precirol® ATO 5, glyceryl monostearate, stearic acid	Pluronic® F68, SDC, Lipoid® E80, sodium deoxycholate	[37]

application examples. Techniques are generally divided into high-energy methods (e.g. ultrasound, high-pressure homogenisation [HPH], and high-speed homogenisation) and low-energy methods (e.g. micro-emulsification, phase inversion, multiple emulsification, and solvent diffusion).

7.3.1 High-Pressure Homogenisation (HPH)

HPH is a technique widely used to prepare lipid systems in research and industrial production due to its versatility, operational easiness, and direct scale-up. The high-pressure homogenisers force a liquid formulation to pass through a hole of micrometric size at high speed, producing shear, and cavitation forces that reduce the size of particles [38]. Normally, 2 to 3 cycles and pressures from 250 to 500 bar are used, but the conditions must be optimised for each formulation. There are two variants of this technique: hot and cold HPH. In cold homogenisation, the API is incorporated into the melted lipid matrix, which is then cooled, ground, and added to the aqueous solution of the selected surfactant to finally pass through the high-pressure homogeniser. In the hot HPH, the API is added to the melted lipids and subsequently to the surfactant solution (at the same temperature) and then subjected to the HPH process. Finally, the mix is cooled for the solidification–crystallisation of the matrix lipid. The disadvantages of this process are the high energy consumption, the risk of damage to the molecular structure, the release of metallic particles, the wide particle size distribution, and in some specific cases, the difficulty of scaling the homogenisation [38].

7.3.2 Ultrasonic Homogenising

In this method, the melted lipid phase, aqueous phase, and surfactant are subjected to high-power ultrasound with the aid of an ultrasonic processor. Frequency waves greater than 20 kHz are generated by a magnetostrictive or piezoelectric transducer, producing pressure gradients that deform the droplets through the cavitation produced by the drop of the value of local pressure below the solvent vapour pressure, generating turbulent flow and shear. The formulation contamination due to the release of metallic particles from the probe tip, the costs, and the difficulties for scaling-up [38].

7.3.3 Solvent Injection

This method was adapted from that used to produce polymeric microparticles. It is based on the precipitation of the lipid dissolved in water-miscible organic solvents, such as ethanol, acetone, or dimethyl sulfoxide (DMSO). These solvents are subsequently injected into the aqueous phase under agitation, with or without surfactant, causing precipitation and formation of lipid particles which are subsequently filtered. This method is restricted to lipids soluble in polar organic solvents but has the advantage of not using high temperatures or high shear rates [39].

7.3.4 Microemulsion-Based Method

This method consists of the precise selection of emulsion components (melted lipids, surfactants, co-surfactants, and water) in order to reduce at a very low level, the interfacial tension at the oil/water interface [40]. Microemulsions are transparent in visible light, and no high-energy input is required to stabilise the system. The proportion of each dilution component and the temperature gradient are factors of great importance for the formation of the microemulsion and can be determined using ternary diagrams as a function of temperature. Steep temperature gradients facilitate the rapid crystallisation of lipids and prevent their aggregation. A disadvantage of this method is the low concentrations of lipid particles attained after preparation (approx. 1%) [41].

7.3.5 Melt Emulsification

In this method, the solid lipids are melted and blended with the liquid lipids and mixed with an aqueous solution of the surfactants (aqueous phase) preheated at the same temperature [42]. The oily and aqueous phases are mixed through a high-efficiency homogeniser (e.g. Ultraturrax) or ultrasonic probe. The pre-emulsion is cooled down to crystallise the lipids forming the lipid particles.

7.4 PHYSICOCHEMICAL CHARACTERISATION OF LIPID SYSTEMS

The lipid formulation characterisation is essential in the development stage to determine the influence of process variables on the product's physicochemical properties. In the industrial production stage, characterisation is also important to guarantee and standardise product quality. The main characteristics evaluated are the load capacity of the API, particle size distribution, physical stability as a function of time, zeta potential, crystallinity degree, and morphology [43].

Encapsulation efficiency is, by definition, the percentage of API incorporated in the lipid particles to the total amount added. On the other hand, the load capacity refers to the maximum amount of API incorporated into the formulation's amount of lipid phase. Encapsulation efficiency and load capacity are intrinsically related to the compatibility between the API, lipids, and surfactants. For this reason, screening is performed to select the lipids to be used in the formulation. The quantification of the API loaded to the lipid formulations is needed and can be performed by analytical techniques such as high-performance liquid chromatography, gas chromatography, and ultraviolet (UV) spectroscopy.

Particle size and morphology are properties linked to the physicochemical stability of the lipidic system. These properties are affected by factors such as the type and concentration of lipid and surfactant used, the preparation method, and the processing temperature. Microscopy methods such as optical, electron, transmission, and atomic force characterise the particle morphology depending on the size range obtained and the resolution required. Special instruments based on physical principles such as light scattering, particle diffusion, and particle settling, among others, are commonly used to measure particle size distribution [44]. Particle size is directly related to the release of the bioactive compound in the pharmacological target [31].

Particle charge is another important property of lipidic formulations since it influences the interaction of the particle with other charged species and surfaces and is related to the system's stability [45]. Particle charge could also influence the adhesion of the particles to solid surfaces on processing equipment or product containers. Three main characteristics define the electrical properties of the particle, the surface charge density, surface electrical potential, and zeta potential. Zeta potential is a property that indicates the surface charge of the particles and is related to the stability of the formulations. The aggregation of particles is less likely to occur in charged particles (high zeta potential—module) due to the repulsion of charges. This parameter is calculated from the migration speed of the particles suspended in a conductive liquid; when an electric field is applied attracting the particles to the electrode of opposite charge, the migration speed is proportional to the surface charge of the particle [43]. The sample preparation procedure is important to avoid erratic measures related to alteration on pH or ionic strength, and the diluting fluid should be as similar as possible to the continuous phase [44].

The physical state of the lipid particles provides information on the molecules' spatial arrangement and structural conformation, allowing the detection of polymorphic phases. Methods such as differential scanning calorimetry, nuclear magnetic resonance, ultrasonics, and X-ray analysis can provide this information. The heating and cooling of lipids during the manufacturing process can cause changes in structural conformation. The most used methods to determine the crystalline state are X-ray diffraction and differential scanning calorimetry [46]. Excellent reviews of procedures for physicochemical characterisation of lipid-based systems were reported elsewhere [42, 47, 48].

7.5 STABILITY OF LIPID-BASED FORMULATIONS

Emulsions are generally described as a disperse system of two immiscible fluids. They are thermodynamically unstable systems since water and oil are not miscible, separating into two phases [49, 50]. Figure 7.2 presents the main physical–chemical destabilisation mechanisms of emulsions, namely gravitational separation (creaming–sedimentation), flocculation, coalescence, phase inversion, and Ostwald ripening.

Gravitational separation is one of the most common instability mechanisms; it results from gravitational or centrifugal external forces. When such forces exceed

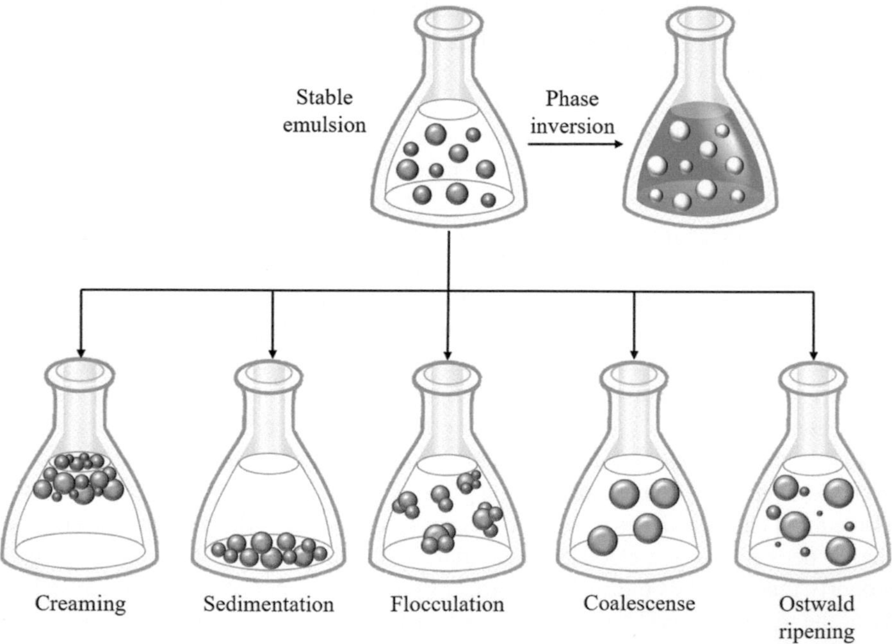

FIGURE 7.2 Representation of the main physical instability mechanism in lipid-based systems.

the Brownian motion of the droplets, a concentration gradient accumulates in the system. Larger droplets with a density less than the medium density move faster to the top of the container, this behaviour known as creaming. When the drop density is greater than the medium density, they move to the bottom of the container, a sedimentation [49]. As the density of most oils used for food or pharmaceutical purposes is lower than the density of water, creaming tends to occur normally O/W emulsions and sedimentation in water-in-oil emulsions (A/O) [51]. The speed at which gravitational separation occurs has been calculated using Stokes' Law which considers the droplet radius, the density of the continuous phase, and the dispersed phase and the force of gravity. If different particle sizes are found in the emulsion, the separation speed is different, with the larger particles separating faster than the small ones [45].

Flocculation is the process by which droplets of emulsions tend to associate, retaining their identity, but are part of a larger aggregate structure, which differs from coalescence in that two or more droplets unite to form a larger droplet [50]. The flocculation process is associated with the attractive and repulsive forces between the particles. It occurs when the repulsion between the droplets is not enough to keep them at distances where the Van der Waals attraction is weak [49]. Drops flocculated by reducing electrostatic repulsion can be redispersed if the repulsive forces are increased by adding emulsifiers or changing the ionic strength or the pH of the continuous phase; therefore, this type of flocculation is considered reversible [50].

Coalescence occurs when two or more droplets merge, inducing phase separation [49]. In O/W emulsions, a lipid phase forms at the top, and in A/O emulsions, an aqueous phase forms at the bottom. Coalescence occurs when the electrostatic repulsion forces that stabilise the surface of the droplets are small or do not repel enough to maintain colloidal stability, or because the attractive Van der Waals forces are high enough to overcome the forces of repulsion, allowing the droplets to contact each other and merge [50]. Coalescence can be minimised by reducing the concentration of the emulsion droplets in the formulation, avoiding subjecting the emulsion to high shear forces, and changing the interfacial membrane's properties by increasing the repulsive forces of the droplets so that they overcome the Van der Waals attractive forces [52].

Ostwald ripening is a mechanism of emulsion instability that increases the size of the larger droplets due to the breakdown of smaller particles induced by the Laplace pressure within the emulsion droplets. In drops with a small radius, the pressure is higher compared to drops with a large radius. The pressure difference causes the lipid droplets to divide from small to large droplets [50]. The droplet size distribution shifts to larger values over time [52].

Phase inversion is the process in which an inversion occurs between the continuous phase and the dispersed phase [53]. An O/W-type emulsion becomes a W/O type [52]. Although this process can be considered a mechanism of instability, this process is carried out intentionally in some cases. It is triggered by changes in the emulsion composition—such as the change in the dispersed phase concentration or the concentration of surfactant—or temperature changes. Flocculation, coalescence, and disruption are involved in this process. The most used method to evaluate the phase inversion is to measure the emulsion's electrical conductivity, which is higher for O/W emulsions than W/O [51].

7.6 DRYING OF LIPID-BASED FORMULATIONS

Removing water from a lipid-based formulation is an efficient method to extend the product's shelf life by reducing the high tension in the oil–water interface, which leads to phase separation and minimising physicochemical and microbiological instability problems. Drying methods such as spray drying, fluidised-bed drying, and freeze-drying could be employed for lipid-based formulations loaded with phytochemicals. Factors such as the physicochemical properties of the phytochemicals, the processing cost, and the drying time should be considered to select the drying method. The main characteristics of these drying methods are presented in Table 7.2. Many bioactive compounds from medicinal plants are heat sensitive, and therefore, it is very important to monitor changes in their contents during the drying process.

Freeze-drying (lyophilisation) is based on a sublimation process, a phase transition from a pre-frozen solid sample to a gas state employing high vacuum conditions. Water removal without high temperatures allows the sample preservation; however, the high costs involved and the batch-type operation can make its industrial application unfeasible.

In fluidised bed drying, the liquid lipid formulation could be atomised over inert support or a bed of particles that could be functional carriers. High heat and mass transfer rates are obtained as a result of the intense particle movement. The drying time is lower than freeze-drying but higher than spray drying [54]. It is commonly a batch-type operation; however, it could be adapted for continuous operation.

The spray drying technique has been used more frequently in the encapsulation and drying of food, pharmaceutical emulsions, and lipid-based formulations as it is more economical and versatile. For this reason, this method will be deeply reviewed in this chapter [20, 55, 56]. Spray drying is a critical step for the degradation or evaporation of the thermolabile and volatile compounds. The composition of the formulation is fundamental for the retention of biological activity associated with the main active principles present in the plant material. The correct selection of wall materials and drying conditions make it possible to encapsulate volatile compounds by spray drying, reducing product losses, and degradation during the process.

TABLE 7.2
Drying Methods Generally Used for Lipid Formulations

	Freeze-Drying	Spray Drying	Fluidised Bed
Temperature range	<0°C	Inlet: 100–200°C Outlet: 60–85°C	30–35°C
Drying time	Hours-days	Seconds-minutes	Minutes-hours
Costs	Fixed: 100% Manufacturing: 100%	Fixed: 20% Manufacturing: 20%	Fixed: 9% Manufacturing: 18%
Output form	Cake	Small particles	Medium particles-granules

Source: Adapted from [57].

Volatile compounds have been successfully encapsulated by spray drying through the development of emulsions and the addition of drying carriers. In this process, the aqueous phase is removed, and consequently, the carrier (solid) encapsulates the dispersed lipid phase, resulting in dry emulsions that can be redispersed in water, restoring the original system [55].

During spray drying encapsulation, water evaporation occurs, but the volatile compounds are retained in the product. In the first phase of the process, the atomised drop loses water from the outside, forming an outer crust that grows inward. When this surface reaches a moisture content from 7 to 23%, it remains permeable to water-soluble molecules, but it is no longer permeable to volatile compounds, therefore acting as a semipermeable membrane, which allows water to evaporate and retain volatiles [58].

The main factors that influence the retention of volatiles during atomisation in a spray dryer are the composition of the formulation, the content of solids, the inlet and outlet gas temperature of the dryer, and the concentration of volatile compounds. One of the most important factors for the retention of volatile compounds is the solids content of the formulation. The higher the solids content of the formulation, the shorter the formation time of the superficial crust, which acts as a semipermeable membrane, thus promoting the retention of volatiles [11, 58, 59].

Huyn et al. [19] optimised the retention of lemon oil (*Backhousia citriodora*) in terms of solids content (20, 30, and 40%), oil concentration (10, 15, and 20%), and outlet air temperature (60, 65, and 70°C), using modified Hi-Cap 100 starch and milk protein as wall material. The optimised conditions were 40% solids content, 18% oil concentration, and 65°C outlet temperature. Concerning the wall material, greater retention was obtained using Hi-cap (64.49–90.07%), compared to milk protein (54.50–77.45%).

The viscosity of the composition is also an important factor since it is directly related to the diameter of the atomised drop. However, very low viscosities affect the formation of the semipermeable membrane of the particles during drying. Therefore, the solids content of the formulation must be optimised as a function of viscosity [59]. Soottitantawat et al. [60] achieved greater retention of l-menthol with the progressive increase of the solids content of the composition of 5, 10, 20, and 30% (w/w) and using the ratio of l-menthol to the wall material (starch of modified corn, Hi-Cap 100) of 2:8 (20% w/w). The type of wall material also influenced l-menthol retention. The authors compared three types of wall materials: Arabic gum, Hi-Cap 100 (modified corn starch), and Capsul (modified corn starch) using a 30% solids content. The results showed that Hi-Cap exhibited higher retention of l-menthol, but with a higher content of l-menthol on the surface of the particles, while Arabic gum showed less retention of l-menthol, but the surface content of the particles was lower, indicating better encapsulation. The viscosity of flaxseed oil emulsions containing Arabic gum as wall material for spray drying directly correlates with the solids content and conversely with the oil concentration. The encapsulation efficiency was higher with more viscous emulsions [61]. The emulsion viscosity associated with Arabic gum depends not only on relative concentration but on the mineralisation, pasteurisation, and total protein content of the gum [8].

Ideally, the wall material or drying carrier must have good emulsifying and film-forming properties. Thus, the addition of surfactants in the formulation allows obtaining stable emulsions, improving the retention of volatiles during drying [11]. The crystalline state of the carrier is also of great importance, as it is related to the diffusion of compounds within the matrix formed in the initial stages of drying. Amorphous materials cause an immobilisation effect that hinders the diffusion of compounds in the matrix, facilitating their encapsulation. On the other hand, in crystalline materials, diffusion is faster, increasing the volatile losses [62].

The physical–chemical characteristics of the compounds to be encapsulated have strong effects on their diffusion through the crust formed during drying, consequently affecting their retention in the product. Therefore, compounds with higher molecular weight, larger size (steric effect), and less volatility diffuse more slowly, reducing losses [62]. Adamiec and Kalemba [63] compared the retentions of elemi oil (*Canarium commune*) and mint (*Mentha piperita*) encapsulated in maltodextrin DE16 by spray drying encapsulation. The results showed superior retention for the mint essential oil retention, attributed to the higher boiling points of its main constituents (oxygenated monoterpenes) compared to those of elemi essential oil (monoterpene hydrocarbons).

The oil concentration has also influenced the retention of volatile compounds. High loads of volatile compounds result in greater losses due to a greater quantity of molecules that will stay close to the surface and diffuse more quickly to the outside, facilitating losses. This behaviour was observed by Garcia et al. [20] in the encapsulation of basil oil by spray drying, using Arabic gum as wall material. The authors observed that the retention decreased with the increase in the initial oil concentration. Similar results also obtained by Adamiec and Kalemba [63] in the mint oil encapsulation, using maltodextrin as wall material. In this study, the encapsulation efficiency decreased from 70.6 to 57.2%, increasing the initial oil concentration from 10 to 30%. The greater the proportion of wall material to the compound to be encapsulated, the greater the retention [64]. Volatile:wall material ratios up to 1:4 (w/w) are usually used [58, 64, 65].

Munoz-Ibanez et al. [66] studied the main factors that influence the spray drying of emulsions. The properties of the emulsion, viscosity, and particle size have significant effects on the product properties. It was considered that the relationship of the internal force, corresponding to the surface tension of the emulsion, and the external force, caused by the external environment where the emulsion is found, might determine the rupture of the droplet [66]. The intense shear and elongation forces suffered by the emulsion during the atomisation stage can cause deformation and rupture of the emulsion structure depending on its physicochemical properties and atomising conditions. High viscosities and emulsion droplet size promote its rupture under the effect of the atomisation process's shear and stress forces. Regarding operational conditions, the influence of variables depends on the type of atomiser. For the double fluid atomiser, the atomising gas flow and pressure have significant effects, while the rotation speed is important in the case of the rotary atomiser.

It has been observed that the retention of volatiles increases with the reduction of the emulsion particle size [20, 64]. Large droplet size emulsions can be broken with the shear force produced during atomisation. However, emulsions with very fine droplets increase the surface area, favouring diffusion [64, 67].

When a liquid formulation is atomised in the spray dryer, the contact of the droplets with the hot air stream evaporates the solvent and forms the outer semipermeable layer [68]. The addition of lipids in the formulation decreases the atomised drop's glass transition temperature and alters the layer's properties. The product adhesion to the spray dryer chamber also increases, which results in less product recovery. Dollo et al. [5] studied the effect of the ratio of the lipid phase to the amount of maltodextrin DE 12.6 and surfactant (sodium caseinate) during the spray drying, using an inlet drying temperature of 110°C and outlet temperatures from 65 to 75°C. The results showed that the wall material ratio (maltodextrin and sodium caseinate) must be 1.35 times greater than the lipid phase for powder production during spray drying.

The effect of drying temperature must be considered for each particular product, depending on the formulation's composition. High drying temperatures favour the rapid formation of the outer semipermeable membrane, allowing water to evaporate and retaining the volatiles [11]. Elevated temperatures also decrease the relative humidity (RH) of the drying air, facilitating heat transfer, and speeding up the drying. On the other hand, high drying temperatures can promote the degradation of the thermosensitive components present in the formulation [58]. Therefore, the inlet and outlet drying gas temperatures are variables commonly optimised in the encapsulation of volatile compounds by spray drying [69, 70]. The microencapsulation of lime oil, by spray drying, was optimised when the inlet and outlet air temperature of 220 and 85°C, respectively, were used. Under these conditions, oil retention was 95.5% and encapsulation efficiency 99.9% [70].

7.7 CASE STUDY: SPRAY DRYING OF *Syzygium aromaticum* LIPIDIC EMULSIONS

Clove (*Syzygium aromaticum* L. Merril. & Perry, syn. *Eugenia aromaticum* or *Eugenia caryophyllata*) is an aromatic spice plant, specifically a medium-size tree (8–12 m) of the Myrtaceae family. It is native to Indonesia, where it grows in areas close to the coast and up to 200 m above sea level. The main clove producers are Indonesia, Madagascar, Tanzania, Malaysia, and Sri Lanka, although today it is cultivated worldwide, mainly in warm zones. Clove buds have a high phenolic compound content such as flavonoids, hydroxybenzoic acids, hydroxycinnamic acids, and hydroxyphenyl propenes. It is classified as one of the plants with the highest antioxidant activity, which has been associated with the presence of eugenol (IUPAC name: 4-allyl-2-methoxyphenyl), the major active compound found in the clove [71]. Eugenol concentrations of up to 89% have been found in clove essential oil, and it has been commonly used as a marker compound in the standardisation and encapsulation process of clove bioproducts [72, 73]. The antioxidant mechanism attributed to eugenol is linked to its characteristic molecular structure, an aromatic ring conjugated to a double-bonded aliphatic chain, also present in resveratrol, the substance linked to the beneficial properties of the red wine. Antioxidant activity higher than Butylated hydroxytoluene (BHT), α-tocopherol, Butylated hydroxyanisole (BHA), and Trolox has been exhibited by the clove oil [74].

TABLE 7.3
Composition of Lipid-Based Formulations of Clove Extract (% w/w)

		Formulation				
Component	**Function**	**F1**	**F2**	**F3**	**F4**	**F5**
Clove extract	Antioxidant's source	63.0	63.0	63.0	63.0	63.0
Glyceryl dibehenate[a]	Solid lipid	8.1	8.1	8.1	—	8.1
Stearic acid	Solid lipid	—	—	—	8.1	—
Buriti oil	Liquid lipid and antioxidants source	0.9	0.9	0.9	0.9	0.9
Polysorbate 80	Surfactant	0.9	0.9	0.9	0.9	—
Poloxamer 188[b]	Surfactant	—	—	—	—	0.9
Lactose	Drying carrier	—	18.0	—	—	—
Maltodextrin	Drying carrier	18.0	—	9.0	18.0	18.0
Arabic gum	Drying carrier	—	—	9.0	—	—
Water	Solvent	9.0	9.0	9.0	9.0	9.0

Source: Cortés-Rojas et al. [73].
[a] Compritol® 888 ATO.
[b] Kolliphor® P 188.

Redispersible dry lipid formulations based on the clove extract as API was developed by Cortés-Rojas et al. [73]. In order to select thc appropriate lipid system, a lipid screening was carried out. Increasing amounts of clove oil were mixed with different lipids such as beeswax, glyceryl monostearate, stearic acid, carnauba wax, Apifil®, Compritol® 888 ATO, stearyl alcohol, and Gelucire 50/13 [75, 76].

After the two solid lipids (stearic acid and Compritol® 888ATO) and the liquid lipid (buriti oil—*Mauritia flexuosa)* were preselected, the formulation design continued with selecting the surfactant and the wall material. Five compositions were designed employing the surfactants: poloxamer 188 and polysorbate 80, and three drying carriers: Arabic gum, maltodextrin DE10, and lactose (Table 7.3). Formulation 5 was selected to compare process parameters such as the homogenisation process and the drying methods. Three homogenisation methods were compared: HPH applying three cycles at 500 bar (Panda Plus GEA Niro Soavi, Parma, Italy), high shear mixing at 18.000 rpm/min for 5 min (Ultraturrax T18, IKA-Wilmington, NC, USA), and ultrasonic homogenisation using an ultrasound probe at 20 kHz, 70% intensity for 3 min (SONICS Vibracell, Newtown, USA). The drying methods evaluated were spray drying and freeze-drying. Spray drying was performed at an inlet air temperature of 90°C, and a fed rate of 4 g/min in a Lab-Plant SD05 spray dryer. The freeze-drying process lasted 36 h with the samples previously frozen at –20°C for 12 h and then at –80°C for 4 h. The response variables evaluated in the microparticulate systems were the retention of the eugenol, antioxidant activity, product recovery, particle size, and the product aqueous dispersibility.

The drying carrier and the type of surfactant showed a direct impact on product recovery. The formulation containing Compritol® 888 ATO and poloxamer 188 (F5) showed the highest product recovery after spray drying (57.6%), while

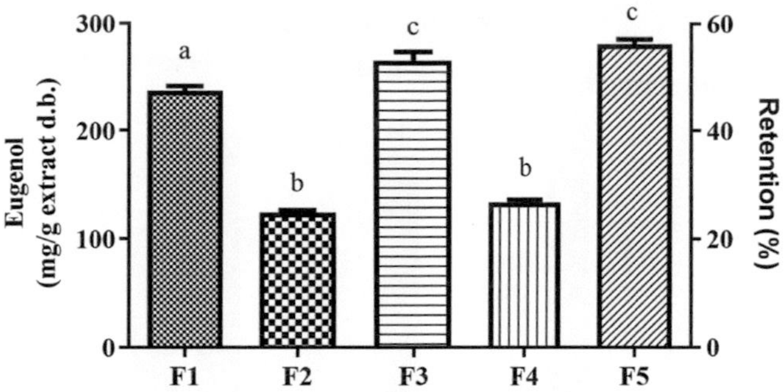

FIGURE 7.3 Eugenol retention as a function of lipid formulation composition. Equal letters in the columns indicate that there is no significant difference between the samples according to the Tukey test ($p \leq 0.05$). (Adapted from Cortés-Rojas et al. [73].)

the formulation containing stearic acid (F4) showed the lowest (21.0%). This result might be related to the higher melting point of Compritol® 888 ATO (~70°C) compared to the stearic acid (~50°C). Dollo et al. [5] obtained product recovery values in the range of 44–74% in the atomisation of emulsions, using Mygliol® 812 and maltodextrin, respectively, as oily phase and carrier. The authors observed that increasing the proportion of oil in the formulation is detrimental to product recovery.

The eugenol retention of the spray dried products was quantified by high-performance liquid chromatography. It can be observed (Figure 7.3) that formulation 5 (F5) showed the highest concentrations of eugenol and eugenol acetate, while formulations 2 and 4 showed the lowest concentrations. The difference between formulations 5 and 4 is the type of surfactant (poloxamer and Tween® 80, respectively) and the solid lipid: Compritol® 888ATO (glyceryl dibehenate) in formulation 5 and stearic acid in formulation 4. Formulation 2 differs from formulation 4 in the type of lipid and wall material, Compritol® 888 ATO (glyceryl dibehenate) and lactose.

Regarding the effect of the surfactant on product recovery, greater recovery was obtained with poloxamer 188 than with polysorbate 80 (formulations 1 and 5). This fact may be related to the melting point of these two components. The melting point of poloxamer 188 is higher than that of polysorbate 80, a viscous liquid at room temperature. Concerning the drying carriers used, formulations containing the maltodextrin DE10 show greater recovery, which can be attributed to its higher glass transition temperature than Arabic gum and lactose [77, 78].

The water dispersibility of the dried formulation containing stearic acid (F4) was higher than formulations containing Compritol® 888 ATO (F1–F5). The type of surfactant did not evidence statistically significant differences ($p < 0.05$) between polysorbate 80 and poloxamer 188 in water dispersibility in formulations containing Compritol® 888ATO. The wall materials used also affected the water dispersibility of the product, which was higher for the formulation containing maltodextrin DE10 (F1) than that containing lactose (F2) or the mixture of maltodextrin and gum arabic (F3). Maltodextrins are carbohydrates derived from the hydrolysis of starch, have good solubility, and are widely used in the food industry as wall materials in spray drying encapsulation [79]. On the other hand, Arabic gum has good emulsifying

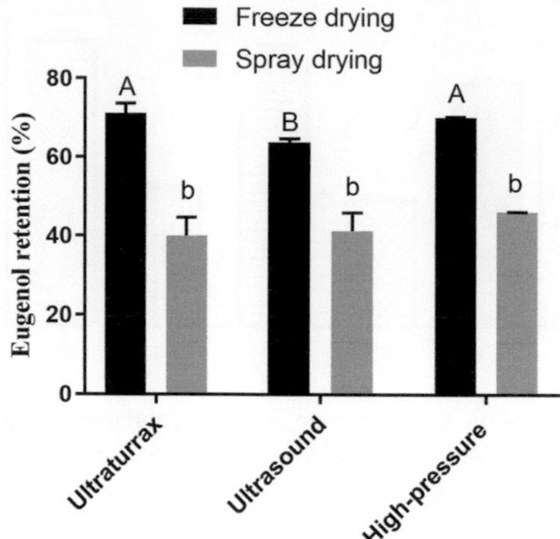

FIGURE 7.4 Effects of homogenisation and drying methods on eugenol retention in dry lipid-based formulations. The same letter means a significant difference according to Tukey's multiple comparison test (p <0.05). (Adapted from Cortés-Rojas et al. [73].)

properties, and greater solubility would be expected. However, the interaction with the lipids in the formulation might affect this property [26].

Based on the retention of eugenol and product recovery, the best result was exhibited by lipid formulation based on Compritol® 888 ATO as a solid lipid, poloxamer 188 as a surfactant, and maltodextrin DE10 as a drying carrier. It was also observed that the homogenisation methods (Ultraturrax, HAP, sonication) did not significantly affect the retention of eugenol for the two drying processes studied, as shown in Figure 7.4 (results obtained for formulation F5). It can be seen in this figure that the concentration of eugenol was higher in powders obtained by freeze-drying than those obtained by spray drying.

As expected, the particle morphology obtained by spray drying and freeze-drying is very different (Figure 7.5). Rounded and rough particles were produced by spray

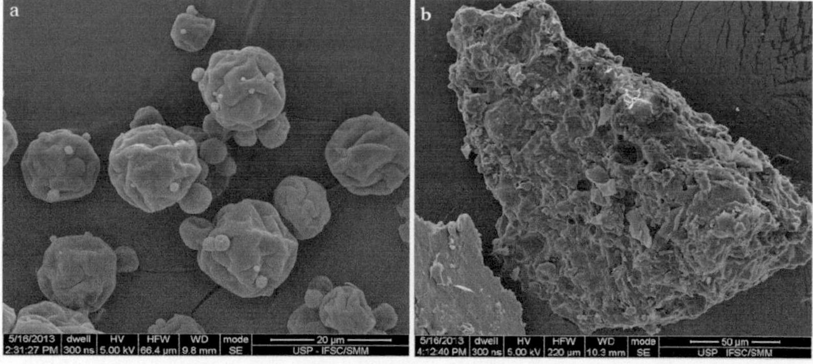

FIGURE 7.5 Particle morphology of lipid-based formulations of clove extract after spray (a) and freeze-drying (b). (From Cortés-Rojas et al. [73].)

drying, while the particles generated by lyophilisation were flat, blade-shaped, and porous. These results are expected since the rounded shapes are obtained when the formulations are atomised, a step not presented in the freeze-drying process.

Confocal microscopy has been used to visualise the distribution of the lipid and aqueous phases in emulsions [80–82]. Oil- and water-soluble dyes are employed to visualise the lipid and aqueous phases through the formulation process. Nile red was employed as the lipophilic stain (excitation maximum: 549 nm; emission maximum: 628 nm), and fluorescein isothiocyanate (FITC) was employed as a hydrophilic stain (excitation maximum: 495 nm; emission maximum: 519 nm). It can also be used to evaluate the encapsulation and homogenisation process [83]. Another advantage of confocal microscopy is the possibility of visualising the interior of the particle through optical sections. Images of the confocal microscopy of the liquid and dry lipid formulation of clove extract are shown in Figure 7.6. The continuous aqueous phase with the dye marker FITC on the outside is green and the lipid particles dispersed within are red. It is observed that in the liquid formulation, the lipid droplets (red) are uniformly distributed in the aqueous medium shown in green (Figure 7.6 a). The image of the dried particles shows the red marker inside the solid particles, indicating the encapsulation of the lipid (Figure 7.6 b).

In another study, the physicochemical properties, storage stability, and *in vitro* intestinal permeation of lipid and non-lipid formulations were compared [84]. The lipid formulation (CSD4) comprises the solid lipid Compritol® 888 ATO, liquid lipid buriti oil, surfactant Gelucire® 50/13, and Arabic gum as the drying carrier. The non-lipid formulation CSD5 is the spray-dried extract of cloves using Arabic gum as wall material.

The non-lipid formulation CSD5 showed greater eugenol retention (70%) than the lipid formulation CSD4 (56%), as the preparation and drying conditions of the formulations were the same, operational variables can be discarded, and differences in retention can be associated with the ability to encapsulate the components of the formulations.

The stability testing was conducted at three temperatures and two RHs. At the most extreme condition, 40°C and 63.5% RH, the non-lipid formulation showed the

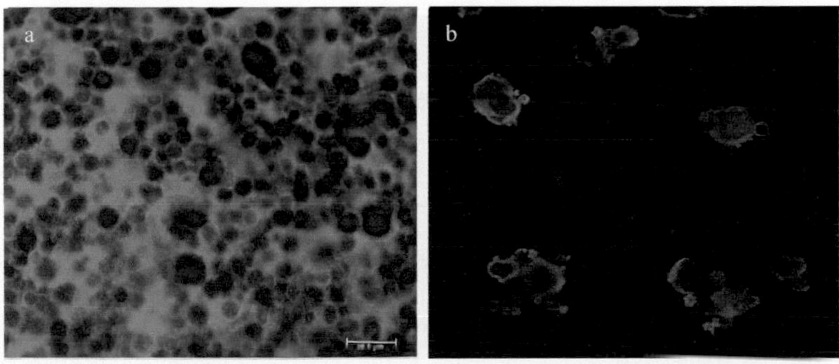

FIGURE 7.6 Confocal microscopy images of the CSD5 lipid formulation. Liquid formulation (a) and spray-dried formulation (b). Red Nile dye was employed for the lipid phase and FITC for the aqueous phase.

lowest eugenol retention over time and the highest retention at 25°C and 32.4% RH, the humidity showed a significant impact on the stability of the non-lipid formulations. In high humidity environments, the eugenol retention of the lipid formulation was higher. Hence, it can be concluded that the hydrophobicity of the lipids in the powdered formulation might confer protection to the clove API in high humidity environments.

The *in vitro* $CaCo_2$ cell model was employed to evaluate the effect of the lipid formulation in the permeation of eugenol. A bidirectional transporter assay indicated that eugenol might not be a substrate of efflux transporters. The permeation of eugenol was moderate $1–10 \times 10^{-6}$ cm/sec, suggesting a moderately intestinal absorption. No significant differences were observed in the apparent permeability coefficient (Papp) of the lipidic and non-lipidic formulations.

7.8 FINAL REMARKS

In this chapter, the advantages of dried lipid-based formulations as delivery systems for API were briefly discussed. In order to achieve the potential protection and improved bioavailability provided by this kind of formulation, the production process and each excipient should be carefully selected. Each API has specific physicochemical characteristics which should be considered in the formulation design. The concentration of the API should be monitored through the formulation process and in different storage conditions to guarantee the amount required for the intended application. The physical characterisation of the particles is also important since these properties are related to the release profile of the API, stability, and protection, among others.

The growing interest in these formulations will improve the industrial-scale production process robust enough for commercial applications. The physiological responses of the lipid formulations associated with the excipients will increase the knowledge of the most suitable components to be used. Thus, appropriate delivery systems that meet the fabrication and functional requirements might be developed for APIs with different physicochemical characteristics.

REFERENCES

1. Porter, C. J. H.; Trevaskis, N. L.; Charman, W. N. Lipids and Lipid-Based Formulations: Optimizing the Oral Delivery of Lipophilic Drugs. *Nature Reviews Drug Discovery*, **2007**, *6* (March), 231–248.
2. Pardeike, J.; Hommoss, A.; Müller, R. H. Lipid Nanoparticles (SLN, NLC) in Cosmetic and Pharmaceutical Dermal Products. *International Journal of Pharmaceutics*, **2009**, *366* (1–2), 170–184.
3. Laffleur, F.; Keckeis, V. Advances in Drug Delivery Systems: Work in Progress Still Needed? *International Journal of Pharmaceutics: X*, **2020**, *2* (June), 119912, 1-15.
4. Lu, W.; Maidannyk, V.; Kelly, A. L.; Miao, S. Fabrication and Characterization of Highly Re-Dispersible Dry Emulsions. *Food Hydrocolloids*, **2020**, *102* (November 2019), 105617.
5. Dollo, G.; Le Corre, P.; Guérin, A.; Chevanne, F.; Burgot, J. L.; Leverge, R. Spray-Dried Redispersible Oil-in-Water Emulsion to Improve Oral Bioavailability of Poorly Soluble Drugs. *European Journal of Pharmaceutical Sciences*, **2003**, *19* (4), 273–280.

6. Müller, R. H. *Lipid Nanoparticles for Improved Formulation of Cosmetic and Pharmaceutical Actives. Free University Technology Presentation*, **2007**, *1*, 1–69.
7. Paulo, B. B.; Alvim, I. D.; Reineccius, G.; Prata, A. S. Performance of Oil-in-Water Emulsions Stabilized by Different Types of Surface-Active Components. *Colloids and Surfaces B: Biointerfaces*, **2020**, *190* (January), 110939.
8. Buffo, R. A.; Reineccius, G. A.; Oehlert, G. W. Factors Affecting the Emulsifying and Rheological Properties of Gum Acacia in Beverage Emulsions. *Food Hydrocolloids*, **2001**, *15* (1), 53–66.
9. Kovačević, A. B.; Müller, R. H.; Keck, C. M. Formulation Development of Lipid Nanoparticles: Improved Lipid Screening and Development of Tacrolimus Loaded Nanostructured Lipid Carriers (NLC). *International Journal of Pharmaceutics*, **2020**, *576* (November 2019), 118918.
10. Rahman, M. A.; Hussain, A.; Hussain, M. S.; Mirza, M. A.; Iqbal, Z. Role of Excipients in Successful Development of Self-Emulsifying/Microemulsifying Drug Delivery System (SEDDS/SMEDDS). *Drug Development and Industrial Pharmacy*, **2013**, *39* (1), 1–19.
11. Jafari, S. M.; Assadpoor, E.; He, Y.; Bhandari, B. Encapsulation Efficiency of Food Flavours and Oils during Spray Drying. *Drying Technology*, **2008**, *26* (7), 816–835.
12. Jafari, S. M.; He, Y.; Bhandari, B. Encapsulation of Nanoparticles of D-Limonene by Spray Drying: Role of Emulsifiers and Emulsifying Techniques. *Drying Technology*, **2007**, *25* (6), 1069–1079.
13. ICI Americas Inc. *The HLB System a Time-Saving Guide to Emulsifier Selection*; Chemmuniqu, ICI Americas Inc.: Wilmington, Delaware, 1980.
14. Carvalho, A. G. S.; Silva, V. M.; Hubinger, M. D. Microencapsulation by Spray Drying of Emulsified Green Coffee Oil with Two-Layered Membranes. *Food Research International*, **2014**, *61*, 236–245.
15. Madene, A.; Jacquot, M.; Scher, J.; Desobry, S. Flavour Encapsulation and Controlled Release a Review. *International Journal of Food Science & Technology*, **2006**, *41* (1), 1–21.
16. Gharsallaoui, A.; Roudaut, G.; Chambin, O.; Voilley, A.; Saurel, R. Applications of Spray-Drying in Microencapsulation of Food Ingredients: An Overview. *Food Research International*, **2007**, *40* (9), 1107–1121.
17. Shah, B.; Ikeda, S.; Michael Davidson, P.; Zhong, Q. Nanodispersing Thymol in Whey Protein Isolate-Maltodextrin Conjugate Capsules Produced Using the Emulsion–Evaporation Technique. *Journal of Food Engineering*, **2012**, *113* (1), 79–86.
18. Rowe, R. C.; Sheskey, P. J.; Owen, S. C. *Handbook of Pharmaceutical Excipients*, 5th ed.; Association Pharmaceutical Press and American Pharmacists: London, 2006.
19. Huynh, T. V.; Caffin, N.; Dykes, G. A.; Bhandari, B. Optimization of the Microencapsulation of Lemon Myrtle Oil Using Response Surface Methodology. *Drying Technology*, **2008**, *26* (3), 357–368.
20. Garcia, L. C.; Tonon, R. V.; Hubinger, M. D. Effect of Homogenization Pressure and Oil Load on the Emulsion Properties and the Oil Retention of Microencapsulated Basil Essential Oil (*Ocimum Basilicum* L.). *Drying Technology*, **2012**, *30* (13), 1413–1421.
21. Ding, Z.; Tao, T.; Wang, X.; Prakash, S.; Zhao, Y.; Han, J.; Wang, Z. Influences of Different Carbohydrates as Wall Material on Powder Characteristics, Encapsulation Efficiency, Stability and Degradation Kinetics of Microencapsulated Lutein by Spray Drying. *International Journal of Food Science and Technology*, **2020**, *55* (7), 2872–2882.
22. Souza, A. L. R.; Hidalgo-Chávez, D. W.; Pontes, S. M.; Gomes, F. S.; Cabral, L. M. C.; Tonon, R. V. Microencapsulation by Spray Drying of a Lycopene-Rich Tomato Concentrate: Characterization and Stability. *LWT – Food Science and Technology*, **2018**, *91* (January), 286–292.

23. Le Priol, L.; Dagmey, A.; Morandat, S.; Saleh, K.; El Kirat, K.; Nesterenko, A. Comparative Study of Plant Protein Extracts as Wall Materials for the Improvement of the Oxidative Stability of Sunflower Oil by Microencapsulation. *Food Hydrocolloids*, **2019**, *95*, 105–115.
24. Chen, F. P.; Liu, L. L.; Tang, C. H. Spray-Drying Microencapsulation of Curcumin Nanocomplexes with Soy Protein Isolate: Encapsulation, Water Dispersion, Bioaccessibility and Bioactivities of Curcumin. *Food Hydrocolloids*, **2020**, *105* (January), 105821.
25. Vu, H. T.; Scarlett, C. J.; Vuong, Q. V. Encapsulation of Phenolic-Rich Extract from Banana (Musa Cavendish) Peel. *Journal of Food Science and Technology*, **2020**, *57* (6), 2089–2098.
26. Coimbra, P. P. S.; Cardoso, F. de S. N.; Gonçalves, É. C. B. de A. Spray-Drying Wall Materials: Relationship with Bioactive Compounds. *Critical Reviews in Food Science and Nutrition*, **2021**, 61 (17), 2809–2826.
27. Pokharkar, V. B.; Shekhawat, P. B.; Dhapte, V. V; Mandpe, L. P. Development and Optimization of Eugenol Loaded Nanostructured Lipid Carriers for Peridontal Delivery. *International Journal of Pharmacy and Pharmaceutical Sciences*, **2011**, *3* (4), 138–143.
28. Mitri, K.; Shegokar, R.; Gohla, S.; Anselmi, C.; Müller, R. H. Lipid Nanocarriers for Dermal Delivery of Lutein: Preparation, Characterization, Stability and Performance. *International Journal of Pharmaceutics*, **2011**, *414* (1–2), 267–275.
29. Fang, J.-Y.; Fang, C.-L.; Liu, C.-H.; Su, Y.-H. Lipid Nanoparticles as Vehicles for Topical Psoralen Delivery: Solid Lipid Nanoparticles (SLN) versus Nanostructured Lipid Carriers (NLC). *European Journal of Pharmaceutics and Biopharmaceutics*, **2008**, *70* (2), 633–640.
30. Liu, C.-H.; Wu, C.-T. Optimization of Nanostructured Lipid Carriers for Lutein Delivery. *Colloids and Surfaces A: Physicochemical and Engineering Aspects*, **2010**, *353* (2–3), 149–156.
31. Tsai, M.-J.; Wu, P.-C.; Huang, Y.-B.; Chang, J.-S.; Lin, C.-L.; Tsai, Y.-H.; Fang, J.-Y. Baicalein Loaded in Tocol Nanostructured Lipid Carriers (Tocol NLCs) for Enhanced Stability and Brain Targeting. *International Journal of Pharmaceutics*, **2012**, *423* (2), 461–470.
32. Tiwari, R.; Pathak, K. Nanostructured Lipid Carrier versus Solid Lipid Nanoparticles of Simvastatin: Comparative Analysis of Characteristics, Pharmacokinetics and Tissue Uptake. *International Journal of Pharmaceutics*, **2011**, *415* (1–2), 232–243.
33. Aman, R. M.; Abu Hashim, I. I.; Meshali, M. M. Novel Chitosan-Based Solid-Lipid Nanoparticles to Enhance the Bio-Residence of the Miraculous Phytochemical "Apocynin." *European Journal of Pharmaceutical Sciences*, **2018**, *124* (September), 304–318.
34. Bankole, V. O.; Osungunna, M. O.; Souza, C. R. F.; Salvador, S. L.; Oliveira, W. P. Spray-Dried Proliposomes: An Innovative Method for Encapsulation of Rosmarinus Officinalis L. Polyphenols. *AAPS PharmSciTech*, **2020**, *21* (5), 1–17.
35. Jia, L.; Shen, J.; Zhang, D.; Duan, C.; Liu, G.; Zheng, D.; Tian, X.; Liu, Y.; Zhang, Q. In Vitro and in Vivo Evaluation of Oridonin-Loaded Long Circulating Nanostructured Lipid Carriers. *International Journal of Biological Macromolecules*, **2012**, *50* (3), 523–529.
36. Outuki, P. M.; Kleinubing, S. A.; Hoscheid, J.; Montanha, M. C.; da Silva, E. A.; do Couto, R. O.; Kimura, E.; Cardoso, M. L. C. The Incorporation of Pterodon Pubescens Fruit Oil into Optimized Nanostructured Lipid Carriers Improves Its Effectiveness in Colorectal Cancer. *Industrial Crops and Products*, **2018**, *123* (July), 719–730.
37. Li, S.; Ji, Z.; Zou, M.; Nie, X.; Shi, Y.; Cheng, G. Preparation, Characterization, Pharmacokinetics and Tissue Distribution of Solid Lipid Nanoparticles Loaded with Tetrandrine. *AAPS PharmSciTech*, **2011**, *12* (3), 1011–1018.

38. Yadav, N.; Khatak, S.; Sara, S. V. U. Solid Lipid Nanoparticles—A Review. *International Journal of Applied Pharmaceutics*, **2013**, *5* (2), 8–18.
39. Schubert, M. A.; Müller-Goymann, C. C. Solvent Injection as a New Approach for Manufacturing Lipid Nanoparticles—Evaluation of the Method and Process Parameters. *European Journal of Pharmaceutics and Biopharmaceutics*, **2003**, *55* (1), 125–131.
40. Battaglia, L.; Gallarate, M.; Panciani, P. P.; Ugazio, E.; Sapino, S.; Peira, E.; Chirio, D. Techniques for the Preparation of Solid Lipid Nano and Microparticles. In *Application of Nanotechnology in Drug Delivery*; Sezer, IntechOpen Istanbul, 2014.
41. Souto, E. B.; Müller, R. H. Lipid Nanoparticles (Solid Lipid Nanoparticles and Nanostructured Lipid Carriers) for Cosmetic, Dermal, and Transdermal Applications. In *Nanoparticulate Drug Delivery Systems*; Thassu, D., Deleers, M., & Pathak, Y; CRC Press, 2007; pp. 213–233.
42. Subramaniam, B.; Siddik, Z. H.; Nagoor, N. H. Optimization of Nanostructured Lipid Carriers: Understanding the Types, Designs, and Parameters in the Process of Formulations. *Journal of Nanoparticle Research*, **2020**, *22* (6).
43. Guimarães, K. L.; Ré, M. I. Lipid Nanoparticles as Carriers for Cosmetic Ingredients: The First (SLN) and the Second Generation (NLC). In *Nanocosmetics and Nanomedicines*; Springer Berlin Heidelberg: Berlin Heidelberg, 2011; pp. 101–122.
44. McClements, D. J. *Nanoparticle- and Microparticle-Based Delivery Systems*; CRC Press: Boca Raton, 2015.
45. Hu, Y. T.; Ting, Y.; Hu, J. Y.; Hsieh, S. C. Techniques and Methods to Study Functional Characteristics of Emulsion Systems. *Journal of Food and Drug Analysis*, **2017**, *25* (1), 16–26.
46. Westesen, K.; Siekmann, B.; Koch, M. H. J. Investigations on the Physical State of Lipid Nanoparticles by Synchrotron Radiation X-Ray Diffraction. *International Journal of Pharmaceutics*, **1993**, *93* (1–3), 189–199.
47. Kathe, N.; Henriksen, B.; Chauhan, H. Physicochemical Characterization Techniques for Solid Lipid Nanoparticles: Principles and Limitations. *Drug Development and Industrial Pharmacy*, **2014**, *40* (12), 1565–1575.
48. Mehnert, W.; Mader, K. Solid Lipid Nanoparticles: Production, Characterization and Applications. *Advanced Drug Delivery Reviews*, **2001**, *47* (2–3), 165–196.
49. Tadros, T. F. *Emulsions—Formation, Stability, Industrial Applications*; De Gruyter: Berlin, Germany, 2016.
50. Wilde, P. J. *Improving Emulsion Stability through Selection of Emulsifiers and Stabilizers*; Elsevier, 2019; Vol. 1. https://doi.org/10.1016/B978-0-08-100596-5.22337-8
51. McClements, D. J. Critical Review of Techniques and Methodologies for Characterization of Emulsion Stability. *Critical Reviews in Food Science and Nutrition*, **2007**, *47* (7), 611–649.
52. Tadros, T. F., Ed. *Emulsion Science and Technology*; Wiley-Vch: Weinheim, 2009.
53. Perazzo, A.; Preziosi, V.; Guido, S. Phase Inversion Emulsification: Current Understanding and Applications. *Advances in Colloid and Interface Science*, **2015**, *222*, 581–599.
54. Broeckx, G.; Vandenheuvel, D.; Claes, I. J. J.; Lebeer, S.; Kiekens, F. Drying Techniques of Probiotic Bacteria as an Important Step towards the Development of Novel Pharmabiotics. *International Journal of Pharmaceutics*, **2016**, *505*, 303–318.
55. Christensen, K. L.; Pedersen, G. P.; Kristensen, H. G. Preparation of Redispersible Dry Emulsions by Spray Drying. *International Journal of Pharmaceutics*, **2001**, *212* (2), 187–194.
56. Bourezg, Z.; Bourgeois, S.; Pressenda, S.; Shehada, T.; Fessi, H. Redispersible Lipid Nanoparticles of Spironolactone Obtained by Three Drying Methods. *Colloids and Surfaces A: Physicochemical and Engineering Aspects*, **2012**, *413*, 191–199.
57. Berninger, T.; Lopez Gonzalez, O.; Bejarano, A.; Preininger, C.; Sessitsch, A. Minireview Maintenance and Assessment of Cell Viability in Formulation of Non-Sporulating Bacterial Inoculants. *Microbial Microbiology*, **2018**, *11* (2), 277–301.

58. Reineccius, G. The Spray Drying of Food Flavors. *Drying Technology*, **2004**, *22* (6), 1289–1324.
59. Rosenberg, M.; Kopelman, I. J.; Talmon, Y. J. Factors Affecting Retention in Spray-Drying Microencapsulation of Volatile Materials. *Journal of Agricultural and Food Chemistry*, **1990**, *38* (5), 1288–1294.
60. Soottitantawat, A.; Takayama, K.; Okamura, K.; Muranaka, D.; Yoshii, H.; Furuta, T.; Ohkawara, M.; Linko, P. Microencapsulation of L-Menthol by Spray Drying and Its Release Characteristics. *Innovative Food Science and Emerging Technologies*, **2005**, *6* (2), 163–170.
61. Tonon, R. V.; Grosso, C. R. F.; Hubinger, M. D. Influence of Emulsion Composition and Inlet Air Temperature on the Microencapsulation of Flaxseed Oil by Spray Drying. *Food Research International*, **2011**, *44* (1), 282–289.
62. Goubet, I.; Voilley, A. J. Retention of Aroma Compounds by Carbohydrates: Influence of Their Physicochemical Characteristics and of Their Physical State. *Journal of Agricultural and Food Chemistry*, **1998**, *46* (5), 1981–1990.
63. Adamiec, J.; Kalemba, D. Analysis of Microencapsulation Ability of Essential Oils during Spray Drying. *Drying Technology*, **2006**, *24* (9), 1127–1132.
64. Soottitantawat, A.; Bigeard, F.; Yoshii, H.; Furuta, T.; Ohkawara, M.; Linko, P. Influence of Emulsion and Powder Size on the Stability of Encapsulated D-Limonene by Spray Drying. *Innovative Food Science and Emerging Technologies*, **2005**, *6* (1), 107–114.
65. Beristain, C. I.; Garcia, H. S.; Vernon-Carter, E. J. Spray-Dried Encapsulation of Cardamom (*Elettaria cardamomum*) Essential Oil with Mesquite (*Prosopis juliflora*) Gum. *LWT—Food Science and Technology*, **2001**, *34* (6), 398–401.
66. Munoz-Ibanez, M.; Azagoh, C.; Dubey, B. N.; Dumoulin, E.; Turchiuli, C. Changes in Oil-in-Water Emulsion Size Distribution during the Atomization Step in Spray-Drying Encapsulation. *Journal of Food Engineering*, **2015**, *167*, 122–132.
67. Soottitantawat, A.; Yoshii, H.; Furuta, T.; Ohkawara, M.; Linko, P. Microencapsulation by Spray Drying: Influence of Emulsion Size on the Retention of Volatile Compounds. *Food Engineering and Physical Properties*, **2003**, *68* (7), 2256–2262.
68. El-sayed, T. M.; Wallack, D. A.; King, C. J. Changes in Particle Morphology during Drying of Drops of Carbohydrate Solutions and Food Liquids. 1. Effects of Composition and Drying Conditions. *Industrial and Engineering Chemical Research*, **1990**, *29* (12), 2346–2354.
69. Bringas-Lantigua, M.; Expósito-Molina, I.; Reineccius, G. A.; López-Hernández, O.; Pino, J. A. Influence of Spray-Dryer Air Temperatures on Encapsulated Mandarin Oil. *Drying Technology*, **2011**, *29* (5), 520–526.
70. Bringas-Lantigua, M.; Valdés, D.; Pino, J. A. Influence of Spray-Dryer Air Temperatures on Encapsulated Lime Essential Oil. *International Journal of Food Science & Technology*, **2012**, *47* (7), 1511–1517.
71. Cortes-Rojas, D. F.; Souza, C. R. F.; Oliveira, W. P. Clove (*Syzygium aromaticum*): A Precious Spice. *Asian Pacific Journal of Tropical Biomedicine*, **2014**, *4* (2), 90–96.
72. Jirovetz, L.; Buchbauer, G.; Stoilova, I.; Stoyanova, A.; Krastanov, A.; Schmidt, E. Chemical Composition and Antioxidant Properties of Clove Leaf Essential Oil. *Journal of Agricultural and Food Chemistry*, **2006**, *54* (17), 6303–6307.
73. Cortés-Rojas, D. F.; Souza, C. R. F.; Oliveira, W. P. Encapsulation of Eugenol Rich Clove Extract in Solid Lipid Carriers. *Journal of Food Engineering*, **2014**, *127*, 34–42.
74. Gülçin, İ. Antioxidant Activity of Eugenol: A Structure-Activity Relationship Study. *Journal of Medicinal Food*, **2011**, *14* (9), 975–985.
75. Xia, Q.; Saupe, A.; Müller, R. H.; Souto, E. B. Nanostructured Lipid Carriers as Novel Carrier for Sunscreen Formulations. *International Journal of Cosmetic Science*, **2007**, *29* (6), 473–482.

76. Nikolić, S.; Keck, C. M.; Anselmi, C.; Müller, R. H. Skin Photoprotection Improvement: Synergistic Interaction between Lipid Nanoparticles and Organic UV Filters. *International Journal of Pharmaceutics*, **2011**, *414* (1–2), 276–284.
77. Islam, M. I. U.; Sherrell, R.; Langrish, T. A. G. An Investigation of the Relationship between Glass Transition Temperatures and the Crystallinity of Spray-Dried Powders. *Drying Technology*, **2010**, *28* (3), 361–368.
78. Mosquera, L. H.; Moraga, G.; Martínez-Navarrete, N. Critical Water Activity and Critical Water Content of Freeze-Dried Strawberry Powder. *Food Research International*, **2012**, *47* (2), 201–206.
79. Cano-Chauca, M.; Stringheta, P. C.; Ramos, A. M.; Cal-Vidal, J. Effect of the Carriers on the Microstructure of Mango Powder Obtained by Spray Drying and Its Functional Characterization. *Innovative Food Science & Emerging Technologies*, **2005**, *6* (4), 420–428.
80. Drusch, S.; Berg, S. Extractable Oil in Microcapsules Prepared by Spray-Drying: Localisation, Determination and Impact on Oxidative Stability. *Food Chemistry*, **2008**, *109* (1), 17–24.
81. Schuster, S.; Bernewitz, R.; Guthausen, G.; Zapp, J.; Greiner, A. M.; Köhler, K.; Schuchmann, H. P. Analysis of W1/O/W2 Double Emulsions with CLSM: Statistical Image Processing for Droplet Size Distribution. *Chemical Engineering Science*, **2012**, *81*, 84–90.
82. Aditya, N. P.; Aditya, S.; Yang, H.-J.; Kim, H. W.; Park, S. O.; Lee, J.; Ko, S. Curcumin and Catechin Co-Loaded Water-in-Oil-in-Water Emulsion and Its Beverage Application. *Journal of Functional Foods*, **2015**, *15*, 35–43.
83. Lamprecht, A.; Schäfer, U. F.; Lehr, C. Characterization of Microcapsules by Confocal Laser Scanning Microscopy: Structure, Capsule Wall Composition and Encapsulation Rate. *European Journal of Pharmaceutics and Biopharmaceutics*, **2000**, *49* (1), 1–9.
84. Cortes-Rojas, D. F.; Souza, C. R. F.; Chen, M. J.; Hochhaus, G.; Oliveira, W. P. Effects of Lipid Formulations on Clove Extract Spray Dried Powders: Comparison of Physicochemical Properties, Storage Stability and In Vitro Intestinal Permeation. *Pharmaceutical Development and Technology*, **2018**, *23* (10), 1047–1056.

84. [illegible]

8 Encapsulation of Essential Oils in Lipid-Based Nanosystems

Iara Baldim, Cláudia Regina Fernandes Souza, and Wanderley Pereira Oliveira

CONTENTS

8.1 Introduction 198
8.1.1 Extraction of Essential Oils 199
8.2 Biological Activities of Essential Oils 201
8.3 Encapsulation of Essential Oils 204
8.3.1 Encapsulation of Essential Oils in Lipid Nanosystems 205
8.3.1.1 Emulsions 206
8.3.1.2 Micelles 207
8.3.1.3 Liposomes 207
8.3.1.4 SLNs 208
8.3.1.5 NLCs 208
8.3.2 Production and Characterisation of Lipid-Based Encapsulation Nanosystems 209
8.3.2.1 High-Energy Emulsification Methods 209
8.3.2.2 Low-Energy Emulsification Methods 211
8.3.2.3 Physicochemical Characterisation of Lipid Nanosystems 211
8.4 Drying of Lipid-Based Compositions Loaded with Essential Oils 212
8.4.1 Spray Drying 213
8.4.2 Freeze-Drying 214
8.4.3 Spray Freeze-Drying 215
8.4.4 Spray Congealing 216
8.5 Applications of Encapsulated Essential Oils in Food and Pharmaceutical Products 217
8.5.1 Food Antimicrobials 218
8.5.2 Natural Antioxidants for Food and Pharmaceutical Products 219
8.5.3 Cosmetics 220
8.5.4 Mouthwashes 221
8.5.5 Phytotherapy 222
8.6 Final Remarks and Prospects 222
Acknowledgements 223
References 223

DOI: 10.1201/9781003225416-10

8.1 INTRODUCTION

The growing interest of consumers for sustainable "green products" has contributed to the increased interest in using plant-derived products and impacted their production methods. This trend has led the industry to look for new and safer approaches to replace existing synthetic active substances or herbal products. In this sense, essential oils (EOs) have a high potential for application in various industrial sectors, including pharmaceutical, food, cosmetic, health, agriculture, and livestock. The application is linked to the EO's inherent biological activities (e.g. antioxidant, bactericide, virucidal, fungicide, antiparasitic, insecticide, analgesic, sedative, anti-inflammatory, spasmolytic, and local anaesthetic). Some isolated EOs and their bioactive compounds (e.g. lemongrass, peppermint, rosemary, chamomile, basil, cloves, thyme, lavender, mustard, rose, menthol, linalool, carvacrol, limonene, citral, *p*-cymene, thymol, linalool) are already listed as generally recognised as safe (GRAS) by the US Code of Federal Regulations [1].

EOs are complex mixtures of various volatile hydrophobic molecules produced by the plant's secondary metabolism. These volatile liquids exhibit high solubility in lipids and organic solvents and generally a lower density than water [2]. They are synthesised in different organs of the plant, such as flowers (jasmine, rose, violet, and lavender), flower buds (clove), leaves (eucalyptus, sage), fruits (anise), branches, bark (cinnamon), seeds (cardamom), wood (sandalwood), and roots (ginger). The term "essential oil" comes from Paracelsus von Hohenheim's theory (1493–1541), a physician and alchemist. He named the effective constituents of the plant as *Quinta essentia* or *Quintessence* to separate the "essential" part from the "nonessential" [3]. To date, nearly 3000 different EOs have been described; around 300 are exploited by the flavour and fragrance market [4].

Typically, EOs have about 20–60 constituents at quite different concentrations, but this number can reach more than 100. The EO constituents include different cyclic and acyclic hydrocarbons compounds and their oxygenated, nitrogen, or sulphur derivatives. The main EO classes of compounds are derived from three biosynthetic pathways: the mevalonate pathway leading to sesquiterpenes, the methyl-erythritol-pathway leading to mono- and diterpenes, and the shikimic acid pathway *en route* to phenylpropenes, and oxygenated compounds (e.g. alcohols, esters, ethers, aldehydes, ketones, lactones, phenolic ethers, and others). Generally, the principal constituent is usually associated with the EO's biological properties [2].

The most representative class of EO constituents are the terpenes, aromatic, and short-chain aliphatic hydrocarbon derivatives. They are formed by a combination of various five-carbon-base (C_5) (isoprene) units. The extension of the chain allows a high diversity of structures. The simplest terpenes are monoterpenes, containing two isoprene units (C_{10}), and constitute around 90% of EOs [2]. Sesquiterpenes have three isoprene units (C_{15}), while diterpenes have four (C_{20}). The increase in the number of carbons (and consequently in the molecular weight) reduces the compound's volatility, requiring more energy to be released from plant parts by steam distillation. Due to their low relative volatility, diterpenes are present in small quantities in many EOs obtained by steam distillation. Heavier terpenes (as tri- and higher—such as sterols or carotenoids) are only present in the non-volatile fractions of plants, for example, resins or gums [4].

Phenylpropanoids, composed of an aromatic ring with a three-carbon side chain (C6C3 skeleton), can also occur but less frequently than terpenes. However, when present, they occur in appreciable amounts, such as eugenol in clove EO, whose concentration can reach 70–90% [5].

Although less common, sulphur- or nitrogen-containing organic compounds may also be present in the EOs of some plant families, such as Alliaceae, Rutaceae, and Brassicaceae [5]. Sulphur confers the pungent and characteristic aroma and taste of garlic, while isothiocyanates are the common constituents of mustard oils [6]. Table 8.1 represents the chemical classification, structure, and properties of various EO constituents.

8.1.1 Extraction of Essential Oils

The content of EOs in fresh aromatic plants is usually low (about 1%), varying according to the species and the plant's organ where it accumulates. For this reason, they are highly valued substances. EOs can be obtained by different extraction methods, classified as conventional/classical or advanced/innovative methods [16]. Examples of conventional methods are hydrodistillation, vapour hydrodistillation, steam distillation, organic solvent extraction, and cold pressing. More efficient extraction processes have been proposed recently to reduce energy consumption and increase the extraction yield, such as supercritical fluid extraction (SFE), ultrasound-assisted extraction (UAE), and microwave-assisted extraction. The selection of an extraction method depends on the plant characteristics, part of the plant used, and EOs properties. The extraction method used has a strong influence on the EO's chemical profile [3]. Due to their density often lower than that of water and hydrophobic nature, EOs can be easily separated from the aqueous phase by decantation. However, some constituents of EOs have high water solubility or may present instabilities in contact with steam and heat, requiring specific extraction methods [16]. Indeed, the most traditional method for EO extraction is the water steam drag and its variants [17]:

1. Hydrodistillation, represented by the Clevenger apparatus, consists of immersing the herbal material directly in the boiling water and recovering the EO by condensation
2. Vapour hydrodistillation, in which the herbal material is placed on a perforated plate system positioned above the boiling water
3. Steam distillation is similar to vapour hydrodistillation, but the vapour is supplied by an external source

Hydrodistillation is a suitable alternative for the extraction of petals and flowers, as it avoids compaction and chomping of the material. However, the long extraction time required can degrade some thermosensitive compounds, changing the EO's chemical profiles. These drawbacks may be minimised or even avoided both in vapour hydrodistillation and steam distillation [16].

TABLE 8.1
Important Essential Oil Constituents: Their Molecular Structure, Properties and Examples

Class of Compound	Subclass	Substance	Structure	Properties	Example of Plant	Part Used
Terpenes	Monoterpene (C_{10})	D-limonene	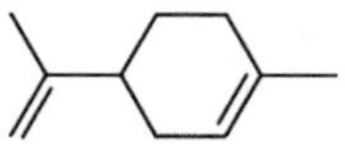	Promotes skin penetration and diffusivity of drugs [7]; excellent flavouring agents and provides effective gastroprotection [8]	*Citrus aurantium*	Fruit peel
	Sesquiterpene (C_{15})	α-Bisabolol	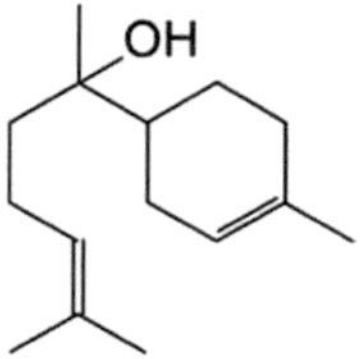	Anti-inflammatory, antinociceptive-like action [5, 9]; skin penetration enhancer [7]; antiglioma activity [10]	*Chamomilla recutita* (L.) Rauschert	Flower
	Diterpene (C_{20})	Phyllocladene	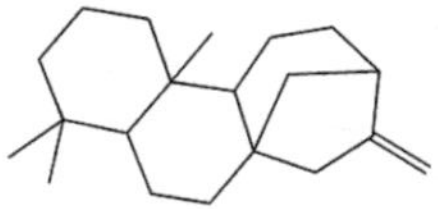	Antibacterial activity [11]	*Araucaria angustifolia*	Leaves
Aromatic compounds	Phenylpropanoids	Eugenol	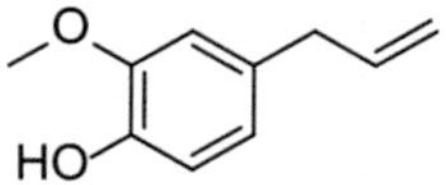	Antimicrobial activity due to its ability to permeate the bacterial cell membrane and interact with proteins [6]; inhibit *Escherichia coli* biofilm formation [12]; improve the stability of nanoemulsion delivery systems [13]; insecticide and herbicide [14]; anti-inflammatory effects [15]	*Eugenia caryophyllata (Syzygium aromaticum* L. Myrtaceae)	Buds and leaves
Other EO constituents	Sulphur- and nitrogen-containing compounds	Allicin	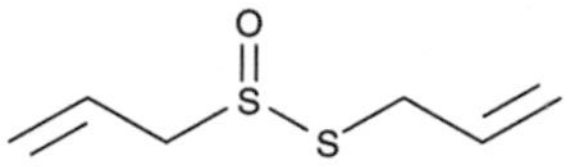	Antibacterial (Gram-negative and Gram-positive), antifungal, antiparasitic, and antiviral properties [6]	*Allium sativum* L.	Bulb
		Allyl isothiocyanate	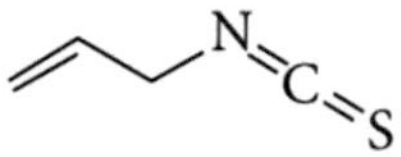	Antimicrobial activity [6]	*Brassica juncea*	Seeds

Organic solvent extraction and cold pressing are also traditional and well-established methods. The first method consists of macerating the plant material in an organic solvent, removed after extracting the EO. This technique is suitable for extracting thermosensitive compounds. On the other hand, organic solvents can compromise the quality and safety of the EO, in addition to being harmful to the environment. Cold pressing is the method of choice for extracting EO from the waxy outer layer of citrus peels. The pressing process breaks the oil bags, releases the EO, and produces an oil/water mixture, separated by pressurised centrifugation [17]. Novel approaches have been proposed to reduce extraction time, energy consumption, and the use of organic solvents.

SFE, an eco-friendly, cleaner, and sustainable extraction technique, has also attracted significant interest, mainly in recent years. The SFE principle is similar to maceration and percolation. However, the extracting fluid (gas) must be kept in conditions above its critical temperature and pressure, which require sophisticated and expensive equipment. This technique also has some restrictions for fresh plants and floral fragrances. Notwithstanding, the EO's quality, with composition similar to that of the raw material and a fresh flavour impression, offsets most of these attributed disadvantages, besides being a fast and gentle process [18].

UAE is an efficient, simple, and inexpensive technique suitable for thermosensitive compounds. It consists of immersing the plant material in a liquid solvent and submitting the mixture to ultrasound, which induces acoustic cavitation bubbles that can break the plant cells, facilitating the EO's release. UAE is commonly coupled with other techniques (e.g. hydrodistillation and solvent extraction) to enhance extraction speed/efficiency [16]. Another technique that also results in higher yields and shorter extraction times is microwave-assisted extraction. The process is based on water present in the plant matrix, whose cells are broken by the absorption of microwave energy, releasing the chemical compounds to the extraction solvent. The moisture content of the plant material allows for quick and uniform distribution of heat, and the extraction solvent (which has a distinct dielectric constant) remains cold, allowing for a reduction in sample temperature [19].

8.2 BIOLOGICAL ACTIVITIES OF ESSENTIAL OILS

The use of EOs in traditional medicine has been recognised and practised by humankind since ancient times [3]. In plants, the volatile constituents of EOs exhibit multiple ecological functions, such as plant defence against pathogens, herbivores attacks, solar radiation, and chemical signalling for pollinator attraction. EOs' multicomponent and complex nature can affect biological systems by various mechanisms of action. The biological effects of EOs are usually, more prominent compared to their isolated substances, caused by the occurrence of synergism between their major and minor constituents [20]. A description of the important biological activities of EO is presented below, and Table 8.2 highlights the biological activities of some EOs with great potential to be used for product development, together with an overview of their mechanism of action.

Antimicrobial activity: The antimicrobial activities of EOs depend on their bioactive constituents and the synergistic interactions between them. The lipophilic nature of EOs allows them to easily interact with the lipids of

TABLE 8.2
Biological Activities of Essential Oils

Bioactivity	Essential Oil	Mechanism of Action	Ref.
Antibacterial	*Syzygium aromaticum* *Melaleuca alternifolia* *Thymus vulgaris* *Origanum vulgare* *Eucalyptus globulus*	Several mechanisms of action involved in its antibacterial activity, among which the following stand out the disturbances in cell membrane integrity and the inhibition of cell wall synthesis, leading to cell lysis by the leakage of protein and lipid contents.	[21, 22, 23]
Antifungal	*Lippia sidoides* *T. vulgaris* *Cymbopogon citratus* *Rosmarinus officinalis* *Ocimum sanctum*	EOs can interact with fungal cell membrane, causing disruption, alteration, or even inhibition of the wall formation; inhibit mitochondrial enzymes, affecting the mitochondrial effectiveness and cellular metabolism; inhibit efflux pumps, modifying the fungal cell physiology; and they can also influence the ROS production in fungi.	[21, 24]
Antiviral	*Laurus nobilis* *E. globulus*	*L. nobilis*—Inhibition of viral replication from SARS-CoV-2. *E. globulus* – inactivates free influenza A (H1N1) virus and disrupt the envelope structures of the virus.	[25, 26]
Anti-inflammatory	*R. officinalis*	Mainly attributed to its major monoterpenes (1,8-cineole and α-pinene), by decreasing the activity of the transcription factor NK-κB, which impedes the synthesis of pro-inflammatory mediators. Also contribute to attenuate inflammation-induced injury by neutralising the reactive species produced in inflammation.	[27]
Antinociceptive	*Thymus capitatus*	The carvacrol-rich essential oil from *T. capitatus* induces antinociception in orally treated mice by exerts its antinociceptive activity through peripheral nervous excitability blockade.	[28]
Antimutagenic	*Citrus sinensis* *Citrus latifolia*	Reduce alkylated DNA damages through a reduction in the expression of base-substitution mutations; reduce the activation of pre-mutagens; and as possible ROS-scavenging mixtures.	[29]

(Continued)

TABLE 8.2 *(Continued)*
Biological Activities of Essential Oils

Bioactivity	Essential Oil	Mechanism of Action	Ref.
Anticancer	*Melissa officinalis* *M. alternifolia*	*M. officinalis*—induces apoptosis in human glioblastoma multiforme cell lines by DNA fragmentation and activation of caspase-9 and caspase-3. *M. alternifolia*—inhibits the growth and induce caspase-dependent apoptotic cell death in melanoma cells, due to the interaction between the lipophilic components of essential oil and the phospholipid bilayer of melanoma cell membranes.	[30, 31]
Antioxidant	*S. aromaticum*	Some EOs are rich in phenolic compounds (or some terpenoids and sulphur containing components) able to stop or delay the aerobic oxidation.	[22]
Immunomodulatory	*Melaleuca alternifolia*	Tea tree essential oil derivative (terpinen-4-ol) reduces the expression of IL-8 through mechanisms related to the protein synthesis inhibition. Also inhibits other inflammatory processes, as contact hypersensitivity and histamine-induced oedema/weal/flare-reaction in human skin.	[15]
Antiprotozoal	*L. sidoides* *C. citratus* *T. vulgaris*	Direct effect on protozoa (disruption of flagellar membranes, mitochondrial swelling, and alterations in the organisation of the chromatins) and interfering with the isoprenoid pathway present in protozoa.	[4, 32]
Antiplatelet	*Foeniculum vulgare* *Artemisia dracunculus* *Wasabia japonica*	EOs containing a higher concentration of phenylpropanoids are related to an inhibition of arachidonate cascade and thrombin activity.	[33, 34]

the microbial cell membrane, and the susceptibility depends on the EO's composition and microorganism strains. Some EOs are active against gram-positive and gram-negative bacteria, yeast, and filamentous fungi. Gram-positive bacteria are more susceptible to EOs than Gram-negative since the former does not have the rigid lipopolysaccharide outer membrane, restricting the diffusion of lipophilic substances [21].

Antiviral activity: Due to their lipophilic nature, EOs can also penetrate viral membranes, easily causing their rupture, leading to a reduction in the host's inflammatory responses [35]. EO constituents can act in synergy at different viral replication stages showing activity against various viruses (e.g. influenza, human herpesvirus, human immunodeficiency, yellow fever, avian influenza). Activity against enveloped viruses, such as the SARS-CoV-2, has also been demonstrated [25].

Antioxidant activity: EOs, especially those with volatile phenolic compounds, are recognised as potent antioxidant ingredients due to their high reactivity with peroxyl radicals [36]. However, some terpenoids and other volatile compounds, as the sulphur-containing substances, also exhibit significant antioxidant activity [20].

Anti-inflammatory and antinociceptive activities: Many aromatic species are used in traditional medicine for anti-inflammatory and antinociceptive purposes to relieve pain and inflammatory diseases. Various experimental studies have demonstrated the anti-inflammatory and antinociceptive activities of various EO active constituents [37].

Antimutagenic activity: The antimutagenic activity of EOs is related to several mechanisms, which includes the ability to inhibit the metabolic conversion of pro-mutagens into mutagens; inhibit the penetration of the mutagenic agent into the cells; make the antioxidant capture of radicals produced by mutagens; activate the enzymatic detoxification of mutagens. The antimutagenic activity depends on both the mutagen and antimutagen doses used [38].

Anticancer activity: Various EOs have shown anticarcinogenic/antimutagenic/antiproliferative effects and can be used for cancer prevention [38]. Interestingly, more than half of the anticancer agents approved between 1940 and 2006 were natural products and their derivatives [39].

Immunomodulatory activity: Some EOs can impact the inflammatory process and the expression of interleukins. Active inflammatory responses are associated with increased circulating cytokines and substantial lymphopenia. EOs can act by reducing the release of pro-inflammatory cytokines from monocytes and macrophages [25].

Antiprotozoal activity: Protozoan diseases are serious public health problems. In recent decades, studies evaluating the antiprotozoal effects of EOs have become increasingly available, both for human and animal health [4].

Antiplatelet activity: Platelets are responsible for preventing blood loss from damage to blood vessels by the blood clotting. However, the clotting process can be especially dangerous when it occurs in healthy blood vessels. Platelet aggregation is irreversible and can block blood flow, compromise oxygen transport to cells, and lead to stroke, pulmonary embolism, and heart attack [36]. The high prevalence of these diseases has led to the continuous search for new antithrombotic agents with low adverse effects. Some EOs have shown influence on the blood clotting process, and their effectiveness and safety have been investigated [33].

8.3 ENCAPSULATION OF ESSENTIAL OILS

EO constituents may exhibit instability, high volatility, and sensitivity to external factors (e.g. light, oxygen, and heat). Thus, during the EO's production chain (extraction, transport and storage), some labile compounds may undergo oxidation and other degradation reactions, losing their function or forming toxic derivatives [16]. Fortunately, these limitations can be overcome by using encapsulation technologies, which can provide new properties to EOs. The use of encapsulation technology can solve several problems related to natural compound stability and bioavailability. The encapsulation of EOs consists of their incorporation in a carrier system (wall material), composed of carbohydrates, gums, proteins, lipids, natural or synthetic polymeric materials, or mixtures between them. The product's characteristics—aqueous solubility, release rate, bioaccessibility, bioavailability—depend on product size (macro, micro, or nanoparticles), wall material (e.g. polymeric and lipid nanoparticles), and lipid system used [40]. Reducing EO volatility and protecting it against environmental factors allows its use in many innovative applications (e.g. incorporation in textiles, surface coating, compositions for agricultural use, or active packing) [3].

The application and the biological activity of the finished product depend on its physicochemical properties. Detoni et al. [10] encapsulated *Zanthoxylum tingoassuiba* EO—rich in α-bisabolol—into liposomes to assess both the increase in oxidative stability and the ability to reduce the glioblastoma's cell viability. The encapsulated system protected the EO from temperature-induced oxidation and performed well against glioma cells, showing potential to be used to treat glioblastoma. Similarly, Hădărugă et al. [41] demonstrated the protective capacity of β-cyclodextrin against the oxidation of labile compounds of *Ocimum basilicum* EO.

In addition to increasing EOs stability, the encapsulation has also shown to be efficient for modulating their release and enhancing bioactivity, improving the E'Os effectiveness. Donsì et al. [42] reported that the encapsulated terpenes extracted from *Melaleuca alternifolia* improved their antimicrobial activity against food-borne pathogens (*Lactobacillus delbrueckii* and *Escherichia coli*), with minimal changes in the organoleptic properties of the treated juice. Baldim et al. [24] encapsulated *Lippia sidoides* EO in lipid nanosystems and evaluated its antifungal efficacy against *Candida albicans*. The encapsulated EO nanosystem successfully retained its antifungal activity. From a technological perspective, this result is very interesting since the lipid nanosystems are more stable, biocompatible, and biodegradable. Saporito et al. [23] encapsulated EOs of *Eucalyptus globulus* or rosemary in naturally based lipid nanosystems to enhance skin wound healing properties. They reported that nanoparticles loaded with the *Eucalyptus* EO showed good bioadhesion, increased cell proliferation *in vitro*, cytocompatibility, antimicrobial activity, and better healing process of skin wounds in the model of burns in rats.

8.3.1 Encapsulation of Essential Oils in Lipid Nanosystems

The encapsulation of active ingredients into lipid systems has increased continuously, mainly in the pharmaceutical and food sectors. Hydrophilic and lipophilic compounds can be encapsulated in these systems, which also present ease and low production cost, low toxicity, increased product aqueous solubility, bioavailability, and stability, and allow sustained release/drug targeting. These systems are also preferred because of their greater drug loading capacity, economic feasibility, suitability

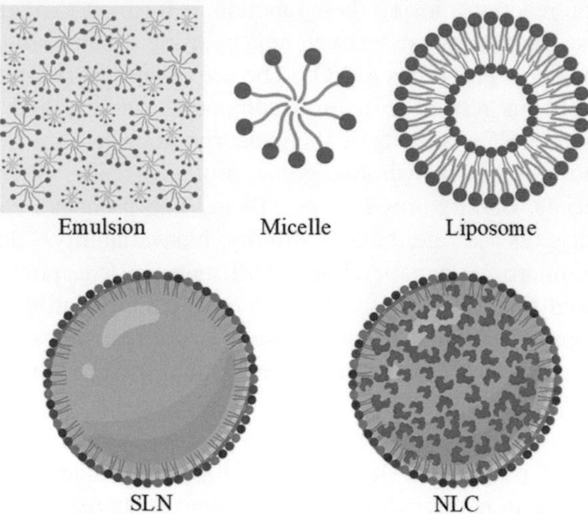

FIGURE 8.1 Schematic representation of distinct lipid nanosystems.

for large-scale production, and versatility. Lipid systems are attractive and efficient methods for EO encapsulation, with advantages over conventional systems, such as better permeation through biological barriers, better bioavailability, and controlled release of bioactive compounds. Most lipid systems are derived from natural sources, biocompatible, and biodegradable and have the GRAS status [40]. They can be used in topical, dermal, transdermal, oral, and parenteral formulations. Nanoemulsions, microemulsions, solid lipid nanoparticles (SLNs), and liposomes are typical lipid systems that have been used to encapsulate EOs [40, 43]. Figure 8.1 shows a schematic representation of different lipid nanosystems, which can be applied for EOs encapsulation.

8.3.1.1 Emulsions

Emulsions are tiny colloidal dispersions formed by mechanical mixing of two immiscible liquid phases plus a surfactant system. They can be classified as water-in-oil (W/O), oil-in-water (O/W), water-in-oil-in-water (W/O/W), or oil-in-water-in-oil (O/W/O) emulsions, being the O/W and W/O/W adequate for EOs encapsulation. Emulsions are classified as coarse emulsions (conventional emulsions—200 nm>1000 nm), nanoemulsions (<200 nm), and microemulsions (10–100 nm). Emulsions and nanoemulsions are thermodynamically unstable systems, although kinetically stable. They are susceptible to instability processes like coalescence, creaming, phase separation, flocculation, and Ostwald ripening. Their stability and functional performance are strictly related to the choice and concentration of appropriate emulsifier systems [44, 45].

Emulsions in the nano-size range (e.g. droplet diameters below 200 nm), also known as nanoemulsions, have functional properties that differ considerably from coarse emulsions. The encapsulation of bioactive in nanoemulsions may enhance its bioactivity [46]. Nanoemulsion production requires high-energy mixing equipment, as high-pressure homogenisers and microfluidisers. However, the concentration of surfactants is relatively less than that required for the formation of microemulsions. They are kinetically stable systems whose stability (even over gravity) can last for several years, being especially attractive to the industry, especially the food and pharmaceutical. The surfactant choice is a critical step since it is desirable that the emulsifier rapidly cover the countless new surfaces formed. However, despite the high kinetic and gravitational stability, the reduced droplet size of nanoemulsions favours the growth of larger droplets inside the emulsion, resulting in the phenomenon of instability known as Ostwald ripening [46]. With the decreasing droplet size, the oil solubility in water also increases, favouring this phenomenon. EOs are unsuitable to be used as the oily phase of nanoemulsions since they are partially miscible in water. EOs should be mixed with a highly lipophilic oil to be loaded in a nanoemulsion to prevent Ostwald ripening [47].

Microemulsions are optically transparent systems, having high thermodynamic stability and low viscosity. These systems are emulsified by a surfactant, normally associated with a co-surfactant [48]. The formation of microemulsions is a very simple and inexpensive process. They are formed spontaneously due to the surfactant hydrophobic group's tendency to associate, reducing their contact with the polar solvent [46]. Microemulsions, however, may be unsuitable for some pharmaceutical applications due to the significant larger amounts of surfactants needed to stabilise them, which can be potentially toxic [47]. Moreover, its loading capacity is limited, and an excess of actives can cause phase separation [46].

8.3.1.2 Micelles

Micelles are dispersed nanosystems structured in the form of a hydrophobic core enclosed by a hydrophilic shell. Some of their main advantages are the high loading capacity, stability, improved solubilisation, prolonged circulation, very small size (1–50 nm), and targeting potential. The shell stabilises the system and interacts with different molecules, such as proteins and cells. Versatility is another strength of micelles, as it allows them to assume several shapes and incorporate various solutes with different structures. Surfactant-based micelles are self-assembled when the surfactant concentration exceeds the so-called "critical micelle concentration" (CMC), reducing the unfavourable interactions between the lipophilic portion of the surfactant and water molecules.

Based on micelle's ability to incorporate lipophilic molecules within its structures, they serve as a suitable delivery system for several functional compounds, among them EOs. The lipophilic bioactive may either be located within the micelle's interior or become part of the surfactant layer. The bioactive is released by diffusion, controlled by pH, chemical, and concentration variations [49].

8.3.1.3 Liposomes

Liposomes are among the most widely studied colloidal delivery systems and formed the first group of lipid-based nanocarriers administered *in vivo* models. They were invented in the mid-1960s but developed for drug delivery purposes only in the 1970s [47]. Liposomes are self-assembled spherical structures formed from amphiphilic lipids (e.g. phospholipids). Cholesterol or ergosterol are also added to give stability, fluidity, and to influence membrane permeability [46]. The phospholipids are organised in a bilayer, which surrounds the aqueous core, with a diameter ranging from 50 to 5000 nm [50]. Depending on both the mean diameter and the number of bilayers, liposomes can be classified into three groups: (i) one bilayer forming unilamellar vesicles, with size usually up to 100 nm and low aqueous-lipid ratio; (ii) one bilayer forming large unilamellar vesicles, with size between 100 nm and 1 μm; and (iii) multilamellar vesicles, with multiple lipid bilayer membrane and size higher than 100 nm [51]. Liposomes may be used to encapsulate hydrophilic (into aqueous core), lipophilic (into lipid bilayer), and amphiphilic drugs (partitioned at the surface of the bilayers). The amphiphilic character of phospholipids molecules is also an attractive approach to encapsulate EOs [52].

The reduced antigenicity and toxicity and high encapsulation efficiency for different biomolecules are some of the advantages of liposomes. In contrast, difficulties in scale-up and reduced long-term stability (by problems as oxidation, hydrolysis, and aggregation of the vesicles) are the most limiting disadvantages for their administration.

8.3.1.4 SLNs

SLNs are colloidal drug delivery systems composed of a biocompatible and biodegradable lipid matrix, in which active molecules can be incorporated. The lipid matrix structure is stabilised by a suitable surfactant, similarly to oil-in-water nanoemulsions, except for the solid lipid (at physiological temperatures), instead of the liquid. The diameter of SLN particles ranged between 150 and 300 nm, though larger or smaller sizes can also be obtained.

These systems are able to encapsulate both lipophilic and hydrophilic molecules. Furthermore, they exhibit excellent biocompatibility and toxicity, promote target release, and have a fabrication process easy and scalable, avoiding the use organic solvents. Hence, it is an excellent nanosystem for EOs encapsulation. On the other hand, its highly crystalline structure and the unexpected dynamics of polymorphic transitions reduce the load capacity of the SLN and favour undesirable drug leakage during storage [40, 53].

8.3.1.5 NLCs

The second generation of lipid nanoparticles, the so-called nanostructured lipid carrier (NLC), was proposed in 1999. NLCs brought solutions to SLN's limitations of SLN, such as high crystallinity, low drug loading, and drug leakage during storage. In these systems, the lipid matrix is composed of a mixture of solid and liquid lipids, which increases its ability to incorporate actives, reduces the degree of crystallinity and, consequently, the occurrence of polymorphic transitions [54]. The strong immobilisation and reduced expulsion of encapsulated molecules during storage are other key advantages of NLCs. Hence, these carriers are convenient systems for encapsulating lipophilic compounds, such as the EOs. The lipophilic nature of EOs favours greater retention efficiency, and the release can be modulated by changing the composition of the lipid matrix.

8.3.2 Production and Characterisation of Lipid-Based Encapsulation Nanosystems

The most commonly used excipients to produce EO lipid nanosystems include the fatty acids (e.g. oleic acid), vegetable oils (e.g. soybean oil), semi-synthetic glycerides (e.g. Miglyol®, Capmul® MCM), polyoxyethylene glycols or derivatives of macrogol glycerides (e.g. Labrasol®, Labrafil®, Gelucire®), ethoxylated glycerides (e.g. Cremophor®), polyalcohol fatty acid esters (e.g. Solutol®, Tween®), cholesterol, and phospholipids (e.g. egg and soybean lecithin) [40]. The excipient's selection should consider the desired product properties (e.g. sustained release, biodegradability, protection) and the intended administration route. The methods usually used to encapsulate EOs in lipid systems can be classified into high- or low-energy emulsification methods [43, 54, 55]. Table 8.3 shows techniques widely used to homogenise and reduce the particle size of these nanosystems as well as recommended characterisation methods.

8.3.2.1 High-Energy Emulsification Methods

These homogenisation methods require high mechanical energy and are carried out in equipment such as high-speed rotor-stator mixers (ultra-turrax), high-pressure homogenisers, microfluidisers, and ultrasonic probes. In the high-pressure homogenisation, a positive displacement pump feeds the lipid composition at high pressure through a homogenising valve promoting its emulsification. In contrast, the microfluidisers have an interaction chamber where the fluid is injected and homogenised by cutting, impact, and cavitation. Factors such as temperature, viscosity, concentration of the emulsified system's internal phase and the equipment used have substantial effects on the physicochemical characteristics of the product. High-pressure homogenisers and microfluidisers apply very high energy to the system, which makes the particle coalescence inevitable. Thus, the appropriate selection of the emulsifying agent's type and concentration, and the process's optimisation are key factors to generate a stable submicrometric emulsion with homogeneously small droplets, minimising the need for over-processing [60].

The production of lipid nanosystems by ultrasound probes has also been widely described in the literature. In homogenisation by ultrasound, reducing the droplet size of a coarse suspension or emulsion is caused using cavitation forces generated by ultrasonic waves generated by an ultrasound probe. Depending on the cavitation energy and homogenisation time, nanosuspensions or nanoemulsions with predefined properties can be produced. However, most of the ultrasonic processing systems still in use cannot be well suited for the aseptic production since ions or particles may be emitted into the product by the cavitation abrasion of the ultrasonic probes, although it is possible to minimise this problem in more sophisticate ultrasonic homogenisers [61].

High-pressure homogenisation and microfluidisation techniques are easily scalable. They are widely used both in laboratory research and on industrial production, while ultrasound homogenisation remains restricted to the laboratory scale. The main disadvantage of these methods is their low-energy efficiency. Only a small parcel of the energy furnished is effectively used for emulsification [62], thus requiring a high energy level to obtain nanometer-scaled droplets.

TABLE 8.3
Commonly Used Methods to Homogenise and Characterise Lipid Nanosystems

Lipid System	Homogenisation Methods	Characterisation Methods	Reference
Microemulsion	Requires low-energy emulsification methods to be formed since they are spontaneous self-assembled (dilution of an oil-surfactant mixture with water)	• Emulsion microstructure: optical microscopy • Particle size distribution: static light scattering; dynamic light scattering (d <2 μm droplets) • Zeta potential • DSC and X-ray diffraction	[56, 57]
Nanoemulsion	• High-energy techniques: high-shear stirring, high-pressure homogenisation, and ultra-sonication • Low-energy techniques: phase inversion temperature, emulsion phase inversion, and spontaneous nanoemulsification	• Emulsion microstructure: electron microscopy (d <500 nm droplets) • Particle size distribution: static light scattering; dynamic light scattering (d <2 μm droplets) • Zeta potential • X-ray diffraction and DSC	[43, 57]
Micelle	Similar to microemulsion, micelles are spontaneously formed self-assembled colloidal structures, requiring only the solubilisation of surfactant in water	• Particle size and zeta potential	[46, 58]
Liposome	• High-energy techniques: ultra-sonication, high-pressure extrusion (through polycarbonate membranes, after lipid hydration) • Low energy techniques: detergent dialysis and solvent injection	• Particle size and zeta potential • Degree of crystallinity and lipid modification (DSC and X-ray diffraction)	[43, 58]
SLN	• High-pressure homogenisation (hot and cold) • Emulsification-solvent diffusion • Emulsification-solvent evaporation • Microemulsion technique • Membrane contactor technique • Solvent injection • Phase inversion • Ultra-sonication	• Particle size and zeta potential • Degree of crystallinity and lipid modification (DSC and X-ray diffraction)	[40, 59]
NLC	• High-pressure homogenisation (hot and cold) • Emulsification-solvent diffusion • Emulsification-solvent evaporation • Microemulsion technique • Membrane contactor technique • Solvent injection • Phase inversion • Ultra-sonication	• Particle size and zeta potential • Degree of crystallinity and lipid modification (DSC and X-ray diffraction)	[40, 59]

8.3.2.2 Low-Energy Emulsification Methods

Low-energy emulsification methods are frequently more energy-efficient and can produce smaller droplet sizes than the high-energy methods (require only gentle stirring) but usually allow lower oil-to-surfactant ratios. These methods generally depend on the modulation of interfacial phenomena/phase transition and intrinsic physicochemical properties of surfactants, co-emulsifiers/co-surfactants, and oil to obtain nanometer-sized droplet emulsions. They are usually called phase inversion and self-emulsification methods, depending on the variations or not of the surfactant system's spontaneous curvature during the emulsification process, respectively [62].

Examples of low-energy emulsification protocols commonly used are the phase inversion temperature (PIT), the phase inversion composition (PIC), the solvent diffusion (also named solvent displacement), and solvent evaporation methods. In the PIT method, the spontaneous emulsification is carried out by changes in temperature at a fixed composition, while in the PIC, the composition (and interfacial properties) is changed at a constant temperature. PIT method uses the temperature-dependent solubility of nonionic surfactants, such as the polyethoxylated surfactants, to modify their affinity for water and oil as a function of temperature. The oily phase, water, and the nonionic surfactant are mixed at room temperature. In the solvent evaporation method, the oil phase is dissolved in a water-miscible organic solvent such as acetone, ethanol, and ethyl methyl ketone. The organic phase is then placed in contact with the aqueous phase containing the surfactant for spontaneous emulsification by rapid diffusion of the organic solvent. The organic solvent is then removed from the emulsified system by evaporation under reduced pressure, thus requiring an additional process step. This technique is simple to be performed on the laboratory scale, but its scale-up for industrial production is tricky.

The main challenges to develop stable emulsified systems reside in the selection and evaluation of their main constituents, namely emulsifiers (tween, span, phospholipids, amphiphilic proteins, and polysaccharides), texture modifiers (sugars, polyols, polysaccharides, and proteins), fillers agents (lipophilic materials), and coalescing retardants or Ostwald ripening agents (e.g. lipophilic materials with low water solubility such as long-chain triglycerides) [49].

8.3.2.3 Physicochemical Characterisation of Lipid Nanosystems

The characterisation of the lipid system is mandatory for product quality control. Particle size, surface area, zeta potential, and structural characteristics of the lipid systems play important roles in controlling the release rate of EOs from the capsules core and on system stability.

The most used techniques for routine particle size measurements are photon correlation spectroscopy (PCS) and laser diffraction (LD). In the PCS, also known as dynamic light scattering, the measurements are based on changes in the intensity of the light scattered by the particle caused by Brownian motion. The normal PCS size dimensions range from few nanometres to about 3 μm. For larger particles, the LD method provides better results. This technique uses static light scattering based on the diffraction angle's dependence on the particle radius. LD measurement range varies from nanometres to millimetres [59].

The zeta potential allows the measurement of the electrical characteristics of a colloidal dispersion. This determination is important because it allows predicting the nanosystem's stability during storage. In general, increasing the zeta potential (modulus) minimises particle aggregation [59].

Although particle size and zeta potential are useful properties for characterising lipid nanosystems, they are not sufficient. The degree of crystallinity and polymorphic transitions also requires special attention since they are linked to the drug incorporation and release rate. The greater the packing density and the thermodynamic stability of the lipids, the lower is the rate of drug incorporation. Differential scanning calorimetry (DSC) and X-ray diffraction are widely used techniques for these characterisations. DSC assesses lipid modifications, determining their melting points and enthalpy of fusion. With X-ray diffraction, it is possible to obtain information on the length of the lipid network's long and short spacings. The drug incorporation decreases in the following order: supercooled fusion <modification α <modification β′ <modification β [59].

8.4 DRYING OF LIPID-BASED COMPOSITIONS LOADED WITH ESSENTIAL OILS

The development of dry, free-flowing lipid-based encapsulation nanosystems has attracted interest from several research groups. These systems may exhibit significant advantages over the liquid and semisolid forms, such as greater stability and shelf-life, easy handling, lower storage volume, and high drug load. Moreover, the dry lipid systems can be directly used to produce conventional solid dosage forms such as pills, tablets, and capsules, enhancing patient compliance [63]. Redispersion of the dry product can recover totally or partially the initial lipid nanosystem characteristics when needed. The properties of the encapsulating composition, drying adjuvants (or cryoprotectants), drying method, and processing conditions affect the product properties and redispersion capability. Several methods, including spray drying, spray chilling, cooling, or congealing, fluidised bed coating, freeze-drying (lyophilisation), centrifugal extrusion, and the physical adsorption on solid carriers (suitable for liquid lipids systems at room temperature), may transform the lipid-based encapsulation nanosystems into free-flow powders or granules [63].

However, the production of dry lipid-based nanosystems loaded with EOs and other active phytopharmaceutical ingredients is challenging since it involves several steps, namely the definition of the original lipid-based encapsulation system, selection of the composition constituents; the choice of the drying method, drying adjuvants, or cryoprotectants; and the definition of the processing conditions. Depending on the choice, it is possible to obtain various particulate systems, including solid dispersions, proliposomes, dry emulsions, dry SLN and NLC, among others [63–65].

However, most of the lipid excipients are liquid at room temperature or have low melting points, and the EOs have high volatility. Thus, the most efficient dryers for these systems work at low temperatures, such as freeze-drying and spray freeze-drying or those that work at high temperatures but with a short residence time of the product in the dryer. A brief description of drying systems widely used to produce dry lipid-based encapsulation nanosystems is presented below.

8.4.1 Spray Drying

Spray drying is a versatile drying technology, which has been widely used in industry to produce dry, free-flowing powders directly from liquid feeds. This technology has been successfully used to manufacture a wide range of products including, pharmaceuticals, cosmetics, clays, pigments, soaps, and detergents, among other products. A great advantage generally attributed to spray drying is its capability to control the product's physicochemical properties by the correct specification of feed composition properties and dying conditions [66].

Spray drying involves atomisation of a liquid feed into a heated flowing gas (normally air), resulting in extremely rapid solvent evaporation (e.g. water). The process is divided into different stages, namely atomisation of the feed liquid, mixing the liquid with the hot gas, solvent evaporation, powder formation, and separation and collection of the dry product. Typical values of the inlet gas temperature during spray drying are around 150–220°C (sometimes higher). However, solvent evaporation occurs very quickly, and the residence time of the product inside the dryer is short. Figure 8.2 presented the main steps of the spray dryer process [67].

The versatility, low operating costs, the short residence time of the product inside the dryers, capability to process thermosensitive materials, and feasibility for continuous and large-scale production have made spray drying a lead drying and encapsulation technology. This technology's successful use to encapsulate volatile substances, including EOs and flavours, is widely described in the literature [68]. The operation relies on applying a protective coating layer surrounding the EO's constituents to protect them from the environment and improve product stability, taste masking, and easy handling. The encapsulated product must show a high retention efficiency of the EO's constituents, which should be maintained during the product shelf life. The encapsulating composition constituents and spray drying conditions affect product properties, such as product granulometry, microstructure, redispersion capability, and bioactive compound retention. These characteristics affect the product functionality, stability, and other technological and biopharmaceutical properties [68]. Wall materials successfully used for EO spray drying encapsulation include mesquite gum [69]. Acacia gum, blends of maltodextrin (DE 16-20), and whey protein/or modified starch/or small molecule surfactant [70], skimmed milk powder and whey protein concentrate [71], molecular inclusion in cyclodextrins [72], and more recently lipid nanosystems [64, 65].

The main factors affecting the volatile's retention during spray drying encapsulation are the feed composition's physicochemical properties (e.g. solids content, density, viscosity, surface tension, type, and concentration of wall materials and EOs) and the spray drying operating conditions (e.g. feed flow rate and pressure of atomisation gas, feed

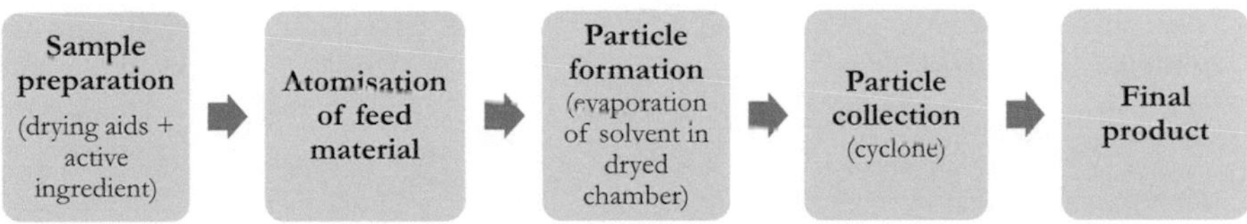

FIGURE 8.2 Main steps involved in spray drying.

flow rate of the encapsulating composition, inlet and outlet temperature of the drying gas, drying gas flow rate, gas humidity, and residence time inside the drying chamber) [69, 73]. The solids content is one of the most important factors linked to the retention of volatile compounds in the encapsulated product. The higher the formulation's solids content, the faster the formation of the superficial crust, which acts as a semi-permeable membrane promoting the volatiles retention [73]. On the other hand, the volatile constituent's retention tends to decrease conversely with the EO amount added to the encapsulating composition. Usually, the ratio of EO:wall material is 1:4 or lower [69, 73].

8.4.2 Freeze-Drying

The freeze-drying or lyophilisation involves the rapid cooling of the material at temperatures and vacuum pressure below the triple point of water (0.01°C and 6.1 mbar). In these conditions, the sublimation of ice occurs. The speed of freeze-drying is generally increased by reducing the pressure with a minimum value. The vapour condenser temperature must be kept below that of the frozen product [74], maintaining a temperature gradient with the frozen sample. Freeze-drying is a drying method widely used in the pharmaceutical industry, and several freeze-dried products are regularly marketed.

The typical freeze-drying operation involves three stages (see Figure 8.3): freezing, primary drying, and secondary drying. The freezing phase is a cooling step where most of the solvent (e.g. water) is separated from the formulation components, resulting in ice formation. The primary drying is initiated when the chamber pressure is reduced to a few millibars. The shelf temperature is increased to supply a sufficient amount of heat to the frozen sample for water sublimation. The water is desorbed from the frozen formulation at a slightly higher temperature and low pressure during the secondary drying stage [75].

The product temperature remains low during freeze-drying, and oxidisable substances are protected under vacuum conditions. The product' reconstitution is easier and quicker (microscopic pores are present in the dry sample and the constituents of dried material remain homogeneously distributed). The flavours and smells generally remain unchanged, with little product contamination owing to an aseptic process. It can be mentioned as disadvantages:

1. The loss of volatile compounds and expensive processing costs.
2. Amorphous (glassy) materials must be maintained at conditions below their critical point to prevent sample thaw or collapse during primary and secondary drying.
3. If too much heat is added, the material's structure could be altered.
4. Freezing damage can occur with labile products.

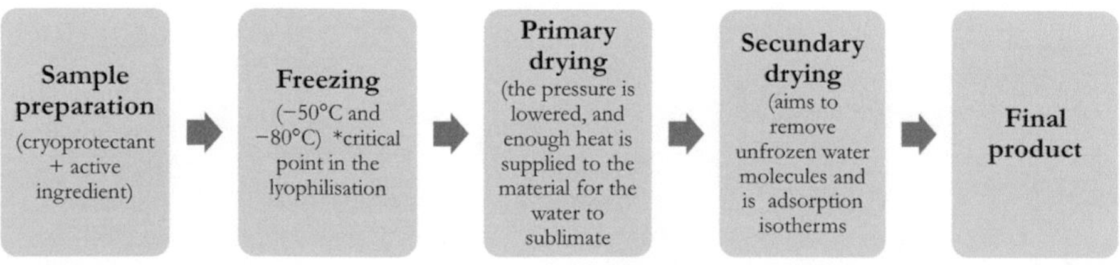

FIGURE 8.3 Main steps involved in the freeze-drying (lyophilisation) procedure.

The formulation of a freeze-dried product may require the addition of various excipients, such as buffers (phosphate buffer), bulking agents (mannitol, sucrose, or one of the other disaccharides), tonicity adjusters (mannitol, sucrose, glycine, glycerol, and sodium chloride), and stabilisers (sucrose, trehalose, glucose, lactose, maltose) aiming to protect and maintain product structure, generating a product of high quality and elegant appearance. The final product quality depends on the freeze-drying conditions (temperature and cooling rate, vacuum operation, heat supply rate), type and amount of excipients, among other factors [74, 76, 77].

8.4.3 Spray Freeze-Drying

Spray freeze-drying (SFD) is a relatively novel technique used in the pharmaceutical field. This process combines the spray drying and freeze-drying. The process steps involved in the SFD include the droplet generation (atomisation), almost instantaneous droplet freezing, primary drying, and secondary drying (see Figure 8.4). Similar to spray drying, the SFD involves the spraying of the liquid composition; however, instead of atomising into a heated gaseous stream, the liquid feed is atomised directly into a cryogenic medium, where the fast freezing of droplets takes place. The frozen droplets are collected by sieves or following the evaporation of the cryogen. The frozen particles are then transferred to pre-chilled shelves of a freeze-dryer, following the conventional freeze-drying. One advantage of SFD is that sublimation and secondary drying of the frozen particles are faster than those achieved in conventional freeze-drying due to the increased surface area of the frozen sample [78, 79]. The SFD is a good option to dehydrate lipid-based encapsulation nanosystems such as emulsions, liposomes, SLNs, and NLCs, forming a product with high aqueous dispersibility.

As heat stress is avoided, this technology may be suitable for processing thermosensitive substances, allowing the formation of powdered particles with optimised properties [75]. It has proven benefits over other drying methods in producing products with improved structural integrity (the shrinkage is minimised), superior quality, and better storage stability [80]. Compared to spray drying, lighter and more porous particles with improved aerosol performance are produced by SFD, and the production yield is almost 100% [81].

The atomisation step is a key factor of the SFD, which affects the particle size distribution of the sprayed droplets directly. Several atomisers can be used for this step, such as centrifugal, ultrasonic, and two-fluid, three fluid, or four-fluid nozzles. Factors influencing atomisation include feed properties (e.g. surface tension, rheology, solids content) and the atomising conditions (e.g. feed flow rate of the composition, feed flow rate, and pressure atomising fluid). Hence, to achieve smaller droplet

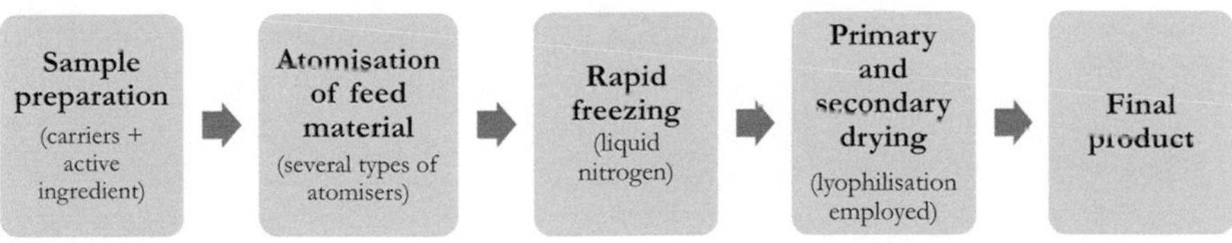

FIGURE 8.4 Steps involved in spray freeze-drying.

sizes, high atomisation pressures (or energy) are required. The atomised composition's fast freezing is carried out below the sub-zero temperatures in a cryogenic fluid such as liquid nitrogen. Surfactants and cryoprotectant can be added to the feed composition to minimise the stresses caused by atomisation, composition freezing, and drying steps. The solid content of the feed composition has significant effects on particle porosity. In general, solid content and particle porosity follow an inverse relation. However, a persistent reduction in the solid content would result in spherical structure breakage due to individual particles' mechanical instability [79].

The physical–chemical properties of SFD particles (sizes, densities, and high specific surface area) show superior stability in the lungs, nasal mucosa, intestine, and skin than those obtained by other drying technologies [79]. SFD processing of poorly water-soluble drugs formulated with polyvinyl alcohol, polyvinylpyrrolidone, poloxamer, and other polymers improved their wetting and dissolution capability [78, 79]. The ability to encapsulate poorly water-soluble drugs and the unique aerodynamic qualities of the porous particles produced have made this process particularly attractive for producing particles for pulmonary delivery [82].

In general, SFD offers some advantages over conventional freeze-drying, including faster drying times, less energy consumption during the dehydration stage and flexibility during scale-up. However, some of these advantages seem to be offset by energy consumption during freezing and difficulties inherent in spray-based processes. Significant amounts of cryogenic fluids may also be required to freeze the atomised composition, and processing under aseptic conditions can be challenging [83].

8.4.4 Spray Congealing

Spray congealing, also named spray chilling, spray cooling, or spray prilling, occurs when a hot molten mixture is atomised into a cooling chamber, where the resulting droplets solidify to form almost spherical powder particles. It is a low-cost, simple, versatile, and eco-friendly method to prepare microparticles without solvent use, showing promising applications in the food, nutraceutical, and pharmaceutical fields [84]. The spray congealing principle also shows similarity to spray drying and includes atomisation, particle formation, and product collection. The key difference between both processes resides in that spray congealing uses a cooling chamber instead of a heated drying chamber. The cooling chamber's temperature is kept well below the matrix material's melting point, which can overcome some limitations of spray drying, particularly concerning the volatile's losses [85]. Figure 8.5 presents the main steps involved in the spray congealing procedure.

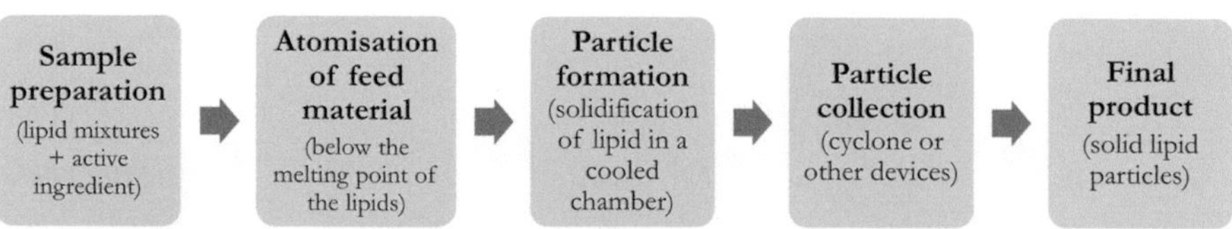

FIGURE 8.5 Main steps involved in the spray congealing procedure.

The production process is often faster because solvents are not used (100% of solids content), and high encapsulation efficiency values (90–100%) can be reached [84]. The ability to control powder characteristics (particle size, morphology, density) without the need for other downstream processing methods (e.g. secondary drying, granulation, milling, pelletisation) offers a remarkable advantage over other particle formation methods.

Spray congealing represents an interesting and successful approach to obtaining solid dispersions/solutions for various purposes, such as mask unpleasant taste and odour, improve the bioavailability of poorly water-soluble substances, and control the drug release. The technique has aroused great interest in the pharmaceutical sector due to the possibility to process lipid-based materials (e.g. fats, waxes, polyethene glycols, fatty acids, and fatty alcohols) without the need for drying aids [85, 86], making the spray congealing an interesting technique to prepare drugs and biopharmaceutical delivery systems [87].

The active compound, matrix material, and spray-frozen particles are also referred to as drug/core, carrier, and microparticles, respectively. The matrix material must exist as a solid at room temperature and have suitable melting point ranges, typically from 50 to 100°C [80]. The lower melting points can cause product agglomeration, and the high melting point can lead to process malfunctioning, such as blocking the feed lines and atomisation systems.

A major disadvantage of spray congealing is that the drug must be stable at the temperature required to melt the matrix material [80]. The heat losses in the feed lines also can cause product solidification inside, causing their blockage. The nozzles or atomisers used in spray congealing must be able to handle viscous mixtures at high temperatures. The cooling chamber dimensions depend on the nozzle, but different chamber designs can be used [85].

The main factors affecting the spray-congealed microparticles can be classified into two groups: equipment configuration and process variables (chamber design, atomiser types, operation temperatures) and formulation variables (matrix constituents, additives, and actives). Microparticles with desired physicochemical properties can be produced by selecting spray congealing variables and strict control of processing conditions.

8.5 APPLICATIONS OF ENCAPSULATED ESSENTIAL OILS IN FOOD AND PHARMACEUTICAL PRODUCTS

The encapsulation of EOs in lipid-based nanosystems is a relatively new and promising strategy, permitting the development of innovative products, expanding the EO's application potential in a wide range of products. A well-designed system can enhance the antimicrobial and antioxidant activity of EOs, improve their stability, and facilitate their incorporation and distribution in food systems without causing changes in the organoleptic properties [88].

Encapsulated EOs have been applied in various commercial products for several purposes. Typical examples include food additives (natural antimicrobials and antioxidants, food flavours); pharmaceuticals (antimicrobials, permeation promoters, herbal medicines); cosmetics (perfumery, cosmeceuticals, mouthwashes); agroindustry (crop protection); veterinary medicine (natural anti-inflammatories); and as growth promoters for farm animals.

Encapsulated EOs can also be used in several other applications, such as antimicrobial and antioxidant active packings, edible packing and coating, insect repellent, medical textiles, and membranes (smart textiles), among others [82, 89]. In this section, we present a brief overview of some food and pharmaceutical applications of EOs, in which the use of encapsulated products may provide better results.

8.5.1 Food Antimicrobials

EOs of aromatic and medicinal plants have demonstrated efficacy against several organisms which cause harmful effects over food products, such as insects, parasites, fungi, and bacteria. Several *in vitro* and *in situ* studies have shown the efficacy of EOs against a broad spectrum of food pathogens, which usually may contaminate processed and unprocessed food products. Common food pathogens include [6, 90]: (a) Fungi (*Fusarium* spp., *Alternaria* spp., *Penicillium* spp., *Aspergillus* spp.); (b) Bacteria (*Salmonella* spp., *Rhizoctonia solani*, *Clostridium perfringens*, *Campylobacter* spp., *Staphylococcus aureus*, *E. coli* O157:H7, *Listeria monocytogenes);* (c) Virus (norovirus, hepatitis A virus); and (d) Parasites (*Toxoplasma gondii*, *Cryptosporidium* spp., *Trypanosoma cruzi*). EOs can also overcome the problems of microorganism resistance to conventional synthetic preservatives. They can be used alone or combined with other synthetic additives (e.g. artificial preservatives).

Successful studies concerning the encapsulation of phytochemicals, EOs, and extracts of aromatic plants in lipid nanosystems have been reported recently and include rosmarinic acid (SLN) [91], Rosemary extract (NLC and proliposomes) [65, 92], Sage and Savoury extracts (SLN) [91], Clove buds extract (NLC) [93], Clove EO (SLN and NLC) [94], Pepper-rosemary EO (*Lippia sidoides*, NLC) [24], Frankincense and Myrrh EO (SLN) [95], and others.

The synergistic effect of EOs constituents when loaded in different lipid-based nanosystems (nanoemulsion, SLNs, liposomes) for the preservation of grains and related food products (e.g. cooked rice, rice flour, sliced bread) has been discussed by Kaliamurthi and co-workers [88]. These authors emphasise the importance of exact quantification of the EO's constituents in the final lipid nanosystems, which is not well addressed in several studies reported in the scientific literature.

The enhancement of EO antimicrobial activity, when incorporated into lipid nanosystems, can be caused by distinct mechanisms of action, namely [96]:

1. Disturbance and disruption of the integrity of the membrane followed by leakage of intracellular content and permeation of extracellular content into the cell interior
2. Diffusion of EO constituents into the cell interior causing the dissociation/disruption of the proton transfer dynamics of the cell, which act simultaneously due to the larger number of substances present.

8.5.2 Natural Antioxidants for Food and Pharmaceutical Products

The oxidation of unsaturated oils and fats in food products is one of the most common food degradation processes, marked by the characteristic rancid odour (rancidity). Rancidity is caused by transforming the unsaturated constituents of oils and fats into hydroperoxides (caused by oxygen). Hydroperoxides can decompose into various volatile compounds (e.g. alcohols, aldehydes, ketones, and hydrocarbons), some of which are responsible for the unpleasant odours exhaled by rancid foods. Oxidation can also degrade proteins, pigments, and other substances present in processed and unprocessed foods. These changes in the product's characteristics significantly reduce its quality (and shelf life), making them unsuitable for consumption. To delay the occurrence of these harmful changes during the whole product shelf life, synthetic and natural antioxidant substances are normally added in small concentrations compared to the oxidising substance [97].

Antioxidants are also beneficial to human health. Many diseases occur due to an overload of oxidative reactions arising from excessive meat, sugar, and fat consumption. Increasing evidence links degenerative diseases, such as diabetes, dementia, cancer, heart disease, and others, with the cell damage caused by reactive oxygen species (ROS), comprising both the free and non-free oxygen intermediates. Common ROS includes superoxide and hydroxyl radicals, hydrogen peroxide, singlet oxygen, and nitrogen dioxide. Antioxidants are synthetic or natural substances able to protect organisms from oxidative stress preventing free radical-induced tissue damage by inhibiting the formation of radicals, scavenging them, or promoting their decomposition.

Several scientific studies have reported that the presence of natural antioxidants in the diet could be an important tool for preventing degenerative diseases. These effects depend on the concentration of the natural antioxidant compounds. However, some studies are showing that high concentrations of certain polyphenols can also induce cellular DNA damage. Antioxidants, such as retinol and tocopherol, also shown to be toxic in high doses, whereas their use in small amounts showed effective antioxidative and antimutagenic activity [98].

Some toxic and even potential carcinogenic effects have been associated with the synthetic antioxidants usually used in food and pharmaceutical products, such as the butylhydroxyanisol (BHA), butylhydroxytoluene (BHT), tert-butylhydroquinone (t-BHQ), trihydroxybutyrophenone (THBP), and propyl gallate (PG). In recent years, as a result of these studies, the Joint Expert Committee on Food Additives (JECFA) of the Food and Agriculture Organization (FAO) and the World Health Organization (WHO) have restricted the values of acceptable daily intake (ADI) of the synthetic antioxidants [99]. Thus, the search for effective and nontoxic natural antioxidants compounds for food or pharmaceutical products has intensified [100].

The use of natural antioxidants in the food, cosmetic, and therapeutic industry is a promising alternative to synthetic antioxidants, concerning their low cost, highly compatible with dietary intake, and does not cause harmful effects inside the human body. Several phytochemicals, mainly the phenolic compounds, have been identified as free radical scavengers. Studies have shown the antioxidant potential of fruits, berries, cherries, citrus, prunes, olives, and aromatic and medicinal plants [101].

Rosemary extracts are commercially available for use as a natural antioxidant for foods in Europe and the USA. It is considered safe and effective and has received the GRAS status [102].

Various studies to evaluate the antioxidant activity of EOs have demonstrated their strong radical scavenging capacity and ability to inhibit lipid peroxidation of fats and oils [103]. However, the antioxidant activity of some EO constituents can also be produced by the transformation of hydroperoxides into stable substances (secondary antioxidant). Besides antioxidant activity, pure EOs and their isolated substances also exhibit other interesting biological activities, which can benefit human health, most linked with their capacity to scavenge ROS. Most of the antioxidant activities of EOs and plant extracts are linked to the high content of phenolic constituents, such as the phenolic acids (e.g. caffeic and rosmarinic acids), phenolic monoterpenes (e.g. thymol, carvacrol, eugenol), and phenolic diterpenes (e.g. carnosol and carnosic acid) [104].

8.5.3 Cosmetics

Today, consumers worldwide are increasingly focused on health and beauty and prefer sustainable, eco-friendly products. The interest in green cosmetics opened a window of opportunity for novel products or reformulation of others by adding phytochemicals and natural functional ingredients. EOs have played a key role in the perfume and cosmetics industry as fragrance ingredients due to their sweet and mild smell [105]. They can enhance the product properties and also act as a preservative agent. EO characteristics allow the formulation of innovative products for health, beauty, and well-being, adding value to the products.

They are cosmetic products containing bioactive ingredients (e.g. antioxidants, skin-whitening and skin-wrinkling agents, phytoextracts, phytochemicals, and UV filters). When phytochemicals or phytoextracts are the main active ingredient, some cosmeceuticals are named phytocosmetics Phytocosmetics are currently used for various beauty treatments for skin, face, lips, hair, and nails with beneficial actions against photoaging, inflammation, hair loss, lip care, psoriasis, ultraviolet toxicity (UV), and so on. Compared to synthetic cosmetic ingredients, phytochemicals and phytoextracts are mostly milder, biodegradable, and have less toxicity. The use of preservatives can be minimised or even eliminated in most phytocosmetics containing EOs (e.g. rosemary oil, eucalyptus oil) due to their inherent antimicrobial and antioxidant activities [106]. However, the low solubility, low penetration, irritability, and physicochemical instability when applied directly to the skin are some of the problems to be overcome in the formulation of phytocosmetics containing EOs. The encapsulation can protect and prevent the loss of the EO's volatile aromatic ingredients and enhance their solubility, stability, bioavailability, and functionality of EOs containing cosmetics. Different nanotechnology-based systems, including lipid nanosystems loaded with EOs, phytochemicals, or phytoextracts, have been successfully developed, and innovative products are already on the market [107]. The wide variety of available biocompatible and biodegradable lipids, surfactants, and phytoactive permits a plethora of interesting possibilities [40], contributing to increasing consumer interest in the phytocosmetics [105]. However, the effective production and implementation of phytocosmeceuticals is a multidisciplinary task and involves selecting and characterising the active ingredients, activity and toxicity assays, product formulation, safety assessment, and product performance and efficacy testing in humans [108].

8.5.4 Mouthwashes

Oral hygiene is an important aspect of periodontal health. There is a balance in a person's oral microbial population, which helps prevent opportunistic microorganism proliferation. An optimum mouthwash has some advantages, such as antiseptic effects on the mouth, washing the food residue on the gingival (gum) medium and teeth, reducing the mouth bacteria, masking and neutralising halitosis, and introducing a good taste and sense of freshness in the mouth [109].

The most prevalent oral infectious diseases, such as dental caries, periodontal inflammations, and gingivitis, are produced by dental biofilm formation in the oral cavity. Dental plaque is a multifaceted biofilm that builds up on the surface of teeth, including more than 500 bacterial species, which can cause severe or chronic infectious diseases [109].

A mouthwash may be recommended to treat infection, reduce inflammation, relieve pain, reduce halitosis, or deliver fluoride locally for caries prevention. Among the active compounds most used in obtaining mouthwashes, it can be mentioned [110]: chlorhexidine gluconate; benzydamine hydrochloride; cetylpyridinium chloride; sodium benzoate; and triclosan (2,4,4'-trichloro-2'-hydroxydiphenyl ether).

Normally, oral hygiene products based on synthetic substances predominate over those containing natural compounds, perhaps due to their easy availability and faster results. However, many of these products have been criticised for their adverse effects on teeth, gums, and mucous membranes. DNA damage in cheek cells is one of the most common side effects of mouthwashes [111]. Thus, phytochemicals are being evaluated and added to oral care products as protective agents. Most EOs have strong antimicrobial and antioxidant activity, having potential for application in oral health products. Mouthwashes containing EOs have been recommended as a complement to mechanical oral hygiene, particularly in patients with inadequate oral hygiene and those suffering from gum inflammation, even with regular brushing and flossing [112].

Examples of EOs used in oral care products include cumin, clove, rosemary, thyme, black sesame, cinnamon, and black pepper. Mouthwashes containing four phenol-related EOs (thymol, eucalyptol, menthol, and methyl salicylate, in up to 26% alcohol) claimed to penetrate the plaque biofilm and kill microorganisms that cause gingivitis. These mouthwashes display broad-spectrum antimicrobial activity, prevent bacterial aggregation, slow bacterial multiplication, retard plaque maturation, and decrease plaque mass and pathogenicity. Their mechanism of action is thought to involve bacterial cell destruction, bacterial enzyme inhibition, and endotoxin extraction from Gram-negative bacteria. They also have anti-inflammatory and prostaglandin synthetase inhibitory activity and act as antioxidants by scavenging free radicals.

8.5.5 Phytotherapy

The knowledge of the composition and several biological activities of EOs have been useful for developing herbal-derived products, including pharmaceuticals, medicinal supplements, and nutraceuticals, which can be used for preventive and curative purposes. Products containing EOs have been used as the main or complementary medicine agent in traditional and complementary medicine systems by several nations, and the interest in these products has been growing continuously [113].

EOs were effective for the treatment of several pulmonary-related disorders, such as cough and nasal congestion (e.g. *Eucalyptus* EO, Mint EO, Thyme EO, menthol, 1,8-cineole), improvement of the lung health (Ginseng EO), chronic obstructive pulmonary disease (Lavender EO), and others. Common examples of medicinal products containing EOs are the "Vicks VapoRub" family and several muscle strains creams and gels. Recently in Brazil, the pharmaceutical company Aché launched the topical anti-inflammatory Acheflan®, which contains in its composition 2.3–2.9% of α-humulene from the EO of *Cordia verbenaceae* (Erva-baleeira), a native Brazilian plant [114].

In the aromatherapy practice, EOs are applied in inhalation, vaporisation, and massages, aiming to relieve various ailments, such as aches, pains, muscle strains, depression, stress, anxiety, and energy, and short-term memory enhancement [115].

At present, the emergence of several pathogens resistant to conventional treatments is one of the world's most serious public health concerns. Resistant microorganisms are generally associated with hospital infections that are difficult to treat. EO's antimicrobial action occurs by several mechanisms since they are constituted by several active molecules acting synergistically. Thus, they are a promising and innovative alternative source of antimicrobial agents to develop new therapies to combat antimicrobial resistance, either in isolated form or in association with traditional antibiotics [24, 116]. EO's encapsulation in lipid systems can facilitate their use in various antimicrobials formulations and enhance their biological activity [24, 52, 117].

8.6 FINAL REMARKS AND PROSPECTS

The encapsulation of EOs is a research subject that has attracted academia, industry, and consumer interests due to several biological properties and the high potential of technological applications. EO encapsulation may improve their physicochemical properties, enhance their biological activity and bioavailability, and reduce volatilisation, taste and odour, and skin irritation. Encapsulation in lipid nanosystems is a promising strategy since different systems can be produced according to the specified objectives. Most lipid materials are also biocompatible, biodegradable, and non-toxic, making them ideal for developing novel pharmaceutical and food formulations.

In the perfumery and cosmetics sector, encapsulated EOs are used in skin creams, body lotions, balms, shampoos, soaps and perfumes, and mouthwashes and breath fresheners. This sector invests significant resources in developing new products to satisfy consumer demand, which prefers sustainable and eco-friendly products formulated with natural ingredients. The use of lipid nanosystems loaded with EOs has enormous potential for developing a future generation of novel "smart products", expanding their applications [108].

In the food and beverage industry, EO encapsulation expands its range of applications. For example, encapsulated EOs can be easily incorporated into hydrophilic food systems. Several conventional and new applications in the food sectors are already being explored, including natural preservatives, flavouring agents, insect repellent to protect stored foods, antimicrobial and antioxidant edible films, and active packings to increase the perishable foods shelf life. The market of encapsulated flavours for use in most diverse food systems is also very relevant and growing significantly.

Another sector with a high potential to use encapsulated EOs is aromatherapy. In Europe, for example, there is a high demand for aromatherapy products, as consumers look for alternative methods to improve their health conditions.

The production of dry, free-flowing, and dispersible lipid nanosystems loaded with EOs is also an important subject and increases the possibilities of applying EOs in the most diversified products. These innovative nanoparticulate systems can be produced by several technologies and involve two stages, the preparation of the emulsified systems (high- or low-energy methods) and the selection of the drying technology (spray drying, SFD, freeze-drying, spray congealing, among others).

The information presented in this chapter is not exhaustive, and readers interested in more information can consult the references cited.

ACKNOWLEDGEMENTS

The authors thank the São Paulo Research Foundation—FAPESP for the continuous financial support (Grants 2011/10333-1, 2012/03427-2, 2014/25934-9; 2014/15905-1 and 2018/26069-0, and 2019/25981-0), and to partial financial support by the Coordination for the Improvement of Higher Education Personnel—Brazil (CAPES)—Finance Code 001.

REFERENCES

1. U.S. Code of Federal Regulations. Title 21, Food and Drugs Part 182—Substances generally recognized as safe, Section 182.20—Essential oils, oleoresins (solvent-free), and natural extractives (including distillates), 2019.
2. Bilia, A. R.; Guccione, C.; Isacchi, B.; Righeschi, C.; Firenzuoli, F.; Bergonzi, M. C. Essential Oils Loaded in Nanosystems: A Developing Strategy for a Successful Therapeutic Approach. *Evid. Based. Complement. Alternat. Med.*, **2014**, *2014*, 1–14.
3. Baser, K. H. C.; Buchbauer, G. *Handbook of Essential Oils: Science, Technology, and Applications*, 2nd ed.; Baser, K. H. C., Buchbauer, G., Eds.; CRC Press: Boca Raton, 2016.
4. Carson, C. F.; Hammer, K. A.; Thormar, H. Lipids and Essential Oils as Antimicrobial Agents; Thormar, H., Ed.; John Wiley & Sons, London, UK, 2011; pp. 255–306.
5. Buckle, J. Basic Plant Taxonomy, Basic Essential Oil Chemistry, Extraction, Biosynthesis, and Analysis. In *Clinical Aromatherapy*, 3rd ed.; Buckle, J., Ed.; Churchill Livingstone: St. Louis, 2015; pp 37–72.
6. Hyldgaard, M.; Mygind, T.; Meyer, R. L. Essential Oils in Food Preservation: Mode of Action, Synergies, and Interactions with Food Matrix Components. *Front. Microbiol.*, **2012**, *3*, 1–24.

7. Herman, A.; Herman, A. P. Essential Oils and Their Constituents as Skin Penetration Enhancer for Transdermal Drug Delivery: A Review. *J. Pharm. Pharmacol.*, **2015**, *67* (4), 473–485.
8. Moraes, T. M.; Kushima, H.; Moleiro, F. C.; Santos, R. C.; Machado Rocha, L. R.; Marques, M. O.; Vilegas, W.; Hiruma-Lima, C. A. Effects of Limonene and Essential Oil from *Citrus aurantium* on Gastric Mucosa: Role of Prostaglandins and Gastric Mucus Secretion. *Chem. Biol. Interact.*, **2009**, *180* (3), 499–505.
9. Alves, A. M.; Gonçalves, J. C. R; Cruz, J. S.; Araújo, D. A. M. Evaluation of the Sesquiterpene (–)-α-Bisabolol as a Novel Peripheral Nerve Blocker. *Neurosci. Lett.*, **2010**, *472* (1), 11–15.
10. Detoni, C. B.; De Oliveira, D. M.; Santo, I. E.; Pedro, A. S.; El-Bacha, R.; Da Silva Velozo, E.; Ferreira, D.; Sarmento, B.; De Magalhães Cabral-Albuquerque, E. C. Evaluation of Thermal-Oxidative Stability and Antiglioma Activity of *Zanthoxylum tingoassuiba* Essential Oil Entrapped into Multi- and Unilamellar Liposomes. *J. Liposome Res.*, **2012**, *22* (1), 1–7.
11. Verma, R. S.; Padalia, R. C.; Goswami, P.; Verma, S. K.; Chauhan, A.; Darokar, M. P. Chemical Composition and Antibacterial Activity of Foliage and Resin Essential Oils of *Araucaria cunninghami*i Aiton Ex D.Don and *Araucaria heterophylla* (Salisb.) Franco from India. *Ind. Crops Prod.*, **2014**, *61*, 410–416.
12. Kim, Y.-G.; Lee, J.-H.; Gwon, G.; Kim, S.-I.; Park, J. G.; Lee, J. Essential Oils and Eugenols Inhibit Biofilm Formation and the Virulence of *Escherichia coli* O157:H7. *Sci. Rep.*, **2016**, *6* (1), 36377.
13. Guan, Y.; Wu, J.; Zhong, Q. Eugenol Improves Physical and Chemical Stabilities of Nanoemulsions Loaded with β-Carotene. *Food Chem.*, **2016**, *194*, 787–796.
14. Oliveira, J. L.; Campos, E. V. R.; Bakshi, M.; Abhilash, P. C.; Fraceto, L. F. Application of Nanotechnology for the Encapsulation of Botanical Insecticides for Sustainable Agriculture: Prospects and Promises. *Biotechnol. Adv.*, **2014**, *32* (8), 1550–1561.
15. Saad, N. Y.; Muller, C. D.; Lobstein, A. Major Bioactivities and Mechanism of Action of Essential Oils and Their Components. *Flavour Fragr. J.*, **2013**, *28* (5), 269–279.
16. Asbahani, A. El; Miladi, K.; Badri, W.; Sala, M.; Addi, E. H. A.; Casabianca, H.; Mousadik, A. El; Hartmann, D.; Jilale, A.; Renaud, F. N. R.; et al. Essential Oils: From Extraction to Encapsulation. *Int. J. Pharm.*, **2015**, *483*(1–2), 220–243.
17. Ríos, J.-L. Essential Oils: What They Are and How the Terms Are Used and Defined. In *Essential Oils in Food Preservation, Flavor and Safety*; Preedy, V. R., Ed.; Academic Press, London, 2016; pp 3–10.
18. Chemat, F.; Abert Vian, M.; Fabiano-Tixier, A. S.; Nutrizio, M.; Režek Jambrak, A.; Munekata, P. E. S.; Lorenzo, J. M.; Barba, F. J.; Binello, A.; Cravotto, G. A Review of Sustainable and Intensified Techniques for Extraction of Food and Natural Products. *Green Chem.*, **2020**, *22* (8), 2325–2353.
19. Rodríguez-Rojo, S.; Visentin, A.; Maestri, D.; Cocero, M. J. Assisted Extraction of Rosemary Antioxidants with Green Solvents. *J. Food Eng.*, **2012**, *109* (1), 98–103.
20. Elshafie, H. S.; Camele, I. An Overview of the Biological Effects of Some Mediterranean Essential Oils on Human Health. *Biomed Res. Int.*, **2017**, *2017*, 1–14.
21. Rai, M.; Paralikar, P.; Jogee, P.; Agarkar, G.; Ingle, A. P.; Derita, M.; Zacchino, S. Synergistic Antimicrobial Potential of Essential Oils in Combination with Nanoparticles: Emerging Trends and Future Perspectives. *Int. J. Pharm.*, **2017**, *519* (1–2), 67–78.
22. Radünz, M.; da Trindade, M. L. M.; Camargo, T. M.; Radünz, A. L.; Borges, C. D.; Gandra, E. A.; Helbig, E. Antimicrobial and Antioxidant Activity of Unencapsulated and Encapsulated Clove (*Syzygium aromaticum*, L.) Essential Oil. *Food Chem.*, **2019**, *276*, 180–186.

23. Saporito, F.; Sandri, G.; Bonferoni, M. C.; Rossi, S.; Boselli, C.; Icaro Cornaglia, A.; Mannucci, B.; Grisoli, P.; Vigani, B.; Ferrari, F. Essential Oil-Loaded Lipid Nanoparticles for Wound Healing. *Int. J. Nanomedicine*, **2017**, *13*, 175–186.
24. Baldim, I.; Tonani, L.; von Zeska Kress, M. R.; Oliveira, W. P. *Lippia Sidoides* Essential Oil Encapsulated in Lipid Nanosystem as an Anti-Candida Agent. *Ind. Crops Prod.*, **2019**, *127*, 73–81.
25. Asif, M.; Saleem, M.; Saadullah, M.; Yaseen, H. S.; Al Zarzour, R. COVID-19 and Therapy with Essential Oils Having Antiviral, Anti-Inflammatory, and Immunomodulatory Properties. *Inflammopharmacology*, **2020**, *28* (5), 1153–1161.
26. Loizzo, M. R.; Saab, A. M.; Tundis, R.; Statti, G. A.; Menichini, F.; Lampronti, I.; Gambari, R.; Cinatl, J.; Doerr, H. W. Phytochemical Analysis and In Vitro Antiviral Activities of the Essential Oils of Seven Lebanon Species. *Chem. Biodivers.*, **2008**, *5* (3), 461–470.
27. Borges, R. S.; Ortiz, B. L. S.; Pereira, A. C. M.; Keita, H.; Carvalho, J. C. T. Rosmarinus Officinalis Essential Oil: A Review of Its Phytochemistry, Anti-Inflammatory Activity, and Mechanisms of Action Involved. *J. Ethnopharmacol.*, **2019**, *229*, 29–45.
28. Gonçalves, J. C. R.; de Meneses, D. A.; de Vasconcelos, A. P.; Piauilino, C. A.; Almeida, F. R. de C.; Napoli, E. M.; Ruberto, G.; de Araújo, D. A. M. Essential Oil Composition and Antinociceptive Activity of *Thymus Capitatus*. *Pharm. Biol.*, **2017**, *55* (1), 782–786.
29. Toscano-Garibay, J. D.; Arriaga-Alba, M.; Sánchez-Navarrete, J.; Mendoza-García, M.; Flores-Estrada, J. J.; Moreno-Eutimio, M. A.; Espinosa-Aguirre, J. J.; González-Ávila, M.; Ruiz-Pérez, N. J. Antimutagenic and Antioxidant Activity of the Essential Oils of *Citrus Sinensis* and *Citrus Latifolia*. *Sci. Rep.*, **2017**, *7* (1), 11479.
30. Calcabrini, A.; Stringaro, A.; Toccacieli, L.; Meschini, S.; Marra, M.; Colone, M.; Arancia, G.; Molinari, A.; Salvatore, G.; Mondello, F. Terpinen-4-Ol, the Main Component of *Melaleuca Alternifolia* (Tea Tree) Oil Inhibits the in Vitro Growth of Human Melanoma Cells. *J. Invest. Dermatol.*, **2004**, *122* (2), 349–360.
31. Queiroz, R. M. de; Takiya, C. M.; Guimarães, L. P. T. P.; Rocha, G. da G.; Alviano, D. S.; Blank, A. F.; Alviano, C. S.; Gattass, C. R. Apoptosis-Inducing Effects of *Melissa officinalis* L. Essential Oil in Glioblastoma Multiforme Cells. *Cancer Invest.*, **2014**, *32* (6), 226–235.
32. Farias-Junior, P. A.; Rios, M. C.; Moura, T. A.; Almeida, R. P.; Alves, P. B.; Blank, A. F.; Fernandes, R. P. M.; Scher, R. Leishmanicidal Activity of Carvacrol-Rich Essential Oil from *Lippia sidoides* Cham. *Biol. Res.*, **2012**, *45* (4), 399–402.
33. Ballabeni, V.; Tognolini, M.; Bertoni, S.; Bruni, R.; Guerrini, A.; Rueda, G. M.; Barocelli, E. Antiplatelet and Antithrombotic Activities of Essential Oil from Wild *Ocotea quixos* (Lam.) Kosterm. (Lauraceae) Calices from Amazonian Ecuador. *Pharmacol. Res.*, **2007**, *55* (1), 23–30.
34. Kumagai, H.; Kashima, N.; Seki, T.; Sakurai, H.; Ishii, K.; Ariga, T. Analysis of Volatile Components in Essential Oil of Upland Wasabi and Their Inhibitory Effects on Platelet Aggregation. *Biosci. Biotechnol. Biochem.*, **1994**, *58* (12), 2131–2135.
35. Hensel, A.; Bauer, R.; Heinrich, M.; Spiegler, V.; Kayser, O.; Hempel, G.; Kraft, K. Challenges at the Time of COVID-19: Opportunities and Innovations in Antivirals from Nature. *Planta Med.*, **2020**, *86* (10), 659–664.
36. Ilijeva, R.; Buchbauer, G. Biological Properties of Some Volatile Phenylpropanoids. *Nat. Prod. Commun.*, **2016**, *11* (10), 1934578X1601101.
37. Gonçalves, N. D.; Pena, F. de L.; Sartoratto, A.; Derlamelina, C.; Duarte, M. C. T.; Antunes, A. E. C.; Prata, A. S. Encapsulated Thyme (*Thymus vulgaris*) Essential Oil Used as a Natural Preservative in Bakery Product. *Food Res. Int.*, **2017**, *96*, 154–160.
38. Bhalla, Y.; Gupta, V. K.; Jaitak, V. Anticancer Activity of Essential Oils: A Review. *J. Sci. Food Agric.*, **2013**, *93* (15), 3643–3653.

39. Efferth, T.; Li, P. C. H.; Konkimalla, V. S. B.; Kaina, B. From Traditional Chinese Medicine to Rational Cancer Therapy. *Trends Mol. Med.*, **2007**, *13* (8), 353–361.
40. Souto, E. B.; Baldim, I.; Oliveira, W. P.; Rao, R.; Yadav, N.; Gama, F. M.; Mahant, S. SLN and NLC for Topical, Dermal, and Transdermal Drug Delivery. *Expert Opin. Drug Deliv.*, **2020**, *17* (3), 357–377.
41. Hădărugă, D. I.; Hădărugă, N. G.; Costescu, C. I.; David, I.; Gruia, A. T. Thermal and Oxidative Stability of the *Ocimum basilicum* L. Essential Oil/β-Cyclodextrin Supramolecular System. *Beilstein J. Org. Chem.*, **2014**, *10*, 2809–2820.
42. Donsì, F.; Ferrari, G. Essential Oil Nanoemulsions as Antimicrobial Agents in Food. *J. Biotechnol.*, **2016**, *233*, 106–120.
43. de Matos, S. P.; Lucca, L. G.; Koester, L. S. Essential Oils in Nanostructured Systems: Challenges in Preparation and Analytical Methods. *Talanta* (Elsevier B.V.), **2019**, *195*, 204–214.
44. Xu, X.; Sun, Q.; McClements, D. J. Enhancing the Formation and Stability of Emulsions Using Mixed Natural Emulsifiers: Hydrolyzed Rice Glutelin and *Quillaja saponin*. *Food Hydrocoll.*, **2019**, *89*, 396–405.
45. Aswathanarayan, J. B.; Vittal, R. R. Nanoemulsions and Their Potential Applications in Food Industry. *Front. Sustainable Food Syst.*, **2019**, *3*, 95.
46. Weiss, J.; Gaysinsky, S.; Davidson, M.; McClements, J. Nanostructured Encapsulation Systems: food antimicrobials. In *Global Issues in Food Science and Technology*; Academic Press, San Diego, 2009; pp 425–479.
47. Gupta, S.; Variyar, P. S. Nanoencapsulation of Essential Oils for Sustained Release: Application as Therapeutics and Antimicrobials. In *Encapsulations*; Grumezescu, A. M., Ed.; Academic Press, Amsterdam, The Netherlands, 2016; pp 641–672.
48. Souto, E. B.; Doktorovova, S.; Boonme, P. Lipid-Based Colloidal Systems (Nanoparticles, Microemulsions) for Drug Delivery to the Skin: Materials and End-Product Formulations. *J. Drug Deliv. Sci. Technol.*, **2011**, *21* (1), 43–54.
49. McClements, D. J.; Decker, E. A.; Park, Y.; Weiss, J. Structural Design Principles for Delivery of Bioactive Components in Nutraceuticals and Functional Foods. *Crit. Rev. Food Sci. Nutr.*, **2009**, *49* (6), 577–606.
50. Sercombe, L.; Veerati, T.; Moheimani, F.; Wu, S. Y.; Sood, A. K.; Hua, S. Advances and Challenges of Liposome Assisted Drug Delivery. *Front. Pharmacol.*, **2015**, *6*.
51. Sharma, A. Liposomes in Drug Delivery: Progress and Limitations. *Int. J. Pharm.*, **1997**, *154* (2), 123–140.
52. Sherry, M.; Charcosset, C.; Fessi, H.; Greige-Gerges, H. Essential Oils Encapsulated in Liposomes: A Review. *J. Liposome Res.*, **2013**, *23* (4), 268–275.
53. Müller, R. H.; Shegokar, R.; Keck, C. M. 20 Years of Lipid Nanoparticles (SLN & NLC): Present State of Development & Industrial Applications. *Curr. Drug Discov. Technol.*, **2011**, *8* (3), 207–227.
54. Arruda, L. M.; Teixeira, M.; Ribeiro, A. I.; Souto, A. P.; Cionek, C. A. Copaíba Essential Oil Microencapsulation: Production and Evaluation. In *Textiles, Identity and Innovation: In Touch*; Montagna, G., Carvalho, C., Eds.; CRC Press, Lisbon, Portugal, 2020.
55. Carbone, C.; Martins-Gomes, C.; Caddeo, C.; Silva, A. M.; Musumeci, T.; Pignatello, R.; Puglisi, G.; Souto, E. B. Mediterranean Essential Oils as Precious Matrix Components and Active Ingredients of Lipid Nanoparticles. *Int. J. Pharm.*, **2018**, *548* (1), 217–226.
56. Flanagan, J.; Singh, H. Microemulsions: A Potential Delivery System for Bioactives in Food. *Crit. Rev. Food Sci. Nutr.*, **2006**, *46* (3), 221–237.
57. McClements, D. J. Critical Review of Techniques and Methodologies for Characterization of Emulsion Stability. *Crit. Rev. Food Sci. Nutr.*, **2007**, *47* (7), 611–649.
58. Mishra, D. K.; Shandilya, R.; Mishra, P. K. Lipid Based Nanocarriers: A Translational Perspective. *Nanomedicine Nanotechnology, Biol. Med.*, **2018**, *14* (7), 2023–2050.

59. Muller, R. H.; Mader, K.; Gohla, S. Solid Lipid Nanoparticles (SLN) for Controlled Drug Delivery—a Review of the State of the Art. *Eur. J. Pharm. Biopharm.*, **2000**, *50* (1), 161–177.
60. Jafari, S. M.; He, Y.; Bhandari, B. Production of Sub-Micron Emulsions by Ultrasound and Microfluidization Techniques. *J. Food Eng.*, **2007**, *82* (4), 478–488.
61. Nejatian, M.; Abbasi, S. Formation of Concentrated Triglyceride Nanoemulsions and Nanogels: Natural Emulsifiers and High Power Ultrasound. *Rsc* Advances, **2019**, *9* (49), 28330-28344.
62. Solans, C.; Solé, I. Nano-Emulsions: Formation by Low-Energy Methods. *Curr. Opin. Colloid Interface Sci.*, **2012**, *17* (5), 246–254.
63. Tan, A.; Rao, S.; Prestidge, C. A. Transforming Lipid-Based Oral Drug Delivery Systems into Solid Dosage Forms: An Overview of Solid Carriers, Physicochemical Properties, and Biopharmaceutical Performance. *Pharm. Res.*, **2013**, *30*, 2993–3017.
64. Baldim, I.; Rosa, D. M.; Souza, C. R. F.; Da Ana, R.; Durazzo, A.; Lucarini, M.; Santini, A.; Souto, E. B.; Oliveira, W. P. Factors Affecting the Retention Efficiency and Physicochemical Properties of Spray Dried Lipid Nanoparticles Loaded with *Lippia sidoides* Essential Oil. *Biomolecules*, **2020**, *10* (5), 693.
65. Bankole, V. O.; Osungunna, M. O.; Souza, C. R. F.; Salvador, S. L.; Oliveira, W. P. Spray-Dried Proliposomes: An Innovative Method for Encapsulation of *Rosmarinus officinalis* L. Polyphenols. *AAPS PharmSciTech*, **2020**, *21*, 143.
66. Santos, D.; Maurício, A. C.; Sencadas, V.; Santos, J. D.; Fernandes, M. H.; Gomes, P. S. Spray Drying: An Overview. In *Biomaterials—Physics and Chemistry—New Edition*; Pignatello, R., Musumeci, T.; InTech.: UK, 2018; pp. 9–35.
67. Masters, K. *Spray Drying Handbook*, 5th ed.; Longman Scientific & Technical. Wiley: New York, 1991.
68. Mohammed, N. K.; Tan, C. P.; Manap, Y. A.; Muhialdin, B. J.; Hussin, A. S. M. Spray Drying for the Encapsulation of Oils—A Review. *Molecules*, **2020**, *25* (17), 1–16.
69. Beristain, C. I.; García, H. S.; Vernon-Carter, E. J. Spray-Dried Encapsulation of Cardamom (*Elettaria cardamomum*) Essential Oil with Mesquite (*Prosopis juliflora*) Gum. *LWT—Food Sci. Technol.*, **2001**, *34* (6).
70. Jafari, S. M.; He, Y.; Bhandari, B. Encapsulation of Nanoparticles of D-Limonene by Spray Drying: Role of Emulsifiers and Emulsifying Techniques. *Dry. Technol.*, **2007**, *25* (6), 1069–1079.
71. Baranauskiene, R.; Venskutonis, P. R.; Dewettinck, K.; Verhé, R. Properties of Oregano (*Origanum vulgare* L.), Citronella (*Cymbopogon nardus* G.) and Marjoram (*Majorana hortensis* L.) Flavors Encapsulated into Milk Protein-Based Matrices. *Food Res. Int.*, **2006**, *39* (4), 413–425.
72. Fernandes, L. P.; Oliveira, W. P.; Sztatisz, J.; Szilágyi, I. M.; Novák, C. Solid State Studies on Molecular Inclusions of *Lippia sidoides* Essential Oil Obtained by Spray Drying. *J. Therm. Anal. Calorim.*, **2009**, *95* (3), 855–863.
73. Fernandes, L. P.; Turatti, I. C. C.; Lopes, N. P.; Ferreira, J. C.; Candido, R. C.; Oliveira, W. P. Volatile Retention and Antifungal Properties of Spray-Dried Microparticles of *Lippia sidoides* Essential Oil. *Dry. Technol.*, **2008**, *26* (12), 1534–1542.
74. Hua, T.-C.; Liu, B.-L.; Zhang, H. Freeze Drying of Pharmaceuticals. In *Freeze-Drying of Pharmaceutical and Food Products*; Hua, T.-C.; Liu, B.-L.; Zhang, H., Eds.; Woodhead Publishing, New York, 2010; pp 187–215.
75. Ingvarsson, P. T.; Yang, M.; Nielsen, H. M.; Rantanen, J.; Foged, C. Stabilization of Liposomes during Drying. *Expert Opin. Drug Deliv.*, **2011**, 375–388.
76. Oliveira, W. P.; Freitas, L. A. P.; Freire, J. T. Drying of Pharmaceutical Products. In *Transport Phenomena in Particulate Systems*; Freire, J. T.; Silveira, A. M.; Ferreira, M. C. Eds.; Bentham Science Publishers Ltd., Oak Park, IL, 2012; pp 148–171.

77. Morais, A. R. D. V.; Alencar, É. D. N.; Xavier Júnior, F. H.; Oliveira, C. M. De; Marcelino, H. R.; Barratt, G.; Fessi, H.; Egito, E. S. T. Do; Elaissari, A. Freeze-Drying of Emulsified Systems: A Review. *Int. J. Pharm.*, **2016**, *503* (1–2), 102–114.
78. Langford, A.; Bhatnagar, B.; Walters, R.; Tchessalov, S.; Ohtake, S. Drying of Biopharmaceuticals: Recent Developments, New Technologies and Future Direction. *Japan J. Food Eng.*, **2018**, *19* (1), 15–25.
79. Vishali, D. A.; Monisha, J.; Sivakamasundari, S. K.; Moses, J. A.; Anandharamakrishnan, C. Spray Freeze Drying: Emerging Applications in Drug Delivery. *J. Control. Release*, **2019**, *300* (October 2018), 93–101.
80. Oh, C. M.; Guo, Q.; Wan Sia Heng, P.; Chan, L. W. Spray-Congealed Microparticles for Drug Delivery—An Overview of Factors Influencing Their Production and Characteristics. *Expert Opin. Drug Deliv.*, **2014**, *11* (7), 1047–1060.
81. Misra, A.; Jinturkar, K.; Patel, D.; Lalani, J.; Chougule, M. Recent Advances in Liposomal Dry Powder Formulations: Preparation and Evaluation. *Expert Opin. Drug Deliv.*, **2009**, *6* (1), 71–89.
82. Ghayempour, S.; Montazer, M. Micro/Nanoencapsulation of Essential Oils and Fragrances: Focus on Perfumed, Antimicrobial, Mosquito-Repellent and Medical Textiles. *J. Microencapsul.*, **2016**, *33* (6), 497–510.
83. Walters, R. H.; Bhatnagar, B.; Tchessalov, S.; Izutsu, K. I.; Tsumoto, K.; Ohtake, S. Next Generation Drying Technologies for Pharmaceutical Applications. *J. Pharm. Sci.*, **2014**, *103* (9), 2673–2695.
84. Bertoni, S.; Dolci, L. S.; Albertini, B.; Passerini, N. Spray Congealing: A Versatile Technology for Advanced Drug-Delivery Systems. *Ther. Deliv.*, **2018**, *9* (11), 833–845.
85. Cordeiro, P.; Temtem, M.; Winters, C. Spray Congealing: Applications in the Pharmaceutical Industry. *Chim. Oggi/Chemistry Today*, **2013**, *31* (5).
86. Saifullah, M.; Shishir, M. R. I.; Ferdowsi, R.; Tanver Rahman, M. R.; Van Vuong, Q. Micro and Nano Encapsulation, Retention and Controlled Release of Flavor and Aroma Compounds: A Critical Review. *Trends Food Sci. Technol.* (Elsevier Ltd), **2019**, *86*, 230–251.
87. Favaro-Trindade, C.; Okuro, P.; de Matos, F. Encapsulation via Spray Chilling/Cooling/Congealing. In *Handbook of Encapsulation and Controlled Release*; Mishra, M., Ed.; CRC Press, Boca Raton, **2015**; pp 71–87.
88. Kaliamurthi, S.; Selvaraj, G.; Hou, L.; Li, Z.; Wei, Y.; Gu, K.; Wei, D. Synergism of Essential Oils with Lipid Based Nanocarriers: Emerging Trends in Preservation of Grains and Related Food Products. *Grain Oil Sci. Technol.*, **2019**, *2* (1), 21–26.
89. Adelakun, O. E.; Oyelade, O. J.; Olanipekun, B. F. Use of Essential Oils in Food Preservation. In *Essential Oils in Food Preservation, Flavor and Safety*; Preedy, V. R., Ed.; Elsevier: London, 2016; pp. 71–84.
90. Pandey, A. K.; Kumar, P.; Singh, P.; Tripathi, N. N.; Bajpai, V. K. Essential Oils: Sources of Antimicrobials and Food Preservatives. *Front. Microbiol.*, **2017**, *7*, 1–14.
91. Campos, D. A.; Madureira, A. R.; Sarmento, B.; Pintado, M. M.; Gomes, A. M. Technological Stability of Solid Lipid Nanoparticles Loaded with Phenolic Compounds: Drying Process and Stability along Storage. *J. Food Eng.*, **2017**, *196*, 1–10.
92. Baldim, I.; Souza, C. R. F.; Durazzo, A.; Lucarini, M.; Santini, A.; Souto, E. B.; Oliveira, W. P. Spray-Dried Structured Lipid Carriers for the Loading of *Rosmarinus Officinalis*: New Nutraceutical and Food Preservative. *Foods*, **2020**, *9* (8), 1110.
93. Cortés-Rojas, D. F.; Souza, C. R. F.; Oliveira, W. P. Encapsulation of Eugenol Rich Clove Extract in Solid Lipid Carriers. *J. Food Eng.*, **2014**, *127*, 34–42.
94. Drying, I.; Val, S.; Sciences, P. Spray Drying of Lipid Nanosystems (SLN and NLC) Loaded with *Syzygium Aromaticum* Essential Oil. **2018**, September, 11–14.

95. Shi, F.; Zhao, J.-H.; Liu, Y.; Wang, Z.; Zhang, Y.-T.; Feng, N.-P. Preparation and Characterization of Solid Lipid Nanoparticles Loaded with Frankincense and Myrrh Oil. *Int. J. Nanomedicine*, **2012**, *7*, 2033–2043.
96. Weiss, J.; Gaysinsky, S.; Davidson, M.; McClements, J. Nanostructured Encapsulation Systems: Food Antimicrobials. In *Global Issues in Food Science and Technology*; Barbosa-Canovas, G., Mortimer, A., Lineback, D., Spiess, W., Buckle, K., Colonna, P., Eds., Elsevier Inc., Amsterdam, The Netherlands, 2009, pp. 425–479.
97. Freitas, I. R.; Cattelan, M. G. Antimicrobial and Antioxidant Properties of Essential Oils in Food Systems—An Overview. In *Microbial Contamination and Food Degradation*; Holban, A. M., Grumezescu, A. M., Eds., Academic Press, Cambridge, MA, 2018, pp. 443–470.
98. Collins, A. R. Antioxidant Intervention as a Route to Cancer Prevention. *Eur. J. Cancer*, **2005**, *41* (13), 1923–1930.
99. Wurtzen, G. Shortcomings of Current Strategy for Toxicity Testing of Food Chemicals: Antioxidants. *Food Chem. Toxic.*, **1990**, *28* (11), 743–745.
100. Zheng, W.; Wang, S. Y. Antioxidant Activity and Phenolic Compounds in Selected Herbs. *J. Agric. Food Chem.*, **2001**, *49* (11), 5165–5170.
101. Lobo, V.; Patil, A.; Phatak, A.; Chandra, N. Free Radicals, Antioxidants and Functional Foods: Impact on Human Health. *Pharmacogn. Rev.*, **2010**, *4* (8), 118–126.
102. Nieto, G.; Ros, G.; Castillo, J. Antioxidant and Antimicrobial Properties of Rosemary (*Rosmarinus officinalis*, L.): A Review. *Medicines*, **2018**, *5* (3), 98.
103. Mimica-Dukić, N.; Orč Ić, D.; Lesjak, M.; Šibul, F. Essential Oils as Powerful Antioxidants: Misconception or Scientific Fact? *ACS Symp. Ser.*, **2016**, *1218*, 187–208.
104. Korntner, S.; Lehner, C.; Gehwolf, R.; Wagner, A.; Grütz, M.; Kunkel, N.; Tempfer, H.; Traweger, A. Limiting Angiogenesis to Modulate Scar Formation. *Adv. Drug Deliv. Rev.*, **2019**, *146*, 170–189.
105. Yang, S.; Liu, L.; Han, J.; Tang, Y. Encapsulating Plant Ingredients for Dermocosmetic Application: An Updated Review of Delivery Systems and Characterization Techniques. *Int. J. Cosmet. Sci.*, *2020*, *42* (1), 16–28.
106. Sarkic, A.; Stappen, I. Essential Oils and Their Single Compounds in Cosmetics—A Critical Review. *Cosmetics*, **2018**, *5* (1), 1–21.
107. Puglia, C.; Santonocito, D. Cosmeceuticals: Nanotechnology-Based Strategies for the Delivery of Phytocompounds. *Curr. Pharm. Des.*, **2019**, *25* (21), 2314–2322.
108. Carvalho, I. T.; Estevinho, B. N.; Santos, L. Application of Microencapsulated Essential Oils in Cosmetic and Personal Healthcare Products—A Review. *Int. J. Cosmet. Sci.*, **2016**, *38* (2), 109–119.
109. Alipour, S.; Dehshahri, S.; Afsari, A. Preparation and Evaluation of a Herbal Mouthwash Containing Oak: Husk of *Quercus Brantii* and *Zataria Multiflora*. *Jundishapur J. Nat. Pharm. Prod.*, **2018**, *13* (3).
110. Farah, C. S.; McIntosh, L.; McCullough, M. J. Mouthwashes. *Aust. Prescr.*, **2009**, *32* (6), 162–164.
111. Jahangir, G. Z.; Ashraf, D. S.; Nasir, I. A.; Sadiq, M.; Shahzad, S.; Naz, F.; Iqbal, M.; Saeed, A. The Myth of Oral Hygiene Using Synthetic Mouthwash Products. *Springerplus*, **2016**, *5* (1).
112. Claffey, N. Essential Oil Mouthwashes: A Key Component in Oral Health Management. *J. Clin. Periodontol.*, **2003**, *30* (suppl 5), 22–24.
113. Raut, J. S.; Karuppayil, S. M. A Status Review on the Medicinal Properties of Essential Oils. *Ind. Crops Prod.*, **2014**, *62*, 250–264.
114. Valli, M.; Bolzani, V. S. Natural Products: Perspectives and Challenges for Use of Brazilian Plant Species in the Bioeconomy. *An. Acad. Bras. Cienc.*, **2019**, *91* (suppl 3), 1–7.

115. Alamgir, A. N. M. *Therapeutic Use of Medicinal Plants and Their Extracts*; Springer: Cham, Switzerland, 2017; Vol. 1, pp. 177–293.
116. Yap, P. S. X.; Yiap, B. C.; Ping, H. C.; Lim, S. H. E. Essential Oils, a New Horizon in Combating Bacterial Antibiotic Resistance. *Open Microbiol. J.*, **2014**, *8*, 6–14.
117. Fazly Bazzaz, B. S.; Khameneh, B.; Namazi, N.; Iranshahi, M.; Davoodi, D.; Golmohammadzadeh, S. Solid Lipid Nanoparticles Carrying *Eugenia caryophyllata* Essential Oil: The Novel Nanoparticulate Systems with Broad-Spectrum Antimicrobial Activity. *Lett. Appl. Microbiol.*, **2018**, *66*, 506–513.

Part III

Technological Applications

9 Plant-Based Cosmetic Products

Patrícia Maria Berardo Gonçalves Maia Campos, Gabriela Maria D'Angelo Costa, and Cláudia Regina Fernandes de Souza

CONTENTS

9.1 Introduction 233
9.2 Trends in the Cosmetic Industry: Botanical Ingredients 235
9.3 Application of Natural Ingredients in the Development of Cosmetic Formulations 240
9.4 Research and Development of Cosmetics with Natural Ingredients 243
9.5 Determination of the Clinical Efficacy of Plant-Based Cosmetics by Biophysical and Skin Imaging Techniques 247
9.6 Final Remarks 250
References 250

9.1 INTRODUCTION

The growing interest in natural products and their health benefits has also been a trend in the cosmetic sector, and novel botanical ingredients have been re searched to reduce consumer exposure to synthetic substances [1]. The composition of cosmetic products consists of active ingredients with protective properties against skin changes resulting from the exposome. These products improve the overall appearance, providing the necessary nutrients for healthy skin. Cosmetics can standardise skin tone, texture, and shine while reducing wrinkles, representing the fastest-growing segment of the personal care industry.

There is a strong tendency in the consumer market for beauty and personal well-being to search for natural and organic ingredients from flora biodiversity to produce innovative cosmetics based on the concepts of sustainability, protection of the environment, and social responsibility. Proof of the biological properties of various botanical ingredients and extracts (phytoextracts) allow their use to develop innovative cosmetic formulations for skin and hair care.

The use of natural ingredients for skin-care purposes has been known since ancient times. Currently, they are becoming more prevalent in cosmetic formulations due to consumer concerns about synthetic ingredient/chemical substances. The desired characteristics of botanical extracts used in skin care include antioxidant and antimicrobial activities, photoprotective effects, tyrosinase inhibition activity, and wetting properties [2–4].

DOI: 10.1201/9781003225416-12

The biological effects of botanical ingredients are linked to secondary metabolites (phytochemicals) such as the phenolic compounds (e.g. anthocyanins, flavonoids, and phenolic acids). Although substances of natural origin have promising applications, additional scientific studies are needed to confirm their beneficial effects when used in different cosmetic formulations to guarantee their safety and effectiveness [1]. *In vitro* and *in vivo* safety and efficacy assays and clinical studies are needed to assess the effect of natural ingredients added to cosmetic products [5, 6].

Preliminary studies include *in vitro* biological activity tests for the selected bioactive compound, compatibility tests between raw materials and botanical extracts or their isolated constituents, selecting the form of presentation of the product under development (e.g. cream, lotion, shampoo, conditioner), and formulation stability tests.

A careful choice of raw materials used during the development of cosmetic products is crucial since it determines how the final product will present itself. For botanical extracts, it is essential to define the part of the plant used, the extraction method, and the standardisation of major compounds according to the proposed biological activities.

The selection of botanical ingredients is usually based on preliminary experimental studies and information reported in the technical literature about the physicochemical and microbiological characteristics, concentrations for use, and incompatibilities of each ingredient. This information contributes to reaching the desired objective of the developmental phase. In addition, the physical–mechanical and sensory properties are determined as well as the clinical benefits of the developed formulations. Figure 9.1 shows a simplified diagram of the main steps in developing herbal cosmetic formulations and evaluation methods.

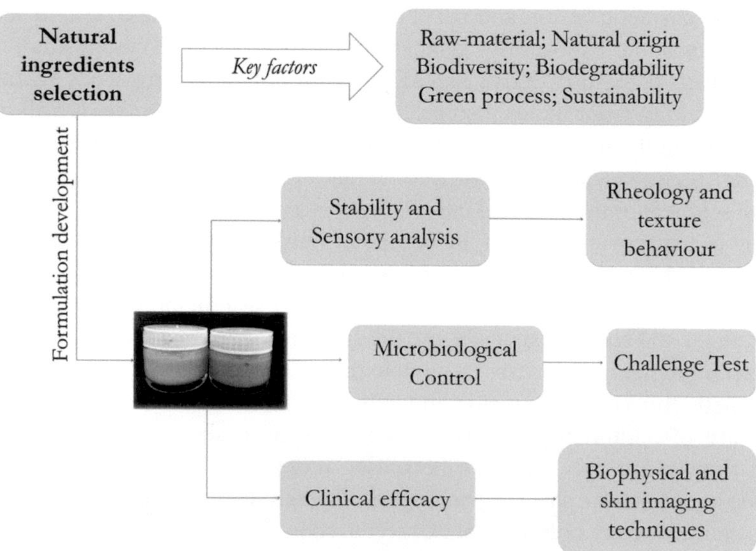

FIGURE 9.1 Steps for the development of plant-based cosmetic formulations.

The product's stability and safety must be evaluated to validate that they attend regulatory standards that guarantee the effectiveness and safety of the cosmetic, even under conditions that accelerate its degradation process. The formulations are subjected to thermal stress conditions through storage in environmental test chambers and refrigerators at extreme temperatures to analyse possible changes in colour, odour, uniformity, pH, and viscosity [7]. The rheological analysis is also an important tool for evaluating the stability and behaviour of the formulation on the skin.

Another important analysis in the development of cosmetic products is their texture profile, which can be defined as the tactile response to a physical stimulus generated by contact between the skin and a product [8–10]. This analysis allows the evaluation of parameters such as consistency, firmness, spreadability, and hardness, among others, which can be related and predict the sensory properties of the formulation. Thus, this analysis determines a group of physical properties of the perceived sensory quality generated by the internal structure of the material, determined by the molecular interactions of its constituents [11, 12]. The importance of the test is to characterise and predict the sensory properties that must be present in the final product and relate them to the consumer sensory perception.

After the definition and evaluation of stability, texture profile, and sensorial properties, the obtained formulations must be submitted to a clinical study for efficacy evaluation. The science of cutaneous biometrics, which seeks to reproduce biological phenomena numerically, has been widely addressed in several studies that aim to evaluate cosmetic products' effectiveness [13–15]. Biophysical and skin imaging techniques are considered an advance in the dermatological and cosmetic area, allowing the real-time and noninvasive analysis of the biological, morphological, structural, and mechanical characteristics of the skin before and after the application of cosmetics [6, 16, 17].

Scientific proof of the biological properties of active botanical principles can lead to innovative cosmetics widely accepted by consumers, having beneficial effects on their health, beauty, and well-being. It is important to emphasise that these natural cosmetics must be safe and effective and comply with regulatory aspects, which are mandatory premises for developing novel plant-based cosmetics (or phytocosmetics).

9.2 TRENDS IN THE COSMETIC INDUSTRY: BOTANICAL INGREDIENTS

The use of botanical ingredients such as polysaccharides, natural dyes and pigments, fragrances, and essential oils in cosmetic products with synthetic ingredients has been carried out for a long time. However, the concept of "natural cosmetic" has gained wide recognition in recent decades, with the establishment of companies such as L'Occitane de Provence (1976, France), Aveda (1978, USA, now owned by Estée Lauder), Melvita (1983, France), and Korres (1996, Greece). These companies started to produce cosmetics containing natural and organic ingredients, avoiding synthetic chemicals, as new marketing strategies [18].

Ingredient suppliers have diversified their product portfolio and have developed new natural active ingredients from plants (phytoactive ingredients) or animals or obtained by biotechnology routes. So, plants traditionally used in small communities for their healing properties have been rediscovered as a source of natural active principles. The cosmetic industry and ingredient manufacturers have embraced environmental conservation programs and sustainability [18].

The search for new functional herbal ingredients is a trend in the ingredients market, driven by the safety concerns of certain groups of consumers who prefer natural ingredients over synthetic ones. The use of ingredients harvested from nature, certified as organic, has contributed to the significant growth in botanical ingredients with antioxidant and anti-pollutant properties in skin and hair care products [18–20]. The use of these ingredients in cosmetic formulations is a topic of great interest that involves the scientific community, the cosmetic industry, and consumers. The cosmeceutical market is constantly growing, as is the demand for phytoactive ingredients to develop innovative skin care products with different activities such as moisturising, sun protection, and anti-ageing and skin whitening effects [21, 22].

The growing demand for cosmetic products for the skin with strong performance has contributed to the development of intense research work aimed at understanding the mechanisms of skin ageing and developing strategies to improve the skin's general health.

In general, the skin health and ageing process result from the contribution by the molecular interactions between our wider genome, our microbiome, and the exposome.

The skin ageing exposome consists of external and internal factors and interactions affecting a human individual from conception to death. The response of the human body to these factors leads to biological and clinical signs of skin ageing. Krutmann et al. [23] propose that environmental factors which are part of the skin ageing exposome fall into the following major categories: solar radiation, air pollution, tobacco smoke, nutrition, and various factors such as stress, sleep deprivation, effects of temperature, and the cosmetic products.

The skin ageing process is affected by numerous factors that can also differ depending on one's ethnic heritage. Some of the main skin ageing factors are the ethnic diversity of the skin ageing mechanism, age and gender (genome), the impact of the microbial ecosystem (microbiome), and various external and lifestyle factors (exposome) [24].

The cutaneous microbiota, a living ecosystem of the outer skin barrier, plays an important role in maintaining health. The skin microbiome is largely affected by the genome (age and gender, genetics) and exposome (external and lifestyle factors). In skin ageing, there is a significant change in the physiology of the skin surface, including pH, lipid composition, and sebum secretion. These physiological changes can affect the composition of the skin's microbiome as well [24, 25].

According to Khmaladze et al. [24], the "genome-microbiome-exposome" model considers both the positive and negative impact of our genome (genes, age/gender), exposome: external (sun, pollution, climate) and lifestyle factors (sleep, stress, exercise, nutrition, skin-care routine), and the role of our skin microbiome. A first application permits us to evaluate the effect of the genome on the synthesis of collagen in the skin and the determination of a suitable target for boosting pro-collagen synthesis.

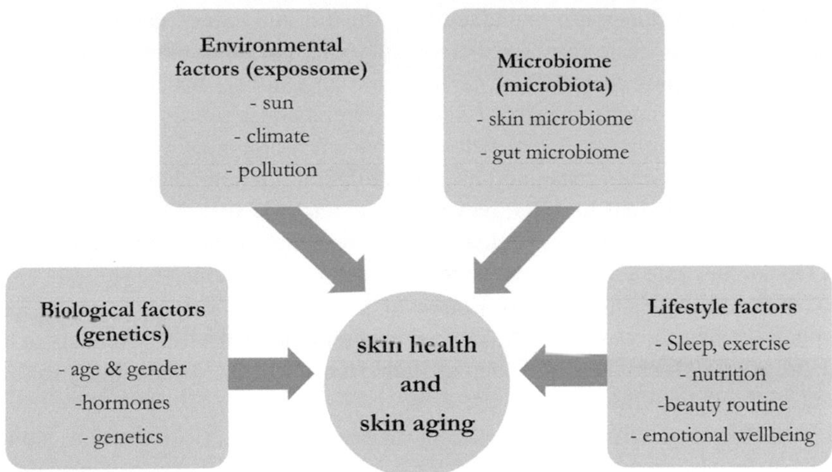

FIGURE 9.2 Factors affecting skin health and skin ageing related to the "genome-microbiome-exposome" interfaces.

Figure 9.2 shows a diagram combining the various factors that affect skin health and ageing concerning genome-microbiome-exposome interfaces.

The high potential of phytoactive ingredients to develop more effective and innovative cosmetic products lead to the introduction in the market of a new generation of products called phytocosmeceuticals. Phytocosmeceuticals can be defined as cosmetic products that claim to contain biologically active ingredients with healing activity or similar properties, which satisfy the needs of beauty and health.

In recent years, growing concerns about the environment and the expansion of "green chemistry" have spurred the development of a myriad of greener extraction techniques to replace conventional extraction methods. The idea of green solvents expresses the objective of minimising the environmental impact resulting from organic solvents. Among these, "green" solvents are water, glycerol, vegetable oils, supercritical fluids, as well as ionic liquids, and organic salts with a low melting point. Concerning the green extraction of natural products, this definition can be modified to include the design of extraction processes that minimise energy consumption, allow the use of renewable natural products and alternative solvents, and guarantee high-quality and safe plant extracts. These technologies should facilitate the simple purification process of plant extracts and produce high-quality extraction of target compounds [26, 27].

Sustainability assessment is commonly defined as an instrument that aims to identify, predict, and evaluate potential environmental, social, and economic impacts. The cosmetic industry needs to adapt and innovate to design products and processes that can improve the sector's sustainability, acting throughout the value chain, always considering consumer safety and following the respective legislation.

With a focus on each phase of a product's life cycle, it is essential to understand what factors to consider when aiming for sustainability; design; sourcing (sustainable agriculture, raw material extraction, chemicals, responsible and ethical sourcing, and economic development); manufacturing (health and safety, energy and water use, emissions and waste formation, transportation, and community involvement); packaging (packaging materials, water use, and emissions); distribution (transport miles, cargo usage, and frequency of deliveries); consumer use (functional benefits, product safety and quality, social benefits, consumer practices, water, and energy consumption); and post-consumer use (formulation biodegradability, packaging waste, landfill, emissions to water, recycling, and reuse) [28].

The greatest limitation of sustainability in cosmetics depends on their ingredients. One of the main challenges is the replacement of unsustainable synthetic ingredients with sustainable alternatives. Bom et al. [28] discuss the relationship between sustainability and the cosmetics industry, the factors that drive developments in this field, the need to assess these and other available tools, and the sustainability impacts produced throughout the product's life cycle.

The certification aims to verify the ingredients, processes, production, storage of raw materials, packaging, labelling, energy resources and waste management, and producer certification to guarantee the quality of the final product. In other words, the certification agencies (e.g., Ecocert – France, Cosmebio – France, BDIH – Germany, Natrue – Belgium, IBD – Brazil, and ICEA – Italy), impose standards, as the COSMOS-standard and ISO16128, that the production industry must meet to ensure the quality of the final product [28, 29].

More and more consumers are looking for products that cause less impact on the environment, and this is why cosmetics must be "environmentally friendly". The development of natural (phytocosmetics) or organic cosmetics is the challenge to ensure stability, safety, and efficiency. The use of botanical ingredients contributes to increasing the sustainable cosmetics market, acquiring a greater market share. These products are classified by regulators into different categories, adding advantages to the product and increasing consumer demand [29].

Biotechnology is currently showing an impact on the cosmetic area in several ways. Cosmetic companies use biotechnology to discover, develop, and produce components of cosmetic formulations and assess the activity of these components in the skin, particularly how they can affect changes associated with ageing. Thus, biotechnology represents a good alternative for the development of new active principles capable of delaying ageing.

A wide range of biotech products is used in the formulation of cosmetics. Based on their molecular structure, the compounds are divided into the following groups: (1) polyphenols, terpenes, and carotenoids; (2) organic acids; (3) amino acids and other nitrogen compound; (4) vitamins and vitamin-like compounds; (5) polysaccharides; (6) polypeptides and proteins; and (7) essential fatty acids, sterols, and lipid derivatives [30].

Other photosynthetic microorganisms, such as microalgae and cyanobacteria, are also rich sources of several bioactive molecules such as carotenoids, lipids, fatty acids, proteins, and amino acids, which have been widely used in cosmetics formulations [31]. Spirulina is a biomass of cyanobacteria (*Arthrospira* sp.) that has been widely used in cosmetics. In some preliminary studies, Maia Campos et al. [32, 33] showed the antioxidant potential, skin compatibility, and immediate effects on skin hydration of formulations containing a spirulina extract obtained by biotechnology. Spirulina contains a bioactive compound, phycocyanin, which has antioxidant properties and can repair premature ageing signs. The use of spirulina extracts in dermo-cosmetic formulations allows for more stable and safer formulations [34].

The green and sustainable manufacture of cosmetics and food products has contributed to another new trend emerging in the last 10 years, i.e., plant cell culture technology. More than 50 products based on cultured plant cell extracts entered the cosmetics industry during this period, with plant cell suspension cultures being the most used. Eibl et al. [35] present the current state of the art in the area and discuss the reasons and characteristics, and challenges of production based on the culture of plant cells for the cosmetics and food industries.

Besides their huge potential, there are some concerns about using phytoactive ingredients in cosmetics, such as low solubility, low penetration, and physical–chemical instability when applied directly to the skin. Different systems based on nanotechnology have been proposed to overcome these problems, and some are already on the market. Nanotechnologies allow the transformation of liquid and volatile products into solids, protect and modulate the release of active compounds, improve the solubility of poorly soluble compounds in water, reduce adverse effects on non-target tissues, and increase their stability against light and temperature [22, 36].

The use of nanosystems in cosmetics also facilitates the permeation/penetration of hydrophilic and lipophilic constituents to the deeper tissues of the skin, increasing the duration of action and stability and avoiding incompatibilities with other formulation ingredients, preventing unwanted effects that may occur locally or systemically.

Micro- and nanostructured systems loaded with phytoactive ingredients can be produced by various methods, including physical processes (spray drying, air suspension, lyophilisation, spray cooling, micronisation, high-pressure homogenisation, and microfluidisation) or by physicochemical processes (simple and complex coacervation, solvent evaporation, among others). Structure, size, and composition have significant effects on the physicochemical properties, stability, release profile, interactions with the skin, and dermo-cosmetic functionality of encapsulated phytoactive ingredients. For skin-care products, which are in direct contact with the human body, assessing the safety of ingredients is a matter of extreme importance [37].

Vesicular delivery systems (e.g. liposomes, nanosomes, phytosomes, and herbosomes), solid lipid nanoparticles, nanostructured lipid carriers, and nanoemulsions are the most preferred delivery systems used in phytocosmectics. Liposomes are used in personal care products due to their benefits such as sustained release, reduced toxicity, greater stability, and greater bioavailability. They are especially used in many anti-ageing products to encapsulate vitamins, antioxidants, and botanical extracts [36–38].

Incorporating delivery nanosystems into cosmetic formulations is one of the most critical phases of new product development. It requires much experimentation since it is not a universal method for all products. Cosmetic formulations can undergo significant changes after application due to interactions with the skin or evaporation of volatile compounds. Hence, after incorporation, it is necessary to guarantee a homogeneous product with long-term stability, sensorily attractive to the customer. Thus, the experimental formulations must be assayed for spreadability, rheological properties, colour changes, pH changes, and storage temperatures [21].

The development of the delivery systems must also follow sustainability criteria, using green technologies and materials that are not toxic to the environment. Furthermore, the development of delivery systems still has a few more issues to be solved. Although the physiology of the skin is relatively well known, further studies must be carried out to understand better the dominant permeation pathways and the interactions of each material in the delivery system with the skin. The use of long-term delivery systems (e.g. nanoparticles) is still unknown, and their effects must be evaluated since they can disrupt the physiological function of the skin. Security assessments are also essential for better public acceptance of new technologies. Delivery systems must use reasonably priced materials to provide an acceptable cost when moving from laboratory scale to industrial and commercial production. Methods must be developed and optimised in order to obtain a uniform and reproducible result [21].

In summary, the use of delivery systems in the phytocosmetic area is a promising technology for developing innovative products with better performance and which have shown good results in protecting the skin from changes caused by skin oiliness and photoaging.

9.3 APPLICATION OF NATURAL INGREDIENTS IN THE DEVELOPMENT OF COSMETIC FORMULATIONS

The publications and patents about natural ingredients in cosmetic products have increased every year, motivated by environmental sustainability trends [28, 39]. Natural ingredients have been used since ancient times to beautify the skin or hair, however, without proper proof of their safety and effectiveness [40].

Concerning botanical products with specific functionalities, the cosmetic industry has experienced a huge demand for essential oils (fragrances, antimicrobials), bioactive phenolics (antioxidants, antimicrobials), dyes and pigments (actives), vegetable oils, waxes, polysaccharides, and others as phytoactive substances.

Vegetable oils can be obtained from fruit or seed and are composed mostly of triglycerides; vitamins A, D, and E; phospholipids; phytosterols; and natural pigments [41]. The fatty acids present in these oils are susceptible to thermal and oxidative degradation that causes poor thermal and oxidative stability. For this reason, it is common to associate the use of antioxidants [41]. The cosmetic function of vegetable oils is to act as emollients with a moisturising effect and sensory properties on the skin, leading to changes in the texture and appearance of the formulations [12, 28].

According to César and Maia Campos [12], vegetable oils are widely used in cosmetic formulations due to their emollient properties (which can protect the skin barrier) and their well-known activities in restoring cutaneous homeostasis. They have also replaced mineral oils because of customers' growing interest in herbal products. Examples of vegetable oils used in cosmetics include coconut (lauric acids), sunflower oil (lecithin, tocopherols, carotenoids), jojoba oil (oleic acids, linoleic and linolenic acids, arachidonic acids), olive oil (carotenoids, polyphenols, tocopherols), mango oil (oleic acids, stearic acids, triglycerides), among others [26, 42].

Natural waxes have a complex chemical composition based on wax esters, straight-chain alkanes, fatty acids, and long-chain alcohols. Also, waxes can be considered crystalline gelators, influencing the viscosity of cosmetic formulations [43]. Physical properties such as hardness, cohesiveness, melting point or range, viscosity, and optical transparency are used to characterise waxes [44] and determine their adequate cosmetic formulation uses.

Most natural waxes are saturated triglycerides or esters with alkyl chain lengths of C_{12}-C_{30}. The triglyceride waxes are normally derived by fractionating or hydrogenating vegetable oil, converting unsaturated to saturated alkyl chains. The most popular natural waxes include Cetyl, Stearyl/Behenyl alcohols, Stearic acid, Carnauba, Candelilla, and Hydrogenated vegetable oils.

Carnauba wax, the most important vegetable wax in terms of economic value and possible applications, is extracted from the leaves of carnauba (*Copernicia prunifera* [Miller] H. E. Moore), a Brazilian palm. Carnauba wax is the hardest wax and has the highest melting point of any commercial natural waxes, has low solubility, and predominantly consists of aliphatic esters and diesters of cinnamic acid [45].

Polymers are an important class of raw materials for cosmetic formulations, essential for preparing high-performance products. They are classified as synthetic, semi-synthetic, or natural macromolecules composed of many repeating units (monomers) usually arranged in a chain. In cosmetic formulations, their structural diversity promotes various functions as rheology modifiers, thickeners, foam stabilisers and destabilisers, emulsifiers, fixatives, conditioners, and film formers. Natural polymers are widely used in cosmetic formulations and are a good alternative to synthetic polymers. They are biocompatible, safe, eco-friendly, highly marketable to consumers, and suitable for many applications, including makeup, skin- and hair care, and formulation modifiers and stabilisers [28, 46].

Polysaccharides have been extensively used in cosmetics to form hydrocolloids and function as film formers, gelling agents, thickeners, conditioners, and emulsifiers. A wide range of polysaccharides is currently used for their physicochemical and bioactive properties. They mostly consist of triglycerides and can be of botanical origin (e.g. starch, cellulose, pectin, guar gum) or may originate from algae (e.g. alginate, agar, carrageenan), animals (e.g. chitosan, gelatin, hyaluronic acid), and microbes (e.g. hyaluronic acid, xanthan, dextran). The botanical polysaccharides most frequently used are starch, guar gum, cellulose, and their functional derivatives obtained by chemical modification [18, 46, 47]. The use of polysaccharides in cosmetic products is important for formulation technology since these compounds can act on rheological properties and increase the stability of the formulation. The sensorial properties of cosmetics can also be enhanced by using these ingredients in the formulation [47].

Essential oils have biologically recognised activities as antioxidants and anti-inflammatory agents, and many of them are employed as cosmetic actives. Essential oils are used as ingredients in cosmetics and fine fragrances due to the presence of volatile and semi-volatile compounds [48] and in soaps and detergents, household products, and other products such as pesticides and aromatherapy oils. They can be used as *co-preservatives* since many essential oils have antimicrobial activity and can be added to synthetic preservatives as supportive agents. *Fragrance* perfumery is the main use of essential oils in cosmetics. Although synthetic fragrances are more stable and have better longevity; they can be used for *hair care* such as conditioning, anti-dandruff, and permanent waving agents; and for *skin care* as topically active ingredients for any skin-care product since they can penetrate the skin and bind to the membranes of skin cells, having sustained effects on the skin [18, 20, 27].

Essential oils and their isolated compounds are widely used in cosmetic products as they offer various health benefits [26]. Their range of biological activities covers analgesic, antiseptic, antimicrobial, carminative, diuretic, spasmolytic, hyperemic, and stimulatory effects [49]. Several essential oils also have antimicrobial, antioxidant, and anti-inflammatory activities. Examples include the essential oils of roses (vitamin C, phenolic acids), eucalyptus (1,8-cineol, *p*-cymene, 2-pinene, β-pinene), rosemary (1,8-cineole, camphor, α-pinene), lemons (limonene, valencene, ocimene), and grapefruit (vitamins A, C, and E). Essential oils are classified as "Generally Recognised As Safe or GRAS" by the US Food and Drug Administration (FDA) and are therefore permitted as food additives/preservatives [50].

In addition to the specific phytoactive ingredients, common cosmeceutical ingredients can also be used, such as hydroxy acids (alpha hydroxy acids [AHAs]: citric acid, malic acid, glycolic acid, lactic acid, pyruvic acid, tartaric acid, lactobionic acid, and beta hydroxy acids [BHAs], salicylic acid referred to as fruit acids), antioxidants (alpha-lipoic acid [ALA], L-ascorbic acid/vitamin C, niacinamide/vitamin B3, N-acetyl glucosamine/NAG, α-tocopherol, and ubiquinone/CoQ10), botanicals (grape seed extract and ferulic acid), depigmenting agents (hydroquinone, ascorbic acid/vitamin C, kojic acid, and liquorice extract), retinoids (retinoic acid/tretinoin, retinol, and retinaldehyde), hyaluronic acid, and ceramides [38].

Cashew apple (*Anacardium occidentale* L.) is a native plant from tropical America, rich in tannins, flavonoids, amino acids, anacardic acids, and vitamin C, which can benefit oily skin. The constituents of cashew apple extracts have effects such as astringency and antimicrobial activity, providing oil control, and acne prevention. A study of the antioxidant activity of cashew extract and the clinical efficacy of a sunscreen formulation containing it to improve oily skin conditions was carried out by Mercurio et al. [51]. A significant reduction in the number of chin pores was observed in the volunteers after 28 days of application and was attributed to the pore constriction caused by the tannins present in this extract, responsible for the astringent antimicrobial activity.

The beneficial photoprotective effects of topical formulations containing combined extracts of *Ginkgo biloba* and green tea have been investigated by Dal Belo et al. [52]. *G. biloba* and green tea glycolic extracts added to a topical formulation provided excellent photoprotective effects against ultraviolet (UV)-induced skin damage (disruption of the skin barrier, erythema, sunburn cell formation, and epidermal hyperplasia). The results indicated that these photoprotective effects are not due to UV absorbance, as is the case for UV filters, but rather to biological effects, mainly observed with the formulation containing *G. biloba* extract.

Gianeti et al. [53] developed cosmetic formulations containing green tea and evaluated their effects on human skin using noninvasive methods. The formulations were applied to the forearm skin of volunteers, and their effects were evaluated by the determination of stratum corneum water content, TEWL, skin viscoelastic-to-elastic ratio, and microrelief. In the long-term study, the formulations increased skin moisture, and after topical application, the skin viscoelastic-to-elastic ratio was significantly enhanced compared to vehicle and control. Also, skin microrelief was significantly improved due to reduced skin roughness, which agreed with Dal Belo et al. [52].

Thus, botanical extracts' complex phytochemical constitution can benefit skin and hair, exhibiting anti-ageing effects, wrinkle reduction, skin lightening, dark spot removal, skin oil control, hair softness, and anti-dandruff action, among others [20].

9.4 RESEARCH AND DEVELOPMENT OF COSMETICS WITH NATURAL INGREDIENTS

The Research and Development (R&D) of cosmetic products is based on the innovation of claims, active substances, and processes, which must obey the laws or resolutions of the regulatory agencies of each country. The innovation process is based on the *development funnel* of Clark and Wheelwright [54], which consists of the funnelling of ideas until selecting the most appropriate one. Thus, the initial stage of development consists of researching the market, patents and scientific and technical literature. After the product concept and formulation definition, preliminary tests can be carried out to verify the viability of its concept. In this stage, adjustments to the cosmetic formulation are made to achieve a stable formulation with good physical–mechanical, rheological, and sensory properties. This step is important to obtain a more accurate cosmetic formulation based on consumer preference [55]. Stability, safety, and efficacy tests are then carried out to guarantee the product's performance according to the requirements of health regulatory agencies. Figure 9.3 shows the steps involved in the development of cosmetic products.

Stability evaluation of cosmetic products ensures the quality and compatibility of the product under different temperatures and over different periods [56]. Extrinsic and intrinsic factors influence the stability of a cosmetic formulation. Extrinsic factors are related to the exposure of the formulation to time, temperature, light, oxygen, humidity, packaging material, and microorganisms. Intrinsic factors are related to the interaction of the formulation ingredients, such as physical and chemical incompatibility. Physical incompatibility produces changes in the formulation appearance, such as phase separation and precipitation. Chemical incompatibility includes changes in pH value, oxidation-reduction reactions, hydrolysis, interactions with formulation ingredients, and interactions of the ingredients with the packaging material [57].

Long-term stability or shelf tests are used to confirm the estimated shelf life in the accelerated stability assays and to verify the actual limits of stability. This test assesses the behaviour of the cosmetic product under normal storage conditions [56, 57]. In addition, the compatibility test of the formulation with the packaging material can also be performed. The same conditions used in the accelerated stability studies can be applied to this test. However, the formulations are stored in the final packaging and not in glass, as done in the accelerated stability tests. Cellulose, metal, plastic, glass, and pressurised packaging can be used [57].

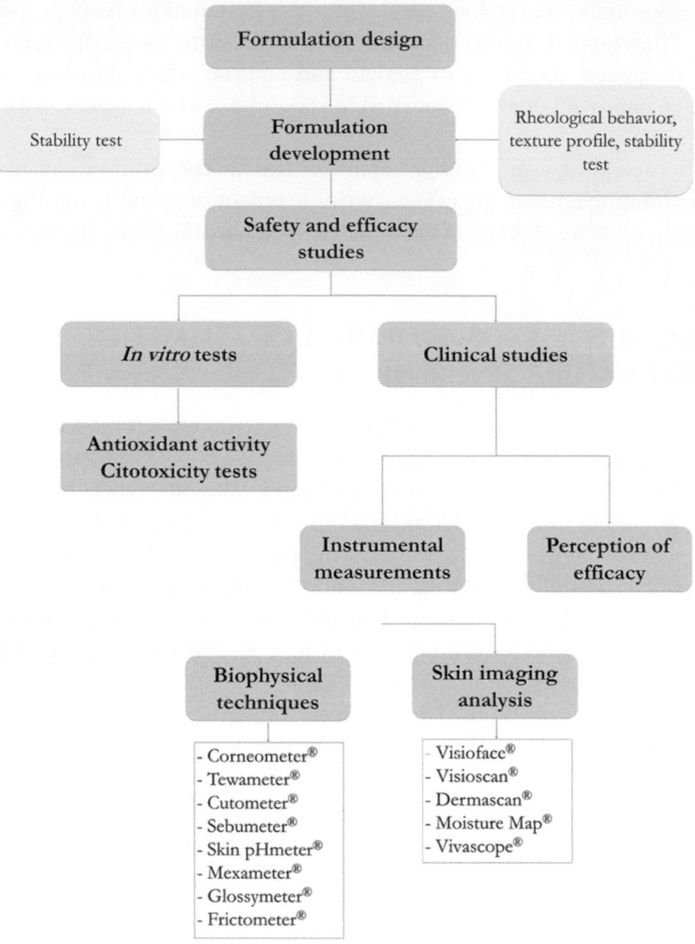

FIGURE 9.3 Flow diagram of cosmetic product development and clinical studies.

Accelerated tests can predict the stability of cosmetic products quickly [58]. The temperature conditions of this test can vary from environmental to high temperature (37, 40, or 45°C), low temperature (5, –5, or –10°C), or freeze-thaw cycles (24-h cycles at two opposite temperatures). The duration of this test can vary from 15 days (preliminary test) to 3 or 6 months or even a year [57, 58]. Organoleptic, physical–chemical, and microbiological parameters can be evaluated. The organoleptic parameters usually evaluated are appearance, colour, and odour. The physical–chemical parameters commonly determined are pH value, viscosity, density, rheological behaviour, and texture profile, and the microbiological parameters that can be evaluated are microbial count and challenge test [57, 59].

It is important to determine the microbiological control of cosmetic products in terms of preservative capacity that should prevent the growth of *fungi*, bacteria, and yeast, microorganisms that can impair the effectiveness and stability of the formulation. The challenge test is the most common microbiological assay used for cosmetics products, consisting of the inoculation of microorganisms and the evaluation of their viability [57, 58].

Usually, four types of microorganisms are inoculated: gram-positive bacteria, gram-negative bacteria, fungus, and yeasts. The most used gram-positive bacterium is *Staphylococcus aureus*, which is present in the skin's microbiome. Examples of gram-negative bacteria are *Escherichia coli* or *Pseudomonas aeruginosa*, which can develop resistance to preservatives. *Aspergillus niger*, which is the main cause of degradation and contamination of cosmetic products, is the fungus usually tested. *Candida albicans* is commonly used to represent the yeasts, which are widespread in the environment and human mucous membranes and are resistant to the preservative system. The microorganisms are usually inoculated separately in up to 1% portions of the cosmetic product to prevent changes in its physicochemical properties. After inoculation, the cosmetic product is incubated at high or environmental temperatures without light for 28 days. The mortality rate of the microorganisms is evaluated 7, 14, 21, and 28 days after inoculation, and microbial activity can be assessed according to acceptance criteria defined by international organisations [59].

Regarding physical stability, the determination of rheological behaviour is an important tool. This analysis evaluates how the cosmetic formulations behave under the action of shear stress according to time and can determine the stability and performance of a cosmetic product over time or process. It can be used to predict or control changes in the formulation [60].

A cosmetic material can exhibit four main behaviours, i.e., viscosity, elasticity, plasticity, and viscoelasticity. Viscoelastic behaviour is the ability of a complex fluid to exhibit elasticity and viscosity simultaneously. The characteristic of this complex fluid is that it is an elastic solid and a viscous liquid. The parameters used to characterise the viscoelasticity of a material are the elastic modulus G' and the viscous modulus G''.

Cosmetics generally exhibit shear-thinning behaviour, which is the current term for pseudoplastic fluids. This behaviour is characterised by a decrease in viscosity with an increase in shear rate. The shear thickening behaviour is the current term for dilating fluids, characterised by increased viscosity as the shear rate increases [60].

Thixotropy is an important parameter for the evaluation of the rheological properties of cosmetics. The thixotropic fluid shows reduced viscosity with time in a condition of shear rate or stress. Viscosity is gradually recovered when the shear rate or stress is removed. This phenomenon is time-dependent and related to the material's breakdown and recovery time [60].

In cosmetics such as sunscreen formulations, viscosity must decrease at a high shear rate to uniformly cover the skin surface. However, viscosity must recover quickly enough after shearing for the formulation to remain as a film on the skin, ensuring effective protection against the sun's UV radiation.

In addition to the rheology, the determination of texture profile is also extensively used to characterise cosmetic products by determining mechanical properties such as work of shear, spreadability, firmness, cohesiveness, consistency, index of viscosity, and hardness. This analysis can help to predict the sensorial properties of the formulations [55].

Spreadability is a desirable characteristic of most cosmetic products. It is a sensory characteristic that refers to the easiness with which the cosmetic product spreads on the skin, usually involving a loss of consistency [61]. This property can be measured with the TA.XT® plus Texture Analyzer using the shear work parameter from the area under the positive curve of the spreadability test [55].

Firmness is a parameter determined by the back extrusion test, which consists of the maximum force needed by the probe to introduce the analysed material [62]. It is related to moderate resistance to deformation of a product and is part of the property spectrum of hardness.

Cohesiveness is the results of intermolecular attraction (internal viscosity) that determines its cohesion (sticking). Measuring cohesiveness involves an amount of force to remove a probe from the analysed material. Cohesiveness is calculated by the maximum value of the negative curve from the back extrusion test [55].

Consistency is related to the firmness or viscosity of a cosmetic product. It is determined by the back extrusion test and is calculated by the area under the positive curve. The viscosity index is determined from the area under the negative curve obtained from the back extrusion test [55].

Hardness is a parameter related to a substantial resistance to deformation of a product and belongs to the same property spectrum as firmness. The penetration test determines this parameter by calculating the maximum force in the first compressive deformation of an object [63].

Sensory analysis is a valuable tool during R&D since it allows the cosmetic formulation to be pleasant and accepted by consumers. To this end, it is necessary to recruit subjects trained or not to evaluate the formulations. Trained subjects are those who receive previous training on how to analyse the sensory characteristics. They are important during the development phase in order to obtain a better targeting of the cosmetic formulation. A small number of subjects ($n = 8$–20) is commonly used. Untrained subjects are generally used when the interest is the evaluation of a cosmetic formulation by potential consumers. However, in this case, it is better to perform the sensory analysis with a greater number of subjects ($n = 50$–100) to minimise the variability of subject response [64].

Sensory analysis carried out by a trained descriptive panel allows obtaining more robust, consistent, detailed, and reproducible results [64]. However, training this descriptive panel can take time and is an expensive process. That is why it is important to correlate this process with some instrumental methods such as those mentioned above that help predict the formulation's sensory behaviour in the early stages of R&D [13].

There are some methods of descriptive sensory analysis, all of them performed with a trained panel, such as Quantitative Descriptive Analysis (QDA) and the Spectrum™ Descriptive Analysis (SDA) method. The QDA method is based on the description of the product's sensory attributes by subjects, while the SDA method classifies the sensory attributes on an absolute or universal scale [13].

The applied method varies according to the study's objective and the type of subject recruited. The methodology for untrained subjects can be, i.e., the Check-all-that-apply (CATA) questions and interest scales. CATA questions are a list of sensory or non-sensory terms defined by the researcher. Consumers answer multiple-choice questions after trying the product. CATA questionnaires are important for obtaining information about consumer perceptions. However, the layout of the list of attributes can influence consumer responses, and the analysis of similar products is not recommended. The intensity scale is a method based on ranking the cosmetic product through an intensity scale containing sensory characteristics defined by the researcher. However, there may be a lack of consensus about consumer responses that can be improved by training the subjects [64].

It is important to perform the set of tests described during R&D in order to obtain a stable and microbiologically safe cosmetic formulation with properties acceptable to the end customer.

9.5 DETERMINATION OF THE CLINICAL EFFICACY OF PLANT-BASED COSMETICS BY BIOPHYSICAL AND SKIN IMAGING TECHNIQUES

The clinical efficacy of cosmetics can be determined in parallel to development to evaluate the performance and benefits of the cosmetic product being developed. Proof of the claims is important to guarantee consumers the effects promised on the label [65]. Thus, clinical efficacy is determined by clinical (*in vivo*) studies with subjects under real conditions of use. The analysis should be carried out in a controlled environment and with well-defined inclusion and exclusion criteria. An ethics committee must previously approve clinical studies, and the safety of the cosmetic formulation should be guaranteed [66].

Biophysical and skin imaging techniques are used to assess the clinical efficacy of plant-based cosmetics. These instrumental and imaging techniques are noninvasive and do not cause any discomfort to the research subject. The biophysical parameters that can be evaluated using these techniques are transepidermal water loss (TEWL), aqueous content of the stratum corneum, mechanical properties, skin microrelief, and sebum content.

TEWL assesses water flow from the stratum corneum, which correlates with the skin's barrier function. The aqueous content of the stratum corneum is used to measure capacitance, conductance, and water impedance, which correlate with skin hydration. Aged skin shows reduced TEWL and skin hydration [67]. Mechanical properties of the skin such as elasticity, viscoelasticity, and plasticity are influenced by the thickness and content of the skin layers [68, 69]. These properties can be assessed using a cutaneous suction method. Loss of elasticity is common for aged skin [69]. Skin microrelief represents the three-dimensional organisation of the dermis and subcutaneous tissue influenced by physiological and environmental factors [70]. Therefore, skin ageing causes progressive changes in skin microrelief with the occurrence of wrinkles [71]. The sebum content of the skin surface can be measured using a photometric method with absorbent papers. This analysis is important for oily skin that contains excessive sebum produced by the sebaceous glands [72].

In addition, advanced skin imaging techniques can be used, such as high-resolution images, high-frequency ultrasound, and Reflectance Confocal Microscopy (RCM).

High-resolution images can be used to evaluate wrinkles, pores, and skin spots [73]. The echogenicity and thickness of the dermis can be determined by high-frequency ultrasound [74], while RCM can assess the morphological and structural characteristics of the epidermis [75]. There are several quantitative and qualitative parameters that the RCM can assess. The quantitative parameters include stratum corneum thickness, granular layer thickness, viable epidermal thickness, dermal papilla depth, and many hyperreflective pixels of the basal layer to assess basal layer pigmentation. Qualitative parameters are assessed using a standardised score from our NEATEC laboratory. The skin film-forming score evaluates the reflectance of the stratum corneum. The film-forming effect can be observed by using polysaccharides on the skin [17]. The skin hydration score is indicative of the furrow size of the stratum corneum and the interkeratinocyte brightness of the granular layer. The moisturising effects can be measured in terms of topical peptides [76]. The skin pigmentation score correlates to the brightness of the basal layer. Skin tone uniformity can be observed using active ingredients of natural origin with an antioxidant action [6].

Several studies have applied these techniques for the characterisation and evaluation of cosmetic products based on ingredients of natural origin for various indications of use, such as film-forming effect, skin tone uniformity, skin hydration, and improvement of skin viscoelasticity, and dermal density, among others.

The immediate film-forming effect on the skin of formulations containing *Kappaphycus alvarezii* and *Caesalpinia spinosa*, quantified by measurements of the water content of the stratum corneum, TEWL, skin microrelief, and morphological and structural characteristics of the epidermis and by sensory analysis, has been reported by Melo and Maia Campos [17]. The cited study demonstrated the benefits of the natural biopolymer based on polysaccharides on the skin surface, reducing furrows and improving the stratum corneum after 1 h of application and reducing TEWL and the skin desquamation [17].

The skin tone uniformity was evaluated in a clinical efficacy study of dermo-cosmetic formulations based on antioxidants such as the fat-soluble derivative of vitamin C—ascorbyl tetraisopalmitate (ATIP), *Spirulina* sp., and olive extract titrated by hydroxytyrosol. The parameters evaluated were the colour difference between lesional and perilesional regions of high-resolution images and the number of hyperreflective pixels of basal layer brightness in RCM images. A significant reduction in the colour difference between lesional and perilesional regions and the number of hyperreflective pixels of basal layer brightness was observed for the formulations containing ATIP and *Spirulina* sp. The olive extract formulation significantly reduced the number of hyperreflective pixels of basal layer brightness, showing the importance of evaluating the RCM images. Thus, the studied formulations based on antioxidants significantly increase skin tone uniformity after 42 days, an effect that was also perceived by the subjects [6]. A clinical study compared the efficacy of the topical application of a dermo-cosmetic formulation with di- and tripeptides extracted from rice (*Oryza sativa*) and oral supplementation based on hydrolysed collagen on the stratum corneum water content, skin viscoelasticity, dermis echogenicity, and skin pore parameters. The combination of these treatments improved the hydration, texture, elasticity, and firmness of the skin, representing a complete treatment acting by different mechanisms [76].

A multifunctional cosmetic formulation containing UV filters; vitamins A, C, and E; *G. biloba*; and *Porphyra umbilicalis* extracts was evaluated in terms of the stratum corneum water content, TEWL, skin microrelief, high-resolution images, echogenicity of the dermis, and morphological and structural characteristics of the epidermis. The studied formulation showed improved skin hydration and barrier function and reduced wrinkles and skin roughness [5].

A broad-spectrum sunscreen containing solid lipid nanoparticles loaded with *Spirulina* sp. and dimethylmethoxychromanole antioxidants was evaluated using stratum corneum water content, TEWL, echogenicity of the dermis, and skin elasticity and pigmentation. The studied formulation significantly improved the skin pigmentation pattern, collagen degradation, and skin network elasticity after 84 days of treatment compared to a vehicle formulation. Thus, the addition of antioxidants to the sunscreen protected the skin from sun-induced damage by improving the photoprotective effect [3].

The efficacy of a multifunctional formulation based on botanical extracts of *Camellia sinensis*, *Vitis vinifera*, *Euterpe oleracea*, vitamins, amino acids, UV filters, and silicones for hair treatment and prevention of UV damage was evaluated by a tensile test and also submitted to combability, shine, and image analysis. In addition, hair strands were submitted to UV radiation in order to evaluate protection against UV damage. The combination of the botanical extracts in the formulation effectively protected the hair from UV damage and prevented and treated hair damage [77].

Biophysical and skin imaging techniques are also applied to the characterisation and evaluation of the skin of populations with different skin characteristics. According to Calixto et al. [16], there are differences in the biophysical properties of the skin between French and Brazilian populations. However, the dermo-cosmetic treatment with a multifunctional formulation containing *Spirulina*-dried extract, *Cichorium intybus* (Chicory) root extract, *Medicago sativa* (Alfalfa) extract, and *Palmaria palmata* extract caused similar improvement of skin hydration, barrier function, and brightness in the two populations.

Another type of clinical investigation to confirm a cosmetic product's safety is the study of its compatibility with the skin and consumers acceptability. After the toxicological evaluation of the ingredients used in cosmetic formulations and *in vitro* preclinical safety tests, the product's safety can be evaluated in a clinical study under real conditions of use [58, 78]. The skin compatibility study assesses the safety of the cosmetic product under conditions maximised by using occlusive or semi-occlusive patches (patch tests) or in open models (open tests) to prove the absence of undesirable effects.

In this context, clinical efficacy and safety studies should be performed during the Research & Development of plant-based cosmetic formulations to guarantee their efficacy and safety. In addition, skin characterisation using biophysical and imaging techniques is very important for developing more specific cosmetic products loaded with phytoactive ingredients according to the type of skin.

9.6 FINAL REMARKS

The use of ingredients obtained from natural sources to develop cosmetic formulations is a new trend and permits obtaining novel and effective products with good texture and sensory properties. Formulation studies, *in vitro* and *in vivo* safety and efficacy trials, and clinical studies are essential for the scientific proof of their real benefits. Therefore, they contribute to the use of flora biodiversity to develop innovative green and sustainable products.

REFERENCES

1. Meira, N. A. N.; Pereira, N. P.; Maciel, L. F.; Menezes-Filho, J. A.; Oliveira, S. S. P. Development and Stability Testing of Emulsions with *Myrciaria cauliflora* (Jaboticaba) Peel Extracts for Cosmetic Application. *J. Cosmetol.*, **2018**, *2* (1), 000106.
2. Ribeiro, A.; Estanqueiro, M.; Oliveira, M.; Sousa Lobo, J. Main Benefits and Applicability of Plant Extracts in Skin Care Products. *Cosmetics*, **2015**, *2* (2), 48–65.
3. Souza, C.; Campos, P. M. B. G. M. Development and Photoprotective Effect of a Sunscreen Containing the Antioxidants Spirulina and Dimethylmethoxy Chromanol on Sun-Induced Skin Damage. *Eur. J. Pharm. Sci.*, **2017**, *104*, 52–64.
4. Bagatin, J. T.; Berardo Gonçalves Ma, P. M.; Bagatin, E. A Pilot Clinical Study to Evaluate the Effectiveness of Olive Extract Containing Hydroxytyrosol for Oral and Topical Treatment of Melasma. *Biomed. Biopharm. Res. J.*, **2020**, *17* (1), 1–15.
5. Gianeti, M.; Maia Campos, P. Efficacy Evaluation of a Multifunctional Cosmetic Formulation: The Benefits of a Combination of Active Antioxidant Substances. *Molecules*, **2014**, *19* (11), 18268–18282.
6. D'Angelo Costa, G. M.; Maia Campos, P. M. B. G. Efficacy of Topical Antioxidants in the Skin Hyperpigmentation Control: A Clinical Study by Reflectance Confocal Microscopy. *J. Cosmet. Dermatol.*, **2021**, *20* (2), 538–545.
7. ANVISA. Guia de Estabilidade Dos Cosméticos. *Anvisa*, **2004**, *1*, 1–52.
8. Bourne, M. C. *Texture, Viscosity and Food*, 2nd ed.; Bourne, M. C., Ed.; Elsevier: Amsterdam, The Netherland, 2012.
9. Bonilha, G. C.; Maia Campos, P. M. B. G.; Costa, G. M. D. Rheological, Texture, and Sensory Analyses and In Vivo Clinical Efficacy of Cosmetic Formulations Containing Ascorbyl Tetraisopalmitate. *Biomed. Biopharm. Res. J.*, **2020**, *17* (1), 1–12.
10. Mercurio, D. G.; Calixto, L. S.; Campos, P. M. B. G. M. Optimization of Cosmetic Formulations Development Using Box-Behnken Design with Response Surface Methodology: Physical, Sensory and Moisturizing Properties. *Brazilian J. Pharm. Sci.*, **2020**, *56*.
11. Calixto, L. S.; Maia Campos, P. M. B. G. Physical-Mechanical Characterization of Cosmetic Formulations and Correlation between Instrumental Measurements and Sensorial Properties. *Int. J. Cosmet. Sci.*, **2017**, *39* (5), 527–534.
12. César, F. C. S.; Maia Campos, P. M. B. G. Influence of Vegetable Oils in the Rheology, Texture Profile and Sensory Properties of Cosmetic Formulations Based on Organogel. *Int. J. Cosmet. Sci.*, **2020**, *42* (5), 494–500.
13. Gilbert, L.; Savary, G.; Grisel, M.; Picard, C. Predicting Sensory Texture Properties of Cosmetic Emulsions by Physical Measurements. *Chemom. Intell. Lab. Syst.*, **2013**, *124*, 21–31.
14. Shirata, M. M. F.; Campos, P. M. B. G. M. Importance of Texture and Sensorial Profile in Cosmetic Formulations Development. *Surg. Cosmet. Dermatology*, **2016**, *8* (3), 223–230.

15. Felippim, E. C.; Marcato, P. D.; Maia Campos, P. M. B. G. Development of Photoprotective Formulations Containing Nanostructured Lipid Carriers: Sun Protection Factor, Physical-Mechanical and Sensorial Properties. *AAPS PharmSciTech*, **2020**, *21* (8), 311.
16. Calixto, L. S.; Picard, C.; Savary, G.; Campos, P. M. B. G. M. Skin Characterization and Immediate Effects of Different Dermocosmetic Treatments in French and Brazilian Skin. *J. Cosmet. Dermatol.*, **2020**, *19* (2), 466–472.
17. Melo, M. O.; Maia Campos, P. M. B. G. Application of Biophysical and Skin Imaging Techniques to Evaluate the Film-forming Effect of Cosmetic Formulations. *Int. J. Cosmet. Sci.*, **2019**, *41* (6), 579–584.
18. Boeriu, C. Plants4Cosmetics: Perspectives for Plant Ingredients in Cosmetics. *Wageningen UR Food Biobased Res.*, **2015**, *1603*, 1–28.
19. Juliano, C.; Magrini, G. Cosmetic Functional Ingredients from Botanical Sources for Anti-Pollution Skincare Products. *Cosmetics*, **2018**, *5* (1), 19.
20. Faccio, G. Plant Complexity and Cosmetic Innovation. *iScience*, **2020**, *23* (8), 101358.
21. Costa, R.; Santos, L. Delivery Systems for Cosmetics—From Manufacturing to the Skin of Natural Antioxidants. *Powder Technol.*, **2017**, *322*, 402–416.
22. Puglia, C.; Santonocito, D. Cosmeceuticals: Nanotechnology-Based Strategies for the Delivery of Phytocompounds. *Curr. Pharm. Des.*, **2019**, *25* (21), 2314–2322.
23. Krutmann, J.; Bouloc, A.; Sore, G.; Bernard, B. A.; Passeron, T. The Skin Aging Exposome. *J. Dermatol. Sci.*, **2017**, *85* (3), 152–161.
24. Khmaladze, I.; Leonardi, M.; Fabre, S.; Messaraa, C.; Mavon, A. The Skin Interactome: A Holistic "Genome-Microbiome-Exposome" Approach to Understand and Modulate Skin Health and Aging. *Clin. Cosmet. Investig. Dermatol.*, **2020**, *13*, 1021–1040.
25. Michalak, M.; Pierzak, M.; Kręcisz, B.; Suliga, E. Bioactive Compounds for Skin Health: A Review. *Nutrients*, **2021**, *13* (1), 203.
26. Yahya, N. A.; Attan, N.; Wahab, R. A. An Overview of Cosmeceutically Relevant Plant Extracts and Strategies for Extraction of Plant-Based Bioactive Compounds. *Food Bioprod. Process.*, **2018**, *112*, 69–85.
27. Burger, P.; Plainfossé, H.; Brochet, X.; Chemat, F.; Fernandez, X. Extraction of Natural Fragrance Ingredients: History Overview and Future Trends. *Chem. Biodivers.*, **2019**, *16* (10).
28. Bom, S.; Jorge, J.; Ribeiro, H. M.; Marto, J. A Step Forward on Sustainability in the Cosmetics Industry: A Review. *J. Clean. Prod.*, **2019**, *225*, 270–290.
29. Fonseca-Santos, B.; Corrêa, M. A.; Chorilli, M. Sustainability, Natural and Organic Cosmetics: Consumer, Products, Efficacy, Toxicological and Regulatory Considerations. *Brazilian J. Pharm. Sci.*, **2015**, *51* (1), 17–26.
30. Sajna, K. V.; Gottumukkala, L. D.; Sukumaran, R. K.; Pandey, A. White Biotechnology in Cosmetics. In *Industrial Biorefineries & White Biotechnology*; Pandey A., Höfer R., Taherzadeh M., Nampoothiri K. M., Larroche C., Eds.; Elsevier: Amsterdam, 2015; pp 607–652.
31. Gomes, C.; Silva, A. C.; Marques, A. C.; Sousa Lobo, J.; Amaral, M. H. Biotechnology Applied to Cosmetics and Aesthetic Medicines. *Cosmetics*, **2020**, *7* (2), 33.
32. Couraucci Neto, D.; Bueno De Camargo Junior, F.; Berardo Gonçalves Maia Campos, P. M. Spirulina-Containing Cosmetic Composition and Cosmetic Treatment Method, 2014.
33. Maia Campos, P. M. B. G.; Camargo Jr, F. B.; Corauce Neto, D. Composição Cosmética Contendo Spirulina, e, Método de Tratamento Cosmético. PI020110032394, 2016.
34. Delsin, S.; Mercurio, D.; Fossa, M. M.; Maia Campos, P. M. B. G. Clinical Efficacy of Dermocosmetic Formulations Containing Spirulina Extract on Young and Mature Skin: Effects on the Skin Hydrolipidic Barrier and Structural Properties. *Clin. Pharmacol. Biopharm.*, **2015**, *04* (04), 1–5.

35. Eibl, R.; Meier, P.; Stutz, I.; Schildberger, D.; Hühn, T.; Eibl, D. Plant Cell Culture Technology in the Cosmetics and Food Industries: Current State and Future Trends. *Appl. Microbiol. Biotechnol.*, **2018**, *102* (20), 8661–8675.
36. Kaul, S.; Gulati, N.; Verma, D.; Mukherjee, S.; Nagaich, U. Role of Nanotechnology in Cosmeceuticals: A Review of Recent Advances. *J. Pharm.*, **2018**, *2018*, 1–19.
37. Yang, S.; Liu, L.; Han, J.; Tang, Y. Encapsulating Plant Ingredients for Dermocosmetic Application: An Updated Review of Delivery Systems and Characterization Techniques. *Int. J. Cosmet. Sci.*, **2020**, *42* (1), 16–28.
38. Yapar, E. A. Herbal Cosmetics and Novel Drug Delivery Systems. *Indian J. Pharm. Educ. Res.*, **2017**, *51* (3s), s152–s158.
39. Siqueira César, F. C.; Carnevale Neto, F.; Porto, G. S.; Campos, P. M. Patent Analysis: A Look at the Innovative Nature of Plant-Based Cosmetics. *Quim. Nova*, **2017**, *40* (7), 840–847.
40. Pernet, G. Skin Diseases and Cosmetics. *BMJ*, **1911**, *1* (2630), 1242–1242.
41. Owuna, F. J. Stability of Vegetable Based Oils Used in the Formulation of Ecofriendly Lubricants—a Review. *Egypt. J. Pet.*, **2020**, *29* (3), 251–256.
42. Jimenez-Lopez, C.; Carpena, M.; Lourenço-Lopes, C.; Gallardo-Gomez, M.; Lorenzo, J. M.; Barba, F. J.; Prieto, M. A.; Simal-Gandara, J. Bioactive Compounds and Quality of Extra Virgin Olive Oil. *Foods*, **2020**, *9* (8), 1014.
43. Doan, C. D.; Tavernier, I.; Okuro, P. K.; Dewettinck, K. Internal and External Factors Affecting the Crystallization, Gelation and Applicability of Wax-Based Oleogels in Food Industry. *Innov. Food Sci. Emerg. Technol.*, **2018**, *45*, 42–52.
44. Fei, T.; Wang, T. A Review of Recent Development of Sustainable Waxes Derived from Vegetable Oils. *Curr. Opin. Food Sci.*, **2017**, *16*, 7–14.
45. de Freitas, C. A. S.; de Sousa, P. H. M.; Soares, D. J.; da Silva, J. Y. G.; Benjamin, S. R.; Guedes, M. I. F. Carnauba Wax Uses in Food—A Review. *Food Chem.*, **2019**, *291*, 38–48.
46. Alves, T. F. R.; Morsink, M.; Batain, F.; Chaud, M. V.; Almeida, T.; Fernandes, D. A.; da Silva, C. F.; Souto, E. B.; Severino, P. Applications of Natural, Semi-Synthetic, and Synthetic Polymers in Cosmetic Formulations. *Cosmetics*, **2020**, *7* (4), 75.
47. Maia Campos, P. M. B. G.; de Melo, M. O.; de Camargo Junior, F. B. Effects of Polysaccharide-Based Formulations on Human Skin. In *Polysaccharides*; Ramawat, K. G., Mérillon, J.-M., Eds.; Springer International Publishing: Cham, 2015; pp 2045–2064.
48. Rasheed, D. M.; Serag, A.; Abdel Shakour, Z. T.; Farag, M. Novel Trends and Applications of Multidimensional Chromatography in the Analysis of Food, Cosmetics and Medicine Bearing Essential Oils. *Talanta*, **2021**, *223*, 121710.
49. Sarkic, A.; Stappen, I. Essential Oils and Their Single Compounds in Cosmetics—A Critical Review. *Cosmetics*, **2018**, *5* (1), 11.
50. Falleh, H.; Ben Jemaa, M.; Saada, M.; Ksouri, R. Essential Oils: A Promising Eco-Friendly Food Preservative. *Food Chem.*, **2020**, *330*, 127268.
51. G. Mercurio, D.; A. L. Wagemaker, T.; Maia Campos, P. M. B. G. *Anacardium occidentale* L. Extract in Cosmetic Formulations: Benefits for Oily Skin. *J. Biomed. Biopharm. Res.*, **2017**, *14* (1), 75–87.
52. Belo, S. E. D.; Gaspar, L. R.; Campos, P. M. B. G. M. Photoprotective Effects of Topical Formulations Containing a Combination of *Ginkgo biloba* and Green Tea Extracts. *Phyther. Res.*, **2011**, *25* (12), 1854–1860.
53. Gianeti, M. D.; Mercurio, D. G.; Maia Campos, P. M. B. G. The Use of Green Tea Extract in Cosmetic Formulations: Not Only an Antioxidant Active Ingredient. *Dermatol. Ther.*, **2013**, *26* (3), 267–271.
54. Clark, K. B.; Wheelwright, S. C. Structuring the Development Funnel. In Revolutionizing Product Development: Quantum Leaps in Speed, Efficiency, and Quality; Wheelwright, S. C., Clark, K. B., Eds.; Simon & Schuster; New York, 1992.

55. Calixto, L. S.; Infante, V. H. P.; Maia Campos, P. M. B. G. Design and Characterization of Topical Formulations: Correlations Between Instrumental and Sensorial Measurements. *AAPS PharmSciTech*, **2018**, *19* (4), 1512–1519.
56. Carmo, A. C. M.; Pereira, R. S.; Gratieri, T. Brazilian Requirements for Stability Indicating Methods. *TrAC Trends Anal. Chem.*, **2018**, *98*, 58–63.
57. National Health Surveillance Agency ANVISA. *Cosmetic Products Stability Guide*, 1st ed.; National Health Surveillance Agency ANVISA: Brasilia, 2005; Vol. 1, p. 52.
58. Cosmetics Europe. *Guidelines for the Safety Assessment of a Cosmetic Product*; COLIPA Guidelines: Brussels, 2004.
59. Halla, N.; Fernandes, I.; Heleno, S.; Costa, P.; Boucherit-Otmani, Z.; Boucherit, K.; Rodrigues, A.; Ferreira, I.; Barreiro, M. Cosmetics Preservation: A Review on Present Strategies. *Molecules*, **2018**, *23* (7), 1571.
60. Huang, N. Rheological Characterization of Pharmaceutical and Cosmetic Formulations for Cutaneous Applications. *Curr. Pharm. Des.*, **2019**, *25* (21), 2349–2363.
61. Gore, E.; Picard, C.; Savary, G. Spreading Behavior of Cosmetic Emulsions: Impact of the Oil Phase. *Biotribology*, **2018**, *16*, 17–24.
62. Liu, H.; Xu, X. M.; Guo, S. D. Rheological, Texture and Sensory Properties of Low-Fat Mayonnaise with Different Fat Mimetics. *LWT—Food Sci. Technol.*, **2007**, *40* (6), 946–954.
63. Tai, A.; Bianchini, R.; Jachowicz, J. Texture Analysis of Cosmetic/Pharmaceutical Raw Materials and Formulations. *Int. J. Cosmet. Sci.*, **2014**, *36* (4), 291–304.
64. Varela, P.; Ares, G. Sensory Profiling, the Blurred Line between Sensory and Consumer Science. A Review of Novel Methods for Product Characterization. *Food Res. Int.*, **2012**, *48* (2), 893–908.
65. Serup, J. Efficacy Testing of Cosmetic Products*. *Ski. Res. Technol.*, **2001**, *7* (3), 141–151.
66. Cosmetics Europe. *Guidelines for the Evaluation of the Efficacy of Cosmetics Products*; COLIPA Guidelines: Brussels, 2008.
67. Berardesca, E.; Loden, M.; Serup, J.; Masson, P.; Rodrigues, L. M. The Revised EEMCO Guidance for the In Vivo Measurement of Water in the Skin. *Ski. Res. Technol.*, **2018**, *24* (3), 351–358.
68. Ohshima, H.; Kinoshita, S.; Oyobikawa, M.; Futagawa, M.; Takiwaki, H.; Ishiko, A.; Kanto, H. Use of Cutometer Area Parameters in Evaluating Age-Related Changes in the Skin Elasticity of the Cheek. *Ski. Res. Technol.*, **2013**, *19* (1), e238–e242.
69. Ryu, H. S.; Joo, Y. H.; Kim, S. O.; Park, K. C.; Youn, S. W. Influence of Age and Regional Differences on Skin Elasticity as Measured by the Cutometer. *Ski. Res. Technol.*, **2008**, *14* (3), 354–358.
70. Lévêque, J. EEMCO Guidance for the Assessment of Skin Topography. *J. Eur. Acad. Dermatology Venereol.*, **1999**, *12* (2), 103–114.
71. Pierard, G. E.; Uhoda, I.; Pierard-Franchimont, C. From Skin Microrelief to Wrinkles. An Area Ripe for Investigation. *J. Cosmet. Dermatol.*, **2003**, *2* (1), 21–28.
72. Sakuma, T. H.; Maibach, H. I. Oily Skin: An Overview. *Skin Pharmacol. Physiol.*, **2012**, *25* (5), 227–235.
73. Sainthillier, J.-M.; Mac Mary, S.; Le Maitre, M.; Humbert, P. Fotografia Digitale in Dermatologia Estetica. *EMC—Cosmetol. Medica e Med. degli Inestetismi Cutanei*, **2021**, *18* (1), 1–9.
74. Lee, H. K.; Seo, Y. K.; Baek, J. H.; Koh, J. S. Comparison between Ultrasonography (Dermascan C Version 3) and Transparency Profilometry (Skin Visiometer SV600). *Ski. Res. Technol.*, **2008**, *14* (1), 8–12.
75. Shahriari, N.; Grant-Kels, J. M.; Rabinovitz, H.; Oliviero, M.; Scope, A. Reflectance Confocal Microscopy. *J. Am. Acad. Dermatol.*, **2021**, *84* (1), 1–14.

76. Maia Campos, P. M. B. G.; Melo, M. O.; Siqueira César, F. C. Topical Application and Oral Supplementation of Peptides in the Improvement of Skin Viscoelasticity and Density. *J. Cosmet. Dermatol.*, **2019**, *18* (6), 1693–1699.
77. Leite, M. G. A.; Maia Campos, P. M. B. G. Photoprotective Effects of a Multifunctional Hair Care Formulation Containing Botanical Extracts, Vitamins, and UV Filters. *Photochem. Photobiol.*, **2018**, *94* (5), 1010–1016.
78. ANVISA. Guia Para Avaliação de Segurança de Produtos Cosméticos. *Anvisa*, **2012**, *2*, 1–71.

10 Uses of Herbal-Derived Products in the Food Sector

Karen Elbert Leal Mazza, Tamires Sousa de Oliveira, André Mesquita Magalhães Costa, Humberto Ribeiro Bizzo, and Renata Valeriano Tonon

CONTENTS

10.1 Introduction 255
10.2 Herbal Extracts and Essential Oils 256
10.3 Micro- and Nanoencapsulation of Herbal Extracts and Essential Oils 261
10.4 Application of Herbal Preparations in Food 268
  10.4.1 Antimicrobial and Antioxidant Agents 268
  10.4.2 Active Films and Coatings 270
10.5 Final Remarks 274
Acknowledgements 274
Abbreviations 274
References 275

10.1 INTRODUCTION

Recently a paradigm shift has been observed in the industry, especially in the food sector. Consumers have been demanding healthier natural products, free of synthetic additives, produced by eco-friendly and sustainable processes, instigated by a greater concern regarding health and environmental problems. This trend is observed in the continuous increase over the years in global sales of herbal products, and this market is estimated to reach US$5 trillion in 2050 [1].

Plants are a rich source of bioactive compounds such as alkaloids, phenolic compounds, and terpenoids. These compounds are associated with an extensive array of activities, such as anti-inflammatory, antiviral, antiproliferative, anticarcinogenic, antioxidant, anti-allergic, estrogenic-like, immune-stimulating, and antimicrobial [2 5].

In this context, the food industry has been focusing on herbal extracts and essential oils (EOs) with antioxidant and antimicrobial activities to develop natural additives, intending to increase the food shelf life and consumers acceptability. However, the bioactive compounds in herbal extracts and EOs are highly reactive and may

DOI: 10.1201/9781003225416-13

have low water solubility. Therefore, these compounds should be stabilised before their application in food products. The food sector has been using encapsulation technologies to enable herbal extracts and EOs applications [6], producing stable additives and ingredients capable of being easily added in different food matrices, including liquids, at any stage of the production process [7].

Supported by new developments in encapsulation techniques, herbal extracts and EOs have also been incorporated in active packaging and coatings, providing them with antimicrobial and antioxidant properties. The development of active films and coatings has received much attention due to their ability to delay deterioration, maintain food integrity, and prevent nutrient and aroma loss in food products. Furthermore, active packaging meets consumer criteria for sustainable products once they can be produced using food industry by-products or underutilised sources of biopolymers as filmogenic matrices [8, 9].

The purpose of this chapter is to present a comprehensive overview of the important applications of herbal extracts and EOs in food products, active films and coatings, and the perspectives in the area.

10.2 HERBAL EXTRACTS AND ESSENTIAL OILS

Spices and herbs play an important role as food preservatives and colourants. These characteristics led to the Age of Exploration, which sought ways to obtain these products to meet the high demand in some European countries, allowing the food storage/preservation for longer periods [10].

Plants have been part of the human diet for millennia [11]. Vegetables in the diet were initially important due to the energy provided by the primary metabolites, such as carbohydrates, lipids, and proteins [12, 13]. Moreover, people observed curative effects of some species, confirming the statement attributed to Hippocrates in the fifth century BC: “Let thy food be thy medicine and medicine be thy food” [14]. Therefore, some herbs are highly valued for their traditional medicinal effects [15].

Herbs comprise an outstanding source of chemical compounds with a wide range of bioactive properties [2–5]. These characteristics are conferred by secondary metabolites, which are compounds present in different plant parts, such as leaves, flowers, buds, seeds, twigs, bark, herbs, wood, fruits, and roots. The secondary metabolites are not involved in the essential biochemical metabolism of plants but exert important functions such as plant defence against microorganisms, insects and herbivores, and the attraction of pollinators [11]. Secondary metabolites major groups are alkaloids, phenolic compounds, and terpenoids, including volatile compounds. Additionally, each major group is further divided into several subclasses extensively explored in the literature [13].

Herbs can be consumed *in natura* or as extracts. Teas—infusion or decoction—and hydroalcoholic beverages are traditionally used [2, 5].

According to the International Organization for Standardization [16], an extract is a “product obtained by treating a natural raw material with one or several solvents”. In the daily diet of the population and folk medicine, phytochemicals are usually extracted with water and consumed as teas. On the other hand, for compound purification, extract standardisation, and bioactive investigative trials, methanol and ethanol are the most commonly used solvents [5, 17–19].

Besides extracts, EOs are also important compounds obtained from plants rich in volatile compounds (aromatic plants). EOs may be defined as volatile products obtained from vegetable raw materials by steam distillation, dry distillation, or, specifically for citrus fruits, by mechanical processing of the epicarp, after separation of the aqueous phase by a physical process, without the use of organic solvents (ISO, 2013); the industry follows this definition. EOs are, therefore, formed by a mixture of volatile compounds, mainly belonging to the terpene family, such as mono, di, and sesquiterpenoids, and by arylpropanoids, including alcohols, ketones, ethers, esters, aldehydes, phenols, and sulphur compounds. Some EO are very complex mixtures (e.g. vetiver EO), while others are simple (e.g. garlic oil). In addition to EO, the composition of the oil extracted from citrus fruits also contains non-volatile compounds, such as wax, skin pigments, flavonoids, and other lipophilic constituents [20–22].

The whole EOs, fractions, and isolated compounds have been extensively used in food and perfumery to impart flavour and fragrance characteristics to their products or raw materials for chemical transformations [23].

As mentioned earlier, the chemical arsenal of plants is associated with many biological activities. Relevant properties of herbal extracts and EOs are summarised in Table 10.1 and Table 10.2, respectively. Among them, antimicrobial and antioxidant are the most important ones due to their high potential application in the food sector [2, 17, 18]. These benefits are associated mainly with phenolic constituents of the herbal extracts and specific volatile components (terpenoids, phenolic compounds, and aldehydes) present in EOs [21, 24].

Herbal extracts and EOs have emerged as promising food additives due to their ability to reduce food oxidation, microbial spoilage, and improve sensory quality [21, 46, 47].

The antimicrobial properties of herbal extracts and EO are commonly exploited for food preservation to inhibit the growth of pathogenic and food spoilage microorganisms. Thus, the product shelf life is extended without needing synthetic preservatives, also avoiding high energy preservation methods that could compromise nutritional food value [45]. The antimicrobial mechanism of action of EO constituents is not fully understood, but it is assumed that these compounds interact with components of microorganism cell membranes leading to membrane disruption and leaking [48].

The antioxidant activity of phytochemicals has also been extensively studied due to their potential to protect the organisms from free radicals (reactive oxygen species, reactive nitrogen species) that cause damaging events and contribute to health problems, such as DNA damage, atherosclerosis, and liver cirrhosis [49]. The antioxidant activity of herbal extracts and EOs is widely applied in the food industry, as lipids and proteins oxidation impact the sensory and nutritional food quality, producing undesirable aroma, flavours, and texture changes [50]. Deterioration of polyunsaturated fatty acids and the formation of residual products, as lipid-derivative volatiles and malondialdehyde, can occur in the food product's preparation, storage, and distribution [20].

TABLE 10.1
Notorious Plant Extracts and Their Potential Biological Activity

Plants	Biological Activity	Solvent	Reference
Agathosma betulina, Datura stramonium, Salacia leptoclada, Schotia brachypetala, Asparagus virgatus, Crotalaria lanceolata, Grewia occidentalis, Callilepis lauréola, Pachycarpus rigidus, Warburgia salutaris, Siphonochilus aethiopicus, Ocotea bullata, Croton gratissimus	Antioxidant (ESR (OH• radical reduction) and DPPP (lipid peroxidation))	Water (infusions) and methanol	[25]
Apium graveolens, Solidago virgaurea, Artemisia dracunculus, Helichrysum arenarium, Achillea millefolium, Onopordum acanthium, Calendula officinalis, Berberis vulgaris, Sambucus ebulus, Vaccinium myrtillus, Galega officinalis, Astragalus glycyphyllos, Mentha spicata, Ocimum basilicum, Polygonum aviculare, Alchemilla vulgaris, Fragaria vesca, Crataegus monogyna, Rosa canina, Cydonia vulgaris, Prunus spinosa, Veronica officinalis, Euphrasia officinalis	Antioxidant (ABTS)	Water (infusion)	[26]
Emilia sonchifolia, Adenostemma lavenia, Blumea balsamifera, Vernonia patula, Ixeris chinensis, Tithonia diversifolia, Siegesbeckia orientalis, Leucas mollissima, Plectranthus amboinicus, Prunella vulgaris, Sida rhombifolia, Hibiscus taiwanensis, Jussiaea repens, Ludwigia octovalvis, Justicia procumbens, Saurauia oldhamii, Bombax malabaricum, Kyllinga brevifolia, Cajanus cajan, Indian pipe, *Rubus parvifolius, Zanthoxylum nitidum, Lindernia anagallis, Solanum verbascifolium, Pteris multifida, Vitis thunbergii*	Antioxidant (DPPH and superoxide anion scavenging activity)	Methanol	[27]
Origanum vulgare, Melissa officinalis, Lavandula angustifolia, Inula helenium, Verbascum phlomoides, Salvia officinalis, Rosmarinus officinalis, Thymus vulgaris, Hypericum perforatum, Mentha longifolia	Antioxidant (DPPH)	Methanol	[28]
Acacia nilotica, Terminalia arjuna, Eucalyptus globulus, Syzygium aromaticum, Cinnamomum zeylanicum	Antibacterial and antifungal (*Escherichia coli, Klebsiella pneumoniae, Candida albicans, Streptococcus mutans, Staphylococcus aureus, Enterococcus faecalis, Streptococcus bovis, Pseudomonas aeruginosa*, and *Salmonella typhimurium*	Ethanol	[18]
Pistacia lentiscus, Thymus vulgaris, Evodia rutaecarpa	Antimicrobial (*S. aureus, Streptococcus pyogenes, E. coli, Proteus mirabilis, Pseudomonas aeruginosa*, and *Candida albicans*)	Ethanol	[29]

(Continued)

TABLE 10.1 ***(Continued)***
Notorious Plant Extracts and Their Potential Biological Activity

Plants	Biological Activity	Solvent	Reference
Phyllanthus emblica, Camellia sinensis, Mangifera indica, Punica granatum, Acacia catechu	Hepatoprotective (*t*-BH-induced cytotoxicity) and antioxidant (ORAC, ABTS, DPPH, CAA)	Methanol, ethyl acetate, ethanol, water, acetone	[17]
Larrea cuneifolia, Zuccagnia punctata, Tetraglochin andina, Larrea nitida, Larrea divaricata	Antimicrobial (*Candida albicans*, *C. glabrata*, *C. tropicalis*, *Saccharomyces cerevisiae*, *C. parapsilosis*, and *C. krusei*) Anti-inflammatory (hydroperoxide) and antioxidant (ABTS, oxidative haemolysis protection, hydrogen peroxide scavenging, and hydroxyl radical scavenge)	Ethanol	[2]
Hibiscus sabdariffa, Withania somnifera, Ocimum sanctum, Emblica officinalis, Allium sativum, Ginkgo biloba	Antioxidant (DPPH, ABTS and FRAP) and ACE (angiotensin-converting enzymes) inhibition	Water	[30]
Camellia sinensis var. *sinensis, Ilex paraguariensis, Aspalathus linearis*	Antioxidant (ORAC, FRAP, FCRC, DPPH, Cu^{2+} chelation, lipoperoxidation), cytotoxic/antiproliferative (against cancer cells), inhibition of α-amylase, α-glucosidase, and angiotensin I-converting enzymes, and inhibition of DNA-induced fission of the peroxyl radical	Water	[31]

Abbreviations: ESR = Electron spin resonance spectrometry; DPPP = Diphenyl-1-pyrenylphosphine; ABTS = 2, 2'-azino-bis (3-ethylbenzothiazoline-6-sulphonic acid); *t*-BH = tert-butyl hydroperoxide; ORAC = Oxygen radical antioxidant capacity; CAA = Cellular antioxidant activity; FRAP = Ferric reducing/antioxidant power; FCRC = Folin–Ciocalteu reducing capacity; DPPH = 2, 2-diphenyl-1-picrylhydrazyl; HORAC = Hydroxyl radical adverting capacity.

TABLE 10.2
Notorious Herbal Essential Oils: Their Major Constituents and Associated Activities

Herbal Essential Oil	Major Constituents	Antioxidant	Antimicrobial	Ref
Coriandrum sativum	δ-3-Carene, γ-Terpinene	No or little DPPH, No, or little ferric reducing power	*B. thermosphacta*, *E. coli*, *L. innocua*, *Listeria monocytogenes*, *P. putida*, *S. typhimurium*, *S. putrefaciens*	[32]
Citrus paradise	Limonene	No or little DPPH, No, or little ferric reducing power	*B. thermosphacta*, *E. coli*, *L. innocua*, *Listeria monocytogenes*, *P. putida*, *S. typhimurium*, *S. putrefaciens*	[32]
Citrus limon	Limonene, α-Phellandrene	No or little DPPH, No or little ferric reducing power	*B. thermosphacta*, *L. innocua*, *Listeria monocytogenes*, *P. putida*, *S. typhimurium*, *S. putrefaciens*	[32]
Citrus sinensis	Limonene	—	*Listeria monocytogenes*	[33]
Mentha piperita	— Menthol, Menthone	DPPH, reducing power, ABTS/H_2O_2/HRP	*S. aureus*, *Streptococcus pyogenes*, *Klebsiella pneumonia*	[34]
		DPPH, hydroxyl radical	—	[35]
Origanum vulgare	*p*-Cymene, Limonene, Carvacrol, Linalool, Thymol	—	—	[36]
	Linalool, Carvacrol, Thymol	High ORAC	—	[37]
	—	ORAC, HORAC	*L. monocytogenes*, *B. cereus*, *S. aureus*, *E. faecalis*, *E. coli*, *S. cerevisiae*	[38]
	Carvacrol	—	*Lactobacillus delbrueckii*	[39]
	Carvacrol	—	*Zygosaccharomyces bailii*	[40]
Cymbopogon citratus	—	—	*E. coli*, *S. aureus*, *L. monocytogenes*, *S. enteritidis*	[41]
	Neral, geranial	—	*E. coli*, *S. aureus*	[42]
Caryophyllus aromaticus or *Syzygium aromaticum*	—	—	*E. coli*, *S. aureus*, *L. monocytogenes*, *S. Enteritidis*	[41]
	Eugenol	High ORAC	—	[37]
	Eugenol, β-Caryophyllene, α-Caryophyllene	High DPPH scavenging capacity and low hydroxyl radical inhibition	*S. aureus*, *E. coli*, *L. monocytogenes*, *S. typhimurium*	[43]
	trans-Caryophyllene, Acetyl-eugenol, Eugenol	High DPPH, High ferric reducing power	*B. thermosphacta*, *E. coli*, *L. innocua*, *Listeria monocytogenes*, *P. putida*, *S. typhimurium*, *S. putrefaciens*	[32]

(Continued)

TABLE 10.2 ***(Continued)***
Notorious Herbal Essential Oils: Their Major Constituents and Associated Activities

Herbal Essential Oil	Major Constituents	Antioxidant	Antimicrobial	Ref
Cymbopogon winterianus	Citronellal, Geraniol, Citronellol	No or little ORAC	—	[37]
	Citronellal, Geraniol, Citronellol	—	*Bacillus subtilis, Staphylococcus epidermidis, S. aureus, Pseudomonas aeruginosa, Klebsiella pneumonia, E. coli*	[44]
Rosmarinus officinalis	β-Pinene, Camphor, Camphene	No or little ORAC	—	[37]
	Limonene, α-Pinene, Camphor, Linalool	DPPH, hydroxyl radical, Lipid Peroxidation	*C. albicans, T. mentagrophytes, T. tonsurans, T. rubrum, E. floccosum, M. canis, P. aeruginosa, E. coli, S. typhi, S. enteritidis, S. sonei, M. flavus, S. lutea, S. aureus, S. epidermidis, B. subtilis*	[45]
	Eucalyptol, Camphor, Bornyl acetate, β-Caryophyllene	No or little DPPH, No or little Ferric reducing power	*B. thermosphacta, E. coli, L. innocua, Listeria monocytogenes, P. putida, S. typhimurium, S. putrefaciens*	[32]

Abbreviations: ORAC = Oxygen radical antioxidant capacity; DPPH = 2, 2-diphenyl-1-picrylhydrazyl; HORAC = Hydroxyl radical adverting capacity; HRP = Horseradish peroxidase.

10.3 MICRO- AND NANOENCAPSULATION OF HERBAL EXTRACTS AND ESSENTIAL OILS

Herbal extracts and EOs are recognised sources of a wide range of bioactive phytochemicals; however, in some cases, the bioactive compounds should not be added directly to food because of their low solubility in free form and high volatility. Additionally, some phytochemicals are highly reactive and may lose their antimicrobial and antioxidant activity due to some processing conditions (presence of light, high temperatures, and pH) and interactions with other compounds in the food, such as specific enzymes and metallic ions. Lastly, direct addition may negatively impact the sensory and textural aspects of food products. The main factors that can affect the stability of the bioactive compounds are presented in Table 10.3 [6].

Therefore, some herbal extracts and EOs should be protected and stabilised before addition in food products to maintain the desired functions of their bioactive constituents [6]. The food industry has been using encapsulation technologies to enable the application of these plant-based natural additives in food products. Encapsulation is a "packing" technique in which an active ingredient (core) is covered by a wall

TABLE 10.3
Factors Affecting the Stability of Selected Bioactive Compounds

Class or Subclass of Compounds	Factors That Affect Bioactive Compounds Stability	Reference
Anthocyanins	High pH, atmospheric oxygen, heat treatment, UV light exposure, presence of specific enzymes, and some metallic ions	[6]
Flavonols	High pH, heat treatment, and exposure to oxygen and light	[6]
Flavan-3-ols	High pH, atmospheric oxygen, and heat treatment.	[6]
Proanthocyanidins	Acid pH and atmospheric oxygen	[6]
Phenolic acid derivatives	Heat treatment	[51]
Curcumin	Neutral and alkaline pH, heat treatment, exposure to light, metallic ions, enzymes, and oxygen.	[6]
Stilbenes	Heat treatments	[52]
Terpenoids	Acid pH and heat treatments	[53]

material, resulting in a stable additive/ingredient capable of being easily added in different food matrices in any stage of the production process [7]. The encapsulated compound is named core or active ingredient, while the covering material is usually defined as wall material, wall system, encapsulant matrix, or carrier agent. According to the desired application, the core and the wall material can be composed of one or more ingredients. The encapsulant matrix may be formed by one or more layers [7]. Encapsulated particles may be classified according to their sizes in: macro- (>5,000 μm), micro- (0.2-5,000 μm), and nano- (<0.2 μm) particles [54].

Encapsulation is often used in the food sector to protect some compounds from adverse processing and storage conditions (light, moisture, oxygen, and UV radiation) and prevent their interaction with other food components. For example, encapsulated methanolic extracts containing polyphenols from *Cordyline terminalis* and *Myristica fragrans* preserved their antioxidant activity and total polyphenolic content for one year at room temperature [55]. This technology also enables controlled release, delivering the active ingredient in the right place at the right time. Recently, a water-soluble extract of *Emblica officinalis* was encapsulated by double emulsion and the *in vitro* simulated digestion indicated that particles resisted the simulated salivary and gastric digestion, releasing the core only in the absorption site [56]. Additionally, encapsulation can mask flavours, which is very convenient when dealing with herbal extracts rich in astringent phenolic compounds such as proanthocyanidins and EOs with a high content of volatile compounds [6, 32].

Encapsulation methods are usually classified according to their manufacturing processes as:

- *Physical*: Spray drying, spray cooling, spray chilling, fluidised bed coating, extrusion, freeze-drying, co-crystallisation, and emulsification

- *Chemical*: Interfacial polycondensation, *in situ* polymerisation, interfacial polymerisation, interfacial cross-linking, and molecular inclusion
- *Physicochemical*: Hot melt coating, ionic gelation, electrospinning, solvent evaporation, simple or complex coacervation, and liposome entrapment

The selection of the encapsulation method is based on economic factors, core sensibility, and the desired microparticles application [11, 57]. Different encapsulation techniques have been applied to herbal extracts and EOs (Table 10.4). Consequently, the industry has filed and published many patents covering the most distinct encapsulation techniques, such as complex coacervation, emulsification, ionic gelation, and spray drying [58–62]. Spray drying is the most common method used in the food industry due to its flexibility, low cost, and ability to produce high-quality particles [12].

Spray drying is a continuous method in which a solution or emulsion containing the core and wall system is atomised in a drying chamber where a hot air flow is injected concurrently with the liquid, promoting fast sample dehydration. In this process, the liquid quickly turns into a free-flowing powder and the atomised droplets maintain a mild temperature throughout the operation [84].

Herbal extracts and EOs encapsulated by spray drying usually show high retention of phenolic and volatile compounds, great antioxidant activity, good solubility, and thermal stability [57, 64, 67, 69, 70]. Fegnoglio et al. [73] encapsulated an antioxidant yerba mate (*Illex paraguariensis*) extract by freeze-drying and spray drying, using maltodextrin as wall material. Maltodextrin efficiently protected the yerba mate polyphenols against oxidation in both encapsulation techniques. The spray-dried microparticles showed superior properties, such as lower moisture content and higher polyphenol content compared to freeze-dried products. The dry products were added to a real food matrix (mayonnaise). The spray-dried microparticles increased the mayonnaise shelf life by 250% compared to the control (without extract addition). A slightly lower increase in mayonnaise shelf life (206%) was observed with the freeze-dried microparticles.

Ghosh et al. [71] designed a polyherbal extract with antimicrobial and antioxidant activity from a blend of tulsi leaves (*Ocimum sanctum*), bay leaves (*Cinnamomum tamala*), and small cardamom seeds (*Elettaria cardamomum*) by using the extraction by supercritical carbon dioxide. The mixture was encapsulated by spray drying using maltodextrin:gum Arabic (60:40) as a wall system. The results showed that the encapsulation process significantly increased the extract shelf life. The antioxidant markers compounds (eugenol and 1,8-cineole) in the encapsulated extract showed a half lifetime of 231 days at room temperature (23 ± 2°C), and 63 days in the non-encapsulated extract. The authors proposed to use the encapsulated extract as a natural food antioxidant.

Spray drying has been a cost-effective method to stabilise EOs, confer protection against oxidation, and increase their thermal stability and solubility. Cortés-Camargo et al. [68] encapsulated lemon (*Citrus aurantifolia* Swingle) EO by spray drying using mesquite gum and nopal mucilage as wall systems. The produced particles showed good physicochemical properties (acceptable moisture content, high volatile retention, and encapsulation efficiency) and protected the EO from oxidation for

TABLE 10.4
Summary of Recent Studies on Major Encapsulation Techniques Applied to Herbal Extracts and Essential Oils

Encapsulation Method	Plant Species	Solvent	Wall System	Main Results	Reference
Acid precipitation	*Cordyline terminalis* and *Myristica fragrans*	Methanol	Casein beads	Beads' polyphenol content and antioxidant activity remained stable for 1 year.	[55]
Molecular inclusion	*Polygonum cuspidatum*	Methanol	β-cyclodextrin	Particles showed high: • Water dispersibility; • Stability; • Antioxidant activity.	[63]
Spray drying	*Ilex paraguariensis*	Water	—	Particles showed high: • Antioxidant activity; • Total phenolic content.	[64]
	Rosmarinus officinalis EO	—	Whey protein isolate and Inulin	Whey protein isolate/inulin blends of 1:1 and 3:1 proved to be effective carriers to entrap rosemary essential oil	[65]
	Orthosiphon stamineus	Methanol	Whey protein and maltodextrin	Wall system components protected *Orthosiphon stamineus*'s phenolics from thermal degradation during drying	[66]
	Zingiber officinale EO	—	Gum Arabic, maltodextrin and inulin	Particles showed high wettability and encapsulation efficiency and low hygroscopicity.	[67]
	Citrus aurantifolia EO	—	Mesquite gum and nopal mucilage	Particles showed high: • Volatile retention; • Encapsulation efficiency; • Thermal stability; Encapsulation protected the oil from oxidation during eight weeks of storage at 35°C.	[68]
	Camellia sinensis	Water	Maltodextrin	Particles showed high: • Antioxidant activity; • Total phenolic content.	[69]

(Continued)

TABLE 10.4 *(Continued)*
Summary of Recent Studies on Major Encapsulation Techniques Applied to Herbal Extracts and Essential Oils

Encapsulation Method	Plant Species	Solvent	Wall System	Main Results	Reference
	Cinnamomum zeylanicum EO	—	Whey protein, maltodextrin and gum Arabic	Particles showed high: • Cinnamaldehyde retention; • Thermal stability.	[70]
Spray drying	*Ocimum sanctum*, *Cinnamomum tamala*, *Elettaria cardamomum* (polyherbal mix)	Supercritical carbon dioxide extraction	Maltodextrin and gum Arabic	Particles showed high: • Extract retention; • Total phenolic content; • Antioxidant activity; Storage stability (231.4 days).	[71]
	Olea europaea	Ethanol	Alginate	Encapsulation promoted the controlled release in the gastrointestinal tract, increasing compounds bioaccessibility and bioavailability.	[72]
	Ilex paraguariensis	Ethanol	Maltodextrin	Particles were produced by freeze-drying in the same conditions; Particles produced by spray drying showed higher polyphenol content properties than freeze-drying particles and showed a higher increase in mayonnaise's oxidative stability.	[73]
Ionic gelation	*Urtica dioica*, *Crataegus laevigata*, *Rubus idaeus*, *Olea europea*, *Achillea millefolium*, and *Glechoma hederacea*	Water	Alginate–chitosan copolymer microbeads	Beads showed high: • Extract retention; • Antioxidant activity.	[74]

(Continued)

TABLE 10.4 *(Continued)*
Summary of Recent Studies on Major Encapsulation Techniques Applied to Herbal Extracts and Essential Oils

Encapsulation Method	Plant Species	Solvent	Wall System	Main Results	Reference
	Thymus serpyllum	Water	Alginate beads	Beads demonstrated high retention.	[75]
	Plectranthus ecklonii, Plectranthus grandidentatus, Plectranthus ornatus, Plectranthus porcatus, and Plectranthus saccatus	Water	Alginate beads	Beads showed high: • Extract retention; • Antioxidant activity; • Acetylcholinesterase inhibition.	[76]
	Thymus serpyllum EO	—	Chitosan microbeads	Microbeads demonstrated sustained release.	[77]
	Stevia rebaudiana	Water	Alginate beads	Alginate beads showed stable total phenolic content and antioxidant activity during 30 days of storage at 4°C.	[78]
Ionic gelation and spray chilling	*Camellia sinensis*	Water	• Ionic gelation (Pectin) • Spray chilling (palm oil and fully hydrogenated and interesterified vegetable oil)	Spray chilling microparticles demonstrated higher encapsulation efficiency and antioxidant activity.	[79]
Double emulsion (DE)	*Emblica officinalis*	Water	Water-in-oil-in-water (W_1/O/W_2)	The DE delivery system promoted a controlled release of *Emblica officinalis* bioactive components.	[56]
Liposome	*Syzygium aromaticum* EO	—	Soy lecithin and cholesterol	Liposome-encapsulated clove oil showed higher shelf life than non-encapsulated clove oil and inhibited *S. aureus* proliferation in tofu.	[80]

(Continued)

TABLE 10.4 ***(Continued)***
Summary of Recent Studies on Major Encapsulation Techniques Applied to Herbal Extracts and Essential Oils

Encapsulation Method	Plant Species	Solvent	Wall System	Main Results	Reference
	Cymbopogon citratus EO	—	Soy lecithin and cholesterol	Liposome-encapsulated lemongrass oil showed antimicrobial activity against *L. monocytogenes* in cheese, and the liposome addition did not affect the physical and sensory properties of the food	[81]
Spouted bed	*Rosmarinus officinalis*	Ethanol	Maltodextrin and HiCap 100	Particles showed high: • Extract retention; • Antioxidant activity; • Solubility.	[82]
Nanoemulsion	*Hyssopus officinalis*	Ethanol	*Lepidium perfoliatum* seed gum and *Orchis mascula*	*Hyssopus officinalis* encapsulated extract was applied in soybean oil and reduced oil oxidation for 40 days of storage at 60°C.	[83]

Abbreviation: EO = essential oil.

eight weeks of storage at 35°C. The wall system also increased lemon's EO thermal stability by acting as a physical barrier preventing oil volatilisation and oxidation.

Recently, aiming at applying EOs with antimicrobial and antioxidant properties in foods, the emulsification technique has gained attention from the food sector. This current enthusiasm is associated with new techniques, namely nanoemulsions and Pickering emulsions, and their potential use in active films and coatings. Emulsions are formed by two immiscible liquids, being one of the liquids dispersed as small spherical droplets in the other. According to the disperse and the continuous phases, they are classified in oil-in-water (O/W) or water-in-oil (W/O) emulsions. Even though with emulsifiers addition, they tend to be physically and thermodynamically unstable due to large droplet sizes (201 nm–100 μm). In this context, nanoemulsions and Pickering emulsions emerge as more stable alternatives to delivery systems [85–87].

The use of EOs in nanoemulsions potentialises their antimicrobial effect, considering the higher surface area per volume observed in this form. Therefore, lower amounts are necessary, representing an advantage from the economic and sensory points of view. The higher efficiency of nanoemulsions concerning the pure EO is also related to the better interaction with the cell membrane. According to Donsí and Ferrari [48], the fusion of the small droplets of the nanoemulsions with the phospholipid bilayer of the microorganisms facilitates their access through the membrane surface, allowing their rupture and leading to cell death. Anwer et al. [88] observed that the clove EO nanoemulsion showed greater antimicrobial activity against several microorganisms when compared to pure EO. Pongsumpun et al. [89] reported that cinnamon EO nanoemulsions showed greater antifungal activity than the conventional emulsion, with inhibition halos more than twice larger.

Unlike traditional emulsions, in which a thin layer of surfactant covers the droplets, Pickering emulsions are stabilised by solid particles, forming a thicker interface layer, leading to higher stability against physical and thermal destabilisation [90]. Along with nanoemulsions, they have been applied in the development of active films and coatings.

Fasihi [91] applied the Pickering stabilisation method to incorporate cinnamon EO (*Cinnamomum zeylanicum*) in a carboxymethyl cellulose-polyvinyl alcohol-based film to obtain a film with antioxidant and antifungal properties. The produced film showed UV inhibitory effect, besides antioxidant and antifungal activity. When this film was applied in bread slices, it completely suppressed fungal growth in all tested concentrations of EO during 15 days of storage at 25°C. The film without EO incorporation did not inhibit fungal growth.

Almasi et al. [92] developed pectin films activated by nanoemulsion and Pickering emulsion stabilised marjoram (*Origanum majorana* L.) EO. Both types of films showed good results. The Pickering emulsion films showed a slower release profile and better mechanical and water barrier properties, while the nanoemulsions demonstrated higher antioxidant activity.

10.4 APPLICATION OF HERBAL PREPARATIONS IN FOOD

10.4.1 Antimicrobial and Antioxidant Agents

The food industries use several technologies to apply natural preservatives to different food products, such as meats, fish, fruits, beverages, and dairy products like ice cream, desserts, yoghurts, fermented milk, and cheeses [50, 93–95].

Some products enriched with herbal preparations can be found in the market. Some examples are fermented milk with aqueous lemongrass preparation (Danone®); a yoghurt enriched with coriander, cornflour, garlic purée, black pepper, and sunflower oil (Tesco®); an aloe vera juice enriched with amla, tulsi, and ginger (International Marketing Corporation [IMC]), and a juice tea blend (Juicy Juice®).

Many studies bring new approaches with good perspectives for the development of novel products. Ivanišová et al. [93] investigated the application of five variants of apple juice enriched by herbal extracts containing phenolic acids and flavonoids. They blended 60% of apple juice with 40% of an herbal aqueous extract, choosing as herbs: mint (*Mentha piperita* L.), lemon balm (*Melissa officinalis* L.), oregano (*Origanum vulgare* L.), wild thymus (*Thymus serpyllum* L.), and sage (*Salvia officinalis* L.). This application had positive biological and sensory effects, showing improved antioxidant activity and good acceptability in the sensory tests.

Taking into account the importance of probiotic cultures preservation in products during storage, Chaikham [96] evaluated the stability of encapsulated probiotics (*Lactobacillus casei* 01, *Lactobacillus acidophilus* LA5, and *Bifidobacterium lactis* Bb-12) added in fruit juices (mulberry, maoberry, longan, and melon). The probiotics were co-encapsulated with plant extracts (cashew flower [*Anacardium occidentale* L.], yanang [*Tiliacora triandra*], pennywort [*Centella asiatica* (Linn.) Urban], and green tea [*Camellia sinensis* L.]) in alginate beads. Among the herbal extracts, green tea and cashew flowers increased the survival of the probiotics in the beads.

One of the major problems of using EOs in food products is their ability to affect the sensory characteristics due to the high content of intense aromatic compounds. In this sense, Donsì [97] encapsulated a mixture of terpenes from *Melaleuca alternifolia* oil and limonene in nanometric delivery systems and evaluated their application in pear and orange juices inoculated with *L. delbrueckii*. Results showed that nanoencapsulated EOs at low concentrations delayed microbial growth or inactivated the microorganisms without significantly changing the fruit juices sensory characteristics. These results corroborate the effectiveness of encapsulation techniques in masking strong flavours and enhancing the functionality of some compounds.

EOs can also be employed in the bakery industry, as reported by Gonçalves et al., [98] in research evaluating the antimicrobial activity of thyme (*Thymus vulgaris*) EO encapsulated by complex coacervation and its potential application as a cake preservative. The microencapsulated EO reduced all the microorganisms tested *in vitro* (*Candida albicans*, *Enterococcus faecium*, *Enterococcus hirae*, *Escherichia coli*, *Salmonella choleraesuis*, *Staphylococcus aureus*, *Salmonella typhimurium*, *Pseudomonas aeruginosa*, and *Aspergillus niger*) and increased cake shelf life without the use of synthetic preservatives.

The short shelf life of fruits is a great concern. In this context, Li et al. [99] had evaluated the impact of Perilla *frutescens* (L.) Britt. encapsulated EO produced by ionic gelation on strawberries preservation. The authors also assessed the antimicrobial activity against *E. coli*, *S. aureus*, and *B. subtilis*. Perilla EO inhibited bacterial strains growth and delayed strawberry decay, minimising nutrient losses and preserving the fruit flavour and quality.

The current demand for healthier products is present in all food sectors, including dairy products. Among the scientific studies, Ribeiro [100] investigated the antioxidant activity of aqueous and hydroalcoholic extracts of *Rosmarinus officinalis* L. (rosemary). The aqueous extract was chosen to be applied in cottage cheese as a functional ingredient due to its higher phenolic content and antioxidant activity. The aqueous extract was added directly or after encapsulation by atomisation/coagulation. Both forms (free and microencapsulated) showed antioxidant activity and did not affect cheese nutritional value. However, the microencapsulated extract was more effective to maintain the antioxidant properties during storage.

Innovative opportunities for the use of herbal-derived products are also emerging in the ice cream market. As an example, Chanmchan et al. [101] evaluated the incorporation of lemongrass (*Cymbopogon citratus*) or ginger (*Zingiber officinale*) extract to obtain an ice cream reduced in sugars. Along with antioxidant activity, they conducted a sensory evaluation based on a 9-point hedonic scale. Herbs application added antioxidant activity to the product and resulted in healthier ice cream with low sugar content. Additionally, the sensory evaluation indicated good acceptance of both herbal ice cream with 15% of extracts.

Safety and quality are also particularly important for seafood products. Fish is extremely perishable, mainly because of microbiological growth and lipid oxidation during processing or storage [94]. Mazandrani et al. [102] analyzed pure and liposomal encapsulated fennel extract and their effect on the quality of silver carp fillets. The authors evaluated the properties of the encapsulated fennel extract (encapsulation efficacy, antioxidant, and antimicrobial activities) and the carp fillets during 15 days of storage at 4°C. Encapsulated fennel reduced lipid oxidation and microbial spoilage in fish during storage, suggesting its potential use as a natural additive.

Regarding meat products, Busatta et al. [103] investigated the effect of marjoram EO in the fresh sausage as a natural antimicrobial agent. The authors tested the EOs in 10 selected aerobic heterotrophic bacterial species *in vitro* and *E. coli* inoculated in fresh sausage. Marjoram EO had a bacteriostatic effect in all the concentrations studied, including for the inoculated *E. coli*. However, higher EO concentrations changed sensory product characteristics.

Recent patents also show the potential use of EOs. For instance, Sandri et al. [104] patented the use of lemongrass and tangerine EOs into ice cream composition, and a patent from Wang et al. [105] showed the use of *Mentha spicata* EO for beverage preservation.

10.4.2 Active Films and Coatings

The main function of films and coatings is to protect the food against physical deterioration and modify the atmosphere and gases exchanges, reducing the respiration rate and increasing product shelf life. Recently, the development of active films and coatings has been reported as promising alternatives for maximising the preservation of food products. They consist of films and coatings incorporated with active substances, such as antioxidant and antimicrobial agents, which improve food quality and further increase its shelf life, allowing for a longer commercialisation time, which is essential in exportation products.

Herbal extracts and EOs have been largely applied in the production of active films and coatings. However, the addition of EOs can present negative sensory effects and low dispersibility, resulting in very heterogeneous materials. The use of EOs in nanoemulsions may minimise these problems, allowing a better dispersion in the filmogenic solution. It may also enhance its antimicrobial and antioxidant effect, probably due to the greater contact surface area by volume reached by EOs loaded in nanoemulsions. In recent years, there has been an increase in investments and research on functional characteristics of films and coatings aimed at food preservation. Active agents are incorporated in the matrix of films and coatings, defining and enhancing their functionality. These active films and coatings could increase shelf life, improve food quality, and ensure greater stability and safety for food products. These benefits are generated according to various characteristics of the active agents used. In this context, studies reported in the literature have shown that EOs, e.g., from clove and citrus fruits, inhibited the growth of *S. aureus* [106, 107]. Other active agents have the antioxidant capacity and therefore can inhibit the oxidation of lipids that causes changes in the odour and taste of many foods. Rosemary EO has some compounds, such as monoterpenes and derivatives (e.g. carnosol and carnosic acid), which confer high antioxidant activity [108], as well as some phenolic compounds from sage extracts [109].

The slow release of the active compounds present in films and coatings can delay the degradation of food and eliminate undesirable compounds from lipid and protein oxidation. Active films and coatings are widely used to cover many food products to assess the antimicrobial, anti-shrink, colouring, flavouring, and antioxidant effects. For example, Naponucena et al. [110] applied soluble coffee (0.76%), cocoa powder (0.22%), and propolis extract (0.82%) in different formulations of active edible coatings for muffins without synthetic additives and succeeded to control the development of fungi and yeasts under accelerated conditions (40 days). Table 10.5 shows some interesting studies in which herbal extracts and EOs have been applied as active agents in films and coatings for foods. The constituents of the extracts and EOs contribute to the chemical stability and maintenance of the quality of various food products.

The antioxidant and antimicrobial effect of the alcoholic extract of red propolis in biodegradable films for cheese and butter has also been reported. Active films could limit the growth of coagulase-positive staphylococci in cheese and delay the oxidation of butter [130].

The *trans*-cinnamaldehyde from cinnamon EO was incorporated into a coating for minimally processed melon peels and pulp and significantly reduced the growth of deteriorating microorganisms during the analyzed period [131].

The extract of the pomegranate peel (*Punica granatum*) was incorporated into coatings for tilapia fillets and increased their shelf life, and caused an improvement in chemical, physical, and microbiological stability [132]. The methanolic extracts of green tea and rosemary were also applied to the coating of tilapia fillets, reducing the oxidative processes of proteins and lipids and increasing the fillet's shelf life [133].

Fried prawns showed lower lipid peroxidation products and a lower degree of hardness when treated with a coating loaded with thymol, a terpenoid from thyme or oregano [134].

The EOs of thyme and garlic incorporated in edible coatings had positive effects on water retention, colour stability, and decreased lipid oxidation of lamb [135]. In this study, the EO of thyme was important in protecting against oxidative damage. Furthermore, in the work of Emiroğlu et al. [122], this EO incorporated in edible film and applied to ground meat reduced the count of *Pseudomonas* spp.

Clove EO incorporated in an edible coating for papaya fruits improved sensory characteristics, such as odour and taste [136]. Clove EO was also incorporated in an edible coating for salmon carpaccio and inhibited the growth of *Enterobacteria* [117].

Many studies in active food coatings have been patented, reassuring the potential of this technology. As an example, Barreto et al. [137] succeed in filing for a patent on the application of grape marc extract in polymeric films based on sodium alginate and pectin. Another patent showed promising results in forming a biodegradable film with pine (*Araucaria angustifolia*) shell extract, generating an edible food packaging [138].

TABLE 10.5
Main Applications of Active Edible Films and Coatings

Biopolymers	Type	Active Agent	Application	Main Results	References
Chitosan	Film	*Camellia sinensis* extract	Pork sausages	Increased shelf life, control of lipid oxidation, and microbial growth.	[111]
	Coating	*Vaccinium* spp. leaf extract	Blueberry	Antifungal effect with the decrease in the rate of deterioration.	[112]
	Coating	*Cymbopogon citratus* EO	Grape berry	Antimicrobial effect and the maintenance of colour.	[113]
	Coating	*Citrus paradisi* seed extract	Cherry tomatoes (*cv. Koko*)	Control of weight loss and antimicrobial effect.	[114]
	Coating	*Citrus limon* EO	Strawberry (*cv. Camarosa*)	Alteration of the metabolic pathway, volatile profile, and antifungal effect.	[115]
Chitosan and alginate	Coating	*Punica granatum* extract	Guava (*cv. Allahabad safeda*)	Maintenance of antioxidant activity and reduced rate of respiration and deterioration.	[116]
Chitosan and gelatin	Film	*Syzygium aromaticum* EO	Salmon carpaccio	Growth retardation of *Pseudomonas*, inhibition of *Enterobacteriaceae*, and lipid oxidation.	[117]
	Coating	*Flourensia cernua* extract	Tomato	Increase the shelf life. Antimicrobial effect. Reduce the respiration rate and ethylene production.	[118]
Chitosan and Hydroxypropyl methyl cellulose	Coating	*Citrus bergamia* EO	Table grapes	Improvement in weight loss and fruit firmness. Control of microbial activity.	[119]
Zein	Film	*Punica granatum* extract	Himalayan cheese	Delay in the oxidation reactions and microbial spoilage during storage.	[120]
Keratin and gelatin	Film	*Syzygium aromaticum* EO	Smoked salmon	Antimicrobial properties against *E. coli* O157:H7 and *Listeria monocytogenes*.	[121]

(Continued)

TABLE 10.5 *(Continued)*
Main Applications of Active Edible Films and Coatings

Biopolymers	Type	Active Agent	Application	Main Results	References
Soy protein isolate	Film	*Thymus vulgaris* EO, *Origanum heracleoticum* EO	Ground beef	*E. coli*, E. coliO157:H7, and *S. aureus* were significantly inhibited by antimicrobial films; *Lactobacillus plantarum* and *Pseudomonas aeruginosa* appeared to be the more resistant bacteria.	[122]
Carboxymethyl cellulose	Coating	*Eucalyptus staigeriana* EO, *Lippia sidoides* EO and *Pimenta pseudocaryophyllus* EO	Papaya	Increase the shelf life. Antifungal effect. Maintain the phytosanitary quality.	[123]
	Coating	*Moringa oleifera* leaf and seed extract	Avocado (cv. Fuerte and Hass)	Firmness and weight loss retention. Reduce the respiration rate. Antimicrobial effect. Increase the shelf life.	[124]
	Coating	*Rosmarinus officinalis* EO	Smoked eel	*Pseudomonas* growth inhibition.	[125]
	Coating	*Thymus vulgaris* EO and *Ocimum basilicum* EO	Roasted sunflower seeds	Improved sensory stability of roasted sunflower seeds during storage, but only thyme EO increased their chemical stability.	[126]
Pectin	Film	*Lippia graveolens* EO	Tomatoes (cv. Saladette)	Antifungal effect. Increase the total phenolic content and antioxidant activity.	[127]
Hydroxypropyl methylcellulose	Film	*Origanum heracleoticum* EO and *Citrus bergamia risso* EO	Fresh Formosa plum	Significantly inhibited the increase in the total bacterial count of apples during storage.	[128]
Whey protein	Coating	*Origanum virens* EO	Sausages	Significantly inhibited the growth of foodborne pathogens in the sausage.	[129]

Abbreviation: EO = essential oil.

These results show that the same extract or EO can be applied to different products and provide different effects. The variety of extracts and EOs allows the industry to develop tailor-made active packaging to improve the final quality and shelf life of different food products. Plant extracts and EOs proved to be promising in preventing food spoilage, and when incorporated into active films and coatings for foods, they can be a functional and sustainable alternative for the packaging industry.

10.5 FINAL REMARKS

The application of herbal extracts and EOs in food products is a reality, which was made possible mainly using encapsulation technologies. In particular, the food industry has used phytochemicals to increase the durability and acceptability of various products. The data presented in this chapter indicate the potential of application of herbal extracts and EOs with antimicrobial and antioxidant activity in a wide range of products such as juices, dairy products, roasted, and meat products.

Active films and coatings applied to fruits, meat products, and cheeses can prevent the loss of weight and firmness of the product, delay oxidation, inhibit microorganism's growth, and reduce the respiration rate of fruits. Therefore, edible films and coatings are emerging as a sustainable technology with great potential for application in the packaging industry.

However, this technology is still embryonic, requiring more research and development to reach an industrial scale.

In summary, stimulated by a current demand of consumers for healthier and more natural products, the food industry has relied on herbal extracts and EOs to provide cost-effective phytochemicals to act as antimicrobial and antioxidant preservatives. The industry has consistently increased the use of herbal extracts and EOs in food products, and this area is growing exponentially. Although some encapsulation technologies, such as spray drying, have produced natural preservatives ready for large-scale production, the use of these ingredients as active in edible packaging still needs more research to fully reach the consumer market.

ACKNOWLEDGEMENTS

This work was supported by Coordination for the Improvement of Higher Education Personnel—Brazil—CAPES (Finance code 001, Grant number 88887.474265/2020-00), Foundation for Research Support of the State of Rio de Janeiro—FAPERJ (Grant numbers E-26/200.399/2020, E-26/202.325/2019, and E-26/202.710/2019), and The National Council for Scientific and Technological Development—CNPq (Grant numbers 310659/2018-3 and 310248/2018-3).

ABBREVIATIONS

ABTS 2, 2'-azino-bis (3-ethylbenzothiazoline- 6-sulphonic acid)
CAA cellular antioxidant activity
DPPH 2, 2-diphenyl-1- picrylhydrazyl
DPPP diphenyl-1-pyrenylphosphine

EO essential oil
ESR electron spin resonance spectrometry
FCRC folin-Ciocalteu reducing capacity
FRAP ferric reducing/antioxidant power
HORAC hydroxyl radical adverting capacity
HRP horseradish peroxidase
ORAC oxygen radical antioxidant capacity
***t*-BH** tert-butyl hydroperoxide

REFERENCES

1. Nirmal, S. A.; Pal, S. C.; Otimenyin, S.; Aye, T.; Elachouri, M.; Kundu, S. K.; Thandavarayan, R. A.; Mandal, S. C. Contribution of Herbal Products in Global Market. *Pharma Rev.*, **2013** (November-December), 95–104.
2. Moreno, M. A.; Zampini, I. C.; Isla, M. I. Antifungal, Anti-Inflammatory and Antioxidant Activity of Bi-Herbal Mixtures with Medicinal Plants from Argentinean Highlands. *J. Ethnopharmacol.*, **2020**, *253* (October 2019), 112642.
3. Morsy, N. F. S.; Abd El-Salam, E. A. Antimicrobial and Antiproliferative Activities of Black Pepper (*Piper Nigrum L.*) Essential Oil and Oleoresin. *J. Essent. Oil-Bearing Plants*, **2017**, *20* (3), 779–790.
4. Barba, F. J.; Zhu, Z.; Koubaa, M.; Sant'Ana, A. S.; Orlien, V. Green Alternative Methods for the Extraction of Antioxidant Bioactive Compounds from Winery Wastes and By-Products: A Review. *Trends Food Sci. Technol.*, **2016**, *49*, 96–109.
5. Atoui, A. K.; Mansouri, A.; Boskou, G.; Kefalas, P. Tea and Herbal Infusions: Their Antioxidant Activity and Phenolic Profile. *Food Chem.*, **2005**, *89* (1), 27–36.
6. Jia, Z.; Dumont, M. J.; Orsat, V. Encapsulation of Phenolic Compounds Present in Plants Using Protein Matrices. *Food Biosci.*, **2016**, *15*, 87–104.
7. Gouin, S. Microencapsulation: Industrial Appraisal of Existing Technologies and Trends. *Trends Food Sci. Technol.*, **2004**, *15* (7–8), 330–347.
8. Jeya Jeevahan, J.; Chandrasekaran, M.; Venkatesan, S. P.; Sriram, V.; Britto Joseph, G.; Mageshwaran, G.; Durairaj, R. B. Scaling up Difficulties and Commercial Aspects of Edible Films for Food Packaging: A Review. *Trends Food Sci. Technol.*, **2020**, *100*, 210–222.
9. Pilar, H. M.; CatalÁ, R.; Gavara, R. Food Aroma Partition between Packaging Materials and Fatty Food Simulants. *Food Addit. Contam.*, **2001**, *18* (7), 673–682.
10. Ceylan, E.; Fung, D. Y. C. Antimicrobial Activity of Spices. *J. Rapid Methods Autom. Microbiol.*, **2004**, *12* (1), 1–55.
11. Dima, C.; Dima, S. Essential Oils in Foods: Extraction, Stabilization, and Toxicity. *Curr. Opin. Food Sci.*, **2015**, *5*, 29–35.
12. Munin, A.; Edwards-Lévy, F. Encapsulation of Natural Polyphenolic Compounds; a Review. *Pharmaceutics*, **2011**, *3* (4), 793–829.
13. Shitan, N. Secondary Metabolites in Plants: Transport and Self-Tolerance Mechanisms. *Biosci. Biotechnol. Biochem.*, **2016**, *80* (7), 1283–1293.
14. Witkamp, R. F.; van Norren, K. Let Thy Food Be Thy Medicine….When Possible. *Eur. J. Pharmacol.*, **2018**, *836* (June), 102–114.
15. Dubick, M. A. Historical Perspectives on the Use of Herbal Preparations to Promote Health. *J. Nutr.*, **1986**, *116* (7), 1348–1354.
16. International Organization for Standardization (ISO). *Aromatic Natural Raw Materials – Vocabulary: ISO 9235*. Geneva, **2013**. p. 8.
17. Deepak, H. B.; Chandrasekaran, C. V.; Dethe, S.; Mundkinajeddu, D.; Pandre, M. K.; Balachandran, J.; Agarwal, A. Hepatoprotective and Antioxidant Activity of Standardized Herbal Extracts. *Pharmacogn. Mag.*, **2012**, *8* (30), 116–123.

18. Khan, R.; Islam, B.; Akram, M.; Shakil, S.; Ahmad, A.; Ali, S. M.; Siddiqui, M.; Khan, A. U. Antimicrobial Activity of Five Herbal Extracts against Multi Drug Resistant (MDR) Strains of Bacteria and Fungus of Clinical Origin. *Molecules*, **2009**, *14* (2), 586–597.
19. Kiselova, Y.; Ivanova, D.; Chervenkov, T.; Gerova, D.; Galunska, B.; Yankova, T. Correlation between the *In Vitro* Antioxidant Activity and Polyphenol Content of Aqueous Extracts from Bulgarian Herbs. *Phytother. Res.*, **2006**, *20*, 961–965.
20. Jayasena, D. D.; Jo, C. Potential Application of Essential Oils as Natural Antioxidants in Meat and Meat Products: A Review. *Food Rev. Int.*, **2014**, *30* (1), 71–90.
21. Pandey, A. K.; Kumar, P.; Singh, P.; Tripathi, N. N.; Bajpai, V. K. Essential Oils: Sources of Antimicrobials and Food Preservatives. *Front. Microbiol.*, **2017**, *7* (January), 1–14.
22. Asbahani, A. El; Miladi, K.; Badri, W.; Sala, M.; Addi, E. H. A.; Casabianca, H.; Mousadik, A. El; Hartmann, D.; Jilale, A.; Renaud, F. N. R.; et al. Essential Oils: From Extraction to Encapsulation. *Int. J. Pharm.*, **2015**, *483* (1–2), 220–243.
23. Bizzo, H. R.; Hovell, A. M. C.; Rezende, C. M. Oleos Essenciais No Brasil: Aspectos Gerais, Desenvolvimento e Perspectivas. *Quim. Nova*, **2009**, *32* (3), 588–594.
24. Maqsood, S.; Benjakul, S.; Shahidi, F. Emerging Role of Phenolic Compounds as Natural Food Additives in Fish and Fish Products. *Crit. Rev. Food Sci. Nutr.*, **2013**, *53* (2), 162–179.
25. Steenkamp, V.; Grimmer, H.; Semano, M.; Gulumian, M. Antioxidant and Genotoxic Properties of South African Herbal Extracts. *Mutat. Res. - Genet. Toxicol. Environ. Mutagen.*, **2005**, *581* (1–2), 35–42.
26. Jang, M. H.; Piao, X. L.; Kim, J. M.; Kwon, S. W.; Park, J. H. Inhibition of Cholinesterase and Amyloid-beta; Aggregation by Resveratrol Oligomers from *Vitis Amurensis*. *Phytother. Res.*, **2008**, *22* (4), 544–549.
27. Shyur, L.-F.; Tsung, J.-H.; Chen, J.-H.; Chiu, C.-Y.; Lo, C.-P. Antioxidant Properties of Extracts from Medicinal Plants Populrly Used in Taiwan. *Int. J. Appl. Sci. Eng. Int. J. Appl. Sci. Eng*, **2005**, *3* (3), 195–202.
28. Spiridon, I.; Bodirlau, R.; Teaca, C. A. Total Phenolic Content and Antioxidant Activity of Plants Used in Traditional Romanian Herbal Medicine. *Cent. Eur. J. Biol.*, **2011**, *6* (3), 388–396.
29. Thuille, N.; Fille, M.; Nagl, M. Bactericidal Activity of Herbal Extracts. *Int. J. Hyg. Environ. Health*, **2003**, *206* (3), 217–221.
30. Chaudhary, N.; Sabikhi, L.; Hussain, A.; Kumar M H, S. A Comparative Study of the Antioxidant and ACE Inhibitory Activities of Selected Herbal Extracts. *J. Herb. Med.*, **2020**, *22* (November 2018), 100343.
31. Santos, J. S.; Escher, G. B.; Vieira do Carmo, M.; Azevedo, L.; Boscacci Marques, M.; Daguer, H.; Molognoni, L.; Inés Genovese, M.; Wen, M.; Zhang, L.; et al. A New Analytical Concept Based on Chemistry and Toxicology for Herbal Extracts Analysis: From Phenolic Composition to Bioactivity. *Food Res. Int.*, **2020**, *132* (February), 109090.
32. Teixeira, B.; Marques, A.; Ramos, C.; Neng, N. R.; Nogueira, J. M. F.; Saraiva, J. A.; Nunes, M. L. Chemical Composition and Antibacterial and Antioxidant Properties of Commercial Essential Oils. *Ind. Crops Prod.*, **2013**, *43* (1), 587–595.
33. Geraci, A.; Di Stefano, V.; Di Martino, E.; Schillaci, D.; Schicchi, R. Essential Oil Components of Orange Peels and Antimicrobial Activity. *Nat. Prod. Res.*, **2017**, *31* (6), 653–659.
34. Singh, R.; Shushni, M. A. M.; Belkheir, A. Antibacterial and Antioxidant Activities of *Mentha piperita* L. *Arab. J. Chem.*, **2015**, *8* (3), 322–328.
35. Schmidt, E.; Bail, S.; Buchbauer, G.; Stoilova, I.; Atanasova, T.; Stoyanova, A.; Krastanov, A.; Jirovetz, L. Chemical Composition, Olfactory Evaluation and Antioxidant Effects of Essential Oil from *Mentha* x *Piperita*. *Nat. Prod. Commun.*, **2009**, *4* (8), 1107–1112.

36. Baranauskiene, R.; Venskutonis, P. R.; Dewettinck, K.; Verhé, R. Properties of Oregano (*Origanum vulgare* L.), Citronella (*Cymbopogon nardus* G.) and Marjoram (*Majorana hortensis* L.) Flavours Encapsulated into Milk Protein-Based Matrices. *Food Res. Int.*, **2006**, *39* (4), 413–425.
37. Bentayeb, K.; Vera, P.; Rubio, C.; Nerín, C. The Additive Properties of Oxygen Radical Absorbance Capacity (ORAC) Assay: The Case of Essential Oils. *Food Chem.*, **2014**, *148*, 204–208.
38. Da Costa, S. B.; Duarte, C.; Bourbon, A. I.; Pinheiro, A. C.; Serra, A. T.; Martins, M. M.; Januário, M. I. N.; Vicente, A. A.; Delgadillo, I.; Duarte, C.; et al. Effect of the Matrix System in the Delivery and in Vitro Bioactivity of Microencapsulated Oregano Essential Oil. *J. Food Eng.*, **2012**, *110* (2), 190–199.
39. Can Baser, K. Biological and Pharmacological Activities of Carvacrol and Carvacrol Bearing Essential Oils. *Curr. Pharm. Des.*, **2008**, *14* (29), 3106–3119.
40. Chavan, P. S.; Tupe, S. G. Antifungal Activity and Mechanism of Action of Carvacrol and Thymol against Vineyard and Wine Spoilage Yeasts. *Food Control*, **2014**, *46*, 115–120.
41. Barbosa, L. N.; Rall, V. L. M.; Fernandes, A. A. H.; Ushimaru, P. I.; Da Silva Probst, I.; Fernandes, A. Essential Oils against Foodborne Pathogens and Spoilage Bacteria in Minced Meat. *Foodborne Pathog. Dis.*, **2009**, *6* (6), 725–728.
42. Leimann, F. V.; Gonçalves, O. H.; Machado, R. A. F.; Bolzan, A. Antimicrobial Activity of Microencapsulated Lemongrass Essential Oil and the Effect of Experimental Parameters on Microcapsules Size and Morphology. *Mater. Sci. Eng. C.*, **2009**, *29* (2), 430–436.
43. Radünz, M.; da Trindade, M. L. M.; Camargo, T. M.; Radünz, A. L.; Borges, C. D.; Gandra, E. A.; Helbig, E. Antimicrobial and Antioxidant Activity of Unencapsulated and Encapsulated Clove (*Syzygium aromaticum,* L.) Essential Oil. *Food Chem.*, **2019**, *276*, 180–186.
44. Timung, R.; Ranjan, C.; Purohit, S.; Goud, V. V. Composition and Antibacterial Activity Analysis of Citronella Oil Obtained by Hydrodistillation: Process Optimization Study. *Ind. Crop. Prod.*, **2016**, *94*, 178–188.
45. Bozin, B.; Mimica-Dukic, N.; Samojlik, I.; Jovin, E. Antimicrobial and Antioxidant Properties of Rosemary and Sage (*Rosmarinus officinalis* L. and *Salvia officinalis* L., Lamiaceae) Essential Oils. *J. Agric. Food Chem.*, **2007**, *55*, 7879–7885.
46. Gutierrez, J.; Barry-Ryan, C.; Bourke, P. The Antimicrobial Efficacy of Plant Essential Oil Combinations and Interactions with Food Ingredients. *Int. J. Food Microbiol.*, **2008**, *124* (1), 91–97.
47. Reyes-Jurado, F.; Franco-Vega, A.; Ramírez-Corona, N.; Palou, E.; López-Malo, A. Essential Oils: Antimicrobial Activities, Extraction Methods, and Their Modeling. *Food Eng. Rev.*, **2015**, *7* (3), 275–297.
48. Donsì, F.; Ferrari, G. Essential Oil Nanoemulsions as Antimicrobial Agents in Food. *J. Biotechnol.*, **2016**, *233*, 106–120.
49. Adhikari, S.; Priyadarsini, K. I.; Mukherjee, T. Physico-Chemical Studies on the Evaluation of the Antioxidant Activity of Herbal Extracts and Active Principles of Some Indian Medicinal Plants. *J. Clin. Biochem. Nutr.*, **2007**, *40* (3), 174–183.
50. Umaraw, P.; Munekata, P. E. S.; Verma, A. K.; Barba, F. J.; Singh, V. P.; Kumar, P.; Lorenzo, J. M. Edible Films/Coating with Tailored Properties for Active Packaging of Meat, Fish and Derived Products. *Trends Food Sci. Technol.*, **2020**, *98*, 10–24.
51. Elhamirad, A. H.; Zamanipoor, M. H. Thermal Stability of Some Flavonoids and Phenolic Acids in Sheep Tallow Olein. *Eur. J. Lipid Sci. Technol.*, **2012**, *114* (5), 602–606.
52. Liazid, A.; Palma, M.; Brigui, J.; Barroso, C. G. Investigation on Phenolic Compounds Stability during Microwave-Assisted Extraction. *J. Chromatogr. A*, **2007**, *1140* (1–2), 29–34.

53. Jerković, I.; Kuś, P. M. Terpenes in Honey: Occurrence, Origin and Their Role as Chemical Biomarkers. *RSC Adv.*, **2014**, *4* (60), 31710–31728.
54. King, A. H. Encapsulation of Food Ingredients—a Review of Available Technology, Focusing on Hydrocolloids. *Encapsulation Control. Release Food Ingredients*, **1995**, *590*, 26–39.
55. Chandrasekhar Reddy, B.; Noor, A.; Sarada, N. C.; Vijayalakshmi, M. A. Antioxidant Properties of *Cordyline terminalis* (L.) Kunth and *Myristica fragrans* Houtt. Encapsulated Separately into Casein Beads. *Curr. Sci.*, **2011**, *101* (3), 416–420.
56. Chaudhary, N.; Sabikhi, L.; Hussain, S. A. Emblicanin Rich *Emblica officinalis* Extract Encapsulated Double Emulsion: Controlled Release of Bioactive during Phagocytosis and in Vitro Digestion. *J. Food Sci. Technol.*, **2020**, *57* (4), 1371–1381.
57. Botrel, D. A.; Vilela Borges, S.; Victória de Barros Fernandes, R.; Dantas Viana, A.; Maria Gomes da Costa, J.; Reginaldo Marques, G. Evaluation of Spray Drying Conditions on Properties of Microencapsulated Oregano Essential Oil. *Int. J. Food Sci. Technol.*, **2012**, *47* (11), 2289–2296.
58. Jafari, S. M.; Assadpoor, E.; He, Y.; Bhandari, B. Encapsulation Efficiency of Food Flavours and Oils during Spray Drying. *Dry. Technol.*, **2008**, *26* (7), 816–835.
59. Casanova, H.; Zapata, C. A. P. Method for Producing Colloidosome Microcapsules. Assignee: Nextia S.A.S. and Universidad de Antoquia. US 20190001294A1. Filed in 18 June 2016. Published in 3 January 2019.
60. Preveraud, D.; Rosilio, V. Nanocapsules comprising a liposoluble active ingredient, production and uses. Assignee: Adisseo France S.A.S. US 20190083414A1. Filed in 17 March 2017. Published in 21 March 2019.
61. Normand, V.; Rada, A.; Schober, A.; Subramaniam, A. Preparation of dried particles comprising menthol. Assignee: Firmenich SA. US 20160165937A1. Filed in 28 May 2014. Published in 16 June 2016.
62. Given, P. Delivery and controlled release of encapsulated water-insoluble flavorants. Assignee: Pepsico Inc. US 20100272859A1. Filed in 28 August. 2007. Published in 28 October 2010.
63. Mantegna, S.; Binello, A.; Boffa, L.; Giorgis, M.; Cena, C.; Cravotto, G. A One-Pot Ultrasound-Assisted Water Extraction/Cyclodextrin Encapsulation of Resveratrol from *Polygonum Cuspidatum*. *Food Chem.*, **2012**, *130* (3), 746–750.
64. Berté, K. A. S.; Beux, M. R.; Spada, P. K. W. D. S.; Salvador, M.; Hoffmann-Ribani, R. Chemical Composition and Antioxidant Activity of Yerba-Mate (*Ilex paraguariensis* A.St.-Hil., Aquifoliaceae) Extract as Obtained by Spray Drying. *J. Agric. Food Chem.*, **2011**, *59* (10), 5523–5527.
65. de Barros Fernandes, R. V.; Borges, S. V.; Botrel, D. A.; Oliveira, C. R. de. Physical and Chemical Properties of Encapsulated Rosemary Essential Oil by Spray Drying Using Whey Protein-Inulin Blends as Carriers. *Int. J. Food Sci. Technol.*, **2014**, *49* (6), 1522–1529.
66. Pang, S. F.; Yusoff, M. M.; Gimbun, J. Assessment of Phenolic Compounds Stability and Retention during Spray Drying of *Orthosiphon stamineus* Extracts. *Food Hydrocoll.*, **2014**, *37*, 159–165.
67. de Barros Fernandes, R. V.; Borges, S. V.; Silva, E. K.; da Silva, Y. F.; de Souza, H. J. B.; do Carmo, E. L.; de Oliveira, C. R.; Yoshida, M. I.; Botrel, D. A. Study of Ultrasound-Assisted Emulsions on Microencapsulation of Ginger Essential Oil by Spray Drying. *Ind. Crops Prod.*, **2016**, *94*, 413–423.
68. Cortés-Camargo, S.; Cruz-Olivares, J.; Barragán-Huerta, B. E.; Dublán-García, O.; Román-Guerrero, A.; Pérez-Alonso, C. Microencapsulation by Spray Drying of Lemon Essential Oil: Evaluation of Mixtures of Mesquite Gum–Nopal Mucilage as New Wall Materials. *J. Microencapsul.*, **2017**, *34* (4), 395–407.

69. Tengse, D. D.; Priya, B.; Kumar, P. A. R. Optimization for Encapsulation of Green Tea (*Camellia sinensis* L.) Extract by Spray Drying Technology. *J. Food Meas. Charact.*, **2017**, *11* (1), 85–92.
70. Felix, P. H. C.; Birchal, V. S.; Botrel, D. A.; Marques, G. R.; Borges, S. V. Physicochemical and Thermal Stability of Microcapsules of Cinnamon Essential Oil by Spray Drying. *J. Food Process. Preserv.*, **2017**, *41* (3), 1–9.
71. Ghosh, S.; Dutta, S.; Kumar Ghosh, P.; Bhattacharjee, P.; Das, S. Design of a Polyherbal Mix by Supercritical Carbon Dioxide Extraction and Its Encapsulation by Spray Drying: Phytochemical Properties and Shelf-Life Study of the Encapsulate. *J. Food Process Eng.*, **2017**, *40* (4), 1–15.
72. González, E.; Gómez-Caravaca, A. M.; Giménez, B.; Cebrián, R.; Maqueda, M.; Martínez-Férez, A.; Segura-Carretero, A.; Robert, P. Evolution of the Phenolic Compounds Profile of Olive Leaf Extract Encapsulated by Spray-Drying during *In Vitro* Gastrointestinal Digestion. *Food Chem.*, **2019**, *279* (November 2018), 40–48.
73. Fenoglio, D.; Soto Madrid, D.; Alarcón Moyano, J.; Ferrario, M.; Guerrero, S.; Matiacevich, S. Active Food Additive Based on Encapsulated Yerba Mate (*Ilex paraguariensis*) Extract: Effect of Drying Methods on the Oxidative Stability of a Real Food Matrix (Mayonnaise). *J. Food Sci. Technol.*, **2020**, 1–11.
74. Belšćak-Cvitanović, A.; Stojanović, R.; Manojlović, V.; Komes, D.; Cindrić, I. J.; Nedović, V.; Bugarski, B. Encapsulation of Polyphenolic Antioxidants from Medicinal Plant Extracts in Alginate-Chitosan System Enhanced with Ascorbic Acid by Electrostatic Extrusion. *Food Res. Int.*, **2011**, *44* (4), 1094–1101.
75. Stojanovic, R.; Belscak-Cvitanovic, A.; Manojlovic, V.; Komes, D.; Nedovic, V.; Bugarski, B. Encapsulation of Thyme (*Thymus serpyllum* L.) Aqueous Extract in Calcium Alginate Beads. *J. Sci. Food Agric.*, **2012**, *92* (3), 685–696.
76. Rijo, P.; Falé, P. L.; Serralheiro, M. L.; Simões, M. F.; Gomes, A.; Reis, C. Optimization of Medicinal Plant Extraction Methods and Their Encapsulation through Extrusion Technology. *Meas. J. Int. Meas. Confed.*, **2014**, *58*, 249–255.
77. Trifković, K. T.; Milašinović, N. Z.; Djordjević, V. B.; Krušić, M. T. K.; Knežević-Jugović, Z. D.; Nedović, V. A.; Bugarski, B. M. Chitosan Microbeads for Encapsulation of Thyme (*Thymus serpyllum* L.) Polyphenols. *Carbohydr. Polym.*, **2014**, *111*, 901–907.
78. Aceval Arriola, N. D.; De Medeiros, P. M.; Prudencio, E. S.; Olivera Müller, C. M.; De Mello Castanho Amboni, R. D. Encapsulation of Aqueous Leaf Extract of *Stevia rebaudiana* Bertoni with Sodium Alginate and Its Impact on Phenolic Content. *Food Biosci.*, **2016**, *13*, 32–40.
79. Cutrim, C. S.; Alvim, I. D.; Cortez, M. A. S. Microencapsulation of Green Tea Polyphenols by Ionic Gelation and Spray Chilling Methods. *J. Food Sci. Technol.*, **2019**, *56* (8), 3561–3570.
80. Cui, H.; Zhao, C.; Lin, L. The Specific Antibacterial Activity of Liposome-Encapsulated Clove Oil and Its Application in Tofu. *Food Control*, **2015**, *56*, 128–134.
81. Cui, H. Y.; Wu, J.; Lin, L. Inhibitory Effect of Liposome-Entrapped Lemongrass Oil on the Growth of *Listeria monocytogenes* in Cheese. *J. Dairy Sci.*, **2016**, *99* (8), 6097–6104.
82. Peshev, D.; Eichner, E.; Goslinska, M.; Pietsch, S.; Trambabova, Y.; Terzieva, T.; Georgieva, N.; Heinrich, S. Particle Formulation of Hydroalcoholic Rosemary (*Rosmarinus officinalis* L.) Extracts Using a Spouted Bed. *Particuology*, **2020**, *51*, 26–34.
83. Rezaei Savadkouhi, N.; Ariaii, P.; Charmchian Langerodi, M. The Effect of Encapsulated Plant Extract of Hyssop (*Hyssopus officinalis* L.) in Biopolymer Nanoemulsions of *Lepidium perfoliatum* and *Orchis mascula* on Controlling Oxidative Stability of Soybean Oil. *Food Sci. Nutr.*, **2020**, *8* (2), 1264–1271.

84. Reineccius, G. A. The Spray Drying of Food Flavors. *Dry. Technol.*, **2004**, *22* (6), 1289–1324.
85. McClements, D. J. Critical Review of Techniques and Methodologies for Characterization of Emulsion Stability. *Crit. Rev. Food Sci. Nutr.*, **2007**, *47* (7), 611–649.
86. Dickinson, E. Hydrocolloids as Emulsifiers and Emulsion Stabilizers. *Food Hydrocoll.*, **2009**, *23* (6), 1473–1482.
87. Given, P. S. Encapsulation of Flavors in Emulsions for Beverages. *Curr. Opin. Colloid Interface Sci.*, **2009**, *14* (1), 43–47.
88. Anwer, M. K.; Jamil, S.; Ibnouf, E. O.; Shakeel, F. Enhanced Antibacterial Effects of Clove Essential Oil by Nanoemulsion. *J. Oleo Sci.*, **2014**, *63* (4), 347–354.
89. Pongsumpun, P.; Iwamoto, S.; Siripatrawan, U. Response Surface Methodology for Optimization of Cinnamon Essential Oil Nanoemulsion with Improved Stability and Antifungal Activity. *Ultrason. Sonochem.*, **2020**, *60* (April 2019), 104604.
90. Berton-Carabin, C. C.; Schroën, K. Pickering Emulsions for Food Applications: Background, Trends, and Challenges. *Annu. Rev. Food Sci. Technol.*, **2015**, *6*, 263–297.
91. Fasihi, H.; Noshirvani, N.; Hashemi, M.; Fazilati, M.; Salavati, H.; Coma, V. Antioxidant and Antimicrobial Properties of Carbohydrate-Based Films Enriched with Cinnamon Essential Oil by Pickering Emulsion Method. *Food Packag. Shelf Life*, **2019**, *19* (August 2018), 147–154.
92. Almasi, H.; Azizi, S.; Amjadi, S. Development and Characterization of Pectin Films Activated by Nanoemulsion and Pickering Emulsion Stabilized Marjoram (*Origanum majorana* L.) Essential Oil. *Food Hydrocoll.*, **2020**, *99* (August 2019), 105338.
93. Ivanišová, E.; Frančáková, H.; Ritschlová, P.; Dráb, Š.; Solgajová, M.; Tokár, M. Biological Activity of Apple Juice Enriched by Herbal Extracts. *J. Microbiol. Biotechnol. Food Sci.*, **2015**, *4* (Special issue 3), 69–73.
94. Hassoun, A.; Emir Çoban, Ö. Essential Oils for Antimicrobial and Antioxidant Applications in Fish and Other Seafood Products. *Trends Food Sci. Technol.*, **2017**, *68*, 26–36.
95. Granato, D.; Santos, J. S.; Salem, R. D.; Mortazavian, A. M.; Rocha, R. S.; Cruz, A. G. Effects of Herbal Extracts on Quality Traits of Yogurts, Cheeses, Fermented Milks, and Ice Creams: A Technological Perspective. *Curr. Opin. Food Sci.*, **2018**, *19*, 1–7.
96. Chaikham, P. Stability of Probiotics Encapsulated with Thai Herbal Extracts in Fruit Juices and Yoghurt during Refrigerated Storage. *Food Biosci.*, **2015**, *12*, 61–66.
97. Donsì, F.; Annunziata, M.; Sessa, M.; Ferrari, G. Nanoencapsulation of Essential Oils to Enhance Their Antimicrobial Activity in Foods. *LWT—Food Sci. Technol.*, **2011**, *44* (9), 1908–1914.
98. Gonçalves, N. D.; Pena, F. de L.; Sartoratto, A.; Derlamelina, C.; Duarte, M. C. T.; Antunes, A. E. C.; Prata, A. S. Encapsulated Thyme (*Thymus vulgaris*) Essential Oil Used as a Natural Preservative in Bakery Product. *Food Res. Int.*, **2017**, *96*, 154–160.
99. Li, N.; Zhang, Z. J.; Li, X. J.; Li, H. Z.; Cui, L. X.; He, D. L. Microcapsules Biologically Prepared Using *Perilla frutescens* (L.) Britt. Essential Oil and Their Use for Extension of Fruit Shelf Life. *J. Sci. Food Agric.*, **2018**, *98* (3), 1033–1041.
100. Ribeiro, A.; Caleja, C.; Barros, L.; Santos-Buelga, C.; Barreiro, M. F.; Ferreira, I. C. F. R. Rosemary Extracts in Functional Foods: Extraction, Chemical Characterization and Incorporation of Free and Microencapsulated Forms in Cottage Cheese. *Food Funct.*, **2016**, *7* (5), 2185–2196.
101. Chanmchan, R.; Sinchaipanit, P.; Disnil, S.; Jittinandana, S.; Nitithamyong, A.; On-nom, N. Formulation of Reduced Sugar Herbal Ice Cream Using Lemongrass or Ginger Extract. *Br. Food J.*, **2017**, *119* (10), 2172–2182.
102. Mazandrani, H.A.; Javadian, S.R.; Bahram, S. The Effect of Encapsulated Fennel Extracts on the Quality of Silver Carp Fillets during Refrigerated Storage. *Food Sci. Nutr.*, **2016**, *4* (2), 298–304.

103. Busatta, C.; Vidal, R. S.; Popiolski, A. S.; Mossi, A. J.; Dariva, C.; Rodrigues, M. R. A.; Corazza, F. C.; Corazza, M. L.; Vladimir Oliveira, J.; Cansian, R. L. Application of *Origanum majorana* L. Essential Oil as an Antimicrobial Agent in Sausage. *Food Microbiol.*, **2008**, *25* (1), 207–211.
104. Sandri, I. G.; Piemolini-Barreto, L. T.; Baruffi, T. Uso de óleo essencial, composição alimentícia e processo de obtenção de composição alimentícia. Assignee: Fundação Universidade de Caxias do Sul. Brazil. BR 102015015325-2A2. Filed in 6 June 2015. Published on 3 January 2017.
105. Wang, Y.; Chen, S.; Zhang, Y.; He, Y.; Liu, Z.; Liu, X. A formula and preparation method of *Mentha spicata* essential oil used for beverage preservation. Assignee: Faming Zhuanli Shenqing, China. CN 104000275A. Filed on 16 May 2014. Published on 27 August 2014.
106. Sun, J. D-Limonene: Safety and Clinical Applications. *Altern. Med. Rev.*, **2007**, *12* (3), 259–264.
107. Yadav, M. K.; Chae, S. W.; Im, G. J.; Chung, J. W.; Song, J. J. Eugenol: A Phyto-Compound Effective against Methicillin-Resistant and Methicillin-Sensitive *Staphylococcus aureus* Clinical Strain Biofilms. *PLoS One*, **2015**, *10* (3), 1–21.
108. Martin-Piñero, M. J.; Ramirez, P.; Muñoz, J.; Alfaro, M. C. Development of Rosemary Essential Oil Nanoemulsions Using a Wheat Biomass-Derived Surfactant. *Colloids Surfaces B Biointerfaces*, **2019**, *173*, 486–492.
109. Nutrizio, M.; Gajdoš Kljusurić, J.; Badanjak Sabolović, M.; Bursać Kovačević, D.; Šupljika, F.; Putnik, P.; Semenčić Čakić, M.; Dubrović, I.; Vrsaljko, D.; Maltar-Strmečki, N.; et al. Valorization of Sage Extracts (*Salvia officinalis* L.) Obtained by High Voltage Electrical Discharges: Process Control and Antioxidant Properties. *Innov. Food Sci. Emerg. Technol.*, **2020**, *60* (September 2019).
110. Naponucena, L. de O. M.; Machado, B. A. S.; Saraiva, L. E. F.; Costa, S. S.; Silva, R. P. D.; Dantas, E. A.; Oliveira, R. S.; Druzian, J. I. Physicochemical and Microbiological Stability of Muffins Packed in Actives Edible Coatings from Cassava Starch: Inverted Sugar/Sucrose and Natural Additives. *African J. Biotechnol.*, **2019**, *18* (10), 206–219.
111. Siripatrawan, U.; Noipha, S. Active Film from Chitosan Incorporating Green Tea Extract for Shelf Life Extension of Pork Sausages. *Food Hydrocoll.*, **2012**, *27* (1), 102–108.
112. Yang, G.; Yue, J.; Gong, X.; Qian, B.; Wang, H.; Deng, Y.; Zhao, Y. Blueberry Leaf Extracts Incorporated Chitosan Coatings for Preserving Postharvest Quality of Fresh Blueberries. *Postharvest Biol. Technol.*, **2014**, *92*, 46–53.
113. Oh, Y. A.; Oh, Y. J.; Song, A. Y.; Won, J. S.; Song, K. Bin; Min, S. C. Comparison of Effectiveness of Edible Coatings Using Emulsions Containing Lemongrass Oil of Different Size Droplets on Grape Berry Safety and Preservation. *LWT—Food Sci. Technol.*, **2017**, *75*, 742–750.
114. Won, J. S.; Lee, S. J.; Park, H. H.; Song, K. Bin; Min, S. C. Edible Coating Using a Chitosan-Based Colloid Incorporating Grapefruit Seed Extract for Cherry Tomato Safety and Preservation. *J. Food Sci.*, **2018**, *83* (1), 138–146.
115. Perdones, A.; Escriche, I.; Chiralt, A.; Vargas, M. Effect of Chitosan-Lemon Essential Oil Coatings on Volatile Profile of Strawberries during Storage. *Food Chem.*, **2016**, *197*, 979–986.
116. Nair, M. S.; Saxena, A.; Kaur, C. Effect of Chitosan and Alginate Based Coatings Enriched with Pomegranate Peel Extract to Extend the Postharvest Quality of Guava (*Psidium guajava* L.). *Food Chem.*, **2018**, *240* (March 2017), 245–252.
117. Gómez-Estaca, J.; López-Caballero, M. E.; Martínez-Bartolomé, M. Á.; de Lacey, A. M. L.; Gómez-Guillen, M. C.; Montero, M. P. The Effect of the Combined Use of High Pressure Treatment and Antimicrobial Edible Film on the Quality of Salmon Carpaccio. *Int. J. Food Microbiol.*, **2018**, *283* (January), 28–36.

118. Salas-Méndez, E. de J.; Vicente, A.; Pinheiro, A. C.; Ballesteros, L. F.; Silva, P.; Rodríguez-García, R.; Hernández-Castillo, F. D.; Díaz-Jiménez, M. de L. V.; Flores-López, M. L.; Villarreal-Quintanilla, J. Á.; et al. Application of Edible Nanolaminate Coatings with Antimicrobial Extract of *Flourensia cernua* to Extend the Shelf-Life of Tomato (*Solanum lycopersicum* L.) Fruit. *Postharvest Biol. Technol.*, **2019**, *150* (December 2018), 19–27.
119. Sánchez-González, L.; Vargas, M.; González-Martínez, C.; Chiralt, A.; Cháfer, M. Use of Essential Oils in Bioactive Edible Coatings: A Review. *Food Eng. Rev.*, **2011**, *3* (1), 1–16.
120. Mushtaq, M.; Gani, A.; Gani, A.; Punoo, H. A.; Masoodi, F. A. Use of Pomegranate Peel Extract Incorporated Zein Film with Improved Properties for Prolonged Shelf Life of Fresh Himalayan Cheese (Kalari/Kradi). *Innov. Food Sci. Emerg. Technol.*, **2018**, *48* (2017), 25–32.
121. Song, N. B.; Lee, J. H.; Al Mijan, M.; Song, K. Bin. Development of a Chicken Feather Protein Film Containing Clove Oil and Its Application in Smoked Salmon Packaging. *LWT—Food Sci. Technol.*, **2014**, *57* (2), 453–460.
122. Emiroğlu, Z. K.; Yemiş, G. P.; Coşkun, B. K.; Candoğan, K. Antimicrobial Activity of Soy Edible Films Incorporated with Thyme and Oregano Essential Oils on Fresh Ground Beef Patties. *Meat Sci.*, **2010**, *86* (2), 283–288.
123. Zillo, R. R.; da Silva, P. P. M.; de Oliveira, J.; da Glória, E. M.; Spoto, M. H. F. Carboxymethylcellulose Coating Associated with Essential Oil Can Increase Papaya Shelf Life. *Sci. Hortic. (Amsterdam).*, **2018**, *239* (March), 70–77.
124. Ortiz-Duarte, G.; Pérez-Cabrera, L. E.; Artés-Hernández, F.; Martínez-Hernández, G. B. Ag-Chitosan Nanocomposites in Edible Coatings Affect the Quality of Fresh-Cut Melon. *Postharvest Biol. Technol.*, **2019**, *147* (September 2018), 174–184.
125. Azarakhsh, N.; Osman, A.; Ghazali, H. M.; Tan, C. P.; Mohd Adzahan, N. Lemongrass Essential Oil Incorporated into Alginate-Based Edible Coating for Shelf-Life Extension and Quality Retention of Fresh-Cut Pineapple. *Postharvest Biol. Technol.*, **2014**, *88*, 1–7.
126. Riveros, C. G.; Nepote, V.; Grosso, N. R. Thyme and Basil Essential Oils Included in Edible Coatings as a Natural Preserving Method of Oilseed Kernels. *J. Sci. Food Agric.*, **2016**, *96* (1), 183–191.
127. Rodriguez-Garcia, I.; Cruz-Valenzuela, M. R.; Silva-Espinoza, B. A.; Gonzalez-Aguilar, G. A.; Moctezuma, E.; Gutierrez-Pacheco, M. M.; Tapia-Rodriguez, M. R.; Ortega-Ramirez, L. A.; Ayala-Zavala, J. F. Oregano (*Lippia graveolens*) Essential Oil Added within Pectin Edible Coatings Prevents Fungal Decay and Increases the Antioxidant Capacity of Treated Tomatoes. *J. Sci. Food Agric.*, **2016**, *96* (11), 3772–3778.
128. Choi, W. S.; Singh, S.; Lee, Y. S. Characterization of Edible Film Containing Essential Oils in Hydroxypropyl Methylcellulose and Its Effect on Quality Attributes of "Formosa" Plum (*Prunus salicina* L.). *LWT—Food Sci. Technol.*, **2016**, *70*, 213–222.
129. Catarino, M. D.; Alves-Silva, J. M.; Fernandes, R. P.; Gonçalves, M. J.; Salgueiro, L. R.; Henriques, M. F.; Cardoso, S. M. Development and Performance of Whey Protein Active Coatings with *Origanum virens* Essential Oils in the Quality and Shelf Life Improvement of Processed Meat Products. *Food Control*, **2017**, *80*, 273–280.
130. Costa, S. S.; Druzian, J. I.; Machado, B. A. S.; De Souza, C. O.; Guimaraes, A. G. Bi-Functional Biobased Packing of the Cassava Starch, Glycerol, Licuri Nanocellulose and Red Propolis. *PLoS One*, **2014**, *9* (11).
131. Zhang, J.; Ozturk, S.; Singh, R. K.; Kong, F. Effect of Cellulose Nanofiber-Based Coating with Chitosan and Trans-Cinnamaldehyde on the Microbiological Safety and Quality of Cantaloupe Rind and Fresh-Cut Pulp. Part 1: Microbial Safety. *LWT—Food Sci. Technol.*, **2020**, 109972.

132. Alsaggaf, M. S.; Moussa, S. H.; Tayel, A. A. Application of Fungal Chitosan Incorporated with Pomegranate Peel Extract as Edible Coating for Microbiological, Chemical and Sensorial Quality Enhancement of Nile Tilapia Fillets. *Int. J. Biol. Macromol.*, **2017**, *99*, 499–505.
133. Zeinab S. Farag, Ashraf M. Sharaf, M. K. M. Influence of Chitosan Based Coating Incorporating Green Tea and Rosemary Extracts on Physicochemical and Microbial Quality of Tilapia Fish (*Oreochromis niloticus*) Fillets under Cold Storage. *Egypt. J. Food Sci.*, **2018**, *46*, 69–82.
134. Khazaei, N.; Esmaiili, M.; Emam-Djomeh, Z. Effect of Active Edible Coatings Made by Basil Seed Gum and Thymol on Oil Uptake and Oxidation in Shrimp during Deep-Fat Frying. *Carbohydr. Polym.*, **2016**, *137*, 249–254.
135. Guerrero, A.; Ferrero, S.; Barahona, M.; Boito, B.; Lisbinski, E.; Maggi, F.; Sañudo, C. Effects of Active Edible Coating Based on Thyme and Garlic Essential Oils on Lamb Meat Shelf Life after Long-term Frozen Storage. *J. Sci. Food Agric.*, **2020**, *100* (2), 656–664.
136. de Vasconcellos Santos Batista, D.; Reis, R. C.; Almeida, J. M.; Rezende, B.; Bragança, C. A. D.; da Silva, F. Edible Coatings in Post-Harvest Papaya: Impact on Physical–Chemical and Sensory Characteristics. *J. Food Sci. Technol.*, **2020**, *57* (1), 274–281.
137. Barreto, L. T. P.; Weschenfelder, E. F.; Sandri, I. G. Filme polimérico e processo de produção do mesmo. Assignee: Fundação Universidade de Caxias do Sul. Br n. 10 2018 008581 6. Filed in 27 April 2018. Published in 12 November **2019**.
138. Barreto, L. T. P.; Fernanda, S.; Weschenfelder, E. F. Filme Biodegradável, Processo e Obtenção Do Extrato Da Casca de Pinhão e Do Filmes Biodegradável e Uso Do Filme Do Filme Biodegradável Como Embalagem Para Alimentos. BR102018075335-5, 2018 (Patent Pending).

11 Essential Oil and Herbal Compounds in the Agroindustry

Thaís Aparecida Santos Oliveira,
Livia Stenico Tanajura,
and Antônio Eduardo Miller Crotti

CONTENTS

11.1 Introduction 285
11.1.1 Agrobusiness and Agroindustry 285
11.1.2 Essential Oils 286
11.2 Applications of Essential Oils in Crop Production 289
11.3 Postharvest Application of Essential Oils 292
11.4 Some Applications of Herbal Products in the Agroindustry 298
11.5 Final Remarks 300
Acknowledgement 301
References 301

11.1 INTRODUCTION

11.1.1 Agrobusiness and Agroindustry

Agrobusiness plays a key role in the economy of many countries. In Brazil, the Brazilian Institute of Geography and Statistics estimates that agroindustry and agribusiness contribute to 21.4% of the gross domestic product (GDP). Agroindustry is an important field of agribusiness, but even though its definition is intuitive. The term "agroindustry" has been given different definitions. For example, according to EMBRAPA, agroindustry is "the large-scale production, processing, and packaging of food through modern equipment and methods" [1]. On the other hand, the Food and Agriculture Organization of the United Nations (FAO) stated that "Agroindustry provides a means of converting raw agricultural materials into value-added products while generating income and employment and contributing to overall economic development in both developed and developing countries" [2]. Therefore, there is no formal or uniform definition for the term "agroindustry". Moreover, the limits between agroindustry and agribusiness are not clear, even for statistical purposes.

The FAO carried out statistical research to show how broad and complex the term "agroindustry" can be. The activities of agroindustry were classified into levels

DOI: 10.1201/9781003225416-14

(section, division, group, and class). The researchers classified the activities of agro-industry into two main groups: activities related to primary products, including agriculture, forestry, fishing, and crop production, and activities related to processed food products and beverages [2].

This chapter will focus on applying essential oils (EOs) in two important classes of activities of agroindustry: support activities for crop production (which involve insect control) and postharvest crop activities (which involve phytopathogen control).

11.1.2 Essential Oils

EOs or volatile oils are hydrophobic mixtures of volatile compounds that originate from the secondary metabolism of aromatic plants. The glandular trichomes and other secretory structures (specialised excretory tissues) diffused on the surface of plant organs (fruits, leaves, flowers, stems, roots, and seeds) produced EOs, which remain stored in secretory cells or their cavities [3, 4].

EOs play an extremely important role in protecting plants against microorganisms and promoting plant interaction with insects: EOs help attract pollen and seed dispersal insects and repel predatory insects [5, 6]. In addition, EOs have several biological activities, such as antibacterial, antifungal, cytotoxic, insecticide, antiviral, anti-inflammatory, and antioxidant actions, and they act against herbivores (reducing their appetite) [5, 7].

Various factors can affect the chemical composition of an EO, including plant genotypic diversity, cultivation environments, harvest time, and extraction process. For instance, (*E*)-2-decenal is the major constituent of the EO of coriander leaves (*Coriandrum sativum* L. Apiaceae), whereas linalool (**4**) is the main component of the EOs of ripe coriander fruits and seeds (86.1 and 91.1%, respectively) [8, 9].

The extraction method is another factor that can affect the quality of EOs. The wrong choice or even incorrect use of an extraction method can cause loss or variations of the chemical constituents of an EO. The EO's extraction can be carried out by numerous techniques, like extraction by supercritical fluid [10], microwave [11], and different distillation techniques. Steam distillation and hydrodistillation are the most widely applied EO extraction methods. Steam distillation is used to extract 93% of the volatile vegetable oils and uses steam to heat the plant material. Hydrodistillation is widely used to extract volatile hydrophobic substances with a high boiling point and condensation temperatures below 100°C [12]. Among the chemical constituents detected in EOs, the most commonly found are terpenoids, phenylpropanoids, and long-chain aliphatic compounds. Because these compounds occur in variable concentrations in each EO, special attention is given to the "major components" (i.e. the components with the largest areas in the gas chromatography (GC) or gas chromatography coupled to mass spectrometry (GC-MS) chromatograms) [5]. Some EOs have a simple constitution (between 20 and 60 substances), e.g., the EO of *Eucalyptus tereticornis* Sm. (Myrtaceae). This oil consists of 23 compounds, and *p*-cymene (**16**, 31.1%), β-phellandrene (**12**, 9.8%), spathulenol (**47**, 8.1%), γ-terpinene (**15**, 7.0%), α-phellandrene (**11**, 6. 8%), and 1,8-cineole (**22**, 5.3%) are its major

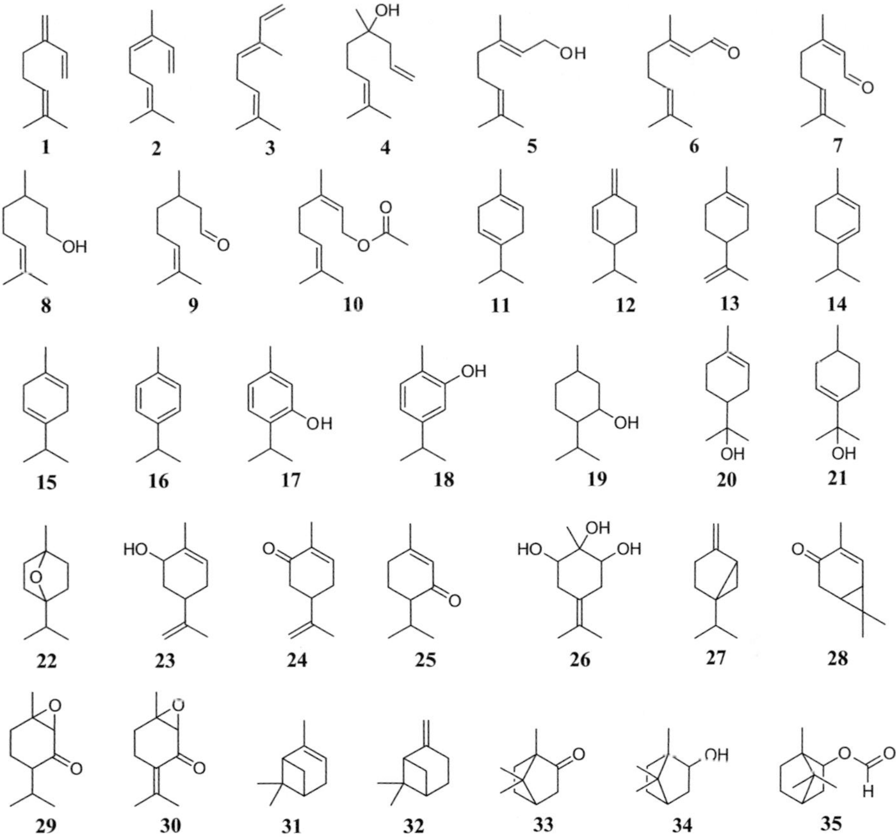

FIGURE 11.1 Chemical structures of monoterpenes **1–35**.

components [13]. On the other hand, some EOs are more complex, such as the EO of Indian rose-scented geranium (*Pelargonium* sp.), in which more than 220 components have been identified [14].

Monoterpenes (Figure 11.1) and sesquiterpenes (Figure 11.2) are the most commonly identified terpenoids in EOs. Monoterpenes (C_{10}) and sesquiterpenes (C_{15}) are formed by two and three joined isoprene (C_5) units, respectively. Some terpenes are hydrocarbons (i.e. they contain only carbon and hydrogen in their structures); for example, myrcene (**1**), alloocimene (**2**), β-terpinene (**12**), *p*-cymene (**16**), α-pinene (**31**), and limonene (**13**), while others have oxygenated functions. Alcohols (e.g. linalool (**4**), geraniol (**5**), carveol (**23**), citronellol (**8**), α-terpineol (**20**), menthol (**19**), borneol (**34**), and α-bisabolol (**38**)), aldehydes [e.g. geranial (**6**), neral (**7**), and citronellal (**9**)], phenols [e.g. thymol (**17**) and carvacrol (**18**)], ketones (carvone (**24**) and camphor (**33**)), ethers (e.g. eucalyptol/1,8-cineole (**22**)), and esters [e.g. citronellyl acetate (**10**)] are the most common oxygenated functions [15]. The EOs of plants like citronella [16], lemon [17], orange [18], and eucalyptus [19] are rich in terpenes. Compared to terpenes, phenylpropanoids (Figure 11.3) occur less frequently,

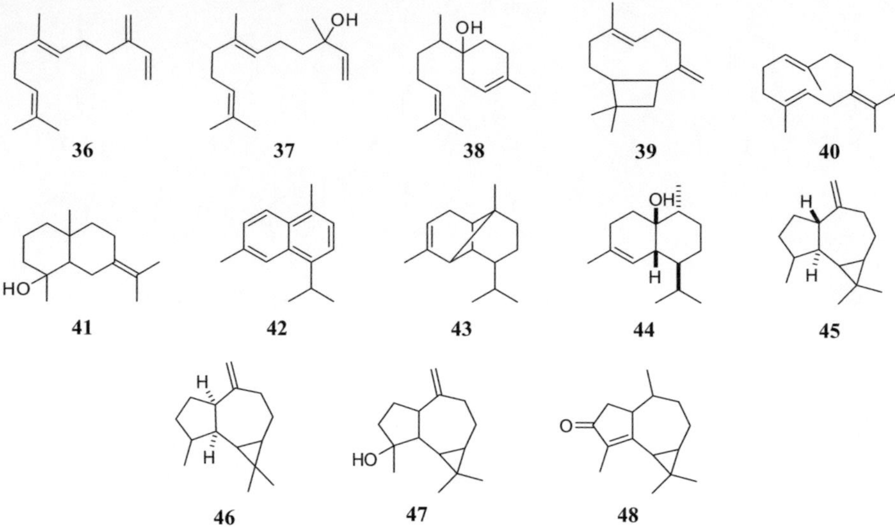

FIGURE 11.2 Chemical structures of sesquiterpenes **36–48**.

but they are abundant in the EOs of plants such as cinnamon [20] and fennel [21]. Phenylpropanoids are crucial for plants because they protect them against pathogens. Countless biological activities have been assigned to these compounds, including anti-inflammatory, antimicrobial, and antioxidant actions. Phenols [e.g. chavicol (**49**) and eugenol (**52**)], aldehydes [cinnamaldehyde (**51**)], and alcohols [e.g. cinnamic alcohol (**50**)] are among the chemical functions that are present in phenylpropanoids [5, 22].

In addition to being widely used in perfumes, cosmetics, food and beverage scents, incense and household cleaning products, and as fragrance fixatives in pharmaceutical and therapeutic compositions [23, 24], the EOs have interesting applications in the agroindustry. This chapter presents some applications of EOs at two important levels of agroindustry–crop production and postharvest food preservation. We will focus on their use to combat insects and phytopathogens during both crop production and postharvest storage.

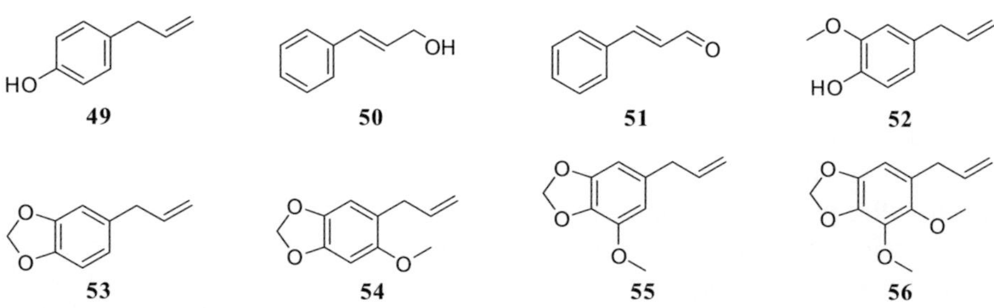

FIGURE 11.3 Chemical structures of phenylpropanoids **49–56**.

11.2 APPLICATIONS OF ESSENTIAL OILS IN CROP PRODUCTION

The widespread application of synthetic insecticides to prevent insects from attacking plantations has caused economic, ecological, social, and environmental impacts, such as the rise of more resistant insects, ecological risks, and toxicity to mammals. These adverse effects have motivated Integrated Pest Management (IPM) strategies, which encourage natural pest control mechanisms. In this scenario, plant EOs are an attractive and ecological alternative: they present fumigant toxicity, repellency, and antifeedant effects (i.e. plants produce EO to inhibit insect attack), and they are widely available and cost-effective [25, 26].

The silverleaf whitefly, *Bemisia tabaci* (Gennadius) biotype B (Hemiptera: Aleyrodidae), attacks more than 500 species of plants worldwide [27]. It is one of the main pests in vegetables, beans, soybeans, peanuts, cotton, vegetables, and plants grown in greenhouses and fields [28]. The silverleaf whitefly not only damages plants directly through feeding, but it is also a vector of several viruses, especially geminiviruses. The incidence of geminivirus transmitted by *B. tabaci* is high in tomato-producing areas in the United States, Mexico, Venezuela, and Brazil, leading to devastating economic consequences. In Mediterranean countries, diseases caused by geminiviruses, like the tomato yellow leaf curl virus (TYLCV), have reduced tomato production by between 40 and 70%. Whitefly management has been carried out primarily through synthetic insecticides of different chemical groups (see Figure 11.4). Typical examples include the carbamates [e.g. cartap (**57**)], pyrethroids [e.g. fenpropathrin (**58**) and imidacloprid (**59**)], neonicotinoids [e.g. thiamethoxam (**60**)], pyriproxyfen (**61**), and organophosphates [e.g. methamidophos (**62**)]. However, the feeding stages of *B. tabaci* colonise the abaxial surface of leaves, so obtaining effective leaf coverage by contact with the spray is difficult and generally requires repeated spraying. In recent decades, these pesticides have gradually become less effective. *B. tabaci* has developed resistance to them, contributing to selecting resistant silverleaf whitefly individuals while its natural enemies have been eliminated. Moreover, cases of poisoning of workers and consumers have been reported [29]. Thus, EOs aimed at silverleaf whitefly control have been extensively investigated [30].

Baldin and co-workers investigated the bioactivity of the EO of *Pelargonium graveolens* L'Her (Geraniaceae), known as geranium, and its major chemical components

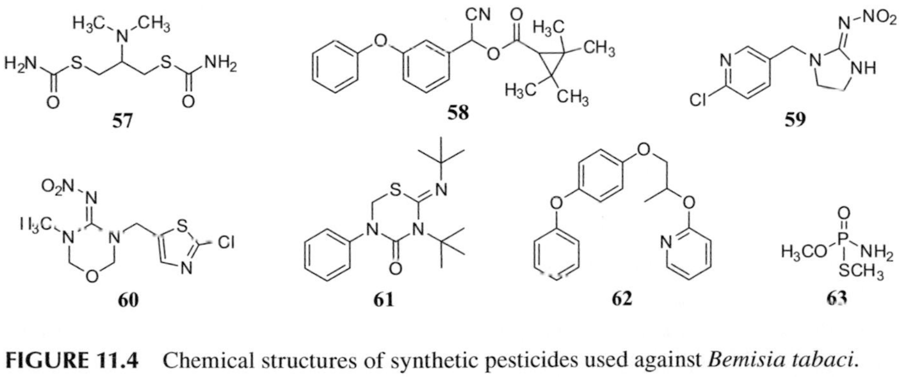

FIGURE 11.4 Chemical structures of synthetic pesticides used against *Bemisia tabaci*.

against *B. tabaci* biotype B in tomatoes. These authors identified 13 components, with geraniol (**5**, 42.3%), linalool (**4**, 16.4%), and citronellol (**8**, 15.6%) being the major ones. In this same study, Baldin et al. employed imidacloprid (**59**, 210 g ha^{-1}) and an aqueous solution of Tween 20 (0.5% v/v) as the positive and negative control, respectively. The EO of *P. graveolens* (PG-EO), the monoterpenes geraniol (**5**), linalool (**4**), and citronellol (**8**), and imidacloprid (positive control) were evaluated in the fumigation assays using 0.5, 1.0, 1.5, and 2.0 μLL^{-1} of air. PG-EO and the tested monoterpenes killed 100% of the insects at all the assayed concentrations. PG-EO was more effective than imidacloprid, one of the insecticides used against *B. tabaci*. For the treated leaves, the repellency tests have shown that PG-EO, citronellol (**8**), and geraniol (**5**) provided higher repellency and reduced the number of whiteflies significantly compared to the control. The number of eggs that were deposited on tomato leaves treated with PG-EO, geraniol (**5**), and citronellol (**8**) was lower as compared to the control and linalool (**4**). These results suggested that PG-EO and its related monoterpenes are potentially applicable in developing effective strategies to manage *B. tabaci* [28].

Fanela and co-workers evaluated the lethal and inhibitory effects of five plant-derived EOs on *B. tabaci* biotype B in tomatoes. Tomato leaflets treated with the EOs of *Piper callosum* Ruiz & Pav. (Piperaceae) (PC-EO), *P. graveolens* L'Hér. (Geraniaceae) (PG-EO), *Adenocalymma alliaceum* (Lam.) Miers (Bignoniaceae) (AA-EO), *Plectranthus neochilus* Schltr. (Lamiaceae) (PN-EO), and thiamethoxam (**60**) were less infested as compared to the controls. These EOs inhibited oviposition as compared to the controls. The LC_{50} (the concentration that kills 50% of the insects) values were obtained only for the treatments with AA-EO, PG-EO, and VA-EO and ranged from 0.1 to 1.2 $\mu L\ L^{-1}$ of air for AA-EO and VA-EO, respectively. AA-EO was the most toxic among the tested EOs and was the only EO to achieve a 50% lethal time (LT_{50}) at the lowest concentration (3.7 h). Additionally, AA-EO was 16.7 times more toxic than VA-EO. Except for PG-EO, LT_{50} decreased with increasing concentrations of EO. AA-EO stood out: its LT_{50} was 2.0 h at 1.0 $\mu L\ L^{-1}$ of air. The main chemical constituents of the EO of *A. alliaceum* were diallyl trisulfide (66.9%) and diallyl sulphide (23.3%), whereas safrole (**53**, 29.3%), α-pinene (**31**, 19.2%), and β-pinene (**32**, 14.3%) were the major compounds in the EO of *P. callosum*. The monoterpenes geraniol (**5**, 42.3%) and linalool (**4**, 16.4%) were the main components of the EO of *P. graveolens*, while the (*E*)-caryophyllene (**39**, 30.7%) and the bicyclic monoterpenes α-pinene (**31**, 11.7%) and β-pinene (**32**, 15.0%) were the major compounds in the EO of *P. neochilus*. Finally, the monoterpenes 1,8-cineole (**22**, 33.2%) and sabinene (**27**, 22.7%) were the main components of the EO of *Vitex agnus-castus*. These results showed that these EOs have great potential to be developed into effective and alternative natural pest management products that can reduce synthetic insecticides use and be employed as a new tool against whiteflies, especially in organic farming [27]. However, further studies are needed to investigate the potential of these EOs in field conditions and to evaluate their compatibility with other pest management methods and strategies.

The velvetbean caterpillar, *Anticarsia gemmatalis* Hübner (Erebidae), is the main soybean defoliator in Brazil, and it harms other economically important crops. In its larval phase, this lepidopteran causes severe damage to soybeans in cultivated areas throughout the country. Each caterpillar consumes about 100–150 cm^2 of leaf area, and approximately 96% of this consumption occurs during the larval phase, which lowers grain production [31]. This pest is primarily controlled by applying synthetic insecticides, but new approaches are necessary to reduce risks to the environment and its natural enemies. Krinski and co-workers screened the EOs of 21 Piperaceae species growing in various regions of Brazil for their ovicidal action against *A. gemmatalis*. These authors sprayed the EOs at five concentrations (0.25, 0.5, 1.0, 2.0, and 4.0% diluted in acetone) on paper containing caterpillar eggs and assessed larval hatching three days after oviposition. The major components that were identified in the most bioactive EOs included asaricin (**54**), myristicin (**55**), spathulenol (**47**), (*E*)-caryophyllene (**39**), germacrene B (**40**), dillapiole (**56**), (*E*)-β-ocimene (**3**), limonene (**13**), (*E*)-nerolidol (**37**), piperitone (**25**), 1-epicubenol (**44**), cadalene (**42**), 4,6-dimethyl-5-vinyl-1,2-benzodioxide, eudesm-7(11)-en-4-ol (**41**), cyclocolorenone (**48**), α-copaene (**43**), (*E*)-α-farnesene (**36**), and allo-aromadendrene (**46**). The highest ovicidal activity was verified for the EOs of 16 Piperaceae species (0.0 ± 0.0 eggs of larvae in three days) at a concentration of 4.0%. Based on the ovicidal effects and lethal concentrations, the EOs of *Piper aduncum*, *Piper caldense* C. DC., *Piper marginatum* Jacq., *Piper mollicomum* (Kunth) Kunth ex Steud., and *Piper mosenii* C. DC. were the most promising to manage *A. gemmatalis* eggs. Therefore, Piperaceae species proved to be toxic to *A. gemmatalis* eggs: they reduced or inhibited the larval hatching of treated eggs and are a relevant alternative to the pesticides currently used in soy plantations [32].

The fall armyworm or cartridge caterpillar, *Spodoptera frugiperda* (Noctuidae), is one of the primary pests in maize and can culminate in huge economic losses. *S. frugiperda* is a polyphagous insect that infests different types of cultures. Its management is usually based on synthetic insecticides, chiefly pyrethroids and organophosphates. However, the efficiency of these insecticides has decreased due to the development of resistance. Moreover, *S. frugiperda* individuals resistant to maize containing the gene Bt (*Bacillus thuringiensis*) and the proteins Cry1F and Cry1Ab are employed to control fall armyworm reported [33]. A recent study examined the efficacy of the EOs of *Corymbia citriodora* (Hook.) K.D. Hill & L.A.S. Johnson (Myrtaceae), *Myrciaria dubia* (Kunth) McVaugh (Myrtaceae), *Lippia microphylla* Cham. (Verbenaceae), and *Piper umbellatum* L. (Piperaceae) in controlling *S. frugiperda*. The EOs were extracted and subjected to topical application tests (30 mg of oil per gram of insect). The EOs that caused mortality above 80% were diluted to achieve concentrations of 1, 5, 10, 15, and 20 mg g^{-1} for dose–response curves. Among the tested EOs, only the EOs of *C. citriodora* and *L. microphylla* were efficient and afforded 100% mortality. For the EO of *C. citriodora*, DL_{80} was 7.06 ± 0.73 mg g^{-1} in the topical application assays and 5.85 ± 0.75 μL via fumigation. In the EO of *L. microphylla*, DL_{80} was 9.95 ± 1.25 mg g^{-1} in the topical application and 18.56 ± 3.55 μL via the volatile application. Citronellal (**9**, 80%) was identified as the major chemical constituent of the EO of *C. citriodora*, whereas (*E*)-caryophyllene (**39**, 32.1%) and (*E*)-nerolidol (**37**, 14.1%) were the main components of the EO of *L. microphylla*. Therefore, citronellal (**9**) can be one of the compounds accounting for the high mortality rates elicited by the EO of *C. citriodora*. These two EOs seem to be promising for controlling *S. frugiperda* on corn plantations [33].

11.3 POSTHARVEST APPLICATION OF ESSENTIAL OILS

Volatility is one of the most striking characteristics of EOs and makes them an attractive alternative to conventional fungicides when it comes to controlling the deterioration of postharvest food. In addition, the vaporisation and distribution of EOs over the fruit surface are advantageous because EOs are less toxic than conventional fungicides [34, 35].

Brown rice and its derivatives are susceptible to postharvest diseases caused by various fungi. *Aspergillus flavus* is one of the main moulds of these products and frequently leads to postharvest losses. This fungus can produce aflatoxins that represent a risk to human health due to their nephrotoxic, immunotoxic, mutagenic, teratogenic, and carcinogenic effects. Numerous studies have detected high levels of fungal contamination owing to *A. flavus* in rice during harvest, handling, transport, and storage. Furthermore, *A. flavus* is one of the most often reported contaminants in agricultural products worldwide [36].

To minimise such effects, Songsamoe and co-workers investigated how the EO of *Michelia alba* DC. (Magnoliaceae) flowers and their main chemical constituents, linalool (**4**, 73%) and (*E*)-caryophyllene (**39**, 7%), in the steam phase, affected *A. flavus* growth in cooked brown rice. The vapour phase of the EO at ≥300 μL L^{-1} of air was active against *A. flavus*. Moreover, a combination of 10:1 linalool (**4**)/(*E*)-caryophyllene (v/v) increased the antifungal activity [37].

Potato (*Solanum tuberosum* L.) is one of the most consumed foods in the world. Because potato tubers are nutritionally rich and easy to grow, potato occupies a special space in humanity's meals. Nevertheless, the potato harvest yield is commonly compromised due to delayed germination and break in its tubers' dormancy, which adversely affects the quality of tubers during storage [38]. After harvesting, the tubers enter the state of growth suspension (i.e. dormancy), but changes in the physiological and environmental conditions interrupt this dormancy stage, so the tubers begin to sprout [39]. Physical and chemical methods are used to manage germination, but each of them has limitations. Cold storage is one of the methodologies that is adopted to delay sprout development. Unfortunately, although storage at low temperatures (3–7°C) delays sprouting, this procedure also causes undesirable sweetening of the tissues [40]. In a recent study, Shukla and co-workers tested 20 EOs at several concentrations in potatoes by fumigation. When stored at room temperature (25 ± 2°C), the EO of lemongrass (*Cymbopogon citratus* (DC.) Stapf. Poaceae) (LG) or clove (*Syzygium aromaticum* (L.) Merr. & L.M. Perry, Myrtaceae) (CL) induced the appearance of potatoes tubers. At the same time, the EOs of palmarosa (*Cymbopogon martini* (Roxb.) W. Watson, Poaceae) (PR) and ajowan (*Trachyspermum ammi* (L.) Sprague, Apiaceae) (AZ) inhibited the potato tubers. Furthermore, treatment with AZ for 7 days inhibited germination for 30 days. According to the results, tubers treated with LG and CL could also increase the potato yield [41].

Besides its high nutritional value, the baobab plant (*Adansonia digitata* L., Malvaceae) has properties that have traditionally been useful in folk medicine. It has been applied to treat malaria and diarrhoea and to prevent microbial infections in wounds. Products made from parts of baobab plants display therapeutic, nutraceutical, and cosmetic potential due to their high antioxidant capacity [42]. Kayode and co-workers investigated the chemical composition and the cytotoxic potential and antimicrobial effects of the EOs of the leaves and stems of the baobab peel on tomato fruits in postharvest storage. The main constituents of these EOs were 3,7,11,15-tetramethyl-2-hexadecen-1-ol (26.3%) and other compounds, such as tetracosane (6.5%), heptacosane (5.8%), tetratetracontane (5.6%), hexacosane (5.4%), octadecane (5.2%), and hexadecane (4.4%). Treatment of experimental tomato fruits stored at 28 ± 1° C with the EO of *A. digitata* leaves at 2000 ppm substantially suppressed the microbial load of tomato fruits at the end of the storage period. The decrease in microbial load during the initial storage stage suggested that EOs may be an alternative to the synthetic fungicides used in food preservation [43].

Nowadays, researchers are also carrying out studies on edible coating materials that can alter the internal atmosphere of fruits and slow down the respiratory process, thus delaying ripening. These coating materials consist of cellulose, chitosan, alginate, and starch, which decrease the rate of water vapour transmission and increase the useful life of coated fruits [44]. The edible guar gum-based coating contains no harmful compounds and is safe for human consumption. It also presents antibacterial activities against contaminating microorganisms. However, when it is used in combination with antimicrobial EOs, its antibacterial properties are enhanced. Following this line, Naeem and co-workers investigated the effect of guar gum coating in combination with EOs. The authors attempted to preserve unripe green mangoes (UGM) by employing edible coatings containing the EO of *Nigella sativa* L. (Ranunculaceae), *C. sativum* L. (Apiaceae), *Foeniculum vulgare* Mill. (Apiaceae), or *Laurus nobilis* L. (Lauraceae). The EOs were extracted with two different solvents (methanol and ethanol) and stored at refrigerator temperature. The results suggested that the EOs extracted with ethanol significantly slowed down the biochemical reactions inside the fruit. The authors analysed these biochemical reactions in the form of bioactive properties of the stored fruits. Along with the biochemical attributes, edible coatings formulated with one of the EOs also delayed the physical–chemical changes in the pulp UGM. The ethanolic EOs conferred greater antioxidant potential to these edible coatings based on guar gum, making them capable of eliminating reactive oxygen species at a high rate. The addition of these aromatic essences to edible coatings affects oxygen transport through the packaging material. These essences act as oxygen scavengers and enrich the fruit coated with antioxidants during diffusion of the bioactive components from the packaging matrix to the mango pulp tissues. These effects indicated that a formulation with guar gum combined with EO is ideal for preserving mangoes in the postharvest period [45].

The quality of apple (*Malus domestica* Borkh., Rosaceae) is influenced by postharvest diseases like blue mould, bull's eye, and soft rot caused by *Penicillium expansum Alternaria* species and *Rhizopus stolonifer*, respectively. The fungus *Botrytis cinerea* can affect fruits at any development stage, leading to rot [46]. Developing countries suffer from the survival of these pathogenic fungi in food, which deteriorates food product quality. El Ouadi and co-workers investigated the antifungal activity of the EO of *Melissa officinalis* L. (Lamiaceae) against *B. cinerea*, *P. expansum*, and *R. stolonifer*. They performed *in vitro* experiments with these fungi using the food poisoning technique and the volatile activity test. The major constituents of this EO were *p*-mentha-1,2,3-triol (**26**, 13.1%), *p*-menth-3-en-8-ol (**21**, 8.8%), piperitenone oxide (**30**, 8.4%), and (Z)-piperitone oxide (**29**, 7.3%). The percentage of growth inhibition rose with increasing concentrations of the EO for all the tested fungal strains. All the assayed strains were sensitive to the vapour of the EO of *M. officinalis*: This volatile fraction at 40, 80, and 160 µL/mycelial discs completely suppressed *B. cinerea*, *P. expansum,* and *R. stolonifer* growth, respectively. The results indicated that the EO of *M. officinalis* is an effective antifungal agent against the tested fungi. Because this type of EO is biodegradable and does not persist in the environment, it can be considered a good alternative to synthetic fungicides to protect apples against the tested phytopathogenic fungi. They can also prevent the deterioration of other food products during storage [47].

Plant species belonging to the genus *Citrus* (Rutaceae) are an important source of fruits, including oranges, tangerines, grapefruits, and pomelo. In 1935, H.B. Frost, in California, USA, developed the "Kinnow" mandarin (*Citrus nobilis* × *C. delicious*). This type of tangerine did not succeed in the United States. However, it revolutionised the citrus industry in India, Pakistan, and Bangladesh, and it currently occupies a large part of the area and production of citrus grown in India [48]. However, the "Kinnow" mandarin is available for a limited time only. During the high production season, this fruit is abundant in the market, which means that farmers profit little from it. To increase its availability, producers store the "Kinnow" tangerine in cold stores for a period, but postharvest losses are huge and range from 25 to 35% [49]. Jhalegar and co-workers examined how the EOs of lemongrass (*C. citratus* (DC). Stapf, Poaceae) (0.16% v/v), clove (*S. aromaticum* [L.] Merrill & Perry, Myrtaceae) (0.06% v/v), eucalyptus (*Eucalyptus globulus* Labill., Myrtaceae) (0.3% v/v), and neem (*Azadirachta indica* A. Juss, Meliaceae) (2.0% v/v) influenced the "Kinnow" tangerine. They aimed to verify how these EOs affected the fungi *Penicillium digitatum* (Trichocomaceae) and *Penicillium italicum* (Trichocomaceae). These fungi cause green and blue mould, respectively, two of the main postharvest diseases affecting the "Kinnow" tangerine, thus preventing its extended availability. *In vitro* and *in vivo* experiments indicated that the tested EOs inhibited the growth (diameter of the colonies) of both pathogens in untreated potato dextrose agar (PDA) plates. At 0.16% (v/v), the EO of lemongrass provided the strongest inhibition: maximum inhibition of 7 ± 1.21 mm for *P. italicum* and 5 ± 0.45 mm for *P. digitatum*. Likewise, under the *in vivo* assay conditions, all the EOs impacted deterioration, loss from deterioration, lesion diameter, respiration rate, ethylene evolution, general acceptance, and physiological weight loss. The EO of lemongrass was also the most effective (*in vivo* tests), probably due to its high citral [a mixture of geranial (**6**) and neral (**7**)] content (approximately 85%). Decaying rot in all storage stages was lower in fruits treated with EOs than untreated fruits, thereby prolonging their shelf life [50].

Decomposition by fungi can critically reduce the durability of pomegranate fruits in the postharvest. The most commonly reported diseases include the appearance of black spots, caused by the fungi *Alternaria alternata* or *Colletotrichum gloeosporioides* [51], and mould due to the action of the fungi *B. cinerea* or *Penicillium* sp. Besides causing economic losses, these fungi pose a potential health risk. Munhuweyi and co-workers investigated the effect of chitosan combined with the EO of cinnamon [*Cinnamomum zeylanicum* Blume, Lauraceae; major constituents: eugenol (**52**), 56.9%; benzyl benzoate, 4.8%; (*E*)-caryophyllene (**39**), 4.8%;

safrole (**53**), 4.7%; and cinnamaldehyde, 3.4%], lemon [*Citrus limonum*, Rutaceae; major constituents: geranial (**6**), 41.4%; neral (**7**), 32.5%; myrcene (**1**), 7.8%; and geraniol (**5**), 3.2%], or oregano [*Origanum vulgare*, Lamiaceae; major constituents: carvacrol (**18**), 51.5%; car-2-en-4-one (**28**), 11.7%; *p*-cymene (**16**), 10.0%; and thymol (**17**), 3.6%] as edible films against the growth of three important pathogens that underlie pomegranate diseases: *Botrytis* sp. (Sclerotiniaceae), *Penicillium* sp. (Trichocomaceae), and *Pilidiella granati* (Schizoparmaceae). The *in vivo* antifungal test conducted on pomegranates artificially inoculated with *Botrytis* sp., treated with chitosan–oregano (emulsions and films) showed that both treatment methods inhibited *Botrytis* sp. growth. Nevertheless, the inhibitory effects were more pronounced for the fruits directly dipped in emulsions of chitosan and one of the EOs (10.0 g L^{-1}) than for the samples exposed to vapour contact through the films. The incorporation of the OEs increased the antifungal activity of the chitosan films. However, the type of EO added to the chitosan emulsion significantly influenced the antifungal efficacy of the films: the chitosan film incorporated with the EO of oregano presented the highest antifungal activity, followed by the EOs of cinnamon and lemongrass [52].

Fresh fruits from diverse plants are susceptible to infection by many pathogenic fungi after harvest. Some synthetic fungicides can control countless vegetables and fruits effectively. Nevertheless, the emergence of resistant fungal strains has limited the effectiveness of synthetic fungicides. Additionally, in some cases, their use in the postharvest phase is prohibited by law. The growing public interest in the risks to health and the environment, associated with the increased levels of pesticides in fruit orchards and the lack of renewed and continuous approval of more effective active molecules spurred the search for alternative methods relying on safe and natural solutions for postharvest control [53]. A study was carried out with peach fruits (*Prunus persica* (L.) Batsch, Rosaceae) aiming to evaluate the potential fungicidal activity of the EOs of thyme (*Thymus vulgaris* L., Lamiaceae) and verbena (*Verbena officinalis* L., Verbenaceae) against *Monilinia laxa* (Sclerotiniaceae), *Monilinia fructigena* (Sclerotiniaceae), and *Monilinia fructicola* (Sclerotiniaceae). The EO's major chemical constituents are (*E*)-β-ocimene (**3**, 56.2%) for thyme, and citral (44.5%) and isobornyl formate (**35**, 45.4%) for verbena. The highest studied concentrations of the EOs of verbena (1000 ppm) and thyme (500 ppm) significantly reduced the diameter of the brown rot lesion. The results attested that the two tested EOs could effectively control infections caused by *M. laxa*, *M. fructicola*, and *M. fructigena*. In particular, the studied EOs succeeded in controlling all the pathogenic fungi tested on peach fruits even though their effectiveness was related to the employed concentrations and the application time [54].

In the postharvest period, most fresh fruits are susceptible to infection by pathogenic fungi. Contamination by filamentous fungi is the main cause of the fast deterioration of fresh fruits, affecting fruit quality and reducing its shelf life [55]. Pathogenic fungi, including *B. cinerea* and *P. expansum*, are the main infectious agents of apples, pears, and other fruits rich in pectin [56]. Nikkah and co-workers investigated the antifungal effects of the EOs of thyme (*T. vulgaris* L., Lamiaceae), cinnamon (*C. zeylanicum* Blume, Lauraceae), rosemary (*Rosmarinus officinalis* L., Lamiaceae), and marjoram (*Origanum majorana* L., Lamiaceae) against *B. cinerea* and *P. expansum*. The authors evaluated the fungicide and growth-inhibiting properties of these EOs and the interaction and possible synergistic impacts of double and triple combinations of these EOs. These authors also assessed the antifungal properties of selected treatments in pear fruits. In an *in vivo* antifungal assay performed by artificially wounding the fruits, the authors evaluated the antifungal efficacy of thyme (625 μg mL^{-1}) or cinnamon (1250 μg mL^{-1}) EOs, and found good antifungal activities. Based on the results, the lowest maximum growth rate (0.37 mm/day) was obtained for *B. cinerea* (Sclerotiniaceae) treated with a triple combination of thyme, cinnamon, and rosemary EOs. The *in vivo* assay also revealed considerable inhibitory effects for the combined use of these EOs. The average diameter of pear lesions treated with a triple combination of the EOs of cinnamon/rosemary/thyme (78, 1250, and 39 μg mL^{-1}) was 6 mm and 8 mm against *B. cinerea* and *P. expansum*, respectively, after 10 days at 25°C. In addition, the results showed the higher inhibitory effects of the double combination of the EOs of thyme/cinnamon (78 and 156 μg mL^{-1}) compared to the treatments with the single EOs [57].

After harvest, table grapes (*Vitis vinifera* L.) are perishable because they are particularly susceptible to drying, mechanical damage, deterioration, and physiological disorders. The most economically significant postharvest disease of table grapes is grey mould, caused by *B. cinerea* [58]. Grey mould is a major obstacle to the long-term storage and transport of grapes because it can develop even at low temperatures (−0.5°C). Once present, grey mould spreads fast among grape berries. Other rot can be caused by *Penicillium* spp., *R. stolonifer*, and *Aspergillus* spp., but they are less common. Servili and co-workers determined how effective exposure to vapours of the EO of rosemary (*R. officinalis* L., Lamiaceae), peppermint (*Mentha* × *piperita* L., Lamiaceae), or thyme (*T. vulgaris* L., Lamiaceae) is to control the postharvest deterioration of table grapes (*V. vinifera*). The authors conducted the tests under atmospheric pressure and in vacuum conditions (50 kPa), with storage at room temperature (20°C) and cold storage (4°C), followed by exposure to conditions of validity. The table grapes were exposed to one of the EOs at atmospheric pressure and then stored at room temperature. The results revealed that only the vapours of the EO of rosemary reduced the incidence and the McKinney Index of grey mould significantly (weighted average of percentages referring to the maximum possible level of grey mould decreased by 63 and 69%, respectively). Treatment with the EO of peppermint tended to reduce both of the measured parameters, whereas the EO of thyme was ineffective. When table grapes were exposed to EO vapours under vacuum conditions for 24 h and then kept at room temperature, the EOs of rosemary and peppermint markedly lowered the incidence and the McKinney Index of grey mould. In particular, the EO of rosemary reduced the measured parameters by 60 and 66%, respectively, while the EO of peppermint decreased the incidence and the McKinney Index of grey mould by 53 and 60%, respectively. When table grapes were exposed to the EO vapours under vacuum conditions for 24 h and then stored at 4°C for seven consecutive days, their validity was guaranteed for three days. Treatment with the vapours of rosemary EO significantly reduced the incidence and the McKinney Index of grey mould by 70 and 66%, respectively. The EO of peppermint also tended to reduce the measured parameters under these experimental conditions [59].

Thymol (**17**) is a component of the EO of thyme (*T. vulgaris* L., Lamiaceae) and applied as a food preservative and beverage ingredient. Chu and co-workers demonstrated that fumigation of sweet cherries (*Prunus avium* L., Rosaceae) with thymol (**17**) effectively controlled the postharvest grey rot caused by *B. cinerea* and the brown rot caused by *M. fructicola*. Fumigation with 30 mg L^{-1} thymol reduced the incidence of grey rot from 35% in untreated fruits to 0.5% [60]. Later, Liu and co-workers showed that thymol (**17**) also effectively controlled the symptoms of brown rot in apricots. In addition, fumigation of plums with relatively low concentrations of thymol (e.g. 2 or 4 mg L^{-1}) significantly decreased postharvest deterioration without causing phytotoxicity [61].

Nabigol and Morshedi evaluated the antifungal potential of the EOs of *Thymus daenensis* Celak. (Lamiaceae) and *Thymus carmanicus* Jalas (Lamiaceae) against four important pathogenic fungi (*R. stolonifer*, *P. digitatum*, *Aspergillus niger*, and *B. cinerea*) that can shorten the useful strawberry life (*Fragaria ananassa* Duch., cv Selva). The EO of *T. carmanicus* contains carvacrol (**18**, 70%), *p*-cymene (**16**, 12.4%), and γ-terpinene (**15**, 2.5%) as major constituents, while the main constituents of the EO of *T. daenensis* are thymol (**17**, 64.8%), α-terpinene (**14**, 11.3%), and *p*-cymene (**16**, 7.9%). Incorporating different concentrations of the EOs (150, 300, 600, and 1200 μL L^{-1}) into the culture medium containing PDA decreased the growth of the four tested strawberry fruit pathogens significantly in a dose-dependent manner. For both EOs, the minimum concentration that completely inhibits the growth of *B. cinerea* and *R. stolonifer* (100% inhibition; minimum inhibitory concentration [MIC]) was 300 μL L^{-1}, while a MIC of 600 μL L^{-1} was obtained for the *P. digitatum* and *A. niger*. The minimum fungicidal concentration (MFC) of the EOs of *T. daenensis* and *T. carmanicus* against *B. cinerea* and *R. stolonifer* was 1200 μL L^{-1}. On the other hand, even the highest tested concentration did not produce a fungicidal effect against *P. digitatum* or *A. niger*. The main compounds in these EOs (*p*-cymene, **16**; α-terpinene; **14**; thymol; **17;** and carvacrol; **18**) also exhibited antifungal activity. The MIC of *p*-cymene (**16**) and α-terpinene (**14**) was 600 μL L^{-1} against *B. cinerea* and *R. stolonifer* and 1200 μL L^{-1} against *A. niger*, while the MFC of both compounds against all the tested pathogens was greater than 1200 μL L^{-1}. The MIC values obtained for thymol and carvacrol against *R. stolonifer* were 300 and 150 μL L^{-1}, respectively. Additionally, the MFC of thymol (**17**) and carvacrol (**18**) was 600 μL L^{-1} against *B. cinerea* and 1200 and 600 μL L^{-1} against *R. stolonifer*. However, the MFC values were higher than 1200 μL L^{-1} for *A. niger*. However, neither of the EOs presented fungicidal activity even at the highest concentration evaluated (1200 μL L^{-1}). When the authors perform *in vivo* antifungal assays of the EOs at a preliminary concentration of 150 μL L^{-1}, they also exhibited inhibitory effects against the assayed pathogenic fungi.

T. carmanicus EO provided the most promising results and significantly decreased the disease incidence in strawberry fruits. For *A. niger*, the immersion of strawberries in one of the EOs reduced disease incidence, 18% for *T. carmanicus* and 30% for *T. daenensis*. In all cases, diving and spraying with EOs were more effective than fumigation. The authors found that *B. cinerea* and *R. stolonifer* were the most sensitive to treatment with EOs, with a total EO concentration of 300 μL L^{-1}. On the other hand, *P. digitatum* and *A. niger* were the fungi most resistant to EOs, and even the concentration of 1200 μL L^{-1} failed to inhibit them [62].

11.4 SOME APPLICATIONS OF HERBAL PRODUCTS IN THE AGROINDUSTRY

The use of plant-derived products can control the most destructive plant diseases. Phytochemicals, such as steroids, tannins, flavonoids, alkaloids, and saponins, are the active compounds underlying the antimicrobial activity of plant extracts [63]. Sheath disease (*Rhizoctonia solani* Kühn—anamorph; *Thanatephorus cucumeris* (Frank) Donk—teleomorph) is one of the main fungal diseases of the rice-producing regions of the world. It has become a serious threat to rice cultivation in Guyana because it can drastically reduce the quantity and quality of rice. The fungus has various hosts and infects over 188 genera of 32 plant families [64]. Recently, Persaud and co-workers assessed the viability of using 11 plant products as an effective approach to manage sheath disease in agricultural environments in Guyana. They employed the poisoned food technique to evaluate the effectiveness of the plant extracts against *R. solani.* They evaluated 11 plant extracts at 5, 10, and 15% in PDA. The extracts were prepared from fresh and healthy parts of neem (*A. indica* A. Juss, Meliaceae), tulsi (*Ocimum basilicum* L., Lamiaceae), lemongrass (*Cymbopogon flexuosus* [Nees ex Steud.] W. Watson, Poaceae), thick leaf thyme (*T. vulgaris* L., Lamiaceae), aloe (*Aloe vera* [L.] Burm.f., Xanthorrhoeaceae), marigold (*Tagetes patula* L., Asteraceae), black sage (*Cordia curassavica* (Jacq.) Roem. & Schult., Boraginaceae), bael (*Aegle marmelos* [L.] Corrêa, Rutaceae), chives (*Allium fistulosum* L., Amaryllidaceae), cloves (*S. aromaticum* [L.] Merr. & L.M. Perry, Myrtaceae), and madar plant (*Calotropis acia* Buch.-Ham., Apocynaceae) for the study. About 100 g of the ground plant were ground with 100 mL of sterile distilled water. The filtrate was collected and stored, and this solution served as a 100% stock of the plant extract. At 15%, the extracts of lemongrass, leafy thyme, and cloves significantly decreased mycelial growth (5.00 mm each) and increased inhibition (94.44% each, respectively) of *R. solani* (*in vitro* methodology). The marigold extract also reduced the mycelial growth (6.66 mm) of *R. solani* significantly compared to the control. The authors show that the application of extracts of lemongrass and thick leaf thyme at 15% markedly reduced the sheath disease caused by *R. solani* [65].

The growth of fungal pathogens in storage cultures creates economic, environmental, and health risks. Fungal toxins, such as aflatoxin [66], can accumulate in infected fruits and easily enter the food chain. Postharvest fungal diseases in apples are primarily caused by *P. expansum* and *B. cinerea* Pers. ex Pe [67]. Losses can be severe, reaching up to 30% in the main harvest and 40% in the second stage [68]. In this scenario, natural compounds, such as crude plant extracts, can be an ingenious technique to control postharvest rot in apple fruits. These extracts may contain several secondary metabolites and other compounds involved in the plant defence process, some of which can be poisonous to some plant pathogens [67]. Apple fruits (golden delicious) are highly susceptible to infection by *B. cinerea* in the postharvest phase. Thus, Gholamnezhad recently investigated the antimicrobial activity of extracts derived from selected plants to obtain a plant-based product to reduce damage and extend the useful life of apple fruits. They studied the inhibitory effects of seven plant extracts (see Table 11.1) on *B. cinerea* spore germination. For each treatment, a concentration of 0.2% (v/v), prepared by dilution of a 100 mg mL^{-1} stock

TABLE 11.1
Data on the Plant Extracts Used in the Experiments

Scientific Name	Common Name	Tissue
Azadirachta indica A. Juss (Meliaceae)	Neem	Seeds
Foeniculum vulgare Mill. (Apiaceae)	Fennel	Sheets
Lavandula spica L.	Lavender leaves	Flowers
Thymus daenensis Celak. (Lamiaceae)	Celak thyme	Sheets
Mentha pulegium L. (Lamiaceae)	Pennyroyal	Sheets
Salvia officinalis L. (Lamiaceae)	Sage leaves	Flowers
Ferula assa-foetida L. (Apiaceae)	Asafoetida	Sheets

aqueous solution, was used to perform the *in vitro* tests. Treatment with distilled water was maintained and used as the negative control. The plant extracts displayed considerable *in vitro* antifungal action against *B. cinerea*. For both extraction methods (water and methanol), exposure to the plant extracts affected the germination rate of pathogen spores. Moreover, plant extracts at 2% inhibited spore germination by between 20.8 and 70.8% compared to the healthy control. The methanol extracts exerted the greatest inhibitory effects. Treatment of wounded fruits with all the plant extracts at 25% significantly reduced the extent of the lesion area by between 52 and 89% compared to the healthy control. In general, the extracts at concentrations of 5% and 15% significantly controlled the grey apple mould caused by *B. cinerea*. The methanol extract of neem at 25 or 5% decreased the lesion area in apples by 89.1 and 73.5%, respectively, compared to the control. The methanol extract of *Salvia officinalis* had the least controlling percentage: 23.7 and 52.8% for concentrations of 5 and 25%, respectively. These plant extracts are promising agents for the organic and ecological management of postharvest apple pathogenic fungi [69].

Numerous pests attack tomato crops, and the whitefly *B. tabaci* (Hemiptera: Aleyrodidae) biotype B is among the most harmful pests in the subtropical, tropical, and temperate regions [70]. *B. tabaci* adults and nymphs feed on phloem, causing chlorosis in tomatoes and irregular fruit ripening [71]. Baldin and co-workers evaluated the insecticidal and inhibitory effects of 13 botanical aqueous extracts at 3% (w/v) on the behaviour of *B. tabaci* biotype B adults and nymphs infecting tomato plants. A distilled water solution was used as the negative control, and thiamethoxam (**60**) (18 g/100 L of water) was employed as the positive control. The leaf extract of *Toona ciliata* M.Roem. (Meliaceae) presented the most efficient inhibitory effect and reduced the number of adults and eggs on tomato leaflets the most drastically. *P. aduncum* L. (Piperaceae) leaf extract afforded the highest ovicidal effect (78.0% of non-hatched nymphs); however, it was not effective against nymphs and adults. The leaf extracts of *Trichilia pallida* SW. (Meliaceae), *Trichilia casaretti* C. DC. (Meliaceae), and *T. ciliata* provided the highest control indexes (67.9, 60.3, and 55.1, respectively). Furthermore, the aqueous extract of *T. pallida* yielded the highest adult mortality percentage (72.8%). The application of *T. pallida*, *T. ciliata*, and *T. casaretti* extracts are promising strategies to manage *B. tabaci* biotype B on tomatoes [72].

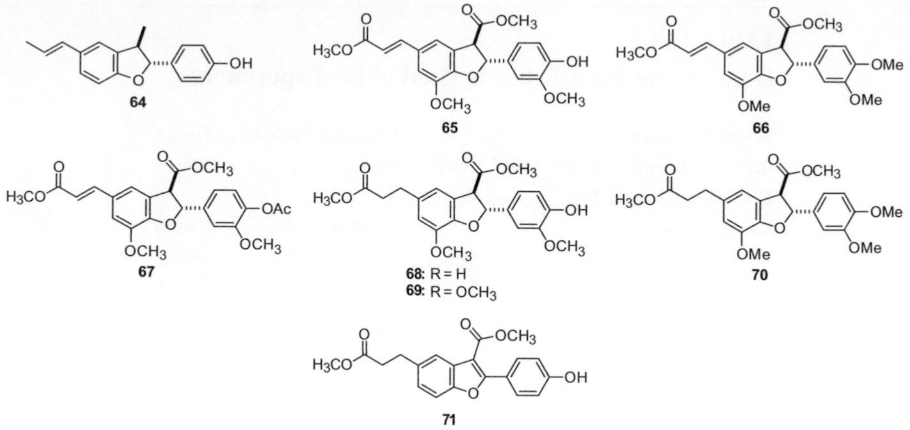

FIGURE 11.5 Chemical structures of neolignans **64–71**.

Conocarpan (**64**), a dihydrobenzofuran neolignans (DBN) isolated from *Piper decurrens* E. Fourn. (Piperaceae), displays larvicidal activity against the European corn borer, *Ostrinia nubilalis* Hübner [73]. Based on these results, Baldin and co-workers synthesised a series of DBNs (**65–71**) structurally related to conocarpan and investigated their insecticidal, repellent, and deterrent effects on *B. tabaci*. Figure 11.5 shows the chemical structures of neolignans **64-71**. For the toxicity tests, the authors diluted these compounds in acetone to achieve a concentration of 5 mg L^{-1} and sprayed them onto the surfaces of *Brassica oleracea* var. *acephala*. Pyriproxyfen (**61**) was diluted in water and used as a positive control at 75 mg L^{-1}. After spraying for 6 days, most of the tested compounds killed 100% of the nymphs. After spraying for three days, the contact toxicity of compounds **65** (*trans*-dehydrodiferulate dimethyl ester), **66** (4-O-methyl-*trans*-dehydrodiferulate dimethyl ester), **67** (4-O-acetyl-*trans*-dehydrodiferulate dimethyl ester), **68** (7′,8′-dihydro-*trans*-dehydrodicoumarate dimethyl ester), **70** (4-O-methyl-7′,8′-dihydro-*trans*-dehydrodiferulate dimethyl ester), and **71** (7′,8′-dihydro-7,8-dehydro-*trans*-dehydrodicoumarate dimethyl ester) was higher as compared to pyriproxyfen (positive control). Compounds **65** and **69** (7′,8′-dihydro-*trans*-dehydrodiferulate dimethyl ester) showed a repellent effect, whereas compounds **65**, **66**, and **69** affected oviposition. DBNs can be employed for effective pest management, especially against whiteflies [30].

11.5 FINAL REMARKS

The use of EOs in agribusiness is an attractive strategy. Besides their proven activity in protecting plants against insects and phytopathogens, the use of EOs is a sustainable and eco-friendly alternative. Moreover, EOs have lower toxicity compared to the currently applied natural insecticides and antifungals. Here, we focused on some EOs extracted from herbaceous plants with easier cultivation and micropropagation, which is an important practical aspect, since they allow the large-scale use of EOs. Volatility is a key feature of EO regarding their fumigation toxicity, making them interesting for greenhouse and postharvest applications.

On the other hand, volatility can be disadvantageous for EO application in the field, which can be solved with its encapsulation. Herbal products, especially aqueous plant extracts, can also be an interesting alternative to EOs in agricultural production. The application of EOs and herbal products is beneficial because they are easily obtained. However, its activities usually is stronger than the isolated compounds, due to additive or synergistic effects between major and minor constituents. Hence, identifying the main chemical components underlying the activity of interest is essential for quality control purposes. Therefore, the application of EOs and herbal extracts in agroindustry represents an innovative and promising research field to be extensively explored in the coming decades.

ACKNOWLEDGEMENT

The authors thank Fundação de Amparo à Pesquisa do Estado de São Paulo (FAPESP) for financial support (Grant number: 07/54241-8).

REFERENCES

1. EMBRAPA. Ciência que transforma. Empresa Brasileira de Pesquisa Agropecuária, Brasília, DF, 2020. Available at: https://www.embrapa.br/grandes-contribuicoes-para-a-agricultura-brasileira/agroindustria. Accessed in 06/08/2020
2. Ramaschiello, V. Defining agro-industry: a statistic perspective. FAO-UNIDO Expert Group Meeting on Agro-Industry Measurement (AIM), Rome, 2015. Available at: http://www.fao.org/economic/ess/ess-events/fao-unido2015/en/. Accessed in 06/08/2020.
3. Burt, S. Essential oils: their antibacterial properties and potential applications in foods - a review. International Journal of Food Microbiology 2004, 94, 223–253.
4. Sharifi-Rad, J.; Sureda, A.; Tenore, G. C.; Daglia, M.; Sharifi-Rad, M.; Valussi, M.; Tundis, R.; Sharifi-Rad, M.; Loizzo, M. R.; Ademiluyi, A. O.; Sharifi-Rad, R.; Ayatollahi, S. A.; Iriti, M. Biological activities of essential oils: from plant chemoecology to traditional healing systems. Molecules 2017, 22, 1–55.
5. Bakkali, F.; Averbeck, S.; Averbeck, D.; Idaomar, M. Biological effects of essential oils - a review. Food and Chemical Toxicology 2008, 46, 446–475.
6. Mittal, R. P.; Rana, A.; Jaitak, V. Essential oils: an impending substitute of synthetic antimicrobial agents to overcome antimicrobial resistance. Current Drug Targets 2019, 20, 605–624.
7. Williams, L. A. D.; Porter, R. B.; Junor, G. O. Biological activities of selected essential oils. Natural Product Communications 2007, 2, 1295–1296.
8. Chahal, K. K.; Singh, R.; Kumar, A.; Bhardwaj, U. Chemical composition and biological activity of *Coriandrum sativum* L.: a review. Indian Journal of Natural Products and Resources 2017, 8, 193–203.
9. Wei, J. N.; Liu, Z. H.; Zhao, Y. P.; Zhao, L. L.; Xue, T. K.; Lan, Q. K. Phytochemical and bioactive profile of *Coriandrum sativum* L. Food Chemistry 2019, 286, 260–267.
10. Yousefi, M.; Rahimi-Nasrabadi, M.; Poumortazavi, S. M.; Wysokowski, M.; Jesionowski, T.; Ehrlich, H.; Mirsadeghi, S. Supercritical fluid extraction of essential oils. TrAC Trends in Analytical Chemistry 2019, 118, 182–193.
11. Cardoso-Ugarte, G. A.; Juárez-Becerra, G. P.; Sosa-Morales, M. E.; López-Malo, A. Microwave-assisted extraction of essential oils from herbs. Journal of Microwave Power and Electromagnetic Energy 2013, 47, 63–72.
12. Aziz, Z. A. A.; Ahmad, A.; Setapar, S. H. M.; Karakucuk, A.; Azim, M. M.; Lokhat, D.; Rafatullah, M.; Ganash, M.; Kamal, M. A.; Ashraf, G. M. Essential oils:

extraction techniques, pharmaceutical and therapeutic potential - a review. Current Drug Metabolism 2018, 19, 1100–1110.

13. Alitonou, G.; Avlessi, F.; Wotto, V. D.; Ahoussi, E.; Dangou, J.; Sohounhloué, D. C. K. Composition chimique, propriétés antimicrobiennes et activités sur les tiques de l'huile essentielle d'*Eucalyptus tereticornis* Sm. Comptes Rendus Chimie 2004, 7, 1051–1055.
14. Rao, B. R. R. Chemical composition and uses of Indian rose-scented geranium (*Pelargonium* species) essential oil—a review. Journal of Essential Oil Bearing Plants 2009, 12, 381–394.
15. Guimaraes, A. C.; Meireles, L. M.; Lemos, M. F.; Guimaraes, M. C. C.; Endringer, D. C.; Fronza, M.; Scherer, R. Antibacterial activity of terpenes and terpenoids present in essential oils. Molecules 2019, 24, 1–12.
16. Zhang, H.; Wang, J. Constituents of the essential oils of garlic and citronella and their vapor-phase inhibition mechanism against *S. aureus*. Food Science and Technology Research 2019, 25, 65–74.
17. Klimek-Szczykutowicz, M.; Szopa, A.; Ekiert, H. *Citrus limon* (Lemon) phenomenon-a review of the chemistry, pharmacological properties, applications in the modern pharmaceutical, food, and cosmetics industries, and biotechnological studies. Plants (Basel) 2020, 9, 1–24.
18. do Evangelho, J. A.; da Silva Dannenberg, G.; Biduski, B.; El Halal, S. L. M.; Kringel, D. H.; Gularte, M. A.; Fiorentini, A. M.; da Rosa Zavareze, E. Antibacterial activity, optical, mechanical, and barrier properties of corn starch films containing orange essential oil. Carbohydrate Polymers 2019, 222, 1–8.
19. Tian, Y.; Dong, F.; Zhou, X.; Yang, X. Repellent, insecticidal and antimicrobial activities of leaf essential oils from three *Eucalyptus* species. Chemistry & Biodiversity 2020, 17, 1–11.
20. Wang, R.; Wang, R.; Yang, B. Extraction of essential oils from five cinnamon leaves and identification of their volatile compound compositions. Innovative Food Science and Emerging Technologies 2009, 10, 289–292.
21. Ilić, D. P.; Stanojević, L. P.; Troter, D. Z.; Stanojević, J. S.; Danilović, B. R.; Nikolić, V. D.; Nikolić, L. B. Improvement of the yield and antimicrobial activity of fennel (*Foeniculum vulgare* Mill.) essential oil by fruit milling. Industrial Crops & Products 2019, 142, 1–7.
22. Balasundram, N.; Sundram, K.; Samman, S. Phenolic compounds in plants and agri-industrial by-products: antioxidant activity, occurrence, and potential uses. Food Chemistry 2006, 99, 191–203.
23. Bizzo, H. R.; Hovell, A. M. C.; Rezende, C. M. Brazilian essential oils: general view, developments and perspectives. Quimica Nova 2009, 32, 588–594.
24. Woolf, A. Essential oil poisoning. Journal of Toxicology: Clinical Toxicology 1999, 37, 721–727.
25. Campolo, O.; Giunti, G.; Russo, A.; Palmeri, V.; Zappalà, L. Essential oils in stored product insect pest control. Journal of Food Quality 2018, 2018, 1–18.
26. Roger, C. R. The potential of botanical essential oils for insect pest control. Integrated Pest Management Reviews 1997, 2, 25–34.
27. Fanela, L. M.; Baldin, E. L. L.; Pannuti, L. E. R.; Cruz, P. L.; Crotti, A. E. M.; Takeara, R.; Kato, M. J. Lethal and inhibitory activities of plant-derived essential oils against *Bemisia tabaci* Gennadius (Hemiptera: Aleyrodidae) biotype B in tomato. Neotropical Entomology 2016, 45, 201–210.
28. Baldin, E. L. L.; Aguiar, G. P.; Fanela, T. L. M.; Soares, M. C. E.; Groppo, M.; Crotti, A. E. M. Bioactivity of *Pelargonium graveolens* essential oil and related monoterpenoids against sweet potato whitefly, *Bemisia tabaci* biotype B. Journal of Pest Science 2015, 88, 191–199.

29. Baldin, E. L. L.; Crotti, A. E. M.; Wakabayashi, K. A. L.; Silva, J. P. G. F.; Aguiar, G. P.; Souza, E. S.; Veneziani, R. C. S.; Groppo, M. Plant-derived essential oils affecting settlement and oviposition of *Bemisia tabaci* (Genn.) biotype B on tomato. Journal of Pest Science 2013, 86, 301–308.
30. Baldin, E. L. L.; Dias, H. J.; Souza, C. M.; Soares, M. C. E.; Grundman, C. O.; Santos, T. L. B.; Crotti, A. E. M. Insecticidal and inhibitory effects of dihydrobenzofuran neolignans on *Bemisia tabaci*. Journal of Pest Science 2019, 92, 861–869.
31. Franco, A. A.; Queiroz, M. S.; Perez, A. R.; Rosa, M. E.; Campos, Z. R.; Campos, A. R. Resistência de cultivares de soja a *Anticarsia gemmatalis*. Revista Inova Ciência & Tecnologia 2016, 2, 7–13.
32. Krinski, D.; Foerster, L. A.; Deschamps, S. Ovicidal effect of the essential oils from 18 Brazilian *Piper* species: controlling *Anticarsia gemmatalis* (Lepidoptera, Erebidae) at the initial stage of development. Acta Scientiarum Agronomy 2018, 40, 2–10.
33. Negrini, M.; Fidelis, E. G.; Schurt, D. A.; Silva, F. S.; Pereira, R. S.; Bizzo, H. R. Insecticidal activity of essential oils in controlling fall armyworm, *Spodoptera frugiperda*. Arquivos do Instituto Biológico 2019, 86, 1–9.
34. Tariq, S.; Wani, S.; Rasool, W.; Shafi, K.; Bhat, M. A.; Prabhakar, A.; Shalla, A. H.; Rather, M. A. A comprehensive review of the antibacterial, antifungal and antiviral potential of essential oils and their chemical constituents against drug-resistant microbial pathogens. Microbial Pathogenesis 2019, 134, 1–20.
35. Tzortzakis, N. G.; Economakis, C. D. Antifungal activity of lemongrass (*Cympopogon citratus* L.) essential oil against key postharvest pathogens. Innovative Food Science & Emerging Technologies 2007, 8, 253–258.
36. Suhem, K.; Matan, N.; Nisoa, M.; Matan, N. Inhibition of *Aspergillus flavus* on agar media and brown rice cereal bars using cold atmospheric plasma treatment. International Journal of Food Microbiology 2013, 161, 107–111.
37. Songsamoe, S.; Matan, N.; Matan, N. Antifungal activity of *Michelia alba* oil in the vapor phase and the synergistic effect of major essential oil components against *Aspergillus flavus* on brown rice. Food Control 2017, 77, 150–157.
38. Teper-Bamnolker, P.; Dudai, N.; Fischer, R.; Belausov, E.; Zemach, H.; Shoseyov, O.; Eshel, D. Mint essential oil can induce or inhibit potato sprouting by differential alteration of apical meristem. Planta 2010, 232, 179–186.
39. Campbell, M.; Segear, E.; Beers, L.; Knauber, D.; Suttle, J. Dormancy in potato tuber meristems: chemically induced cessation in dormancy matches the natural process based on transcript profiles. Functional & Integrative Genomics 2008, 8, 317–328.
40. Alamar, M. C.; Tosetti, R.; Landahl, S.; Bermejo, A.; Terry, L. A. Assuring potato tuber quality during storage: a future perspective. Frontiers in Plant Science 2017, 8, 1–6.
41. Shukla, S.; Pandey, S. S.; Chandra, M.; Pandey, A.; Bharti, N.; Barnawal, D.; Chanotiya, C. S.; Tandon, S.; Darokar, M. P.; Kalra, A. Application of essential oils as a natural and alternate method for inhibiting and inducing the sprouting of potato tubers. Food Chemistry 2019, 284, 171–179.
42. Besco, E.; Braccioli, E.; Vertuani, S.; Ziosi, P.; Brazzo, F.; Bruni, R.; Sacchetti, G.; Manfredini, S. The use of photochemiluminescence for the measurement of the Integral Antioxidant Capacity of baobab products. Food Chemistry 2007, 102, 1352–1356.
43. Kayode, R. M.; Azubuike, C. U.; Laba, S. A.; Dauda, A. O.; Balogun, M. A.; Ajala, S. A. Chemical composition and antimicrobial activities of the essential oil of *Adansonia digitata* stem-bark and leaf on postharvest control of tomato spoilage. Lwt-Food Science and Technology 2018, 93, 58–63.
44. Eum, H. L.; Hwang, D. K.; Linke, M.; Lee, S. K.; Zude, M. Influence of edible coating on quality of plum (*Prunus salicina* Lindl. cv. 'Sapphire'). European Food Research and Technology 2009, 229, 427–434.

45. Naeem, A.; Abbas, T.; Ali, T. M.; Hasnain, A. Effect of guar gum coatings containing essential oils on shelf life and nutritional quality of green-unripe mangoes during low temperature storage. International Journal of Biological Macromolecules 2018, 113, 403–410.
46. Casanova, E.; Garcia-Mina, J. M.; Calvo, M. I. Antioxidant and antifungal activity of *Verbena officinalis* L. leaves. Plant Foods for Human Nutrition 2008, 63, 93–97.
47. El Ouadi, Y.; Manssouri, M.; Bouyanzer, A.; Majidi, L.; Bendaif, H.; Elmsellem, H.; Shariati, M. A.; Melhaoui, A.; Hammouti, B. Essential oil composition and antifungal activity of *Melissa officinalis* originating from north-east Morocco, against postharvest phytopathogenic fungi in apples. Microbial Pathogenesis 2017, 107, 321–326.
48. Sharma, R. R.; Saxena, S. K. Rootstocks influence granulation in Kinnow mandarin (*Citrus nobilis* × *C. deliciosa*). Scientia Horticulturae 2004, 101, 235–242.
49. Jhalegar, M. J.; Sharma, R. R.; Pal, R. K.; Rana, V. Effect of postharvest treatments with polyamines on physiological and biochemical attributes of kiwifruit (*Actinidia deliciosa*) cv. Allison. Fruits 2012, 67, 13–22.
50. Jhalegar, M. J.; Sharma, R. R.; Singh, D. In vitro and in vivo activity of essential oils against major postharvest pathogens of Kinnow (*Citrus nobilis* × *C. deliciosa*) mandarin. Journal of Food Science and Technology-Mysore 2015, 52, 2229–2237.
51. Martinovic, T.; Andjelkovic, U.; Gajdosik, M. S.; Resetar, D.; Josic, D. Foodborne pathogens and their toxins. Journal of Proteomics 2016, 147, 226–235.
52. Munhuweyi, K.; Caleb, O. J.; Lennox, C. L.; van Reenen, A. J.; Opara, U. L. *In vitro* and *in vivo* antifungal activity of chitosan-essential oils against pomegranate fruit pathogens. Postharvest Biology and Technology 2017, 129, 9–22.
53. Lopez-Reyes, J. G.; Spadaro, D.; Prelle, A.; Garibaldi, A.; Gullino, M. L. Efficacy of plant essential oils on postharvest control of rots caused by fungi on different stone fruits *in vivo*. Journal of Food Protection 2013, 76, 631–639.
54. Elshafie, H. S.; Mancini, E.; Camele, I.; De Martino, L.; De Feo, V. In vivo antifungal activity of two essential oils from Mediterranean plants against postharvest brown rot disease of peach fruit. Industrial Crops and Products 2015, 66, 11–15.
55. Tejeswini, M. G.; Sowmya, H. V.; Swarnalatha, S. P.; Negi, P. S. Antifungal activity of essential oils and their combinations in *in vitro* and *in vivo* conditions. Archives of Phytopathology and Plant Protection 2013, 47, 564–570.
56. van Kan, J. A. L. Licensed to kill: the lifestyle of a necrotrophic plant pathogen. Trends in Plant Science 2006, 11, 247–253.
57. Nikkhah, M.; Hashemi, M.; Najafi, M. B. H.; Farhoosh, R. Synergistic effects of some essential oils against fungal spoilage on pear fruit. International Journal of Food Microbiology 2017, 257, 285–294.
58. Feliziani, E.; Romanazzi, G.; Smilanick, J. L. Application of low concentrations of ozone during the cold storage of table grapes. Postharvest Biology and Technology 2014, 93, 38–48.
59. Servili, A.; Feliziani, E.; Romanazzi, G. Exposure to volatiles of essential oils alone or under hypobaric treatment to control postharvest gray mold of table grapes. Postharvest Biology and Technology 2017, 133, 36–40.
60. Chu, C. L.; Wei, T. L.; Zhou, T. Fumigation of sweet cherries with thymol and acetic acid to reduce postharvest brown rot and blue mold rot. Fruits 2001, 56, 123–130.
61. Liu, W. T.; Chu, C. L.; Zhou, T. Thymol and acetic acid vapors reduce postharvest brown rot of apricots and plums. Hortscience 2002, 37, 151–156.
62. Nabigol, A.; Morshedi, H. Evaluation of the antifungal activity of the Iranian thyme essential oils on the postharvest pathogens of strawberry fruits. African Journal of Biotechnology 2011, 10, 9864–9869.
63. Oloum, H. Phytochemistry and ethno-pharmaceutics of *Calotropis procera*. Ethno-Pharmaceutical Products 2014, 1, 1–8.

64. Srinivasachary; Wiullocquet, L.; Savary, S. Resistance to rice sheath blight (*Rhizoctonia solani* Kuhn) [(teleomorph: *Thanatephorus cucumeris* (A.B. Frank) Donk.] disease: current status and perspectives. Euphytica 2011, 178, 1–28.
65. Persaud, R.; Khan, A.; Isaac, W. A.; Ganpat, W.; Saravanakumar, D. Plant extracts, bioagents and new generation fungicides in the control of rice sheath blight in Guyana. Crop Protection 2019, 119, 30–37.
66. Janisiewicz, W. J.; Conway, W. S. Combining biological control with physical and chemical treatments to control fruit decay after harvest. Stewart Postharvest Review 2010, 6, 1–16.
67. Gholamnejad, J.; Etebarian, H. R.; Roustaee, A.; Sahebani, N. A. Biological control of apples blue mold by isolates of *Saccharomyces cerevisiae*. Journal of Plant Protection Research 2009, 49, 270–275.
68. Ceredi, G.; Antoniacci, L.; Montuschi, C.; De Paoli, E.; Mari, M.; Gengotti, S. Ten years of field trials on grey mold control on strawberries. Acta Horticulturae 2009, 842, 327–330.
69. Gholamnezhad, J. Effect of plant extracts on activity of some defense enzymes of apple fruit in interaction with *Botrytis cinerea*. Journal of Integrative Agriculture 2019, 18, 115–123.
70. Srinivasan, R.; Riley, D.; Diffie, S.; Sparks, A.; Adkins, S. Whitefly population dynamics and evaluation of whitefly-transmitted tomato yellow leaf curl virus (TYLCV)-resistant tomato genotypes as whitefly and TYLCV reservoirs. Journal of Economic Entomology 2012, 105, 1447–1456.
71. Firdays, S.; van Heusden, A. W.; Hidayati, N.; Supena, E. D. J.; Visser, R. G. F.; Vosman, B. Resistance to *Bemisia tabaci* in tomato wild relatives. Euphytica 2012, 187, 31–45.
72. Baldin, E. L. L.; Fanela, T. L. M.; Pannuti, L. E. R.; Kato, M. J.; Takeara, R.; Crotti, A. E. M. Botanical extracts: alternative control for silverleaf whitefly management in tomato. Horticultura Brasileira 2015, 33, 59–65.
73. Chauret, D. C.; Bernard, C. B.; Arnason, J. T.; Durst, T.; Krishnamurty, H. G.; Sanchez-Vindas-P.; Moreno, N.; San Roman, L.; Poveda, L. Insecticidal neolignans from *Piper decurrens*. Journal of Natural Products 1996, 59, 152–155.

Part IV

Regulation Aspects

12 Registration of Phytomedicines

Technical Requirements and Highlights on Regulation Instruments

Wagner Luiz Ramos Barbosa, Wanderley Pereira Oliveira, Andressa Santa Brígida da Silva, and Ailton Castro Pinheiro

CONTENTS

12.1 Introduction 309
12.2 Technical Features of Phytomedicine Development Associated with the Registration Process 311
  12.2.1 Selection of a Medicinal Plant Species for the Development of Herbal Products 311
  12.2.2 Characterisation of the Active Phytopharmaceutical Ingredient...... 312
12.3 Highlights on Regulatory Instruments of Herbal Medicines in Brazil: The Resolutions 313
  12.3.1 The ANVISA Collegiate Board Resolution Nr. 17/2000 313
  12.3.2 The ANVISA Collegiate Board Resolution Nr. 48/2004 315
  12.3.3 The ANVISA Collegiate Board Resolution Nr. 14/2010 317
  12.3.4 The ANVISA Collegiate Board Resolution Nr. 26/2014 319
12.4 Further Documents Associated with Phytomedicine Regulation 322
  12.4.1 The Brazilian Pharmacopoeia Formulary of Phytomedicines 322
  12.4.2 The Brazilian Pharmacopoeia Phytotherapeutical Memento 322
12.5 Concluding Remarks 323
References 323

12.1 INTRODUCTION

The regulatory standards for herbal medicines are essential requirements to ensure their quality, safety, and efficacy to exert their healing properties with minimal health risk. However, the definitions, requirements, scope, or even terminology in which herbal medicines are classified vary from country to country [1]. Depending

DOI: 10.1201/9781003225416-16

on the country, these products are defined as traditional medicines, herbal medicines, herbal supplements, herbal pharmaceuticals, phytoprotectants, phytotherapeutical agents, health food, among others [2]. Therefore, the approaches used to license, dispense, manufacture, and trade herbal medicines are not harmonised worldwide. In some countries and regions, the regulatory issues are being addressed and evolved for a long time, establishing national offices, specific regulations, accepted status and health claims, and registration systems.

Notwithstanding, in other nations, the regulatory framework is rudimentary or inexistent, being the herbal products regarded as health foods or even foods, without therapeutic claims [1, 3, 4]. These differences in the regulatory frameworks of herbal medicines globally have been pointed out in several studies reported continuously [1, 3–9]. In 1998, the World Health Organization (WHO) published a non-formal document reviewing the regulatory situation of the herbal medicines of 52 members states, aiming to share national experiences in formulating policies and in the measures for their registration and regulations; which can contribute to support the preparation of a model of harmonised guidelines [1]. A WHO survey conducted in 2001 showed that 57 countries had regulations requiring traditional medicines to meet the safety assessment criteria as those in place for conventional pharmaceuticals, while another 82 listed some requirements, which run in parallel. Concerning the production, 73 countries enforced the same rules of conventional pharmaceuticals, and 28 nations reported no requirements to guide the production [2].

Reddy and Thomas [7] presented an extensive and detailed evaluation of the regulatory framework for herbal medicines globally, covering over 180 countries, distinctly explaining existing regulatory situations and registration requirements. Other important publications also compare the differences in the regulatory frame worldwide or regionally, as can be seen in Metta et al. [3], Mtewa et al. [9], Knoess and Wiesner [6], Thakkar et al. [4], Knöss [5], and Calixto [8].

Therefore, establishing a global harmonised regulation for herbal medicines are the basic requirements for the production of standardised herbal products, with the same safety, quality, and efficacy requirements to be accepted globally. The harmonised regulation rules will contribute significantly to the increase in trading of these products between the nations. Regulatory bodies of several countries and regions, like United States Food and Drug Administration (USFDA) and European Medicines Agency (EMA), together WHO have been addressing efforts to establish a uniform and harmonised regulation for herbal products, but much work is still to be done.

In the European Union (EU), common law has been enforced to harmonise assessment of herbal medicinal products and facilitate access to the market in different member states; establishing the basic definitions, common standards, and requirements for the herbal medicinal products [5]. According to Knöss and Wiesner [6], the standards defined in the EU herbal monographs of the Committee on Herbal Medicinal Products (HMPC) and the quality requirements laid down in the European Pharmacopoeia is an excellent model for the harmonisation of the regulatory frameworks for herbal and traditional medicines valid worldwide; which can contribute to the worldwide availability of traditional medicines based on appropriate standards.

In this chapter, we will examine, as a model, the Brazilian experience on the regulations for the manufacturing and registration of herbal medicinal products, which has evolved over half a century and currently has a long period of stability and efficiency. Since the normative instruments for registering herbal medicines can be changed at any time in the face of new scientific data or trends of the herbal medicine market, a predominantly chronological discussion will be avoided. Some technological aspects of the development of herbal medicines associated with registration processes will also be addressed briefly.

12.2 TECHNICAL FEATURES OF PHYTOMEDICINE DEVELOPMENT ASSOCIATED WITH THE REGISTRATION PROCESS

12.2.1 Selection of a Medicinal Plant Species for the Development of Herbal Products

The selection of plant species is the initial and most relevant step in investigating medicinal plants as a active phytopharmaceutical ingredient (API) in therapeutic formulations. The selection of the plant material to develop herbal medicine can be performed based on the traditional knowledge (including the ethnoguided survey), random, ecological, and chemotaxonomic approaches.

The selection based on popular knowledge regarding the plant species used involves the claims of medicinal effects and aspects associated with the stages of harvesting and processing the plant; therefore, allowing the proposition of a rational and precise product development protocol. This approach provides important and necessary information for obtaining the intermediate pharmaceutical ingredient, such as parts of the plant used, extraction solvent (water or hydroethanolic solvents), and other factors. This knowledge can also guide pharmacological studies to scientific verification of the assigned pharmacological activity, assisting in selecting experimental models that simulate the nosological frame characterised by the health symptoms reported by the plant's users. This approach are essential for a rational development of a phytomedicine. Information regarding the traditional or popular uses of the plant and the alleged pharmacological activities, when historically registered or documented, can supply the need for safety studies, facilitating the registration process of the developed herbal medicine [10] strongly.

The plant species selection can also be carried out through the chemotaxonomic survey. Substances belonging to a secondary metabolite class are associated with a certain pharmacological activity based on data already published in the scientific literature. For example, salicylates are linked to anti-inflammatory, antiphlogistic, and analgesic activities. Hence, *Salix* spp. could serve as a source of an active pharmaceutical ingredient of a herbal medicine.

The random approach to select plant species for the development of herbal medicine can also be used. This method involves the random collection of the plant species that will supply the active phytopharmaceutical ingredient according to their availability. Although the pharmacological utility of the selected species is imprecise, this procedure most likely leads to discovering new substances and, at best, phytomedicines.

An ecological survey following the observation of interactions between plants and other organisms existing at the collection site is another method used to select plant species to develop herbal medicines. It presents a variation, zoopharmacognosy, which proposes the selection of species regularly ingested by animals.

12.2.2 Characterisation of the Active Phytopharmaceutical Ingredient

The phytochemical characterisation of herbaceous active pharmaceutical ingredients begins with extracting the substances present through popular or traditional phytotherapy techniques systematised by pharmaceutical science. The product of this process, an extract, must be tolerable by the animal organism; therefore, it must not contain aggressive solvents. Ideally, water or a mixture of water and ethanol at known proportions are used, and adults can directly take mixtures of up to 40°GL (approx. 40%). The substances present in the extract belong to metabolic classes that chemical reactions can detect. Together with the chromatographic profile obtained by thin-layer chromatography, this data is necessary to register the herbal medicine, as expressed in the Collegiate Board Resolution (RDC) Nr. 26/2014 [11].

The definition of the phytochemical and chromatographic profiles of the extract allows tracing the analytical strategy to isolate substances that may be responsible for the alleged biological activity, to be characterised by pharmacological tests. The most used technique for this step, the high-performance liquid chromatography—HPLC, has been coupled with spectroanalytical techniques such as ultraviolet spectroscopy—HPLC-UV(DAD) or mass spectrometry—HPLC-MS, in addition to nuclear magnetic resonance—HPLC-NMR. Obtaining the substances of interest in an adequate quantity allows pharmacological tests to link, experimentally, the alleged and detected activity, to the isolated substance(s). The quantification of this substance permits the standardisation of the extract, the active phytopharmaceutical ingredient. This procedure can be considered a gold standard for quality control of herbal medicine and positively impacts herbal medicine registration.

After detecting and quantifying the substances chosen as markers, it is necessary to validate the method developed for standardisation, to ensure that the data generated is reliable and reproducible within limits defined previously when the method was created. The Brazilian National Agency of Health Surveillance (ANVISA) regulates the validation of quality control methods through the Resolutions of the Collegiate Board, accessible free of charge, specific for this purpose, and the most recent is the RDC 166 published in 2017 [12]. A validated quality control method is a mandatory requirement for a successful registration process.

Other parameters of chemical and microbiological quality, such as the content of heavy metals and the concentration of bacteria and fungi in the active pharmaceutical ingredient, are determinants for the quality of the final product and are linked to the cultivation and manufacturing of plant material, including its collection, storage, and processing.

Clinical and nonclinical trials are also essential requirements for registering any drugs, including those of plant origin, and parameters of efficacy and safety must also be guaranteed. However, in herbal medicines, the safe and effective use over decades or generations can prove the safety and effectiveness of the product, provided that data are faithfully registered or documented and reported in the scientific literature [11].

12.3 HIGHLIGHTS ON REGULATORY INSTRUMENTS OF HERBAL MEDICINES IN BRAZIL: THE RESOLUTIONS

In Brazil, there is a specific regulatory framework to regulate herbal medicines that date back to 1967, when Ordinance 22, which establishes rules for the use of herbal preparations, was enacted [13]. The specific regulation on herbal medicines registration has its beginning, after the creation of the Brazilian Unified Health System (SUS) in 1990, with the verification of the use and availability of herbal remedies by the health system's users. The finding of the widespread use of this type of therapeutic resource by primary care patients and the increase in the sale of herbal medicines led to the promulgation of Ordinance Nr. 6 of 1995 [14]. This Ordinance institutes and regulates the registration of herbal products in the Brazilian health surveillance system and defines these products as follows:

> Herbal medicines are therapeutic resources obtained technically and elaborated exclusively from active botanical raw materials for curative purposes. They are characterised by the effectiveness and safety of use, reproducibility and constancy of their quality. It is the finished product packaged and labelled. Only pharmaceutical adjuvants authorised by the enforced legislation may be used to prepare the herbal medicine. Phytomedicines cannot include isolated active substances alone or in mixtures, even of plant origin. In situations where this occurs, the product is not considered a herbal medicine [14].

This definition remains the same today.

After the creation of the Brazilian National Health Surveillance Agency - ANVISA - (1999), the Collegiate Board Resolution—RDC Nr. 17—was published in 2000 [15], being the first to deal specifically with the registration of herbal medicines. As a result of a review of the criteria, RDC Nr. 48 was published on 16 March 2004 [16]. The advancement of the qualification of products and services related to phytotherapy leads to RDC 14/2010 published on 5 April 2004 [17]. Aiming to improve the rules for granting registration, enhancing the quality of herbal medicines authorised by the Surveillance Agency, the current regulation—RDC 26—was published on 13 May 2014 [11]. Only industrialised herbal medicines for human use are registered at the Brazilian Surveillance Agency (ANVISA). The significant growth of the herbal medicine production sector led to establishing the so-called regulated sector formed by the herbal medicines manufacturing companies.

12.3.1 The ANVISA Collegiate Board Resolution Nr. 17/2000

The creation of the Brazilian National Health Surveillance Agency (ANVISA) on 26 January 1999 increased the professionalisation of the quality control of services and products related to the collective health of Brazilian society. To contribute to the qualification of the therapeutic resources used in Phytotherapy, ANVISA promulgates on 24 February 2000, the Resolution of the Collegiate Board (RDC) Nr. 17 [15], that approved the Technical Regulation (TR) to Standardise the Registration of Herbal Medicines in the Health Surveillance System and introduced the categories "*Traditional Herbal Products*" and "*Similar Herbal Medicines*".

RDC 17/2000 categorises and characterises three types of products to be registered and define "*Herbal Medicine*" as a therapeutic resource "obtained by adequate technological processes from only botanical raw materials, having prophylactic, curative, palliative, or diagnostic purposes. It is characterised by well-established information on effectiveness and risks, and by the reproducibility and constancy of its quality". Products that include isolated active substances of any origin or associated with plant extracts are not considered herbal medicine.

The first category of herbal medicines cited in RDC 17/2000 is the *New Herbal Medicine*, a product with effectiveness, safety, and quality scientifically proved at the competent federal agency at the time of registration. It can be used as a reference for the registration of similar products. Technically, the selection of plant species of interest for the development of herbal medicine can be carried out based on the traditional or folk knowledge (accessed by an ethnoguided search), random, chemotaxonomic, and ecological approaches as described in Section 12.2.1.

A curious example of the ecological approach was the development of an antiophidic remedy, very popular in Northeastern Brazil. The tale tells about a practitioner-pharmacist who circulated throughout the Brazilian Northeastern inland, selling handmade medicines and pharmaceutical products. On one of these trips, the apothecary would have observed a fight between a lizard and a poisonous snake. At each snakebite, the lizard run to a bush and chew some leaves. Based on this observation, Mr Pessoa, the surname of the practitioner, developed an association of herbs that for decades was marketed by him as a remedy for snakebites in the cities of the Northeastern Brazilian inland. On his deathbed, Pessoa, when making his last confession, told the priest the formula of the product "Específico P. Pessoa" and offered the marketing rights to the Brazilian Catholic Church. It so happens that, with the improvement of the regulation on herbal medicines in Brazil, the product became irregular, and its sale prohibited throughout the Brazilian territory. It was impossible to regularise the "Específico P. Pessoa" production and commercialisation by registering its composition at ANVISA, since this information is a religious confession with guaranteed secrecy. Hence, the antiophidic remedy of recognised effectiveness continues to be produced and marketed without registration, being regularly apprehended at each inspection action of the Health Surveillance Agency.

The RDC 17/2000 also addresses the most common and well-founded category of phytomedicine—*Traditional Herbal Product*, which has its origin in medicinal plants traditionally or popularly used due to its alleged effect and perception of the risks to the user's health, even lacking scientific verification. The product effectiveness is documented by technoscientific information, indexed publications, and ethnoguided research.

In ethnopharmacological research, the main focus remains on explaining the action mechanism and identifying the active substance(s). Details on the formulation and studies on it are subject for further investigation. Medicinal plant's ethnobotanical survey is also used to select plant species to develop a phytomedicine. The centrality of the approach is to know and describe the botanical characteristics of the plant: taxonomy, anatomy, microscopic characteristics, among others, and environmental description with ecological and economic purposes [18].

More recently, beside the insertion of the pharmacists in search for information on the use and preparation of herbal medicines by residents of Brazilian inland, as a cultural heritage of this population, the ethnopharmaceutical approach emerged as another strategy for the investigation of popular/traditional herbal medicines. Many articles published in scientific journals dealing with medicinal plants and their pharmacological activities and chemical constituents often report data obtained from extracts that do not resemble the traditional or popular use. On the other hand, the published information about the composition and activity of herbal preparations using the same part of the plant, solvent and extraction method traditionally used are very useful in the development of traditional herbal medicines; and can contribute very efficiently to compose the registration report, according to the regulatory framework [19].

The development of phytomedicine through an ethnopharmaceutical approach is based on information regarding the botanical classification of medicinal plants. This information is complemented by a botanical investigation aiming the complete characterisation of plant material.

Information is also available on the alleged use of the plant, which can be fully investigated by models or pharmacological systems that resemble the pathological frame of the disease for which the plant is indicated; and, mainly, information on how to prepare and use the traditional medicine. Ethnopharmaceutical research is a multidisciplinary subject at the interface between basic and applied disciplines such as Sociology, Economics, Chemistry, and Pharmacology, which allows obtaining vital information from the interviews and participating observations carried out during the research [19].

Finally, RDC 17 characterises *Similar Herbal Medicine* as the one that contains the same botanical raw materials, the same concentration of active pharmaceutical ingredient or marker substances, has the same route of administration, pharmaceutical form, dosage, and the therapeutic indication of the reference herbal medicine. The product report for registration of a similar phytomedicine must present the technical description of the plant raw material, the active pharmaceutical ingredient, and the final product and include analyses of marker substance and toxicological and pharmacological tests at clinical and nonclinical levels to confirm the dose–activity relationship.

This resolution was effective until part of the regulated sector reacted to the demanding rules set for the registration of traditional products. They required quality parameters obtained in relatively sophisticated and expensive equipment, impossible to obtain considering the size of the sector's companies. Hence, the RDC 17/2000 was revoked and replaced by the RDC 48/2004 [16], which will be commented on in the next section.

12.3.2 The ANVISA Collegiate Board Resolution Nr. 48/2004

In its sanitary, scientific, and technological aspects, the agency responsible for the regulation of phytotherapy started to consider the manifestations of the regulated sector, whether questioning or collaborative, which led ANVISA to incorporate constructive criticism in the review of regulatory instruments (through public consultations, more recently). Thus, RDC Nr. 48, published on 16 March 2004 [16], was drafted, changing the terms of the previous resolution by excluding the "traditional herbal products" provided in RDC 17/2000 [15]. The document provides information for the transition between the two resolutions, giving a deadline for providing data and reports for the new registration conditions.

The TR instituted by this RDC defines the active principle as the "substance, or chemical classes (for example, alkaloids, flavonoids and fatty acids), chemically characterised, whose pharmacological action is known and responsible—totally or partially—for the therapeutic effects of herbal medicine". Identifying these substances allows the standardisation of the active herbal pharmaceutical ingredient, which characterises a standardised extract according to the regulation of the EMA [20].

TR also describes: *herbal drug*—medicinal plant or some of its parts, after collection, stabilisation, and drying processes, which can be whole, scraped, crushed, or pulverised; *herbal drug derivative*—products of the extraction of botanical raw material: extract, tincture, oil, wax, exudate, juice, among others; *phytomedicine*—medicine obtained from exclusively active plant raw materials. It is characterised by knowledge of the effectiveness, risks of use, and constancy of its quality. The efficacy and safety are validated through ethnopharmacological research, techno-scientific documentation from the literature, or phase 3 clinical trials. The products containing isolated active phytochemicals alone or associated with plant extracts are not considered herbal medicines.

This resolution also guides the preparation of the quality control report of the finished product, highlighting: (1) the applicant must present a detailed description of all methodologies used in the control of the phytomedicine quality, describing the analytical methods, duly validated, according to the official methods [12], indicating the bibliographic references or development description, and (2) the results of phytochemical screening (by metabolic classes) or high-performance liquid chromatography—HPLC or gas chromatography—GC chromatographic profile (with peaks for separate substances) should also be provided, when applicable. Provide translation when the language is not English or Spanish (or Portuguese).

RDC 48/2004 brings the innovation of allowing the validation of the safety of use and the therapeutic indication(s) through a scoring system where the proposed formulation must reach at least 6 points; earned according to safety and efficacy studies reported in the references contained in the "Bibliographical Reference List for the Assessment of the Safety and Effectiveness of Phytomedicines" (updates are published regularly) [21]. The listed literature is divided into four categories, scoring three (3), two (2), one (1), or half a point (0.5), according to their importance. References include WHO monographs, theses, and dissertations on the subject and even books with empirical knowledge about the use of medicinal plants. These references must contain information on the safety of use and the therapeutic indications proposed, derived from studies in humans, corresponding to at least 50% of the score.

Also, the document infers another way to validate data about de phytomedicine to be registered; that is, the applicant must provide proof of the safety of use (nonclinical toxicology, clinical toxicology) and therapeutic effectiveness (nonclinical pharmacology, clinical pharmacology) of the phytomedicine. Clinical and nonclinical toxicological tests must meet the official requirements established in guides and by regulatory research committees.

Finally, to ensure the effectiveness and safety of the registering phytomedicine, the resolution foresees the possibility of, use a bibliographic survey (ethnopharmacological (in general, ethnoguided) on the use of the proposed plant, technical–scientific documentation, or publications), which will be evaluated according to the following criteria: (a) indication of use: episodic or for short periods; (b) consistency concerning the proposed therapeutic indications; (c) absence of toxic risk to the user; (d) absence of toxic chemical groups or substances, or present within proven safety limits; (e) proof of safe use for 20 years or more.

RDC 48 brings as an innovation the possibility of "if the medicine" to be registered "is part of the latest issue of the List of Simplified Phytomedicine Registration", and presents the same characteristics there defined, there is no need to validate the therapeutic indications and safety of use [22]. It is a simplified registration system in which the specifications mentioned above must be fully respected: botanical part used, standardisation, forms of use, therapeutic indications/actions, dose, route of administration, dosage—when described—and restriction of use. Other pharmaceutical forms for the same administration route may be formulated, provided that the dose equivalence calculations between the regulated formulation and the proposed pharmaceutical forms are presented. Inclusions in the List of Simplified Phytomedicine Registration will be published periodically according to the experience accumulated by the herbal medicine registration area of ANVISA with the support of external consultants [16].

The intensification of the commercialisation of medicinal plants, such as raw herbal medicines or in the form of products with low technological content, led ANVISA to seek for regularisation of such herbal medicine marketing, promulgating the RDC Nr. 10, on 9 March 2010, which regulated the notification of "medicinal" plant species at ANVISA [23]. Then, to modernise the regulations for phytomedicines, the RDC 48/2004 was replaced by RDC 14/2010, presented as follow.

12.3.3 The ANVISA Collegiate Board Resolution Nr. 14/2010

On 31 March 2010, ANVISA published RDC Nr. 14 [17], in which phytomedicines are still considered therapeutic products obtained exclusively from active plant materials, whose effectiveness and safety are validated through ethnopharmacological or uses surveys, technical–scientific documentation, or clinical evidence.

Resolution 14/2010 [17] provided guidelines for registering herbal medicines in their context, without presenting a TR, such as the previous resolutions. For example, the document directly defines several and diversified items necessary for the registration required for the proposed phytomedicine, for example, "derived from herbal medicine: product obtained by extraction of the natural medicinal plant or herbal medicine, which can be presented in the form of extract, tincture, alcoholate, fixed and volatile oil, wax, exudate and others".

The document expands the possibility of investigating the traditional/popular use of medicinal plants in the development of phytomedicine. It presents a definition for ethnoguided studies, such as collecting information on the use of medicinal plants based on ethnological aspects of the human group that uses them. This possibility has already been discussed in the previous section of this chapter (see Section 12.2.1).

The resolution also brings the definition of phytocomplex as a set of substances synthesised by the primary and secondary plant metabolism, which combined are responsible for the biological effects of a medicinal plant or its derivatives, altering the understanding of what expresses the activity of a plant. In the previous resolutions, the active principle was mentioned and defined, as an expression that goes back to the Victorian era of pharmaceutical science when there was not much knowledge about the structure of chemical substances and their occurrence in plant organisms.

The document defines terms related to the presence of chemical substances in medicinal plants and their derivatives, such as phytocomplex, to build an identity for the regulatory framework for the registration of phytomedicines, disconnecting it from the current procedure for synthetic drugs, although maintaining the character of the biological action of herbal medicines. The term marker is defined as a substance or class of plant chemical substances (for example, alkaloids, flavonoids, and fatty acids) present in the plant raw material, preferably correlated with the therapeutic effect. The marker is used to reference the quality control of the herbal ingredient and herbal raw material, leading to the quantification or even standardisation of the extract, as explained earlier in this chapter.

In line with world events at the time the resolution was enacted, the recommended quality control report should provide information on the control of transmissible spongiform encephalopathy (TSE); results of the accelerated stability study of three pilot batches, accompanied by long-term stability studies in progress, or long-term stability studies already completed, each following the "Guide to conducting drug stability studies" published by ANVISA Special Resolution Nr. 1, of 29 July 2005 [24], and its updates.

This resolution brings the possibility of regulating herbal medicines that contain more than one plant species designated as an association of plant species. For the quality control of this type of product, the text considers that the quantitative determination of a marker by species is not possible, being possible to present the chromatographic profile(s) to demonstrate the presence of at least one specific marker for each species presented in the association, complemented by the quantitative determination of the largest possible number of characteristic markers for each species.

The section Effectiveness and Safety Report exposed in the RDC 14 recommends that the presentation of a technical report must contain information on safety and efficacy proven by one of the options already discussed in the previous section [17]: punctuation in the technoscientific literature; pre-clinical and clinical safety and efficacy trials; traditional use; and presence in the "List of herbal medicines for simplified registration", published by ANVISA in the Normative Instruction - IN Nr. 5, from 11 December 2008 [25], and updates. When proof of safety and efficacy is made by punctuating only with references from the "List of bibliographic references for assessing the safety and efficacy of herbal medicines", at least one reference must comprise information from studies in humans. At least 50% of the score must be obtained from information on studies in humans.

Finally, the resolution presents some characteristics such as the phytochemical prospecting of the metabolic classes present in the herbal active pharmaceutical ingredient through the performance of chemical, qualitative, or semi-quantitative screening tests, using specific reagents to detect the presence of functional groups characteristic of the substances present in the plant species used in the formulation. The determination of the chromatographic profile of the herbal active pharmaceutical ingredient must be obtained under defined conditions and using a standard chromatographic substance, characteristic of the plant species, to enable the identification or characterisation of the plant species used in the formulation or, in a given case, the differentiation of other species.

Another innovation brought by the resolution refers to the relationship "herbal drug:plant derivative": an expression that defines the ratio between an amount of herbal drug and the respective volume of plant derivative obtained. The numeric expression consists of a first element—defined as a number or an interval—corresponding to the quantity of the herbal drug used to prepare the derivative; followed by a double dot (:) and then the number corresponding to the volume obtained from the herbal drug derivative [11].

12.3.4 The ANVISA Collegiate Board Resolution Nr. 26/2014

Resolution Nr. 14 was revoked by RDC No. 26/2014, published on 13 May 2014, which is the most recent and brings as innovation the categorisation of herbal medicines in two classes [11]: phytomedicines (MF) and traditional *herbal products* (PTF), giving their respective conceptualisation. PTFs are herbal medicines produced exclusively based on local, popular, or traditional knowledge, obtained from exclusively active vegetable raw materials, whose safety and efficacy are based on data published in the technical–scientific literature, which are intended to be used without the supervision of a health professional for diagnosis, prescription, or follow-up. The proof of use time was also made official based on technical–scientific literature to prove the PTF's safety and efficacy and regulate the formulation's production and use.

This resolution states that herbal medicines are subject to registration and traditional herbal products are subject to registration or notification. Medicinal plants in the form of a herbal drug, called medicinal teas, will be exempted from registration and must be notified as described in this resolution, in the traditional herbal product category. Such products, to be notified, cannot contain excipients in their formulations, including only herbal drugs. The RDC does not recommend the registration or notification of remedies prepared by the traditional healers and communities of the country, in a non-industrialised way and with non-profit purposes.

This resolution (currently in force) brings more definitions for the registration and notification of phytomedicines and traditional herbal products, respectively, such as those listed as follow:

Medicinal tea: Herbal drug with medicinal purposes to be prepared, by the consumer, by infusion, decoction, or maceration.

Infusion: Is a form of use, which consists of pouring boiling drinking water over the herbal drug and then covering the container for about 5 minutes, in general. This method is indicated for soft to less rigid pharmacogen, such as leaves, flowers, inflorescence, and fruits, or with volatile active substances or with good solubility in water.

Decoction: A form of use, which consists in boiling the herbal drug in drinking water for a previously defined time. This method is indicated for plant drugs with rigid consistency, such as bark, roots, rhizomes, stems, seeds, and leathery leaves or that contain substances with low water solubility.

Water maceration: It consists in maintain the herbal drug in contact with drinking water at room temperature for a given time, specific to each herbal drug. This method is indicated for herbal drugs containing substances that can degrade with heating.

Along with the characterisation presented in previous resolutions, RDC 26/2014 adds that phytomedicine can be simple—when the active ingredient is obtained from a single medicinal plant species—or composite—when the active ingredient is from more than one plant species.

In line with the updating of concepts related to phytotherapy and improvement of the concept of the active ingredient, the Brazilian Pharmacopoeia, in cooperation with the Brazilian Health Surveillance Agency (ANVISA), introduced the term active pharmaceutical herbal ingredient (IFAV) to designate the active botanical material, that is, the herbal drug or plant derivative used in the development and production of the herbal medicine. The Brazilian organisations responsible for the resolutions discussed here, based on the exchange with their foreign counterparts, adopted the term chemical marker, which has been defined previously in another RDC. Here, it is complemented with the following information: marker can be active when it is responsible for the therapeutic activity of the phytocomplex, or analytic when its relation to the therapeutic activity of the phytocomplex has not yet been demonstrated. The quantification of the active marker allows the standardisation of the IFAV. When analytical markers are used, the extract is considered quantified, since the marker has no demonstrated relation to the activity.

This resolution was prepared in a context, in which, the bibliographic production in pharmaceutical science gains identity and, even in an initial way, deals with issues relevant to regulating the registration and notification processes of phytomedicines. The technical–scientific documentation used to compose the technical reports, to support the data related to the product to be registered, can be based on bibliographic references, national or international indexed scientific publications, and technical publications, such as those issued by health and government agencies, for example, pharmacopoeia and other codices recognised by ANVISA.

Within the innovative aspect of the current regulatory framework, resulting from the strengthening of pharmaceutical science and the exchange with EMA and other similar organisations, the notification is presented as a procedure to formalise the PTF. Notification is a prior communication to ANVISA stating the intention to manufacture, import, or commercialise traditional herbal products. For phytomedicines, the registration is an instrument whereby the Ministry of Health, in the use of a specific attribution, determines the prior registration of phytomedicine at the competent organisation or entity by assessing compliance with the legal–administrative and technical–scientific character related to the effectiveness, safety, and quality of these products, for their introduction in the market and their commercialisation or use.

To complete the registration process of a phytomedicine, the applicant must prepare a technical report that consists in the documentation presented by the company, describing the elements that constitute and characterise the product, and that clarifies its peculiarities, purposes, way of use; declaring the indications and contraindications among other information that enable the health authority to decide on the registration application.

The innovation of RDC 26/2014 consists in the inclusion of product notification, a simplified form of registration applied to PTF. According to the resolution, only traditional herbal medicinal products containing herbal active pharmaceutical ingredients that are listed in the latest edition of the Brazilian Pharmacopoeia Formulary of Phytomedicines (FFFB) [26], and that has a specific monograph on quality control published in a pharmacopoeia recognised by ANVISA, will be allowed as a traditional herbal product, following the criteria reported in the resolution [11].

Table 12.1 shows the differences between phytomedicines [MF] and traditional herbal medicinal products [PTF] concerning the characteristics and requirements for their registration and notifications, including, in addition to RDC No. 26/2014,

TABLE 12.1
Characterisation and Differences Regarding the Regulation of Phytomedicines—MF and Traditional Herbal Medicinal Products—PTF

Phytomedicine	Common or simplified registration	Common registration: it is based on the presentation of efficacy and safety data from an experimental investigation. Simplified registration: if the active plant is one of the plant species listed in normative instruction (IN)/MS nr. 02 of 13 May 2014 (or in its updates).
Traditional herbal medicinal product	Can be notified or registered	Notification: possible for the products listed in the Brazilian Pharmacopoeia Phytomedicine Formulary and which have a specific quality control monograph, published in a pharmacopoeia recognised by ANVISA, according to the criteria of Art. 38 of RDC Nr. 26/2014 [11]. Record: • Prepared according to the literature that describes the safe and effective use for at least 30 years; • If it is obtained from a plant species listed in Normative Instruction/MS No. 02 of 13 May 2014). • Presence in herbal monographs of traditional use by the European community (community herbal monographs with traditional use). Prepared by the Committee on Herbal Medicinal Products of the European Medicine Agency.

Source: RDC No. 26/2014 and IN/MS No. 02 of 13 May 2014.

Normative Instruction of the Ministry of Health No. 02 13 May 2014, which deals with the simplified registration of phytomedicines and traditional herbal medicinal product [27].

12.4 FURTHER DOCUMENTS ASSOCIATED WITH PHYTOMEDICINE REGULATION

12.4.1 The Brazilian Pharmacopoeia Formulary of Phytomedicines

The Brazilian Pharmacopoeia Formulary of Phytomedicines was prepared by the Technical-thematic committee for Policy for Medicinal Plants and Herbal Medicines Support; which dealt with handling and dispensing Herbal Medicines in the Phytotherapy Programs of the SUS, aiming at an effective therapeutic response. The formulary contains definitions of terms and expressions related to handling herbal medicines and formalises formulations to be produced in the laboratory, supported by scientific literature, and by formulations traditionally used in recognised herbal programs of different Brazilian regions. The formulations described can be used as a basis for the development of registered or notified herbal medicines, as explained in the previous section.

The first edition of the formulary was launched in November 2011 by the Brazilian Health Surveillance Agency (ANVISA), through the Brazilian Pharmacopoeia (RDC 60/2011) [28], with a supplement added in 2018 (RDC 255/2018) [29]. The formulary was fully revised and restructured, and a second edition has been published recently (February 2021) [26], with previous versions being revoked.

The Brazilian Pharmacopoeia Formulary of Phytomedicines presents manufacturing rules, and the formulations prepared under standardised form are considered official. The formulations included are pharmaceutical forms and products used in phytotherapy programs in different Brazilian regions. The second edition of the Brazilian Pharmacopoeia Formulary of phytotherapy contains 85 (eighty-five) monographs, including 85 (eighty-five) species, associated with traditionally used pharmaceutical formulations, with 236 different formulations.

The formulations listed in the Brazilian Pharmacopoeia Formulary of phytotherapy are recognised as pharmacopoeial and can be manipulated to establish a minimum stock in *Living Pharmacies* (the Phytotherapy Program of the Brazilian Health Ministry); establishments authorised by Ordinance 886 (20 April 2010), for the exclusive handling of medicinal plants and herbal medicines. The Formulary contains information on the appropriated manipulation, use indications, and restrictions for each plant species, with the quality requirements defined in specific rules for *Living Pharmacies*, as stated in the RDC Nr. 18/2013 [30].

12.4.2 The Brazilian Pharmacopoeia Phytotherapeutical Memento

Another document produced with the contribution of the Technical-thematic committee for the National Policy on Medicinal Plants and Herbal Medicines Support of the Brazilian Pharmacopoeia, is the Brazilian Pharmacopoeia Phytotherapeutical Memento—*Memento Fitoterápico* [31]. It is a document for fast consultation by prescribing professionals to ensure safe and pertinent information on plant species for therapeutic use, to support prescriptions of herbal medicines in primary health care. Memento presents important information concerning the plant species: common name, plant part used, main therapeutic indications and contraindications, precautions, side effects, interactions, pharmaceutical forms used, way of administration, and other important data. The document brings 28 monographs and must be used together with the monographs of Brazilian Pharmacopoeia Formulary of Herbal Medicines [26]. The monographs contain data based on scientific evidence that may help the prescribing professional adopt effective and rational therapeutic conduct.

12.5 CONCLUDING REMARKS

The research and use of herbal medicines have experienced a strong development in the pharmaceutical sector, especially in recent decades. However, the definitions, requirements, scope, terminology, and even therapeutic indications of herbal medicines vary from country to country. Similarly, the approaches used to license, dispense, manufacture, and trade herbal medicines are not harmonised worldwide. The establishment of a global harmonised regulation for herbal medicines is essential for the production of standardised herbal products, with the same safety, quality, and efficacy requirements to be accepted globally, contributing to the increase in the trading of these products between the nations.

In Brazil, the regulation rules for herbal medicines development, production, use, and registration have evolved continuously and consistently. Efforts have also been directed to implement herbal medicines in the SUS. In this chapter, the Brazilian experience in constructing policies, technoscientific documents, and regulations for the development, registration, and use of herbal medicines was concisely examined. We believe that the information presented here can serve as an excellent framework for harmonising the rules for regulating herbal medicines that are currently being conducted by health authorities globally.

REFERENCES

1. WHO. W. H. O. Regulatory Situation of Herbal Medicines. A Worldwide Review. *Geneve*, 1998, 45.
2. Robinson, M. M.; Zhang, X. The World Medicines Situation 2011—Traditional Medicines: Global Situation, Issues and Challenges. *World Heal. Organ.*, **2011**, 3rd Edition, 1–14.
3. Metta, A. M.; Kingumahanthi, N. L. N.; Kalidindi, V. R.; Juturi, R. K. R.; Boddu, V. Scope for Harmonisation of Herbal Medicine Regulations. *Int. J. Pharm. Sci. Res.*, **2021**, *12* (4), 2012–2020.
4. Thakkar, S.; Anklam, E.; Xu, A.; Ulberth, F.; Li, J.; Li, B.; Hugas, M.; Sarma, N.; Crerar, S.; Swift, S.; et al. Regulatory Landscape of Dietary Supplements and Herbal Medicines from a Global Perspective. *Regul. Toxicol. Pharmacol.*, **2020**, *114* (January), 104647.
5. Knöss, W. Harmonization of Regulatory Requirements in Europe to Ensure Quality, Safety and Efficacy of Herbal Medicinal Products. In *Evidence-Based Validation of Herbal Medicine*; Mukherjee, P. K., Ed.; Elsevier: Amsterdam, The Netherland, **2015**; pp. 201–216.

6. Knoess, W.; Wiesner, J. The Globalization of Traditional Medicines: Perspectives Related to the European Union Regulatory Environment. *Engineering*, **2019**, *5* (1), 22–31.
7. Reddy, K. J.; Sciences, S. L.; Thomas, A.; Limited, C. *Regulations for Herbal Medicine—Worldwide: A Focus on Current Regulations and Their Requirements*; LAP Lambert Academic Publ: Beau Bassin, **2017**.
8. Calixto, J. B. Efficacy, Safety, Quality Control, Marketing and Regulatory Guidelines for Herbal Medicines (Phytotherapeutic Agents). *Brazilian J. Med. Biol. Res.*, **2000**, *33* (2), 179–189.
9. Mtewa, A.G.; Egbuna, C.; Beressa, T.B.; Ngwira, K.J.; Lampiao, F. Phytopharmaceuticals: Efficacy, Safety, and Regulation. **2021**, 25–38.
10. Teixeira, F. M.; Barbosa, W. L. R. N.; Nascimento, M. S. *Plataforma Tecnológica para o Desenvolvimento de Fitoterápicos*; CRV Publ.: Curitiba—BR, 2013.
11. BRAZIL. Ministry of Health. National Health Surveillance Agency. **Resolution of the Collegiate Board—RDC Nr. 26**, May 13, 2014. Provides on the registration of herbal medicines and the registration and notification of traditional herbal products. *Diário Oficial União.* 14 maio 2014; Seção 1:52.
12. BRAZIL. Ministry of Health. National Health Surveillance Agency. **Resolution of the Collegiate Board—RDC n.r 166**, of July 24, 2017. Characteristics to be considered during the validation of analytical procedures. *Diário Oficial União.* 25 julho 2017; Seção 1:87-89.
13. BRAZIL. Ministry of Health. **Ordinance Nr. 22**, October 30, 1967. Establishes standards for the use of herbal preparations, *Diário Oficial da União.* 16 November 1967; Seção 1:45-46.
14. BRAZIL. Ministry of Health. National Health Surveillance Agency (ANVISA). **Ordinance Nr. 6**, January 31, 1995. Establishes and regulates the regulation and herbal products with the Department of Health Surveillance. *Diário Oficial da União.* 1 fev 1995; Seção 1:1378-1379.
15. BRAZIL. Ministry of Health. National Health Surveillance Agency. **Resolution of the Collegiate Board—RDC Nr. 17**, February 24, 2000. Registration of herbal medicines. *Diário Oficial da União.* 25 fev 2000; Seção 1:25-26.
16. BRAZIL. Ministry of Health. National Health Surveillance Agency. **Resolution of the Collegiate Board-RDC Nr. 48**, March 16, 2004. Provides on the Registration of Herbal Medicines. *Diário Oficial da União.* 18 March 2004; Seção 1:39-41.
17. BRAZIL. Ministry of Health. National Health Surveillance Agency. **Resolution of the Collegiate Board—RDC Nr. 14**, March 31, 2010. Provides on the Registration of Herbal Medicines. *Diário Oficial da União.* 5 abr 2010; Seção 1:85-87.
18. Flor, A. S. S.; Barbosa, W. L. R. Sabedoria Popular no Uso de Plantas Medicinais pelos Moradores do Bairro do Sossego no Distrito de Marudá - PA. *Rev. Bras. Plantas Med.*, **2015**, *17* (4), 757–768.
19. Barbosa, W. L. R.; Nascimento, M. S.; Pinto, L. N.; Maia, F. L. C.; Sousa, A. J. A.; Silva Junior, J. O. C.; Monteiro, M. M.; Oliveira, D. R. Selecting Medicinal Plants for Development of Phytomedicine and Use in Primary Health Care. *Bioact. Compd. Phytomedicine*, **2012**, 3–24.
20. EMA, European Medicines Agency. **Guideline on Declaration of Herbal Substances and Herbal Preparations in Herbal Medicinal Products/Traditional Herbal Medicinal Products**, London, 29 January 2009.
21. BRAZIL. Ministry of Health. National Health Surveillance Agency (ANVISA). **Reference Guide for Registration of Herbal Medicines**. **2010**, 123 p.
22. BRAZIL. Ministry of Health. National Health Surveillance Agency (ANVISA). **Resolution - RE Nr. 89**, March 16, 2004. Provides the List of Simplified Registration Herbal Medicines. *Diário Oficial da União.* 18 March 2004; Seção 1:32-34.

23. BRAZIL. Ministry of Health. National Health Surveillance Agency. **Resolution of the Collegiate Board—RDC Nr. 10**, March 9, 2010. Provides on the Notification of Herbal Medicines. *Diário Oficial da União*. 10 March 2010; Seção 1:52-59.
24. BRAZIL. Ministry of Health. National Health Surveillance Agency (ANVISA). **Resolution—RE Nr. 1**. July 29, 2005. Guide for Conducting Stability Studies. *Diário Oficial da União, Suplemento*. 01ago 2005; Seção 1: 119, 1-2.
25. BRAZIL. Ministry of Health. National Health Surveillance Agency (ANVISA). **Normative Instruction—IN Nr. 5**, March 31, 2010. Provides the List of Bibliographic References for Evaluating the Ssafety and Efficacy of Herbal Medicines, *Diário Oficial da União*. 5 abr 2010; Seção 1:91.
26. BRAZIL. Ministry of Health. National Health Surveillance Agency (ANVISA). **Brazilian Pharmacopoeia Formulary of Phytomedicines (Formulário de Fitoterápicos da Farmacopeia Brasileira)**, 2021. 217 p.
27. BRAZIL. Ministry of Health. National Health Surveillance Agency (ANVISA). **Normative Instruction—IN Nr. 2**, March 13, 2014. List of Simplified Registration Herbal Medicines. *Diário Oficial da União*. 14 March 2014; Seção 1:58-61.
28. BRAZIL. Ministry of Health. National Health Surveillance Agency (ANVISA). **Brazilian Pharmacopoeia Formulary of Phytomedicines (Formulário de Fitoterápicos da Farmacopeia Brasileira)**, 2011. 125 p.
29. BRAZIL. Ministry of Health. National Health Surveillance Agency (ANVISA). **Brazilian Pharmacopoeia Formulary of Phytomedicines—First Supplement (Formulário de Fitoterápicos da Farmacopeia Brasileira—Primeiro Suplemento)**, 2018. 156 p.
30. BRAZIL. Ministry of Health. National Health Surveillance Agency (ANVISA). **Resolution of the Collegiate Board—RDC Nr. 18**, April 3, 2013. Good practices in the processing and storage of medicinal plants, preparation and dispensing of original and official medicinal and herbal products in living pharmacies within the scope of the Unified Health System (SUS). *Diário Oficial da União*, 5 abr. 2013. Seção 1:67.
31. BRAZIL. National Agency of Sanitary Surveillance—ANVISA. **Brazilian Pharmacopoeia Phytotherapeutical (Memento Memento Fitoterápico da Farmacopeia Brasileira)**, 2016. 114 p.

13 Phytopharmacovigilance

Ricardo Tabach

CONTENTS

13.1 Introduction 327
13.2 Importance of Pharmacovigilance 328
13.2.1 A Brief History of Pharmacovigilance 328
13.3 Toxicity and Safety of Plant-Based Medicines 330
13.4 Phytopharmacovigilance of Herbal Medicines in Brazil 336
13.5 Challenges of Phytopharmacovigilance of Herbal Medicines in Brazil 339
13.6 Pharmacovigilance Legislation in Brazil 341
13.7 Final Remarks...343
References 344

13.1 INTRODUCTION

The use of plants for medicinal purposes in the treatment, cure, and prevention of diseases is one of humanity's oldest forms of therapeutic practice. Herbal medicines also have a long history of use and better acceptance by the population. Among the factors that contribute to this situation are the difficulty of access to health centres, the high costs of obtaining medical tests and medicines, the grand tradition of using medicinal plants associated with the ease of getting them, and a relatively lower price when compared to synthetic drugs [1].

In the early 1990s, the World Health Organization (WHO) reported that 65–80% of the developing countries' population depended on medicinal plants as the only form of access to primary health care. Moreover, medicinal plants as an alternative and complementary therapy in Western countries have been gaining significant popularity. A global survey of national traditional medicine policy and regulation of herbal medicines indicated that around 50 countries, including China, Japan, and Germany, have national laws regulating the use of traditional medicines [2].

The emergence of the concept of "natural" has contributed significantly to the increase, in recent decades, in the use of medicinal plants by the general population. For many peoples, this concept means the absence of potentially harmful chemical substances or, in other words, they are products that do not pose a health hazard. It is also common to believe that medicines of natural origin are devoid of risks to the consumer. This idea is part of the cultural background of the population, not only in Brazil but also in many other countries. However, the "natural" character of such products is no guarantee of exemption from adverse reactions or other problems arising from their improper use [3]. The lack of information on the risks associated with using some materials, including natural products, is one of the main factors

DOI: 10.1201/9781003225416-17

leading to intoxications. At first glance, it may seem trivial when compared to that presented by conventional medicines. However, the toxicity of medicinal plants is a public health problem, precisely due to the common belief that natural products do not entail risks and, consequently resulting in possible improper use and adverse effects [4]. Thus, natural products have become synonymous with healthy, safe, and beneficial products. Nothing could be further from reality, mainly because there is a danger of picking the wrong plant, often toxic, or even obtaining preparations based on commercial plants after the intentional addition of several undeclared synthetic substances. Ascertaining the origin and quality of starting materials is the first step in developing reliable and safe herbal medicines—avoiding contamination, errors in identification, preparation, and even dosages. As a result, scientists have expressed growing concerns with the subject as reports of adulteration and adverse reactions caused by this category of products are now common, compromising their quality. Thus, these substances cannot be considered harmless, and toxicological tests are necessary to provide scientific information on their safety and efficacy [5].

The lack of regulation and marketing control, easy access, the risk of contamination or adulteration of the material, and the specific characteristics of users are risk factors for the occurrence of adverse reactions and other problems arising from their use. Unfortunately, most herbal medicines currently used through self-medication or prescription do not yet have a well-known toxicity profile. On the other hand, the inappropriate use of a product, even with low toxicity, can induce serious problems as long as other risk factors may be present such as contraindications or concomitant use with other medications.

Products of natural origin have been widely used for centuries, with wide global acceptance over time, suggesting their safety and effectiveness. However, there is a lack of guarantee of these parameters is mainly due to the insufficient pharmacokinetic, pharmacological, and clinical data on most herbal medicines, aggravated by their complex chemical composition. Although there has been an increase in herbal medicine clinical trials in recent years, there is still a long way to go to reach the same level of information currently available on synthetic drugs [2].

13.2 IMPORTANCE OF PHARMACOVIGILANCE

The WHO defines pharmacovigilance as "the science and activities related to the identification, evaluation, understanding, and prevention of adverse effects or any problems related to the use of medicines" [6]. The role of pharmacovigilance includes identifying, evaluating, and monitoring the occurrence of adverse events related to the use of medicines sold in a particular country, including Brazil, thereby ensuring that the benefits related to the use of these products are greater than the risks caused by them. In addition to adverse drug reactions, relevant pharmacovigilance issues are adverse events caused by deviations in the quality of medicines, therapeutic ineffectiveness, medication errors, the use of drugs for indications not approved in the registry, abuse, intoxications, and drug interactions.

13.2.1 A Brief History of Pharmacovigilance

Problems related to the use of medicines have been reported since the end of the 19th century, such as sudden deaths caused by using chloroform in anaesthesia and jaundice caused by arsenic in the treatment of syphilis. However, the historic milestone of pharmacovigilance in the world was given by the "thalidomide disaster". Thousands of phocomelia cases (a rare congenital malformation) were reportedly caused by using this substance to prevent nausea in pregnant women in the 1950s and 1960s of the last century. After the product was removed from the market in 1962, about 4,000 cases were recorded, with 498 deaths during or after delivery. A review of studies carried out in the pre-marketing phase of the drug development process indicated that data misinterpretation contributed to the emergence of these cases.

From 1962, the North American regulatory agency (Food and Drug Administration [FDA]) demanded more rigorous pre-clinical and clinical studies from drug manufacturers. In 1968, the WHO initiated the pilot phase of the International Adverse Drug Reaction Monitoring Program, with the participation of ten countries. Since 1978, the program has been operated by the Uppsala Monitoring Center (UMC) in Sweden and today brings together more than 140 countries.

In general terms, pharmacovigilance is the study of the safety of medicines under the usual conditions of clinical use in large communities [7], monitoring and detecting adverse events for all types of drugs. Although this concept was initiated to monitor pharmaceutical products, it is also currently used for the additional safety assessment of other drugs, including natural products such as medicinal plants, blood, vaccines, and even medical devices [8].

The inclusion of medicinal plants in pharmacovigilance systems has been encouraged in several countries around the world. The WHO, based on the recognition of the growing importance of the use of medicinal plants and the possible risks of their uncontrolled use in combination with other drugs, published in 2004 the guidelines for monitoring and pharmacovigilance, with the proposal to include medicinal plants, traditional and complementary medicine in the International Pharmacovigilance System [9]. Within this context, the existing systems were adapted for plant-based products, expanding their scope of action and contributing to information development on the safety of all types of medicines, including those of vegetable origin.

In Brazil, in the 1960s and 1970s, the sanitary medicine legislation that prevails until today, highlighting Federal Law No. 6360/76 of September 23, 1976, establishes the notification of accidents or harmful reactions to the competent health authority. In 1990, the Brazilian Society for the Monitoring of Medicines (Sociedade Brasileira de Vigilância de Medicamentos, SOBRAVIME) was created, encouraging studies on the surveillance of medicines and pharmaceutical supplies. In the same period, Medicines Information Centres—such as the Drug Abuse Prevention Group (Grupo de Prevenção ao Uso Indevido de Medicamentos, GPUIM) at the Federal University of Ceará—appeared in some Brazilian cities. The GPUIM later housed the Ceará Pharmacovigilance Centre (Centro de Farmacovigilância do Ceará, CEFACE). In 1998, the State Program for reducing iatrogenic harm, coordinated by the Health Surveillance Centre (Centro de Vigilância Sanitária [CVS-SP]), was implemented in the State of São Paulo. Under this program, sending notifications of adverse events by drug registration holders to the health authority has become mandatory in the State since the year 2000. Thus, we can generally say that the role of pharmacovigilance is to define and reduce the risks and damages associated with the use of medicines as much as is humanly possible.

13.3 TOXICITY AND SAFETY OF PLANT-BASED MEDICINES

"The use of medicinal plants is widespread and is expanding worldwide" (WHO, 2004) [9]. Some factors contributed to the marked increase in this practice, such as, for example, the cyclical economic crises that periodically affect different countries around the world, the high cost of medicines, and the difficulty in access to health care by the population. These factors are in addition to a generalised trend among consumers to use natural origin products more frequently, which is due to the increase of ecological awareness verified in the last decades. Unfortunately, this growing use is also being encouraged in a non-judicious way by misleading advertisement, which often claims miraculous properties of certain plants. In most cases, this information ignores the empirical knowledge accumulated over time regarding the desired or unwanted effects, precautions, and contraindications of certain herbal medicines, arising from rigorous and careful scientific work developed in the last decades.

When it comes to medicinal plants, the chemical constituents responsible for pharmacological effects have some peculiarities, namely: variation and complexity; ununiform distribution across the plant; quantitative and qualitative variation according to the part of the plant used; seasonal variation, which must be taken into account; a single part of the plant, such as the leaf, for example, may have intraspecific variations in its chemical components; influence of climate, collection, drying, storage, transport, and extraction method. Also, herbal products are often complex mixtures of various plants, of which little is known about toxicity and the adverse reaction profile of each of them. In addition to these peculiarities are other aggravating factors such as the concomitant—but not always revealed—use of natural products with prescription drugs; the absence of government standards on the quality of medicinal plants in most countries; the lack of scientific knowledge and standardised tests on these products; and a revealing panorama of the difficulties in establishing the toxicity and safety of herbal medicines.

As the use of herbal medicines by the population increased, so did reports of suspected toxicity and adverse events. Such unwanted reactions are due to different factors: a) side effects, generally predictable and detectable through pharmacodynamics; b) reactions resulting from an overdose, tolerance, or dependence; c) hypersensitivity, allergy, and idiosyncratic responses; d) toxic effects due to continued use for medium and long terms. Problems related to quality, incorrect or poorly identified plants, inadequate processing methods, contamination and adulteration, have also been associated with unexpected toxicity problems reported for herbal products [10]. It is known that some medicinal plants have substances that can trigger adverse reactions. Scientific studies have reported toxic effects on different organs and systems of the body (e.g. liver, kidneys, and nervous system), in addition to mutagenic and carcinogenic effects [11]. These problems are compounded by the fact that many of these products come from countries with different manufacturing and regulatory standards. Therefore, there is a need for further toxicological studies and the implementation and strengthening of phytopharmacovigilance policies that must be of priority for public health.

The idea that herbal medicines are products that do not cause harm to health is still prevalent and, for this reason, as in all forms of self-medication, the use of plants represents a potential risk to human health. Although scientific data on the toxicological profile of these products is limited, the premise that the traditional use of a plant for hundreds of years would be sufficient to establish its safety is not necessarily true. Some subtle and chronic forms of toxicity, such as carcinogenicity, mutagenicity, and hepatotoxicity, might have either gone unnoticed or not associated with the use of this type of substance for an extended period [12].

The capacity of each plant to cause toxicity is only verifiable through pre-clinical toxicological assessment in which the whole extract or isolated compound is administered to experimental animals before clinical toxicology studies. In this manner, data on dosage, signs, and effects may be obtained, thereby contributing to assessing the product's potential toxicity. This information must be taken into account to determine the quality, safety, and efficacy standards and, eventually, their commercialisation. The main objectives of these tests in terms of safety involve the determination and characterisation of the toxic effects related to the target organ, the dose and dependence relationship, the exposure time, the reversibility of the effects, and the time interval in which the signs of toxicity appear and disappear [13]. Analysis of these parameters allows the determination of possible acute, subchronic, or chronic toxicity. Acute toxicity causes a rapid response within a short period, generally causing high mortality, whereas chronic toxicity effects result from prolonged use of the product in question [14]. Thus, investigating the toxic potential of medicinal plants can elucidate critical pharmacological aspects of their active ingredients, allowing for safe use and identifying possible health risks [3]. From the analysis of the pre-clinical data obtained, the possibility of continuing the studies in the clinical phase may be evaluated. Controlled and scientifically conducted clinical trials, in turn, must confirm that these drugs are safe for short-, medium-, and long-term use. Clinical trials are considered fundamental prerequisites to provide additional information to patients regarding product quality, efficacy, and safety [15].

Although herbal products are considered less risky than synthetic drugs, they are not entirely exempted from the possibility of causing adverse effects [16]. The emergence of adverse reactions associated with Ephedra or Aristolochia, for example, revealed that these types of medication could produce high toxicity in humans. Although the toxicity inherent in certain plants may be well known, undesirable effects can also result from the contamination of products with toxic metals, adulteration with pharmacologically active synthetic compounds, incorrect identification, or replacement of herbal ingredients with processed products [1, 17, 18]. Interactions with other medications or even foods can also occur when used concomitantly without proper care [19, 20].

In recent years, there has been a significant increase in the number of studies related to the safety of medicinal plants and herbal medicines and an effort to improve the regulation of these products. These actions minimise the risk of manifestation of undesirable effects while also serving as a stimulant for the rational use of herbal medicines. A literature survey on the topic reveals an increase in the number of studies describing the toxic effects or adverse reactions explicitly caused by herbal medicines or other products based on medicinal plants. Within this line of reasoning, Franco et al. [21] evaluated the effects of administering valerian extract for 30 days in Swiss mice. Valerian is a plant widely used in the composition of different herbal medicines due to its known hypnotic/sedative effect. It was verified that in the experimental group, the liver parenchyma showed disorganised hepatocytes, with apparent disruption of the cell wall and the network of sinusoid capillaries exhibiting vasodilation and vascular congestion. In addition, the cytoplasm of these cells showed the deposition of fat droplets. These changes were caused by the chemical components of valerian, which even interfered with the activity of liver enzymes [21]. Similar results had been observed by Barreiro and Fraga [22] while verifying the harmful action of *Valeriana officinalis* L. on the biological activity of two liver isoenzymes, 3A4 and 2D6, of cytochrome P450. The prolonged presence of valerian extract inside hepatocytes was associated with the histological lesions and signs of nuclear disintegration observed in the experimental group [21]. In the same study, the medullary region of the kidneys of the experimental group presented with changes in the collecting tubules and the loops of Henle. An increase in both the quantity and the diameter of blood vessels in these regions was also observed. The nephrotoxicity was probably caused by terpenes present in *V. officinalis* L. [21].

There are also some plants used in folk medicine and even in cooking that have potentially toxic chemicals. Examples include the sassafras oil (*Sassafras albidum*), which is hepatotoxic; parsley oil (*Petroselinum crispum*), which has an abortive and hepatotoxic action after its use for an extended period; and tarragon oils (*Artemisia dracunculus*), fennel (*Foeniculum vulgare*), sweet basil (*Ocimum basilicum*), and chervil (*Anthriscus cerefolium*), which all show a carcinogenic potential [23].

Plants ingested in the form of tea or ingested "*in natura*" can also cause numerous adverse reactions, for example, heart problems, allergic reactions, hormonal changes, irritation, and purgative effects, both in pre-clinical experimental models as well as in humans. Hence, it can be said that the plant species belonging to the genera *Crotalaria*, *Heliotropium*, and *Senecio*, chemically constituted of pyrrolisidine alkaloids, cause high hepatotoxicity even when used in food or teas—a widespread habit in African Caribbean countries and South America [24,25].

Within the subject of health problems related to plant use, excessive consumption of some plants is another topic that must be considered [12]. Sesquiterpene lactones are known to have allergenic properties. These metabolites occur predominantly in plants of the *Asteraceae* family, such as chamomile (*Matricaria chamomilla*). The general population widely uses this plant for its soothing properties, but it can cause hypersensitivity reactions, as is the case with other family plants [26].

Few conventional drugs are considered safe during pregnancy. It is well known that no drug substance should be taken at this stage unless the benefits outweigh the risks and under close medical supervision. This rule also applies to plants used in folk medicine, which are often mistakenly considered safe alternatives. However, it is important to note that some plants that contain volatile oils in their composition are abortifacients as they induce uterine contractions. Typical examples include the ivy (*Hedera helix*), parsley (*P. crispum*), pennyroyal (*Mentha pulegium*), sage (*Salvia officinalis*), feverfew (*Tanacetum parthenium*), and common yarrow (*Achillea millefolium*) [23].

In order to highlight the risks that herbal medicines can pose to the patient, Lombardo (2018) conducted a survey of the data available in the literature on their potential to cause adverse reactions, emphasising mainly those with simplified registration and those sold under medical prescription. According to the pharmacological action, the drugs were grouped into seven categories for the treatment of; (a) *Infections*: bearberry (*Arctostaphylos uva-ursi*) and echinacea (*Echinacea purpurea*); (b) *Intestinal Disorders*: plantago (*Plantago major*) and peppermint (*Mentha piperita*); (c) *Circulatory Disorders*: ginkgo (*Ginkgo biloba*); (d) *migraine*: feverfew (*T. parthenium*); (e) *Mental Disorders*: St. John's wort (*Hypericum perforatum*), kava-kava (*Piper methysticum*), and valerian (*V. officinalis*); (f) *Prostate Hyperplasia*: saw palmetto (*Serenoa repens*); (g) *Climacteric*: cimicifuga or black cohosh (*Cimicífuga racemosa*). The negative aspects that stood out the most in this survey were: hepatotoxic potential due to prolonged use, allergic or irritating reactions, photosensitising effect, interference with blood clotting and the consequent increased risk of bleeding, uterotonic effect and the consequent possibility of abortion, cognitive changes such as impairment in the capacity of concentration and attention, interference in hormonal regulation, in addition to drug interactions with different classes of drugs. It was found that the available data on the safety of these drugs targeted at pregnant women, nursing mothers, and children are still insufficient and, therefore, their use is not recommended, except under medical supervision. The study showed that herbal medicines with simplified registration and classified as prescribed have, in general, significant contraindications and precautions for use. They can cause serious adverse reactions and important drug interactions, depending on the patient's clinical peculiarities. In pregnant women, nursing mothers, and babies, their use must be carefully evaluated in these groups as the available data are insufficient. In addition to the adverse potential, which justifies the need for a prescription, the health problems for which these drugs are indicated do not correspond to self-limited and specific problems, highlighting the importance of medical monitoring so that more critical pathological conditions are not neglected or masked. Therefore, health professionals must prioritise the rational and safe use of herbal medicines, similar to conventional medicines. The required actions will include proper prescription, therapeutic monitoring, and notification of adverse reactions, thereby contributing significantly to developing and improving the pharmacovigilance system for medicinal plants [27].

Drug interactions, another pertinent item when it comes to herbal medicines, should also be taken into account, as there is little information about the interaction of plants when ingested with conventional medicines, for example, in the form of teas. Due to the increasing popularity and use of products of plant origin, the dangers resulting from the concomitant use of conventional plants and medicines have become a significant public health problem. This association increases the potential for pharmacokinetic and pharmacodynamic interactions since medicinal plants can affect absorption, metabolism (through metabolic enzyme induction or inhibition), distribution, and excretion. However, one can identify which plants interfere with specific drugs based on their chemical constituents, pharmacological properties, and known side effects [28]. For example, plants containing high coumarins content can increase blood clotting time when consumed in high doses; the prolonged or excessive use of a plant with diuretic action may potentiate some ongoing diuretic therapy or the effect of certain cardioactive drugs—this inappropriate use resulting in hypokalaemia [29, 30].

The concomitant use of medicinal plants with conventional drugs must consider safety, efficacy, consistency, and quality. Safe use requires strict control over the presence of adulterants, correct dosage, standardisation of extracts, contraindications, manufacturing techniques, and the list of all components, which is not always done. Thus, under these conditions, interactions between conventional drugs and plant-based medicines are not only challenging to assess but sometimes impossible to identify. This current situation could be better controlled by improving regulatory processes, accompanied by an efficient inspection network.

An extensive review study reported by Izzo and Ernst [31] revealed that 15% of patients taking conventional medicines for a health problem concomitantly use products of plant origin. Among them, potential drug interactions were reported in 40% of patients. Further analysis revealed that only one-third of these users inform the doctor of the use of these products. In turn, the health professional is also not in the habit of asking the patient about this subject. This situation of insufficient information exchange, together with the fact that herbal products often have several substances in their composition, increases the likelihood of drug interactions [31]. The association between synthetic medicines and medicinal plants is relatively common, for example, between chamomile (*M. chamomilla*) and passion fruit (*Passiflora edulis*), due to their soothing properties, and benzodiazepines, which may eventually cause undesirable drug interactions. In the case of St. John's wort (*H. perforatum*), used to treat depression, there is a record of a large number of occurrences of this type. Several factors contribute to the triggering of drug interactions or even cases of poisoning involving medicinal plants [32]. Among them, the lack of knowledge of the conditions of cultivation, problems of inaccurate plant identification, lack of information on posology, time of use, and very little data on the mechanisms of action can be highlighted. Studies on drug interactions involving plant drugs increased considerably and revealed that health damage could be significant depending on the products involved. In order to have better contact between the notifier and the prescriber, it is imperative to disseminate the available data regarding the pharmacovigilance of medicinal plants among health professionals. This practice can contribute to a better understanding of the possible harmful effects, the improvement of the medication (if applicable), and its effectiveness and safety.

Posadzki et al. [33] also evaluated the possible drug interactions between plants and drugs in a related study. Ginkgo (*G. biloba*), ginseng (*Panax ginseng*), green tea (*Camellia sinensis*), kava-kava (*P. methysticum*), mistletoe (*Viscum album),* saw palmetto (*S. repens*), and St. John's wort (*H. perforatum)* were the most cited plants. Common interacting drugs were anticoagulants, anti-inflammatories, and antiplatelet agents. The results indicated that the most probable interaction mechanisms involve inhibiting syntheses of thromboxane and cyclooxygenase (in the case of anti-inflammatories). Some products of plant origin could also act as agonists or antagonists of drugs administered concurrently, interfering with the mechanism of action and consequently impairing the pharmacological effect.

Drug interactions involving herbal medicines used to treat insomnia (problem that affects many people worldwide), and other medications was evaluated by Ferreira [34]. The most used herbal medicines for insomnia are based on *Passiflora incarnata* and *V. officinalis* and, most of the time, without the proper monitoring of a health professional. According to the author, simultaneous use of these herbal medicines and alcoholic beverages or illicit drugs, such as cocaine, should be avoided. Often, the patient does not understand that these substances cause side effects when interacting with other products or medications. The concomitant use of hypnotics with one of the herbal medicines mentioned previously for the treatment of anxiety or panic syndrome, for example, could potentiate their pharmacological effect, causing an increase in drowsiness and more prolonged sedation, or even an additive effect when administered together with monoamine oxidase (MAO) inhibitors for the treatment of depression. The results of this work also revealed that *P. incarnata*, when administered in conjunction with some anticoagulants, antiplatelet agents, or anti-inflammatory drugs, increases the risk of bleeding. The author stresses the necessity to guide patients appropriately and the general populace, especially the younger ones, on the use of *P. incarnata* and stimulants. As a common cause, such individuals use substances such as caffeine or guarana throughout the day to ensure an extra dose of energy and at night use *P. incarnata* due to sleeping difficulty. This association should be avoided, as there is a risk of high blood pressure resulting from this interaction. Nausea and vomiting have also been linked to interactions between the alcoholic extract of *V. officinalis* with drugs such as metronidazole and disulfiram [34].

Although there has been an increase in the number of articles on the subject in recent years, little is still known about drug interactions and food or between drugs and herbal medicines. An inappropriate combination of prescription drugs with food or medicinal plants can cause adverse effects or produce unexpected and undesirable therapeutic results. Besides, this situation is aggravated by a cultural issue since the doctor does not ask, and the patient does not usually report on the use of herbal products. Thus, possible drug interaction and adverse reactions arising from such occurrences cannot be associated and adequately reported. Therefore, routine activities of health professionals should include questioning patients on the use of medicinal plants and herbal medicines to report any inadequacies to the National Pharmacovigilance System.

Over the past few years, the WHO has been promoting specific strategies for the prevention of these types of pharmacological interactions through the establishment of public policies to support the dissemination of knowledge about the subject. A systematic review on the topic would contribute to the prevention of reactions caused by pharmacological interactions and complications due to toxicity and avoiding the worsening of the patient's clinical condition, reducing the hospitalisation period and the consequent hospitalisation costs. For drug interactions and adverse effects to be avoided, interdisciplinary work is necessary, with different health professional involvement, thus contributing to the health, well-being, and improvement of the patient's quality of life.

At global levels, the WHO-UMC (Uppsala Monitoring Centres) records and organises the adverse reactions resulting from the plant/drug interaction reported by the national pharmacovigilance centres, although in a still insignificant number [32]. This system is ineffective because, besides the small number of countries that send their data to UMC, underreporting is also a reality. It is essential that health professionals, consumers, and other agents—including regulatory authorities and suppliers of raw materials and herbal products—are aware of the possible adverse reactions and drug interactions caused when herbal drugs are co-administered with allopathic medicines. This awareness aims at a better level of information and may promote the rational use of herbal medicines.

13.4 PHYTOPHARMACOVIGILANCE OF HERBAL MEDICINES IN BRAZIL

Phytotherapy is considered one of the oldest forms of disease prevention and cure. In Brazil, it was institutionalised in the Public Health System with the publication of the National Policy of Integrative and Complementary Practices (2006), a guiding document of the National Policy of Medicinal and Herbal Plants, which aims to guarantee access to and quality of this type of products offered to the population.

More and more of the population has been using medicinal plants and herbal medicines in their treatments in Brazil. A survey carried out between the years 2013 and 2015 indicated that the search for natural products increased about 160% in Paraná State, reaching almost 16 thousand people who received these products through the Unified Health System (SUS) [35]. Another study conducted within the elderly population of the same State showed that 64% of the people interviewed used medicinal plants, 54% of whom used them together with some synthetic medicine, showing a worrying situation due to frequent drug interactions [36].

At the end of the 1990s, with the approval of the National Medicines Policy and the creation of the National Health Surveillance Agency, the responsibility to establish, coordinate, and monitor toxicological and pharmacological surveillance systems was institutionalised. These responsibilities are in addition to regulating, controlling, and inspecting medicines for human use, culminating in implementing a National Pharmacovigilance Program. Today, this program is coordinated by the National Monitoring Centre for Medicines (Centro Nacional de Monitorização de Medicamentos [CNMM]), based in the pharmacovigilance area of ANVISA. In 2001, the CNMM was accepted as the 62nd member of the WHO International Program. In 2009, the National Notification System for Health Surveillance (Sistema Nacional de Notificações para a Vigilância Sanitária [NOTIVISA]) was created in Brazil, to receive notifications of adverse events and technical complaints of several products, including medicinal plants and herbal medicines. The information and complaints received have aided the National Health Surveillance System (Sistema Nacional de Vigilância Sanitária [SNVS]) to identify the products' adverse reactions or unwanted effects. This work can improve the knowledge concerning the product effects and, when indicated, lead to changes in the recommendations on its use. In addition, the agency may publish statements of caution relating to such recommendations and promote actions that protect public health through the regulation of products sold in the country. It is important to remember that not every notification generates a sanitary measure, be it regulatory or not. Often, a set of notifications is necessary for the information generated to be consistent to the point of triggering actions by the SNVS. It is, therefore, vital to notify the organ whenever an incident, adverse event, or technical complaint is suspected [37].

Proof of the efficacy and safety of herbal medicines must be carried out during the product registration phase with the National Health Surveillance Agency (ANVISA). This proof can be done through either non-clinical and clinical trials or simplified registration. The latter is based on traditionality/history of use over a long period and on a significant amount of literature data proving the efficacy and safety of that product [27]. This registration modality is in line with the worldwide trend on the regulation of this class of product. It is founded on monographs of well-established use, prepared by the Committee for Medicinal and Herbal Products of the European Medicines Agency (EMA), which consider evidence of efficacy and safety within at least ten years [38].

Despite the benefits in the use of herbal medicines and the fact that the population often considers them as safe medicines—and idea often relayed under the maxim "what comes from the earth does not hurt"—there has been an increase in the number of adverse event notifications in the pharmacovigilance database of the Brazilian National Health Surveillance Agency—ANVISA [39]. This fact negates claims that medicinal plants and their derivatives are entirely harmless because they are natural products. Even with the current level of reporting, it is believed that the number of cases is much higher; that is, there currently exists an underreporting of adverse reactions caused by these products.

This lapse in notifications in the country might reflect negligence by health professionals and users, who are often unaware of the risks that these products can offer to health [6]. Following this line of reasoning, Leal and Tellis [40] identified several reasons for the great difficulty in obtention and dissemination of data regarding interactions between medicines and medicinal plants/herbal medicines in Brazil. Among them is the lack of preparation of health professionals; the belief that what is natural does not hurt; and self-medication, a rampant habit. Self-medication is one example of drug misuse and is considered a public health problem not only in Brazil but also in other parts of the world. According to data from the National Toxic-Pharmacological Information System, medicines are responsible for about 28% of all poisoning notifications [41].

Although natural products are widely used, relatively little is known about the frequency of suspected adverse reactions related to these products. This information is more difficult to monitor because underreporting is more common for these products than conventional drugs. One of the reasons, as previously mentioned, is that many consumers believe that these products are safe due to their natural origin [42]. Consumers often self-medicate without reporting this to healthcare professionals. If natural products have a potentially harmful effect on their own or caused by interaction with other drugs, they should be monitored.

The difficulty found in the reports of adverse reactions of herbal medicines occurs, therefore, for three main reasons: (1) the user population does not have the culture of complaint registration; (2) the user population has the belief that "whatever comes from the earth does not harm"; (3) in regions or countries where phytotherapeutics are the main source of remedies, there is, in most cases, no developed and efficient pharmacovigilance system. As herbal medicine use is growing, the need to create an efficient pharmacovigilance system for these products proportionally increases. In the case of herbal medicines, several factors must be taken into account, as many aspects that contribute to the emergence of adverse reactions are unique to this type of medicine, such as factors related to cultivation, the difficulty in identifying or distinguishing a medicinal plant from another innocuous plant (plants from different families, but of similar morphology), and seasonality among others. The population and professional resistance to recognising the symptoms and reactions caused by herbal medicines also constitute significant challenges. Another critical factor that health professionals often overlook is the possibility of drug interactions between a phytomedicine and a synthetic drug, compromising treatment outcomes in terms of health [43].

The pharmacovigilance of medicinal plants and herbal medicines is an emerging concern and deserves to be highlighted since, in recent years, there has been a significant increase in the prescription, use, and consumption of these products by the population. Currently, package inserts of phytotherapeutics describing them as largely safe and with little or no side effects are typically found on account of being natural products. Consumers of medicinal plants, in turn, consider phytotherapy as a low-cost therapeutic alternative and free from adverse reactions or even that it does not cause drug interactions and, for this reason, they often do not inform the doctor about their use of this product type.

Within this context, the Brazilian Centre for Information on Psychotropic Drugs (Centro Brasileiro de Informações Sobre Drogas Psicotrópicas [CEBRID]) at the Federal University of São Paulo (UNIFESP) created the Medicinal Plant Pharmacovigilance System, with the launch of Planfavi, a quarterly bulletin whose first edition, Planfavi Bulletin Number 1 (electronic format) was published in 2007. Besides this bulletin, CEBRID also implemented, at the time, a System for the Collection of Information on Adverse Reactions produced by Phytotherapics and Medicinal Plants (Reações Adversas Produzidas por Fitoterápicos e Plantas Medicinais [RAMF]). These activities are in line with the public health mandate of CEBRID, which includes, among others, conducting research in the area of medicinal plants, creating awareness on the problems related to the inappropriate use of plant-based products, and contributing to curtailing this scenario. This work aimed to establish an herbal medicine pharmacovigilance system and create a database on the main adverse reactions caused by this type of medicine. The original idea was that spontaneous reports obtained through doctors and health professionals, case reports in scientific publications, and clinical research results would form part of a database for the survey of the national picture of occurrences of adverse reactions caused by herbal medicines and medicinal plants. For the success of this initiative, it was envisaged that the system for collecting and recording adverse reaction cases and the dissemination of these data through the Planfavi Bulletin would count on the indispensable participation of health professionals to provide information on possible adverse reactions caused by herbal medicines. This is towards contributing not only to the diagnosis but also to the analysis of the conditions of use of these substances, thereby gathering evidence and providing suggestions that would be useful for establishing policies for the Pharmacovigilance of Medicinal and Herbal Plants in Brazil. In this sense, the content of the bulletins would aim to inform about the potential health risks that herbal medicines, when used indiscriminately or associated with other medicines, could cause. It is important to note that phytotherapy is an important therapeutic option, especially in a country like Brazil, but it is not without risks, which need to be considered when choosing this type of treatment. Among the objectives of the Planfavi Bulletin was also to expand its reach in such a way that it could reach the largest possible number of professionals and be an important source of information about adverse reactions caused by medicinal plants. This anticipated collaboration by health professionals was unfortunately below expectations. Despite this, this work continues in progress, albeit at a slow pace due to the numerous difficulties. At least the Planfavi Bulletin (https://planfavi-cebrid.webnode.com), thanks to the collaboration of dedicated colleagues, continues to be published and is currently at number 59 (07/2021).

13.5 CHALLENGES OF PHYTOPHARMACOVIGILANCE OF HERBAL MEDICINES IN BRAZIL

There are several challenges related to the pharmacovigilance of medicinal plants/herbal medicines. Herbal medicines, unlike synthetic drugs, are chemically rich and complex products, and several factors can influence the quality and chemical profile of these products, including geographical origin (climate, soil, photoperiod); genotype; plant parts utilised (leaves, stems, root, root bark); harvest time (year, season, time of day); storage, processing, and extraction; combination or processing with other types of drugs.

The identification and analysis of safety associated with herbal medicines and products are subject to the same challenges related to synthetic medicines, alongside more specific ones, such as insufficient information due to underreporting, absence of toxicological information about the components of that product, or inconclusive reports of adverse reactions.

A robust product profile can be developed in the regulatory context via analysis of safety and the careful clinical assessment of possible adverse reactions using available pharmacological and toxicological information.

Although the literature contains many plants that have been used for centuries as traditional medicines, there are only a few clinical studies, making post-marketing pharmacovigilance a critical source of information on the safety and efficacy of these products [44, 45].

The evaluation of these products also concerns quality and quantity, as incomplete information is usually found in the case reports of adverse reactions involving herbal products. These problems have been observed in articles published in the scientific literature and reports submitted to regulatory authorities. There is also a gap in the toxicological information on most of these products. The procedures to improve this situation include training health professionals on what information is necessary to adequately evaluate plant origin products regarding their quality, safety, and effectiveness. Another important aspect is related to underreporting, which, as previously mentioned, is more common with natural products than with synthetic products.

Poison control centres could act as a potential source of additional data on adverse drug reactions mainly because, in most cases, the reports sent to these centres generally outnumber those submitted to official pharmacovigilance systems [1].

Another challenge in the toxicological evaluation of these products concerns the use of isolated active principles in the medicine compared to the reality, in which the population often uses whole plants or plant extracts. Although this is a challenge, it has been shown that the toxicity of certain chemical compounds isolated from plants, such as aristolochic acid, correlates with the known toxicity of extracts obtained from plants in the genus *Aristolochia* in which this acid is generally found [46]. However, this similarity does not always occur, and this aspect deserves special attention.

The product's quality is also a challenge. It is very common to find herbal products whose composition involves the association of different plant extracts, making it complicated to analyse quality, safety, and efficacy, unless the necessary procedures have been taken to identify and analyse each of the chemical constituents of the product in question, which is not always done. In addition, the illegal trade and misleading advertising that often accompanies these products in a bid to circumvent official inspection systems is a considerable challenge, bringing risks to the population. Despite the efforts of the regulatory bodies, this problem persists, and new strategies must be developed to minimise this situation.

The most recent technologies, such as omics and predictive toxicology, have been applied more frequently to evaluate the therapeutic efficacy and perform toxicological screening in the development of herbal medicines, contributing to the emergence of quality products that the population can safely use.

General recommendations for the treatment of various health problems related to the inappropriate use of medicinal plants and herbal medicines.

The rational use of medicines is an essential tool for improving the population's quality of life and life expectancy through disease prevention, health maintenance, and recovery. Its practice aims to better medication effect, at a reasonable cost, for the shortest possible time [1]. The following are some general recommendations to be followed for the treatment of various health problems with medicinal plants:

1. Continuing education of consumers, health professionals, and industry stakeholders on the most appropriate way to report adverse reactions in order to build a database, with the consequent increase in the quantity and quality of information available on the topic.
2. Contribution to the existing body of knowledge on the subject by sharing existing data in Poison Centres.
3. Provision of incentive to research and scientific work on pharmacology, and pre-clinical and clinical toxicology of medicinal plants.
4. Continuous exploration of new technologies such as omics and predictive toxicology in medicinal plant assessment.
5. Continuous exploration of new active surveillance methods (pharmacies, hospitals, points of sale), as important tools in detecting adverse reactions and potential toxicity of these products.
6. Strengthening the public pharmacovigilance policies, including medicinal plants.

13.6 PHARMACOVIGILANCE LEGISLATION IN BRAZIL

The need to make international efforts on drug safety issues gained importance after the global thalidomide tragedy in 1961. As a result, the 16th World Health Assembly (1963) adopted a resolution that reaffirmed the need for immediate action concerning disseminating information on adverse drug reactions, which subsequently led to the creation of the WHO Pilot Research Project for International Drug Monitoring in 1968. The program currently brings together more than 140 countries, including Brazil [47].

Pharmacovigilance actions in Brazil are already supported by general legislation, such as *Federal Law No. 6360/76*, *Federal Law No. 9782/99*, the *Resolution of the National Health Council No. 3/89*, and the *Ordinance of the Ministry of Health 3916/98*. In addition, several drug registration laws solicit pharmacovigilance data at the time of registration renewal.

The Ministry of Health Ordinance *MS No. 696* of May 7, 2001, instituted the National Monitoring Centre for Medicines (Centro Nacional de Monitorização de Medicamentos, CNMM). The CNMM is responsible for implementing and coordinating the National Pharmacovigilance System [48].

In 2009, ANVISA published the first specific pharmacovigilance standard for drug registration holders, the Resolution of the Collegiate Board (*Resolução da Diretoria Colegiada, RDC—No. 04*) of February 10, 2009. In the same year, there was a publication, through the Normative Instruction (*Instrução Normativa, IN—No. 14*) of October 27, 2009, on the Pharmacovigilance Guides for Drug Registration Holders linked to RDC 04. Since the promulgation of the RDC No. 04, the notification of adverse events related to the use of medicines has become mandatory for all holders of medicines registration in the national territory. In addition, pharmacovigilance inspection was established—a procedure carried out by the regulatory agency to verify the existence of a pharmacovigilance system in pharmaceutical companies, in addition to compliance with other legal requirements. Furthermore, it is now required that a Periodic Pharmacovigilance Reports (Relatórios Periódicos de Farmacovigilância [RPF]) and Plans on Pharmacovigilance be submitted to ANVISA regularly. In the case of specific problems related to medication safety, ANVISA may also require the elaboration of risk minimisation plans.

As a consequence of strengthening the pharmacovigilance legal bases in Brazil, ANVISA has increasingly included post-marketing surveillance actions for medicines. Examples of these actions include the publication of norms that establish the notification, by health professionals, of adverse events associated with oseltamivir (*RDC 45/2009*), thalidomide (*Resolution of the Ministry of Health, 11/2011*), and sibutramine (*RDC 50/2014*).

ANVISA also published *RDC 36/2013*, which instituted actions for patient safety in health services and made the notification of adverse events by the Service's Patient Safety Centre mandatory.

In addition to the laws already cited, several other laws, ordinances, and federal resolutions provide legal support for pharmacovigilance actions in Brazil. These laws are shown in Table 13.1.

TABLE 13.1
Other Laws That Support Pharmacovigilance Activities in Brazil

Ordinance No. 802, of October 8, 1998	It determines that distributors must immediately separate the batch and report it to the registry holder and the health authority in case of complaints, observations, and adverse reactions.
Ordinance No. 06, of January 29, 1999	It defines that the local health authority must establish mechanisms for the pharmacovigilance of drugs based on the substances contained in the lists of Ordinance SVS/MS No. 344/98 (and updates), instituting a specific model of pharmacovigilance form for retinoid drugs for systemic use and a notification form for suspected adverse reactions.
Ordinance of the Ministry of Health No. 696, of May 7, 2001	It institutes the National Medicines Monitoring Centre (CNMM), based in the Pharmacovigilance Unit of ANVISA.
Decree No. 3.961, of October 10, 2001	Amends Decree No. 79,094/77, which regulates Law No. 6,360/76, including pharmacovigilance in health surveillance actions, such as investigating the effects that compromise the safety, effectiveness, or risk–benefit ratio of a product.
Resolution of the Collegiate Board—RDC No. 233, of August 17, 2005	It determines that the manufacturer of extracts and allergenic products should make available a registration and statistics system to study pharmacovigilance. Then, when there is clinical experience, the pharmacotoxicological data can be substituted by studies of pharmacovigilance or clinical trials.
Resolution of the Collegiate Board—RDC No. 67, of October 8, 2007	It defines as the pharmacist's duty in the compounding pharmacy to participate in pharmacovigilance studies and inform the health authorities about the occurrence of adverse reactions and drug interactions that are not foreseen.
Ordinance No. 1660, of July 22, 2009	It institutes the Health Surveillance Notification and Investigation System—Vigipos, within the scope of the National Health Surveillance System, as an integral part of the Unified Health System (Sistema Único de Saúde, SUS).
Resolution of the Collegiate Board—RDC No. 44, of August 17, 2009	It establishes that pharmacists in pharmacies and drugstores must contribute to pharmacovigilance, notifying the occurrence or suspicion of an adverse event or technical complaint to health authorities.
Resolution of the Collegiate Board—RDC No. 47, of September 8, 2009	It determines that ANVISA may require changes to the instructions for use, whenever deemed necessary, based on information from pharmacovigilance.
Resolution of the Collegiate Board—RDC No. 60, of November 26, 2009	It establishes that the procedures adopted for the notification of adverse drug events must be the same for free samples.
Resolution of the Collegiate Board—RDC No. 64, of December 18, 2009	It includes, in the documentation for the registration of radiopharmaceuticals, the presentation of the updated Pharmacovigilance Report, according to the legislation in force, with data obtained from clinical studies and the commercialisation of the product in other countries, when applicable. For registration renewal, pharmacovigilance data must be submitted. ANVISA can request this data before the defined deadlines.

(Continued)

TABLE 13.1 ***(Continued)***
Other Laws That Support Pharmacovigilance Activities in Brazil

Resolution of the Collegiate Board—RDC No. 49, of September 20, 2011	On the occasion of renewing the registration of biological medicines, it requires presenting the Periodic Pharmacovigilance Report, the Pharmacovigilance Plan, and the Risk Minimisation Plan in specific situations related to the medicine's safety.
Resolution of the Collegiate Board—RDC No. 26, of May 13, 2014	The documentation for the registration of herbal medicines must include a Document of the Description of the company's Pharmacovigilance System. For the renewal of the registration, the requirements of the RDC 04/2009 should also be attended.
Portaria No. 650, of May 29, 2014	Approves and promulgates the Internal Regulations of the National Health Surveillance Agency (ANVISA) and provides other measures.
Resolution of the Collegiate Board—RDC 406/2020	It addresses Good Pharmacovigilance Practices and establishes the requirements, responsibilities, and work standards to be observed by all those who have records of medicines for human use distributed or marketed in the country.
Normative Instruction—IN 63/2020	It deals with the Periodic Benefit-Risk Assessment Report (Relatório Periódico de Avaliação Benefício-Risco, RPBR) to be submitted to ANVISA.

13.7 FINAL REMARKS

Although used for thousands of years, herbal medicinal products have gained popularity in recent decades, with the consequent increase in their use by the population. Consequently, the concomitant use of herbal medicines and synthetic medicines has become a common practice in recent years. Many people believe that since herbal products are natural, they are safe and free from side effects or adverse reactions. Recent pieces of evidence have shown that this presumption is a dangerous simplification of its status. The information gap, associated with the fact that herbal products often have many substances in their composition, increases the likelihood of adverse effects and drug interactions.

Several factors contribute to the triggering of drug interactions or even cases of poisoning involving medicinal plants. Among them is insufficient knowledge of the conditions of cultivation, identification of the plant, adulterations, lack of information on posology, time of use, and mainly, little data on the mechanisms of action responsible for these problems. In recent years, work on plant-drug interactions has increased significantly and revealed that health damage could be significant depending on the products involved. To ensure better interaction between the notifier and the prescriber, the training of health professionals, the awareness of the population, and the improvement of pharmacovigilance systems for medicinal plants and herbal medicines are of fundamental importance. These measures can mitigate the situation and provide safe and rational use of these products, contributing to improving the population's quality of life.

REFERENCES

1. Ernst, E. Challenge of Phytopharmacovigilance Postgrad. Med J **2004** May, 80 (943), 249–250.
2. Parveen, A.; Parveen, B.; Parveen, R.; Ahmad, S. Challenges and Guidelines for Clinical Trial of Herbal Drugs. J Pharm Bioall Sci **2015**, 7, 329–333.
3. Mengue, S.S.; Ments, L.A.; Schenkel, E.P. Use of Medicinal Plants During Pregnancy [Uso de Plantas Medicinais Durante a Gravidez]. In: Sanseverino, M. T. V; Spritzel, D. T.; Schüler-Faccini, L., Ed. Manual de Teratogênese. Porto Alegre: Ed. UFRGS, **2011**, 32, 347–364.
4. Lima, C.S. Non-Clinical Toxicity Study in Rats Undergoing Treatment with *Copaifera duckei* Dwyer Resin Oil (Subchronic and Reproductive) [Estudo de Toxidade Não Clínica Em Ratos Submetidos ao Tratamento com Óleo Resina de *Copaifera duckei* Dwyer (Subcrônico e Reprodutivo)]. Tese (doutorado)—Fundação Universidade Federal do Amapá. Macapá, **2014**. 265f.
5. Oga, S; Camargo, M.M.A.; Batistuzzo, J.A.O. Fundamentals of Toxicology [Fundamentos de Toxicologia].São Paulo: Atheneu. 3rd Ed., **2008**, 677
6. World Health Organization. WHO Guidelines on Good Agricultural and Collection Practices (GACP) for Medicinal Plants. Geneva: WHO, **2003**.
7. Mann, R.D.; Andrews, E.F. (Eds.). Pharmacovigilance. Chichester: Wiley, **2007**, 2nd Ed, 702.
8. Shaw, D.; Ladds, G., Duez, P.; Williamson, E.; Chan, K. Pharmacovigilance of Herbal Medicine. J Ethnopharmacol. **2012**, 140, 513–518.
9. World Health Organization. WHO Guidelines on Safety Monitoring of Herbal Medicines in Pharmacovigilance Systems. Geneva: WHO, **2004**.
10. Shaw, D. Toxicological Risks of Chinese Herbs. Planta Medica **2010**, 76, 2012–2018.
11. Soares, J.A.B. Medicinal herbs: the need to be cautious? [Ervas Medicinais: é preciso ter cuidado!] Available at: http://www.geocities.com/paraciencia/fitoterapia.html, 2008. Last accessed on 12/06/2020.
12. Newall, C.A.; Anderson, L.A; Phillipson, J.D., Medicinal Plants: Guide for Health Professionals [Plantas Medicinas: Guia para Profissional de Saúde]. São Paulo: Premier, **2002**, 308.
13. FDA. **2010**. Available at http://www.fda.gov/downloads/Drugs/GuidanceCompliance RegulatoryInformation/Guidances/ucm073246.pdf. Last accessed on 28/06/2020.
14. Dias, A; Aires, C; Silva, M; Catarino, R. *Artemia salina* Toxicity Test: Contaminants (K_2CrO_7) and Chemical Effluents (treated and untreated) [Teste de Toxicidade em *Artemia salina*: Contaminantes (K_2CrO_7) e Efluentes Químicos (tratados e não tratados)]. Faro: Universidade do Algarve, **2002**.
15. Veiga-Júnior, V.F; Pinto, A.C. Medicinal Plants: Safe Cure? [Plantas Medicinais: cura segura?] Quim. Nova **2005**, 28 (3), 519–528.
16. De Smet, P. Health Risks of Herbal Remedies: An Update. Clin. Pharmacol. Ther **2004**, 76, 1–17.
17. Van Breemen, R.B.; Fong, H.H.S.; Farnsworth, N.R. Ensuring the Safety of Botanical Dietary Supplements. Am J Clin Nutr **2008**, 87 (Suppl), 509S–13S.
18. Ankli, A.; Reich, E.; Steiner, M., Rapid High-Performance Thin-Layer Chromatographic Method for Detection of 5% Adulteration of Black Cohosh with *Cimicifuga foetida*, *C. heracleifolia*, *C. dahurica*, or *C. americana*. J AOAC Int **2008**, 91, 1257–1264.
19. Foster, B.C.; Arnason, J.T.; Briggs, C.J. Natural Health Products and Drug Disposition. Annu Rev Pharmacol Toxicol **2005**, 45, 203–226.
20. Goldman, R.D.; Rogovik, A.L.; Lai, D.; Vohra, S. Potential Interactions of Drug-Natural Health Products and Natural Health Products-Natural Health Products Among Children. J Pediatr **2008**, 152, 521–526.

21. Franco, A.T.M; Moura, R.M.X.; Battochio, A.P.R.; Marcelino, M.C.L.; Cardoso, V.M.; Andrade, J. Histomorphometry of Liver and Kidneys of Swiss Mice Subjected to the Infusion of *Valeriana officinalis* [Histomorfometria de Fígado e Rins de Camundongos da Linhagem Swiss, Submetidos à Infusão da *Valeriana officinalis* L]. Revista Conexão Saúde **2014**, 9 (1), 63–79.
22. Barreiro, E.J.; Fraga C.A.M. Medicinal Chemistry: The Molecular Bases of Drug Action [Química Medicinal: As Bases Moleculares da Ação dos Fármacos]. São Paulo: ArtMed, 1rd Ed, **2001**, 243.
23. Tisserand, R.; Balacs, T. Essential Oil Safety: A Guide for Health Care Professionals Edinburgh: Churchill Livingstone, **1995**, 279.
24. De Smet, P.A.G.M.; Keller, K.; Hãnsel, R.; Chandle, R.F. Adverse Effects of Herbal Drugs. Berlin: Springer Verlag, **1992**, 1. 252.
25. D'Arcy, P.F. Adverse Reactions and Interactions with Herbal Medicines. Part 1. Adverse Reactions. Adverse Drug React Toxicol Review **1991**, 10, 189–208.
26. Deboyser, P. Traditional Herbal Medicines Around the Globe: Modern Perspectives. Swiss Pharm **1991**, 13, 86–89.
27. Lombardo, M. Potential Adverse of Herbal Medicines: A Study Focusing on Simplified Registration Medicines [Potencial Adverso de Medicamentos Fitoterápicos: Um Estudo com Foco em Medicamentos de Registro Simplificado]. Rev Ciên Saúde **2018**, 3 (1), 1–11.
28. Argenta, S.C.; Argenta, L.C.; Giacomelli, S.R.; Cezarotto, V.S. Medicinal Plants: Popular Culture Versus Science [Plantas Medicinais: Cultura Popular Versus Ciência]. Vivências **2011**, 7, (12), 51–60.
29. Anderson, L.A.; Phillipson, J.D. Herbal Medicine Education and the Pharmacist. Pharm J **1986**, 236, 306–308.
30. D'Arcy, P.F. Adverse Reactions and Interactions with Herbal Medicines. Part 2. Drug Interactions. Adverse Drug React Toxicol Review **1993**, 10, 147–162.
31. Izzo, A.; Ernst, E. Interactions between Herbal Medicines and Prescribed Drugs: An Update Systematic Review. Drugs **2009**, 69, 1777–1798.
32. Skalli, S.; Bencheikh, R.S. Safety Monitoring of Herb Drug Interactions. Drug Saf **2012**, 35 (10), 785–791.
33. Posadzki, P; Watson, L.; Ernst, E. Herb–Drug Interactions: An Overview of Systematic Reviews Br J Clin Pharmacol **2012**, 75 (3), 603–618.
34. Ferreira, F.S. Interaction of Herbal Drugs Used in the Treatment of Insomnia: A Brief Review [Interações Medicamentosas de Fitoterápicos Utilizados no Tratamento da Insônia: Uma Breve Revisão]. Curitiba: Visão Acadêmica **2019** 20 (3), 60–71.
35. Paraná, S.S. Use of Herbal Medicine and Medicinal Plants Grows in SUS [Uso de Fitoterápicos e Plantas Medicinais Cresce No. SUS]. 2017. Available at <http://portalms.saude.gov.br/noticias/agencia-saude/24205-uso-de-fitoterapicos-e-plantas-medicinais-cresce-no-sus>. Last accessed on 02/06/2020.
36. Silva, N.C.S. Everything natural is good? Investigation on the use of Medicinal Plants and Herbal Medicines by the Elderly, in the city of Iapu—Eastern Minas Gerais [Tudo que é natural não faz mal? Investigação sobre o uso de Plantas Medicinais e Medicamentos Fitoterápicos por Idosos, na cidade de Iapu—Leste de Minas Gerais]. Unica Cadernos Acadêmicos **2016**, 2 (2), 1–12.
37. ANVISA. Resolution-RDC 14 of March 31, 2010. Establishes the minimum requirements for the registration of herbal medicines [Resolução-RDC 14, de 31 de março de 2010. Estabelece os requisitos mínimos para o registro de medicamentos fitoterápicos]. 2010. Available at: http://portal2.saude.gov.br/saudelegis/Leg. Last accessed on 14/08/2020.
38. EMA. European Medicines Agency. Herbal Medicinal Products. Available at: <https://www.ema.europa.eu/en/human-regulatory/herbal-medicinal-products>. Last accessed on 14/08/2021.

39. ANVISA. Herbal medicines and medicinal plants [Medicamentos fitoterápicos e plantas medicinais]. **2018**. Available at: http://portal.anvisa.gov.br/fitoterapicos>. Last accessed on 21/10/2020.
40. Leal, L. R., Tellis, C.J.M. Pharmacovigilance in Medical Plants and Phytotherapics in Brazil: A Brief Review. Revista Fitos **2015**, 9 (4), 253–303.
41. SINITOX—National Toxic-Pharmacological Information System [Sistema Nacional de Informações Tóxico-Farmacológicas]. Estatística anual de casos de intoxicação de medicamentos e envenenamento: Brasil, Rio de Janeiro: Fundação Oswaldo Cruz: Centro de Informação Científica e Tecnológica, **2018**. Available at <http://www.fiocruz.br/sinitox_novo/cgi/cgilua.exe/sys/start.htm?sid=349>. Last accessed on 13/08/2020
42. Walji, R.; Boon, H.; Barnes, J.; Austin, Z.; Welsh, S.; Baker, G.R. Consumers of Natural Health Products: Natural-Born Pharmacovigilantes? BMC Complement Altern Med **2010**, 10, 8.
43. Balbino, E.E., Dias, M.F. Pharmacovigilance: A Step Towards the Rational Use of Medicinal and Herbal Plants [Farmacovigilância: Um Passo em Direção ao Uso Racional de Plantas Medicinais e Fitoterápicos]. Revista Brasileira de Farmacognosia **2010**, 20, 992–1000.
44. Farah, M.H.; Edwards, R. International Monitoring of Adverse Health Effects Associated with Herbal Medicines. Pharmacoepidemiol Drug Safety **2000**, 9, 105–112.
45. Gardiner, P.; Sarma, D.; Low Dog T.; Barrett, M.; Chavez, M.K.R.; Mahady, G.; Marles, R.; Pellicore, L.; Giancaspro, G. The State of Dietary Supplement Adverse Event Reporting in The United States. Pharmacoepidemiol Drug Safety **2008**, 17, 962–970.
46. Jordan, S.A; Cunningham, D.G.; Marles, R.A. Assessment of Herbal Medicinal Products: Challenges, and Opportunities to Increase the Knowledge Base for Safety Assessment. Toxicol Appl Pharmacol **2010**, 243, 198–216.
47. UMC—The Uppsala Monitoring Centre. The Uppsala Monitoring Centre & WHO Collaborating Centre for International Drug Monitoring. **2015**. Last accessed on 10/09/2020.
48. Arrais, P.S.D. The Irrational Use of Medicines and Pharmacovigilance in Brazil [O Uso Irracional de Medicamentos e a Farmacovigilância no Brazil]. Cad. Saúde Pública. Rio de Janeiro **2002**, 18, 1478–1479.

Index

Italicized pages refer to figures and **bold** pages refer to tables.

A

Abascal, K., 130
Acacia senegal, 176
Acacia seyal, 176
Acceptable daily intake (ADI), 219
Aché laboratory, 11
Acheflan®, **9**, 11, **13**, 222
Achyrocline satureioides (Marcela), 124
Active films and coatings, 270–274, **272–273**
Active packaging, 256, 274, 277
Active phytopharmaceutical ingredients (API), 131, 173, 174–175, **177**
Acute respiratory distress syndrome, 36–37
Adamiec, J., 184
Additives, 54, 109, 217–219, 242, 255–257, 261, 271
  food, 54, 217, 219, 242, 257
  functional, 109
  natural, 255, 261
  synthetic, 218, 255, 271
Adenovirus, 27
Adjuvant, 4, 36–37, 49, 112, 120–126, **127–128**, 131, 137, 147–148, 151, **152–155**, 157, 159–160, 162–166, 212, 313
Adulteration, 111
Aesculus hippocastanum, 8, **9**
Agrobusiness and agroindustry, 285–286
Agroindustry, 133, 218, 285–286, 288, 298–299, 301
Agronomic studies, 110
  applications of herbal products in, 298–300
Alcantara-Rodriguez, M., 5
Alibas, I., 65
Alkaloid(s), 12, **28**, **32**, 37, 54, 86, **88**, **102**, 106–108, 135, 142, 255–256, 298, 316, 318, 332
  harmane, harmine, and harmol, 12
Aloe (*Aloe vera* L.) leaves, 53
Alpinia zerumbet leaves, 13
Amazon Forest, 5
Amerindian, 22–23, 42
Analytical chromatography, 101–102
Analytical methodologies development, 110
Anthocyanins, **28**, **33**, 47, 142, 234, 262
Anti asthmatic, **28–29**
Anticancer activity, 204
Anticoagulant, 27, **29–31**, **33–34**, 36, 40, 44, 49, **334–335**
Antifungal activity, **128**, 205, 268, 277, 280, 292–293, 295, 297
Anti-inflammatory (AI), 54, 65
Anti-inflammatory and antinociceptive activities, 204
Anti-inflammatory drugs, 37
Antimicrobial (AM) actions, 54, 65
Antimicrobial activity, **200**, 201, 205, 218, 221, 241–242, **267**, 268–269
Antimicrobial and antioxidant agents, 268–270
Antimutagenic activity, 204
Antinociceptive activity, 202, 204
Antioxidant activity (AA), 77–78, 204
Antioxidant capacity (AC), 54, 65
Antiplatelet activity, 204
Antiprotozoal activity, 204
Antituberculosis, **28**
Antitussive, **32–33**, 86
Antiviral, 27, **28–34**, 37, 66, 108, **200**, **202**, 203, 255, 286
Antiviral activity, 203–204
ANVI SA Collegiate Board Resolution Nr. 14/2010, 317–319
ANVI SA Collegiate Board Resolution Nr. 26/2014, 319–322
ANVI SA Collegiate Board Resolution Nr. 48/2004, 315–317
ANVISA Resolution of the Collegiate Board Nr. 17/2000, 313–315
Apsen Farmacêutica Laboratory, 12
Arabic gum, 176, 186–187
Aristolochia species, 37
Ascorbyl tetraisopalmitate (ATIP), 248
Aspergillus flavus, 292
Atlantic Forest, 5, 22, 23, 25
Aveda, 235
Avicenna, 4

B

Babu, A. K., 56
Bacopa monnieri, 8
Baldim, I., 205
Ball mills, 116
Barbatimão (*Stryphnodendron adstringens* [Mart.] Coville), 22, 23
Barreiro, E.J., 332
Basil *(Ocimum basilicum)* leaves, 55, 66
Basil leaves in a vibrofluidized dryer, 67–70

Bauhinia forficata (Bf), 121, 148
Bemisia tabaci (Gennadius) biotype, 289
Bidens pilosa, 125, 164
Bilberry (*Vaccinium myrtillus* L.) leaves, 53
Bioactive compounds, 77–78
Bioavailability, 16, 120, 132, 173–174, 176, 190, 205–206, 217, 220, 222, 239, **265**
Biocompatible, 205–206, 208, 220, 222, 241
Biodegradable, 205–206, 208, 220, 222, 241, 271, 294
Biodiversity, 4–5, 8, 10, 12, 13–14, 16, 22–23, 26, 37–38, 53, 108, 233, 250
Biological activity studies, 110
Biological materials complexity, 14
Biomolecules
  extraction from raw plant material, 87–96, **88**
    extraction by steam drag, 91
    maceration, 90, *91*
    percolation, 92
    pressing extraction, 91–92
    soxhlet extraction, 90–91
    supercritical fluid extraction (SFE), 92–96, **95**, *95*
    turbolysis extraction, 89
    ultrasound extraction method (UEM), 89
  identification of, 101–102, **102**
    analytical chromatography, 101–102
    by chemical reactions, 101
  liquid solvents used in the extraction of, **88**
Biopolymers, 256, **272–273**
Böhm, M.E., 65
Bonaparte, N., 23
Botanical products, 6, **7**
Botanical studies, 110
Bott, R.F., 165
Botrytis cinerea, 293
Brazil
  authors' nationalities, phytogeographical domains, and period of studies in, **24**
  biodiversity, 4, 5, 10, 22, 53
  Brazilian Institute of Geography and Statistics, 285
  drug market in, 22
  entrepreneur, 11
  flora and fauna, 5
  health regulatory framework for herbal products in, 15
  in herbal medicine area, 4–5, 11, 22
  impact from World Wars, 10
  market for medicines, 6
  medicinal plants, 122, *160*, 160–163, *161*, *162*
  in medicines' area, 4
  native vegetation, 22
  natural wealth, 5
  pharmaceutical companies, 11
  pharmacovigilance activities in, **342–343**
  pharmacovigilance legislation in, 341
  phytopharmaceuticals market, 8, **9**, *9*, 12
  phytopharmacovigilance of herbal medicines in, 336–339
  plant protection market, **7**, 8
  Portuguese royal family in, 5
  R&D of phytopharmaceuticals, **13**
  records on plants, 23–26
  regulations for phytomedicines, 106
  regulatory instruments of herbal medicines in, 313–322
  soybean defoliator in, 290
  traditional use of plants, 27–37
Brazilian Association of the Phytoterapic Sector, Food Supplement, and Health Promotion (ABIFISA), 53
Brazilian Health Surveillance Agency (ANVISA), 12, 36
Brazilian National Health Surveillance Agency (RDC no. 26/2014—ANVISA), 22, 313
Brazilian Pharmacopoeia Formulary of Phytomedicines, 322
Brazilian Pharmacopoeia Phytotherapeutical Memento, 322–323
Brazilian Society for the Monitoring of Medicines, 329
Brazilian Unified Health System (SUS), 313
Bronchodilator, **29–30**, **32**
Butua (*Chondrodendron platyphyllum* [A. St.-Hil.] Miers), 25
Butylhydroxyanisol (BHA), 219
Butylhydroxytoluene (BHT), 219

C

Caatinga, 5
Caminha, P. V., 5
Canabarro, N. I., 76
Candida albicans, 205
Capillary electrophoresis (CE), 96
Carbohydrates, 175
Carnauba wax, 241
Caroba (*Jacaranda caroba* [Vell.] A. DC.), 23
Carotenoids, 142
Ceará Pharmacovigilance Centre, 329
Centella Asiatica L. (aerial parts—infusion), 122
Cerrado, 5
César, F. C. S., 240
Ceylon cinnamon (*Cinnamomum verum* J. Presl), 23
Chard (*Beta vulgaris* L.) leaves, 65
Chemat, F., 116
Chemical drying, 56
Chemical studies, 110
Chernoviz, P.N., **24**, 24–25
Chest affection (CA), 27, 34

China, 6
Chromatographic methods, 165
Chromatography-mass spectrometry (CG-MS) technique, 69
Circular dichroism, 97, 101
Citrus (Rutaceae), 294
Clinical study, **28**, 235, 248–249
Clove, 185
CM-5 Konica Minolta spectrophotometer, 73
Coalescence, 181
Collares, F., 158
Collegiate Board Resolution (RDC) No. 26/2014, 312
Collegiate Board Resolution—RDC No. 17, 313
Colloidal silicon dioxide, 150, 158, *158*, *160*, *161*, *162*, 163
Color-changing enzymes, 57, 74
Color degradation, *73*, 73–74, **74**
Color preservation, 65, 71, 74
Column liquid chromatography, 99, *99*, **102**
Comminution, 115–116
Concentrated extractive solutions of dry leaves, characterisation, **161**
Concentration of extractive solution, 117
Concerning gums, 176
Confocal laser scanning microscopy (CLSM), 163
Convective, 54–57, 65–67, 76, 78–79, 115
  drying, 55–56, 65–67, 78, 115
  heat coefficient, 76
Conveyor belt dryers, 56, *75*, 75–78, **76**
Copaiba balsam (*Copaifera* spp.), 23
Cordia verbenacea, 8, **9**, **13**, 222
Corrêa, M. P., **24**, 24–25
Cortés-Rojas, D. F., 164, 186
Cosmetics, 220–221; *see also* Plant-based cosmetic products
Countercurrent chromatography, 96
COVID-19, 26, 34, 36–37
Creaming, 189
Critical micelle concentration (CMC), 207
Crop production, 286, 288–289
Crozier, A., 107
Current GMP (cGMP), 111
Cyclodextrins, 176
Cymbopogon citratus, **60**, **128**, **202**, **260**, **267**, **269**, **272**, 292
Cynara scolymus L. (leaves—infusion), 122
Cytokine storm, 37

D

Dataplamt, 26, **28–34**, **35–36**, 37
Design of experiments (DoE), 123
Detoni, C. B., 205
Dialysis, 97
Dialysis separation, *98*
Dietary Supplement and Non-prescription Drug Consumer Protection Act (DSNDCPA), 8
Dietary Supplement Health and Education Act of 1994 (DSHEA), 8
Differential scanning calorimetry (DSC), 147, 212
Disc mill, 116
Dollo, G., 185, 187
Drug Abuse Prevention Group, 329
Drugs obtained from plant extracts, **86**
Dry emulsions, 183, 212
Drying
  adjuvant (s), 120–121
  aids, 120–121
  carrier, 120–121
  of herbal material, 115
  of lipid-based formulations, **182**, 182–185
  of lipid systems loaded with phytochemicals, 173–190
  of phytochemical compositions by spouted bed, 142–166, *see also* Spouted bed drying
  of phytochemicals, 141–166
  rates, 56–57, 67, 71–72, 76, 79
  temperature, 67, 70, **127**, **152**, **174**, 185
Drying Center at the Department of Chemical Engineering/Federal University of São Carlos (DEQ/UFSCar, Brazil), 55, 66
Drying of medicinal and aromatic plants, 53–80
  herbs, 55–65
  leaves, 66–78
    basil leaves in a vibrofluidized dryer, 67–70
    mint leaves in a modified rotary dryer, 70–74, **74**
    olive leaves in conveyor belt dryer, 75–78, **78**
  nomenclature, 79–80
  overview, 53–55
Dry phytochemical preparations, 142

E

Ecological, 23, 53, 110, 201, 289, 299, 311–312, 314, 330
  alternative, 289
  approach, 314
  aspects, 23
  awareness, 330
  functions, 201
  interrelationship, 110
  management, 299
  risks, 289
  survey, 312
  waves, 53

Economic costs of innovation process, 14–15
Ecosystem 22, 236
Eibl, R., 239
Electron microscopy, 163
Elemi oil *(Canarium commune),* 184
Elsholtzia ciliata, 130
Emulsification process, 174, 211
Emulsifiers, 174–175, 181, 211, 241, 267
Emulsions, 180, 206–207
Encapsulation
  of essential oils in lipid-based nanosystems, 197–223
Energy balance, **76**
Ernst, E., 334
Erva-baleeira (*Varronia curassavica* Jacq.), 22
Espinheira-santa *(Monteverdia ilicifolia),* 22
Essential oils (EO), 54, **69**, 69–70, **200**
  in agroindustry, 285–301
  applications of, 217–222
    cosmetics, 220–221
    food antimicrobials, 218
    mouthwashes, 221
    natural antioxidants for food and pharmaceutical products, 219–220
    phytotherapy, 222
  biological activities of, 201–204, **202–203**
    anticancer activity, 204
    anti-inflammatory and antinociceptive activities, 204
    antimicrobial activity, 201–203
    antimutagenic activity, 204
    antioxidant activity, 204
    antiplatelet activity, 204
    antiprotozoal activity, 204
    antiviral activity, 203–204
    immunomodulatory activity, 204
  in crop production, 289–291
  drying of lipid-based compositions loaded with, 212–217
    freeze-drying, *214*, 214–215
    spray congealing, *216*, 216–217
    spray drying, *213*, 213–214
    spray freeze-drying (SFD), *215*, 215–216
  encapsulation of, 204–212
    high-energy emulsification methods, 209
    in lipid nanosystems, 205–208, *206*
    low-energy emulsification methods, 211
    methods, **210**
    physicochemical characterisation of lipid nanosystems, 211–212
    production and characterisation of, 209–212
  encapsulation techniques applied on, **264–267**
  extraction of, 199–201
  herbal-derived products in the food sector, 256–257
  Lippia sidoides, 205
  micro- and nanoencapsulation of, 261–268
  Ocimum basilicum, 205
  overview, 198–199
  postharvest application of, 292–297
  Zanthoxylum tingoassuiba, 205
Eucalyptus (*Corymbia citriodora* H.) leaves, 55
Eugenol retention, *187*
Euphorbia genus, 37
European Medicines Agency (EMA), 111
European Mistletoe *(Viscum album),* 131
Experimental studies, 121–126
Extraction, 75, 77, 87, 91, 116
Extraction
  of bioactive compounds, 116
  by cold pressing, 199, 201
  by steam drag, 91
  efficiency, 87–89, 201
  mechanisms of vegetable drug, *87*
  percolation, 67, 92, 116, 122–124, 201
  yields (EY), 75, 77

F

Federal Fluminense University, 12
Federal Law No. 9, 787, 11
Federal Law No. 13, 123, 13
Federal University of Pernambuco, Brazil, 11
Federal University of Santa Catarina, 12
Film-free inert bodies, 145
Fitoscar®, 12, **13**
Fixed beds, 55, 56, 58, **60**, 144
Flocculation, 181
Flora Fluminensis, 23
Fluidized dryers, 56–57
Fluorescein isothiocyanate (FITC), 189
Food additives, 54, 217, 219, 242, 257
Food and Agriculture Organization (FAO), 219
Food and Drug Administration (FDA), 8, 111, 329
Food antimicrobials, 218
Food industry, 7, 121, 187, 255–257, 261, 263, 274
Food preservation, 256–257, 270, 288, 293
Formulation studies, 110
Fractionation, 37, 87–89, 93–94, 96–97, 101, 103
Fraga, C.A.M., 332
Fragmentation, 115–116
Fraxinus excelsior, 124
Freeze-drying (FD), 57, 126–131, 142, 182, *214*, 214–215
Fungal contamination, 292

G

Galen, 4
Garcia, L.C., 184

Gardner, E.G., 23
Gardner, G., **24**
Gas chromatography (GC), 101, 179
Generally recognised as safe (GRAS), 198, 206, 220
Genome-microbiome-exposome model, 236, *237*
Germany, 11, 327
Giamebil®, 11, **13**
Ginger (*Zingiber officinale* Roscoe), 23,
Ginkgo biloba, 8, **9**, 242, **259**, 333
Glass transition temperature, 121–122, 147, 150, 164, 166, 174–175, 185, 187
Gomes, B.A., 23, **24**
Good Agricultural and Collection Practices (GACP), 111
Good Manufacturing Practices (GMP), 110; *see also* Current GMP (cGMP)
Grave, G.M., 5
Gravitational separation, 180–181
Green Chemistry, 87, 94, 103
Grinding, 115–116
Guaco (*Mikania glomerata* Spreng.), 22
Guaraná (*Paullinia cupana* Kunth), 22, 25

H

Hădărugă, D. I., 205
Hamamelis virginiana L. (leaves—decoction), 122
Hammer mills, 116
Hardy, K., 4
Health regulatory agencies, 111
Heat pump dryers, 57
Hebron Laboratory, 13
Hedera helix, *8*
Herbal compounds
  in agroindustry, 285–301
Herbal-derived products in the food sector, 255–275
  application of, 268–275
    active films and coatings, 270–274, **272–273**
    antimicrobial and antioxidant agents, 268–270
  encapsulation techniques applied on, **264–267**
  essential oils (EO), 256–257
  herbal extracts, 256–257
  micro- and nanoencapsulation of, 261–268
  notorious plant extracts and biological activity, **258–261**
  overview, 255–256
Herbal drugs, 111–112, *112*
Herbal drug derivative, 111–112
Herbal medicinal products (HMPs)
  drying technologies, *114*
    standardisation of herbal extracts by, 117–131
  stability testing, 131–132
  technological development of, 110–111
  unit operations used in processing of, 111–117
    bioactive compounds extraction, 116
    comminution, 115–116
    drying of herbal material, 115
    extractive solution concentration, 117
    fragmentation, 115–116
    grinding, 115–116
    macroscopic analysis—cleaning, 114
    milling, 115–116
    primary operations, 113–116
Herbal medicines and products
  Dataplamt, 26
  data searching, 27–37
  development of, 10–14
    importance of historical records for, 21–38
  market of, 5–8
  overview, 21–22
  records on plants from Brazilian traditional medicine, 23–26
  research and development (R&D) of, 3–17
  standardisation of, 109–117
Herbarium Laboratory, 12
Herbs, 4, 25, 53–57, 65, 67, 74, 79, 108, 115, 122, 142, 256, 268–269, 314
Herbs drying, 55–65
High-performance liquid chromatography, 96, 179
High-pressure homogenisation (HPH), 177–178
High-pressure liquid chromatography (HPLC), 99–100
Hippocrates, 4, 256
História Natural do Brasil (Piso), 5, 23
Historical 4, 21, 26, 38
  evidence, 2, 26, 38
  records, 4
HIV-1, 27
Hohenheim, P., 198
Hot air, 54, 56–57, **58–59**, 61, **63–64**, 65, 67, 70, **74**, 75, 79, 185, 263
Human coronavirus, 27
Huynh, T. V., 183
Hydrodistillation, 199; *see also* Vapour hydrodistillation
Hypericum perforatum, 8, 122
  aerial parts—infusion, 122

I

Identification of biomolecules, 89, 101, 119
Immunomodulatory activity, 204
Indigenous, 23
Influenza virus, 27
Infrared spectrometry, 165
Initial and boundary conditions, **76**

In silico analysis, 27
Integrated Pest Management (IPM), 289
Integration between industry and university, 15
International Conference on Harmonisation, 131
In vitro, 27
Ionic gelation, 263, **265–266**, 269
Ipecac (*Carapichea ipecacuanha* [Brot.] L. Andersson), 23, 25
Izzo, A., 334

J

Jaborandi (*Pilocarpus jaborandi* Holmes), 25
Jackfruit (*Artocarpus heterophyllus* Lam.), 23
Jaenicke, C., 6, **7**
Japan, 6
Joint Expert Committee on Food Additives (JECFA), 219
Justicia pectoralis, 36

K

Kalemba, D., 184
Khmaladze, I., 236
Klebsiella pneumoniae, 27
Knife mill, 116
Knudsen diffusion, 67
Korres, 235
Krutmann, J., 236

L

Lab-Plant SD-05 spray dryer, 121
Langsdorff, G.I., 23, **24**
Laser diffraction (LD), 211
Leaf drying, 56, **58–64**
- applications, 66–78
- chemical drying, 56
- special drying, 56
- thermal drying, 56

Leaves
- basil *(Ocimum basilicum),* 55, 66
- eucalyptus (*Corymbia citriodora* H.), 55
- mint (*Mentha* x *villosa* L.), 55, 66
- olive (*Olea europaea* L.), 55, 65, 66
- physical properties and initial moisture content of, **66**

Lemon oil *(Backhousia citriodora),* 183
Lipid-based formulations, 173–190
- case study, 185–190
- of clove, **186**, *188*
- CSD5, *189*
- drying of, 174–176, **182**, 182–185
- microemulsion-based method, 178
- overview, 173–174
- physical instability mechanism in, *180*
- physicochemical characterisation of, 179–180
- preparation method, 176–179, **177**
- preparation steps for dry, *175*
- stability of, 180–181
- wall materials, 175–176

Lipid matrix, 178, 208
Lipid nanoparticles, 173, 205, 206, 208, 239, 249
Liposomes, 207–208
Lippia sidoides EO, 205
Liquid capillary flow, 67
Liquid chromatography, 96
Liquid diffusions, 67
Liquid lipid, 186
Liquid-liquid partition, 97
Liquid soap (phytocosmetic), 11
Liquid solvents used in the extraction of biomolecules, **88**
L'Occitane de Provence, 235
Lombardo, M., 332
Lung injury, **28–30**, **32–33**, 37
Lyophilisation/cryodesiccation, 126; *see also* Freeze-drying

M

Maceration, 90, *91*
Maia Campos, P.M.B.G., 240
Mango (*Mangifera indica* L.), 23
Mango pulp (*Espada* variety), 155–156
Manoel, D., 5
Martius, F.P., 5, 23, **24**, 25
Mass fraction of dyed branches, 71, *71*
Mass spectrometer, 97
Mate (*Ilex paraguariensis* A. St.-Hil.), 25, 65
Maytenus aquifolium, 12
Maytenus ilicifolia (Mi), 12, 122
Mechanism of action, 37, 109, 201, **202–203**, 218, 221, 257, 334, 343
Medical Dictionary and Guide (*Dicionário e Guia Médico*) (Chernoviz), 25
Medicinal plants, 105
Medicinal Plants Research Program (PPPM), 11, 12, 15
Medicine Center of the Brazilian Ministry of Health (CEME), 11, 12
Melissa officinalis, 59, **203**, **258**, 268, 293
Melt emulsification, 179
Melvita, 235
Mentha crispa, 11
Mentha piperita, **63**, 184, **260**, 268, 333
Methicillin-resistant *Staphylococcus aureus,* 27
Micelles, 207
Micro- and nanostructured systems, 239
Microbial ecosystem (microbiome), 236
Microemulsions, **177–178**, 206, 207, 210
Microencapsulation, 121, 131, 185
Microwave dryers, 57, 65
Microwave drying, 57, 65, 74, 115, 117
Mikan, J.C., 5

Mikania glomerata, 36
Mikania guaco, 36
Mikania laevigata, 36
Milling, 115–116
Mills, 116
Mint *(Mentha piperita),* 184
Mint (*Mentha* x *villosa* L.) leaves, 55, 66, 71
Mint branches, 71–72
Mint leaves in a modified rotary dryer, 70–74, **74**
Moisture content, 54–55, 65, **66**, 67–68, 71, 75–77, 79, 118, 122–124, 126, **127–129**, 131, 148, 151, **152–153**, **155**, 160, 162, 183, 201, 263
Moisture reduction ratio of mint leaves, *72*
Molecular interaction, *94*
Monographs, 8, 25–26, 310, 316, 322, 323, 337
Monoterpenes 1–35, *287*
Morphological characteristics, 55, 76, 110
Mouthwashes, 221
Munoz-Ibanez, M., 184
Mycobacterium abscessus, 27
Mycobacterium tuberculosis, 27

N

Nagoya Protocol, 13
Nanoemulsions, **200**, **206**, 207–209, **210**, 218, 239, **267**, 268, 270
Nanoencapsulation, 261
Nanostructured lipid carrier (NLC), 208
National pharmaceutical industry's denationalisation process, 10
National Policy of Integrative and Complementary Practices, 336
Natterer, J., 5
Natural additives, 255, 261
Natural antioxidants for food and pharmaceutical products, 219–220
Natural History of Brazil, 5
Naturalists, 5, 23, 37
Natural waxes, 241
Natureza, doenças, medicina e remédios dos índios brasileiros (Martius), 5
Neanderthals, 4
Neolignans 64–71, *300*
Niro Atomiser (type Minor), 125
N-octenyl succinyl anhydride (OSA), 176
Nomenclature, 79–80, 166

O

Ocimum basilicum EO, 205
OECD, *see* Organisation for Economic Co-operation and Development
Oliveira, W.P., 122, 123, 125, 148, 151, 164
Olive (*Olea europaea* L.) leaves, 55, 65, 66
Olive leaves in conveyor belt dryer, 75–78, **78**
Ordinary vapor, 67
Organic solvents, 87–89, 92–93, 103, 116, 176, 178, 198, 199, 201, 208, 211, 237, 257
Organisation for Economic Co-operation and Development (OECD), 3
Ostwald ripening, 181, 207
Oxidative stability, 205, 240, 265
Oxygen radical absorption capacity (ORAC), 126

P

Pampas, 5
Pantanal, 5
Paris, 25
Particle 97, 119, 122–123, 125, **127–128**, 131, **152**, **154**, 163–164, 178–179, 184, 186, 209, **210**
  charge, 179
  size, 97, 119, 122–123, 125, **127–128**, 131, **152**, **154**, 163–164, 178–179, 184, 186, 209, **210**
  size and morphology, 122, 131, 179
Passiflora alata (Pa), 122
Passiflora incarnata (P. incarnata), 12, 335
Passion fruit (*Passiflora alata* Curtis), 25
Patents, 6, 12, 240, 243, 262, 270
Pathogenic fungi, 293–295, 297, 299
Peckolt, T., **24**, 24–25
Pelargonium graveolens, 289
Pelargonium sidoides, 8, 9
Percolation, 92
Percolator, *93*
Persian walnut *(Juglans regia),* 131
Peumus boldus Mol. (leaves—infusion), 122
Pfaffia glomerata, 13
Pharmaceutical products, 3, 11–12, 86, 117, 146, 217–222
  based on vegetal species, 4
  cosmetics, 220–221
  in COVID-19 pandemic, 4
  food antimicrobials, 218
  mouthwashes, 221
  natural Antioxidants for, 219–220
  phytotherapy, 222
Phase
  diagram, 93, *94*, 126
  inversion, 181
Phenolic acid(s), 107, 142, 220, 234, 242, 268
Phenolics, 142
Phenylpropanoids 69, 199, **200**, **203**, 286–287, *288*
Photo diode array, 97, 101
Photon correlation spectroscopy (PCS), 211
Physicochemical characterisation of lipid nanosystems, 211–212
Phytochemicals, 86, 106–109
  applications of, 108–109

carotenoids, 142
chemical structures, *107*
compositions by spouted bed, 141–166
concentration of, 108
drying of, 141–166
pharmacokinetics of, 132
phenolics, 142
systemic bioavailability of, 132
uses of, 142
Phytocosmeceuticals, 237
Phytogeographical domains, **24**
Phytomedicine, 112
Phytomedicines registration, 309–323
documents associated to, 322–323
overview, 309–311
resolutions, 313–322
ANVI SA Collegiate Board Resolution Nr. 14/2010, 317–319
ANVI SA Collegiate Board Resolution Nr. 26/2014, 319–322
ANVI SA Collegiate Board Resolution Nr. 48/2004, 315–317
ANVISA Resolution of the Collegiate Board Nr. 17/2000, 313–315
characterisation and differences, **321**
technical features of, 311–312
characterisation of the active phytopharmaceutical ingredient, 312
selection of plant species, 311–312
Phytopharmaceuticals, 7
adequate development of, 11
extraction of biomolecules from raw plant material, 87–96, *see also* Biomolecules
fractionation and isolation, 96–101
column liquid chromatography, 99
dialysis, 97
high-pressure liquid chromatography (HPLC), 99–100
liquid-liquid partition, 97
precipitation, 97
supercritical fluid chromatography (SFC), 100–101
thin-layer chromatography (TLC), 97–99, *98*
identification of biomolecules, 101–102
market and participation, *9*
overview, 85–87
turnover evolution of top 12, **9**
turnover of genuine Brazilian R&D of, **13**
worldwide consumption of, **7**
Phytopharmacovigilance, 327–343
challenges of, 339–340
of herbal medicines in Brazil, 336–339
importance of, 328–329
laws, **342–343**
legislation in Brazil, 341
overview, 327–328
toxicity and safety of plant-based medicines, 330–336
Phytotherapy, 222
Piso, G., **24**
Piso, W., 5, 23
Plant-based cosmetic products, 233–250
application of natural ingredients in, 240–243
biotechnology in, 238
botanical ingredients, 235–240
determination of the clinical efficacy of, 247–249
developmental steps for, *234*
overview, 233–235
research and development of, 243–247, *244*
Pohl, J.E., 5
Polymers, 241
Polysaccharides, 241
Pop, C., 131
Porous media, 67, 76
Posadzki, P, 334
Post-harvest, 53, 11
Potato (*Solanum tuberosum* L.), 292
Precipitation, 97
Pressing extraction, 91–92
Propylene glycol (PEG), 174
Propyl gallate (PG), 219
Pseudo-homogeneous model, 76
Pseudomonas aeruginosa, 27
Psidium guajava leaves, 125
PubMed, 27
Pulmonary disease (PD), 27, 34

Q

Quality attributes, 55–57, 65, 76, 132
Quantitative Descriptive Analysis (QDA), 246
Quina-docampo (*Strychnos pseudoquina* A. St.-Hil.), 25
Quina-mineira (*Remijia ferruginea* [A. St.-Hil.] DC), 25
Quinta essentia or *Quintessence,* 198

R

Raddi, G., 5
Reactive oxygen species (ROS), 219
Reflectance confocal microscopy (RCM), 247–248
Relative percentage area (RPA), 69
Renisus, 15
Repellency, 289, 290
Research and development (R&D) of herbal medicines, 3–17
challenges in, 14–16

biological materials complexity, 14
economic costs of innovation process, 14–15
integration between industry and university, 15
unreasonable legal requirements, 15–16
economic expenditures in, 3
history of, 4–5
overview, 3–4
Respiratory disease(s) (RD), 26, 27, **34**, **36**
Retention indices (RI), 69
Rhamnus purshiana (bark—maceration and percolation), 8, **9**, 122
Rheum palmatum, **9**
Rhinovirus, 27
Rhizopus stolonifer, 293
Rio de Janeiro, 12, 23, 24–25
Rocha, S.C.S., 148
Rosmarinus officinalis, 122
Rotary dryers, 56–57, **70**, 70–74, *72*
Rotavirus, 27
Roussel Laboratory, 10
Rue *(Ruta graveolens)* leaves, 53

S

Saint-Hilaire, A., 5, 23, **24**, 25
Salvia officinalis, **63**, **258**, 268, **299**, 332
Sambucus australis, 37
SARS-CoV-2, 26–27, 36–37, **202**, 204
Scanning probe microscopy techniques, 163
Schinus terebinthifolius, **13**
Sesquiterpenes 36–48, *288*
Shade drying, 54, 65
Sigaud, J.F.X., **24**
Sigaud, X., 24
Silva, R. A., 25
Silva Araújo Laboratory, 10
Silva Araújo Roussel S/A (SARSA), 10
Simões, C.M.O., 107
Solar dryers, 56
Solid lipid nanoparticles (SLNs), 206, 208
Solid lipids, 186
Soottitantawat, A., 183
Souza, C. R. F., 116, 121, 123, 124, 151
Souza, G. S., 23, **24**
Soxhlet extraction, 90, 116
Special drying, 56
Spectrum Descriptive Analysis (SDA), 246
Spix, J., 5
Spodoptera frugiperda, 291
Spouted bed drying (SBD), 117
aspects of, 142–145
of *Bauhinia forficata*, *149*
changes of the spouting regimes, *149*
fluid dynamic curves, *144*
of liquid feeds, 145–146
of liquid materials, *146*
nomenclature, 166
of phytochemical preparations, 150–160, **152–155**
effects of processing conditions, 151
evaluation of experimental studies, 151–160
product stability during storage, 165
properties, 162–164
flow properties, 163–164
loss on drying and water activity, *162*, 162–163
particle size and size distribution, 163
product morphology, 163
product solubility, 164
X-ray diffraction, 164
schematic diagram of, *143*
solid–fluid flow patterns, *144*
solids flow, *149*
stickiness issues, 146–150
instabilities issues, 148–150
Teflon beads just after, *159*
Spray congealing, *216*, 216–217
Spray chilling, 212, 216, 262, **266**
Spray drying (SD), 117–126, *118*, 142, *213*, 213–214
of herbal extracts, 119–126
of plant extracts, **127–129**
of *Syzygium aromaticum* lipidic emulsions, 185–190
Spray freeze-drying (SFD), *215*, 215–216
Stability testing, 131–132
Standardisation of herbal extracts by drying technologies, 117–131
challenges and prospects, 132–133
freeze-drying (FD), 126–131
spray drying (SD), 117–126
stability testing, 131–132
Standardisation of herbal medicinal products, 109–117, *113*
Standardised dried phytoextracts, 142
Staphylococcus aureus, 27
State of Minas Gerais, 22
Steam distillation, 199
Steam puller, *92*
Stokes' Law, 181
Streptococcus pneumoniae, 27
Streptococcus pyogenes, 27
Structural conformation, 180
Sun drying, 56
Supercritical carbon dioxide (scCO_2), 93
Supercritical chromatography (SCC), 96–97
Supercritical extraction, 77–78
Supercritical fluid chromatography (SFC), 96, *100*, 100–101
Supercritical fluid extraction (SFE), 87, 92–96, **95**, *95*, 199

Supercritical fluids, 92–94, 237
Surface diffusion of water molecules, 67
Sustainability assessment, 237
Synergistic effect, 65, 218, 301
Synthetic pesticides used against *Bemisia tabaci*, *289*
Systema de materia medica vegetal brasileira (Martius), 5
Syzygium aromaticum, 185, **200**, **202**, **259**, **260**, **266**, **272**, 292

T

Tarhan, S., 74
Tert-butylhydroquinone (t-BHQ), 219
Thamkaew, G., 115
Thermal calorimetry, 165
Thermal drying, 56
Thermodynamic stability, 207, 212
Thin-layer chromatography (TLC), 96, 97–99, *98*
Thin-layer drying methodology, 67
Thymus vulgaris, **202**, **258–259**, 269, **273**, 295
Total flavonoid content (TFC), 121
Total phenolic content (TPC), 77–78
Total phenolics (TP), 65
Total polyphenol (TPC), 123
Traditional Chinese medicine system (TCM), 27
Traditionality, 21–22, 26, 337
Transepidermal water loss (TEWL), 247
Transmission electron microscopy (TEM), 163
Tratado descritivo do Brasil em 1587 (Souza), 23
Travels in Brazil (Martius), 5
Trihydroxybutyrophenone (THBP), 219
Turbolysis extraction, 89

U

Ultra-high-pressure liquid chromatography (UHPLC), 100
Ultrasonic homogenising, 178
Ultrasound-assisted extraction (UAE), 199, 201
Ultrasound extraction method (UEM), 89
Ultra-turrax, *90*
Ultraviolet (UV) spectroscopy, 179
Unha-de-gato (*Uncaria tomentosa* [Willd. ex Roem. & Schult.] DC), 22
Unified Health System (SUS), 336
United States, 6–8
University of Ribeirão Preto, 12
Uppsala Monitoring Center (UMC), 329
US Code of Federal Regulations, 198
US Food and Drug Administration (USFDA), *see* Food and Drug Administration
UV-spectrophotometry, 165

V

Valeriana officinalis L. (rhizomes, roots, and stolons—infusion), 122
Vapour hydrodistillation, 199
Velloso, F., 23
Vellozo, M. C., **24**
Vesicular delivery systems, 239
Vibration energy, defined, 68
Vibrofluidized bed dryers, 56
Vibrofluidized dryer, 67–70, *68*
Volatile compounds, 54, 57, 67, 69, 116, 119, 129, 150, 176, 182–185, 204, 214, 219, 239, 241, 256–257, 262–263, 286
Volatile oils, 57, 70, **88**, 91, 286, 332
Volatility, 184, 198, 204–205, 212, 261, 292, 300–301
Von Hohenheim, Paracelsus, 4, 198

W

Wall materials, 175–176
Water mass balance, **76**
Web of Science, 119, *120*
White willow bark *(Salix alba),* 131
WHO Pilot Research Project for International Drug Monitoring, 341
World Health Assembly, 341
World Health Organization (WHO), 14, 21, 106, 111, 131, 219, 327

X

Xie, L., 65
X-ray diffraction, 212

Z

Zanthoxylum tingoassuiba EO, 205
Zeta potential, 179, **210**, 211–212